WHAT IS QUANTUM MECHANICS?

A Physics Adventure

SECOND EDITION

Written by

Transnational College of LEX

Foreword by

Dr. Yoichiro Nambu

Translated by John Nambu

Language Research Foundation

Cambridge, Massachusetts

What is Quantum Mechanics? A Physics Adventure

Language Research Foundation 90 Sherman Street, Cambridge, MA 02140
www.lexlrf.org, publisher@lexlrf.org

Second Edition Published 2009
First Edition Published 1996
Second Printing 1997
Third Printing 2000
Fourth Printing 2002
Fifth Printing 2004

Library of Congress Catalog Card Number: 2009927745

ISBN 978-0-9643504-4-1

Printed in the United States of America

10 9 8 7 6 5 4 3 2 1

Acknowledgments

Writing and producing the original version and the translation of this book has involved many people. It gives us great pleasure to acknowledge those people who have taken time to help and advise us with our projects.

Advisors to the English version

Yoichiro Nambu, Ph.D., Elementary Particle Physics at Enrico Fermi Institute, University of Chicago

Dr. Matthias Nolte, Ph.D., Crystallography, Harvard University

Japanese Language Services, Boston

Advisors to the original Japanese version

Genpei Akasegawa, artist, writer, photographer

Jiro Ohta, Ph.D., Cell Biology, President of Ochanomizu University

Tan Sakakibara, Automatic Control Engineering, Director of LEX Institute

Hiroshi Shimizu, Ph.D., Biological Complexity and Information, The *Ba* Research Institute, Kanazawa Institute of Technology & International Media Foundation

Yusuke Tsukahara, Technical Research Institute in Toppan Printing Co.

Yao Nakano, Senior Fellow at the LEX Institute

Teru Hayashi, Ph.D., Control and System Engineering, Professor Emeritus of Tokyo Institute of Technology / Professor of Toin University of Yokohama

Toyoo Maeda, Ph.D., Metallurgist, IHI Research Institute Vice-Director

Junichi Miida, Ph.D., Nuclear Engineering, Japan Atomic Energy Research Institute (1956-1981), Deputy Director / Nuclear Science and Engineering, OECD Nuclear Energy Agency, Paris (1976-1979), Deputy Director

Shigeyuki Minami, Ph.D., Electromagnetism, Osaka City University

Kazuo Yamazaki, Ph.D., Theoretical Physics, Professor Emeritus of Kyoto University / Professor of Kobegakuin University

Keiko Nakamura, Ph.D., Biohistory, Biohistory Research Hall Deputy Director General / Professor of Osaka University

Takao Saito, Ph.D., Space Physics, Professor Emeritus of Tohoku University

Hippo Family Club Members who joined in the Quantum Lectures

Cover

Illustration by Karyl Klopp, Boston, MA.

Designed by Rodelinde Albrecht, Lee, MA.

FOREWORD

Early in 1990, I received an unexpected phone call from Japan. The caller, a student from the Tokyo-based Transnational College of LEX, requested a meeting. He explained the group was involved in family-oriented activities centered around the natural acquisition of multiple languages. Though language acquisition is not exactly my specialty, I agreed to meet with him and his colleagues.

A month later, three young people arrived at the University of Chicago. As they talked about their natural language acquisition activities, I wasn't quite sure what to think. But when the topic shifted to their research, my curiosity was piqued by their natural science approach to the investigation of language. My interest was enhanced through the subsequent visits of Mr. Yo Sakakibara, Founding President of the LEX Institute.

There was something very exciting about their enthusiasm and their distinctive approach to topics spanning language, mathematics, and physics. Soon I became an advisor to the Transnational College of LEX. In 1993 I lent my support to the publication of the English versions of the well received, "What is Quantum Mechanics? A Physics Adventure" and "Who is Fourier? A Mathematical Adventure." LEX happened at the time to be searching for an English translator for "What is Quantum Mechanics?" and my son, John's name was mentioned.

My son is an architect, not a physics expert. For a long time, I had been wishing he could know a little more about my work. This seemed the perfect opportunity. One thing that makes LEX's books more appealing than other books on these topics is that they take the reader through the same journey of understanding that the student authors, ordinary people, not scientists or specialists, have traveled themselves. It seemed particularly interesting to have my son, a layperson, work on the translation and experience this process for himself. I agreed to oversee the technical descriptions, and so the English version of "What is Quantum Mechanics?" was born.

"Who is Fourier?" is an equally interesting journey of discovery. I have long been fascinated by one of the experiments described in this book. The LEX students examined the structure of Japanese vowel sounds. They collected samples of the five vowel sounds (a, i, u, e, o) from a randomly selected group of Japanese speakers. When these sounds were graphed, no order could be found in the distribution of each individual's vowel sounds. However, when the average of the whole group was taken, the graph revealed a perfectly beautiful, symmetrical distribution.

I am pleased that both "What is Quantum Mechanics?" and "Who is Fourier?" have already been enjoyed by so many readers in North America. Now, on the occasion of the second edition of "What is Quantum Mechanics?" it is my deepest wish that, through this unique book, more and more people will come to appreciate the mystery and the beauty of physics.

Dr. Yoichiro Nambu
Professor of Physics Emeritus
Enrico Fermi Institute, University of Chicago
2008 Winner of the Nobel Prize in Physics

Chicago, IL
May 15, 2009

CONTENTS

PREFACE to the English-Language Edition

What is Quantum Mechanics? A Physics Adventure is the English translation of *Adventures in Quantum Mechanics* (original title : 量子力学の冒険) which was first published in Japan in 1991. Like its predecessor, *Who is Fourier? A Mathematical Adventure*, which is now on sale in the U.S., it was translated from Japanese. Both books were originally written by students of the Transnational College of LEX, or TCL. The English editions were a cooperative effort between the TCL students and the translators in the U.S., and were produced in Japan.

We are very thankful for the continued support we have received since 1991 from the readers of the original Japanese version of *What is Quantum Mechanics?*. It has sold over 40,000 copies (as of September 1995) and has become a long running best-seller. The majority of our readers are in their 20's and 30's, with one quarter of the total consisting of students. In addition, the book has been well received by many high school teachers and university professors who have utilized it as supplementary reading for their classes.

In a world where technological advances are happening at a rapid pace, people who have up until now not had as much as a hint of interest in quantum mechanics are beginning to discover and study it. One can see this increased interest just by browsing through the natural sciences section of major bookstores in Japan and counting the number of books related to quantum mechanics. Being chosen as one of the most sought after books on the subject by readers is an honor and has provided us with much confidence and support.

The most unique aspect of this book, if it was summed up in a few words, would be the process by which this book was produced. In most cases, a person well versed in the sciences, such as a physics or mathematics professor, would be the author. This book, however, was written by a group of over 30 lively TCL students who took up the challenge to understand quantum mechanics. In addition, the first drafts of each chapter were written by those who least understood the subject when the project began. The joy was overwhelming when those who didn't understand suddenly did after repeated discussions with members in the same group. People who listened to the explanations of how these students came to understand were literally drawn into the presentations because of the happy and powerful mood in which they were conveyed. Another unique feature of this book is that it can be easily understood by any reader. Its step by step approach starts at the basics and leaves no stone unturned, down to the very last equation.

This book is derived from the discussions of those students. We think that the reason why the original Japanese version was so well received was because it is easily understood and its inclusion of the basics lets even the least knowledgeable feel closer to the subject matter. Great care was taken to be sure that the happiness and power present in the original version was not lost in the process of translation. Our hope is that this can be conveyed to the readers of the English edition. At the same time, we also hope that you will enjoy the real experience of learning the equations.

Lastly, we would especially like to thank Dr. Yoichiro Nambu, Professor Emeritus of the University of Chicago, who advised us, and his son, John Nambu, who did the translation work, for their invaluable help in producing the English edition. Many thanks to all the others who took the time to assist and support us.

Of course, any errors in this work are strictly our responsibility. We hope that this book will bring forth many new acquaintances.

January 1996
Transnational College of LEX

OVERVIEW Transnational College of LEX

WHAT IS HIPPO FAMILY CLUB?

Say, listen! Isn't it about time we set off on our next adventure. . .

Everyone had already gathered, hoping Hyon would say exactly that.

This is Shibuya, a lively quarter of Tokyo and a popular haunt for crowds of young people. Moving past the big department stores and away from the energetic shopping streets, you find your way to Shoto, with its array of large private homes. There is a white, seven-story building at one corner. When you look up, bright blue and yellow jump out at you from the signboard on the middle section of the building. You can be sure that at certain times, the place is aglow with the kaleidoscopic stir of people turning, twisting, hands and feet going up and down. Few can pass by without hearing music, laughter and all manner of odd sounds coming forth.

Every day, this modest-sized building rings with the light steps of casual young people, smiling mothers with nursing babies, fathers in suit and tie, rambunctious children, bright-faced office ladies, and shuffling grandmothers and grandfathers. Not all of these people coming and going are Japanese — quite a few are from other countries.

This cheerful, unique place is the main headquarters of the Hippo Family Club, where their motto is "Let's speak in seven languages!"

1. Our favorite phrase is "Let's speak in seven languages", but in the last several years we have added new languages, and are currently acquiring eleven languages - Japanese, English, Korean, Spanish, French, Chinese, German, Italian, Russian, Thai and Malay - the natural way.

2. What is "natural learning"? We don't study so much as naturally grow fluent in a language, like a small child does.

3. We play tapes all the time — at home, inside the car, on the way to school or work, wherever we happen to be. Like so much background music, we constantly listen to cheerful songs and conversations in a multitude of different languages and hum these sounds to ourselves.

4. We don't do it alone, of course, in isolation. Groups of families gather together at "multilingual parks" called "Families" and sing, dance and practice saying the sounds and words heard on the tapes back and forth to each other. We all have a great deal of fun while chanting our new languages.

5. As the name Family Club implies, people of all ages join, from babies, children and students to young, single working adults, fathers, mothers and grandparents. Anyone can participate no matter who they are.

6. Since we can go abroad to various countries on our homestay exchange programs, or host visitors from abroad at our homes, we can get to know people and their families from all over the world.

For details, please call LEX AMERICA,
the North American headquarters of HIPPO!
Tel: **(617) 354-1140**

Serving as the research division of the Hippo Family Club is the Hippo institute called the Transnational College of LEX (Tokyo, Japan), commonly known as TCL, for short. It takes up the entire second floor of the white building. At TCL there are no tests, and no grades or marks given. Classes are not divided by grade levels, and attendance is not taken. About fifty students are currently enrolled, from freshmen to experienced research students. They range from recent high school graduates to elderly grandmothers.

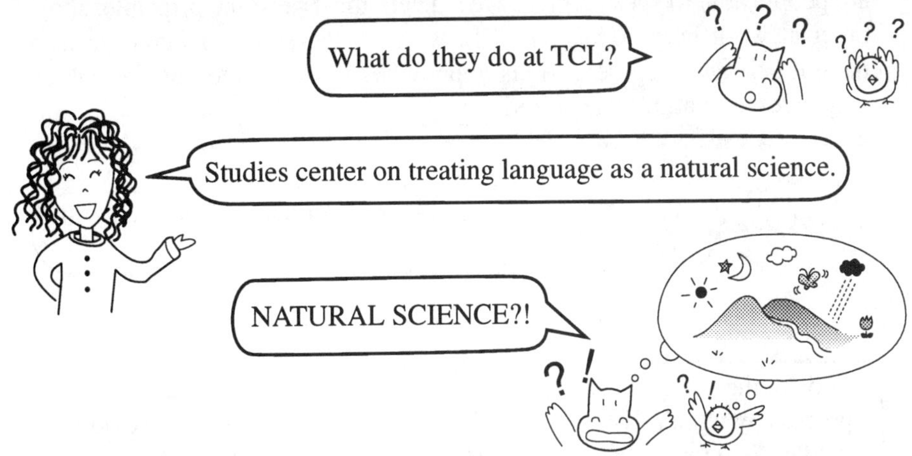

At first, I had absolutely no idea what it meant to treat language as a natural science, either. The word "nature" evokes images like mountains and seas. So I could understand studying the earth and living things in the natural sciences. In physics as well, I could understand why things like how the planets rotate are questions for natural science, but as to why an apple falls from a tree, or why a ping-pong ball bounces or rolls — that was too much. How could these possibly be the objects of natural science, much less human language. . .?

About the third year after I entered TCL, I finally grasped what it meant to treat language as a natural science. That's because I discovered that language shares a trait found in other objects of natural science. That common trait is "repetition." To find a language by which we can explain things that occur repeatedly is the basis for natural science.

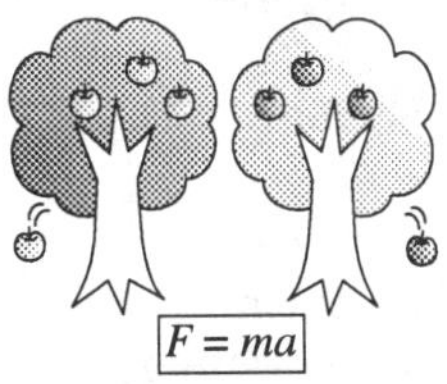

An apple falls from a tree. This happens repeatedly, every time an apple grows bigger and its stem weakens. No matter what sort of apple it may be, if the conditions are the same, an apple should fall in just exactly the same way. It never happens that one apple falls to the ground, while another apple climbs up the tree. In the language of physics, which uses equations rather than words, this predictable, regular occurrence is described by $F = ma$.

Discovering these regularities is natural science. Human language also is a phenomenon of natural science. A baby born in Japan is eventually able to speak Japanese, while a baby born in Luxembourg, where four languages are used, is ultimately able to speak all four: Luxembourgeois, German, French and English. Wherever a person is born, he or she will always develop the ability to speak a language as long as there is a natural environment where that language is used.

Achieving language ability is a regular phenomenon throughout human history, so much so that we take it for granted. Just how and why are people able to speak a language? There must be some principle, some order at work here. Thus, at TCL, we treat the study of language as a natural science and use various approaches to study the path by which languages are naturally acquired.

I see. What are those various approaches you use to pin down language?

Look at the process by which toddlers acquire language.

Above all, we do it through Hippo's multilingual activities!! Once you have experienced them, you will see how adults and children alike can use the same path to learn how to speak. We're looking for a natural process of learning languages that will work for adults, too.

Close in on the phonemes of speech. Explore the mysteries of vowels and consonants and phoneme recognition, including things such as tone and rhythm.

How did the Japanese language form and develop? By reading and deciphering the very oldest extant texts — *Kojiki*, *Nihonshoki*, *Manyoshu*—we can find out a great deal about the principles behind language.

Hitomaro's Code
by Yuka Fujimura

Nukata no Ookimi's Code
by Yuka Fujimura

We musn't forget to mention the interesting and varied lectures at TCL by our senior fellows, all of them people at the top of their fields. TCL may be lacking in material resources, but when it comes to things to do, ideas that you want to follow, those it has in abundance. It's an interesting place to be!

By all means, please come and pay us a visit at TCL.

WHAT'S NEXT?

Now then, on that day something was in the air at TCL. "Big brother" Hyon had started talking about the "next adventure."

Gosh, the Fourier adventure sure was fun!

You bet it was! I never dreamed we could get into something that exciting.

We got hold of some terrific treasures during that adventure, didn't we?

Setting out on the track of Fourier — that adventure is a treasure in itself!

During the course of our fieldwork on phoneme recognition, we came across a mathematical concept, called Fourier analysis, which is necessary for the analysis of the wave form of phonemes. I used to detest mathematics. After my second year of high school, I thought I was finally able to say "再見(zai-jian)," or "good-bye," to math. How amazing that after so many years, I should run into it again at TCL. But this time when math came back into my life, it was neither threatening nor incomprehensible. I recognized it as a beautiful language for describing nature.

We all took up mathematics at TCL and at Hippo. That truly was an adventure as we went through the process of understanding the Fourier series together, reliving the experience of discovery while talking about it in front of others, and preparing a series of lectures based on this. All that is encapsulated in *Who is Fourier? A Mathematical Adventure.*

When I think that we have another wonderful adventure ahead, my heart starts pounding with excitement.

Me too, but what kind of adventure is it this time?

Good question. I was wondering about that, and so I asked you all to get together.

So we're meeting to talk strategy. First off, what do you think, Hyon?

Well, since it comes after Fourier, I think something like mechanics would be good, but what does everyone else think?

Hyon continued speaking.

I mean, if we take care of mechanics now we'll be in great shape, don't you think?

Everyone remained silent. Feeling a little awkward, Hyon said,

I really want to hear everyone's opinion. If there's anything at all you want to try, speak up. How about you, Furta?

Called on first, Furta was a little flustered.

Umm, let's see,. . .

Furta is always like this. Finally he seemed to have made up his mind, but his answer was halting.

Well, um. . . What I would like. . .
I'd sort of like to do quantum mechanics. . . Um hmn.

Huh?! Q—qua—quantum mechanics?!

Without thinking, Hyon let out a great shout. And then he stammered,

Heh heh, quantum mechanics, eh? Ha ha ha, I see.

He was smiling uneasily.

What about you, Hana?

Me? Oh, I want to do quantum mechanics too.
I really admire all that Dr. Heisenberg did.

I want to do quantum mechanics too!

Me, too!

Same goes for me!

I say quantum mechanics too!

How about that? Everyone spoke up, and they all wanted to do quantum mechanics. Hyon's smile became even more uncomfortable.

Now look, I'd like to do quantum mechanics too, but do you realize how difficult it is? Envision a stairway of mathematics. It starts with 1 + 1, and then follows subtraction, multiplication, division, algebra, differentials, integration, matrices. . . As you climb up higher and higher, there at the top of the staircase up above the clouds is quantum mechanics. Even smart people only get halfway up and then stumble and fall. Only a few are able to arrive at the top.

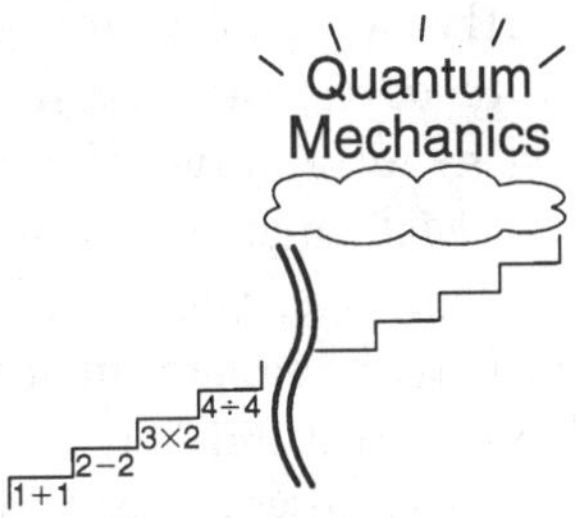

Hearing this everyone started to look a bit troubled. Only Hyon was chuckling merrily to himself. Soon the chuckles rose into giggles, and then into loud and merry laughter.

Okay, since everyone wants to do it, let's do quantum mechanics! Since we're doing it the Hippo way, it'll be possible to do it. Didn't we find that out with Fourier?

Instead of climbing the stairway step by step from the very bottom, you can just hop on and start at any step. And rather than climbing from there, you go down. Climbing takes great effort and you quickly tire and stop, but going down is easy. If you start at the highest, most difficult step, you can then go down the rest in one breath.

It was just as Hyon said. We experienced that in *Who is Fourier? A Mathematical Adventure.* That is to say, we found that mathematics is a human language.

Learning mathematics at school is exactly the same as learning English at school. You are taken forward step by step from the beginning levels, and when you stumble, that's when you stop. People who make their way up above the clouds in math are rare, when it is learned that way. It's just like English. Most people in Japan still can't speak English even after studying it for more than six years in the classroom.

Babies and toddlers don't formally study languages, yet within only four or five years they are able to speak a language. And young children don't just learn their ABC's and then put them together one by one to finally speak a language. It's not as if they start to talk only using simple, discrete words. They don't do that because they are listening to and absorbing the speech going on around them, which is far from "simple."

They hear complete strings of sentences spoken by adults and their elder brothers and sisters, and they begin to speak using rough, general sounds like Ah-Ah and Ooh-Ooh. They certainly do not start speaking just by adding more and more words. They hear the whole first and then tackle the parts, which is the way of nature. And the Hippo way.

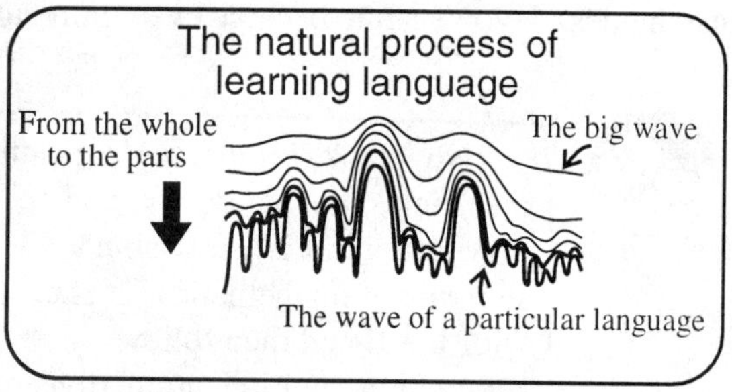

First we must seize the big wave of language, all at once. No matter how carefully we put together separate parts, the result is almost never a wave of real speech. Mathematics, too, is a human language, and we find that exactly the same principle holds true. If it did not, it probably would have been impossible for someone like me, who always got bad marks in high school math, to be able, after just one short month, to lecture on the Fourier series.

The children, even three- and four-year-olds, enjoyed the Fourier adventure lectures. They astonished us with their sharp observations. That could never have happened if math weren't something natural to us.

Every one of us has learned to speak any number of foreign languages here at Hippo. We treat mathematics as just one more language that you can pick up by following nature. As long as we stick to natural processes, there is nothing more to hold us back. We can do it!

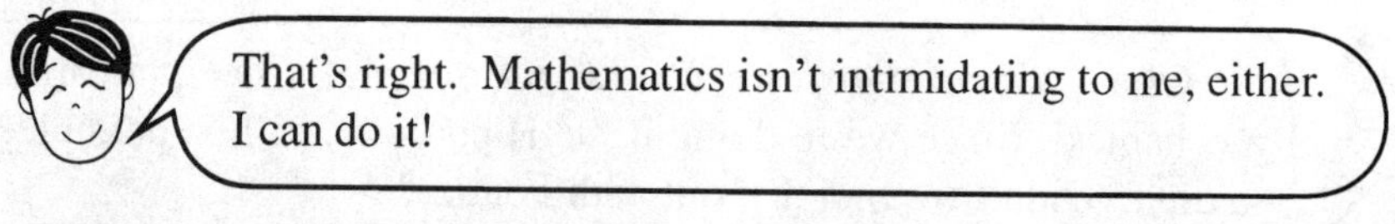

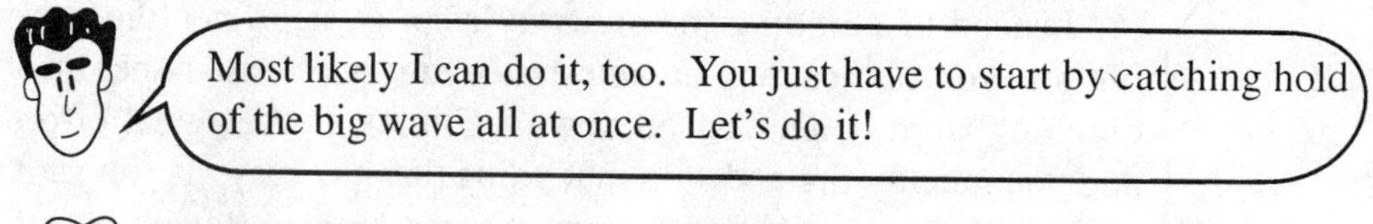

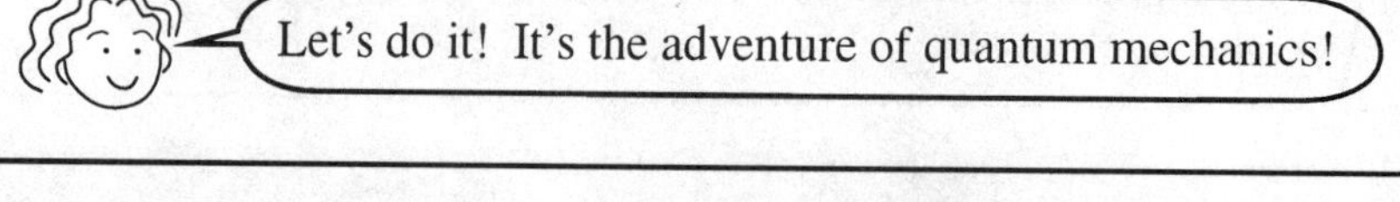

By now everyone was totally inspired by happy anticipation. I was grinning through the strategy meeting from start to finish. It didn't bother us in the least to learn that quantum mechanics is considered exceedingly difficult. For us, there was not much difference between Fourier and quantum mechanics, mainly because we had absolutely no idea how difficult either was compared to the other.

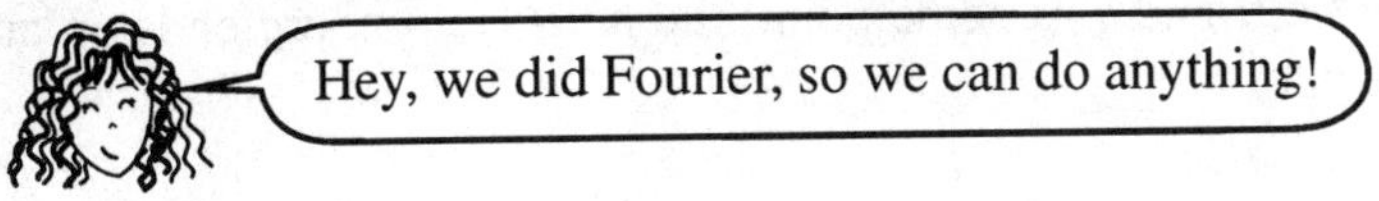

Unfamiliar things can be frightening. Yet we're undaunted by a whole new project.

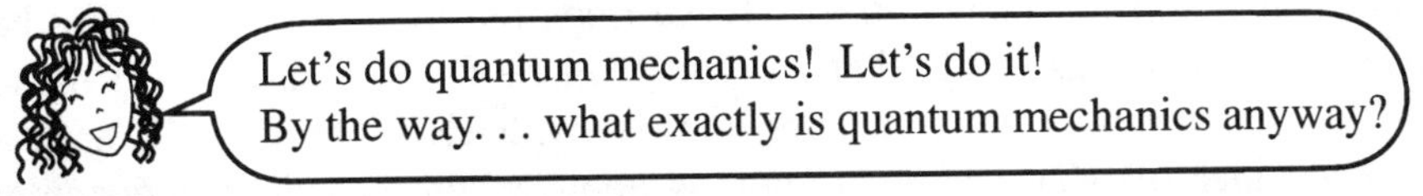

That's the kind of place TCL is. But there was a reason that TCL students were so unanimous in wanting to do quantum mechanics, while knowing nothing about it. They wanted to understand what some of their friends had done.

PHYSICS AND BEYOND

Although there are no entrance examinations at TCL, certain assignments must be tackled before entering. One is to wholeheartedly enjoy the activities at Hippo. The other is to read *Physics and Beyond* by Werner Heisenberg over and over. The book *Physics and Beyond* is something of an autobiography of a physicist named Werner Heisenberg. It is the grand drama of the emergence of a new physics called quantum mechanics, based on the work of Heisenberg and his colleagues.

The thing is, it is impossible to sit down and just read it. When you try reading two or three pages, you start to feel sleepy! In short, it's an unspeakably difficult book for us. Being told to read it again and again, you begin to experience a feeling of hopelessness.

But that's Hippo too. If you had to read through it and understand it perfectly passage by passage, page by page, you probably would never finish. Not in a lifetime. So, more experienced TCL students tell us, "Just plow quickly through the book." Even if you don't understand it, they say, just keep turning the pages until you finish it. And then you do it again, from the beginning. You repeat this many times over.

You can't just listen to the Hippo multilingual tapes and understand them phrase by phrase. You listen to the whole tape, like background music. With time, some phrases gradually settle in your mind. That's because you're taking on a big wave. A book is like that, too.

Now, when you begin to read *Physics and Beyond* that way, the parts that most people understand first have no relation to the substance of what we call quantum mechanics. When you read it several times, you at least begin to remember the names of people who appear in the book. And then as you look at the photographs, you start to think, "Good old Heisenberg is wonderful!" or "I love Hans Euler!" and start feeling as if you've become good friends with them. When you come across their names in another book or somewhere, you feel glad, like you've met a friend. At some point, the hero Heisenberg ends up an intimate friend of us all.

His is the story of quantum mechanics, a new field that he and his colleagues struggled to develop. The beautiful sunrise he saw on Helgoland Island. I want to know about what he did, and to see a sunrise like that over Helgoland. If I could feel the happiness he felt. . . We can never meet Heisenberg, for he is gone, but we can get to know him through his writing.

The most difficult parts of *Physics and Beyond* are those dealing with the content of quantum mechanics itself. If we trace the intellectual path that he followed, it seems reasonable that we will then be able to understand those parts. As we become more and more familiar with Heisenberg, we'll have a much better idea of what people are talking about when they discuss quantum mechanics.

From the time we first encountered *Physics and Beyond*, it was inevitable that we would someday tackle quantum mechanics. That time had now come.

QUANTUM MECHANICS ADVENTURE PART I

So we decided, just like that, to plunge into the adventure of quantum mechanics. We are going to stalk the trail of the physicists who formulated quantum mechanics: M. Planck, A. Einstein, W. Heisenberg, D.L.V. de Broglie, E. Schrödinger, M. Born, and back again to Heisenberg.

We decided to split up into groups, each taking one physicist. Everyone indicated which group they wanted. We determined that we could get through quantum mechanics in ten weeks. The lectures were to be given on Monday afternoons, and the groups would take turns making presentations of their selected topics. Done in this relay fashion, in ten weeks, after ten lectures, our adventure would end. Shinichiro Tomonaga's *Quantum Mechanics I-II* became our official guidebook to the adventure. Making that book our foundation, each group worked hard to prepare their material for their lecture presentation.

When the adventure groups were formed, Hyon consulted some people who had already gone through the adventure of quantum mechanics.

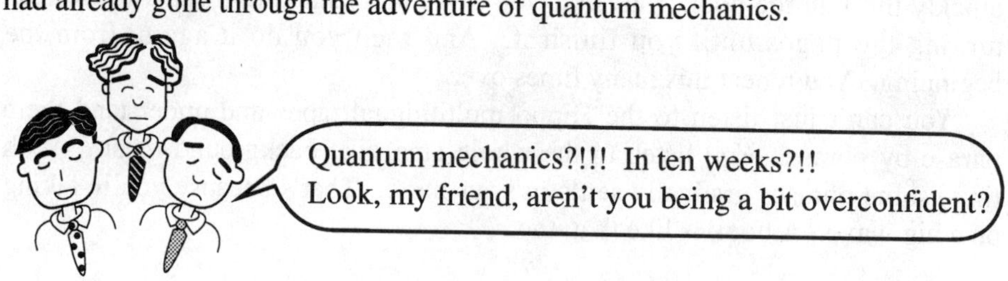

They were seasoned veterans who had encountered the difficulties of quantum mechanics first hand. They had fought their way through quantum mechanics, and it had been a struggle for them. It was only natural that they should warn us off.

To do the highest level of physics, quantum mechanics, with a band of complete novices who couldn't even handle derivatives and integrals very well, and in ten weeks no less, seemed a joke. To learn quantum mechanics, you have to know this, that and a dozen other things first; if you don't you'll get nowhere, or so they said. But if we believed that, we'd never get even close to quantum mechanics, not in a lifetime.

No matter how famous or exceptional they were, when people told us, "To try quantum mechanics, that's pushing things!" we were unimpressed.

We all know from our own experience that by following the ways of small children, we can learn to speak even the most unfamiliar foreign language. In the course of about a year, I learned to speak Russian, a language I had never encountered before in my life. Of course, this was accomplished through the Hippo method of natural learning.

But, come to think of it, I couldn't give you the Japanese equivalents for many Russian words, nor could I come up with the Russian for a number of Japanese words. Even so, I can still say what I want to in Russian. I think I speak like a two- or three-year-old Russian child. Yet children keep on picking up new words, one after the other, and so do I. Last week I knew more than I did two months ago; yesterday, more than last week; and today, more than yesterday. That's the way I've been learning to talk. At some point, my Hippo friends, who were listening to me, began speaking Russian themselves, too.

You need to prepare yourself first, as if you had a big, empty vessel inside you. After that, you keep putting things in it, slowly filling it. You need that "vessel" in which to put all that you acquire. "Capturing the big wave" is filling that vessel with language.

We knew from experience in the Fourier adventure that mathematics could also be done that way. Instinctively we knew it would work for quantum mechanics, too. I say "instinctively" because not a single student at TCL had any notion of what quantum mechanics was.

I wasn't too concerned and remained nonchalant about it all, but it was quite different with Hyon.

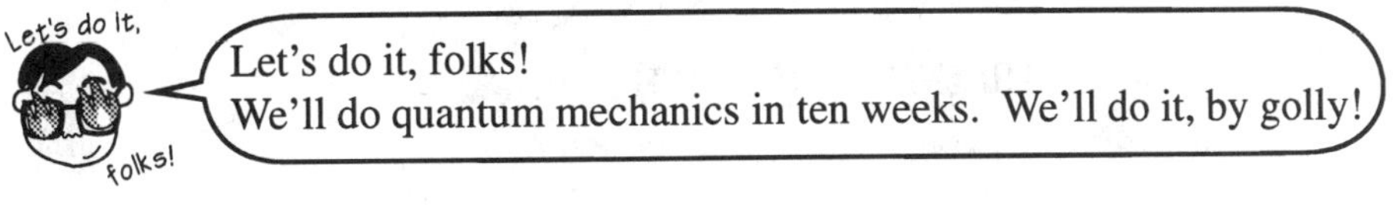

Being told it was impossible, his eyes were burning with determination.

So the TCL students listened to advice from wise experts and promptly forgot it as they set out on the adventure of quantum mechanics.

Ten weeks later, we saw for ourselves the beautiful sunrise on Helgoland. Well, maybe it was not quite Helgoland, but wherever we saw that sunrise, it was as beautiful as the one Heisenberg saw.

Catching the "big wave," we had pulled off our adventure in quantum mechanics. Once you capture the big wave, afterwards it's just a matter of filling in the details. The way we framed our original question was correct after all. Going a step further, we came close to seeing the sunrise as Heisenberg saw it on Helgoland, and we knew we were right.

QUANTUM MECHANICS ADVENTURE PART II

Half a year later, we had completed a one-volume pilot text recording our adventure in quantum mechanics. Some of the expressions in it were rudimentary, but our narrative, told in beginners' voices, reflects our genuine enthusiasm for quantum mechanics. This book was going to be the guidebook for our next adventure.

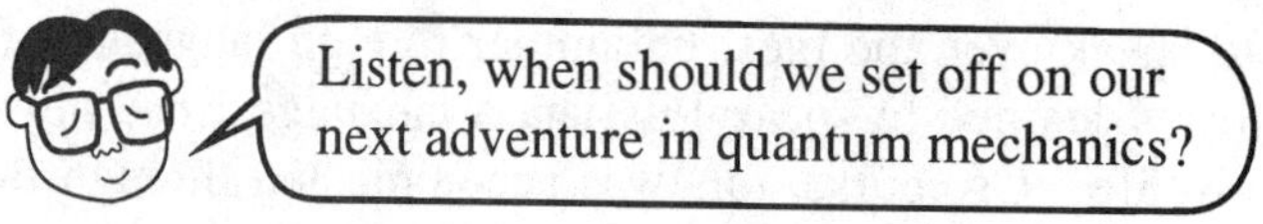

Even before we had time to catch our breath after completing the guide to our adventure in quantum mechanics, Hyon laid this new project upon us.

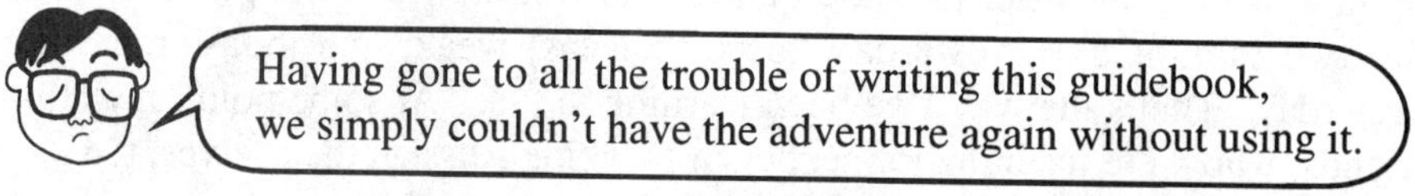

We all started thinking. Everyone wanted to go off on another adventure. But at TCL, there were many other projects that we wanted to pursue, that we had to do. We couldn't just keep doing quantum mechanics.

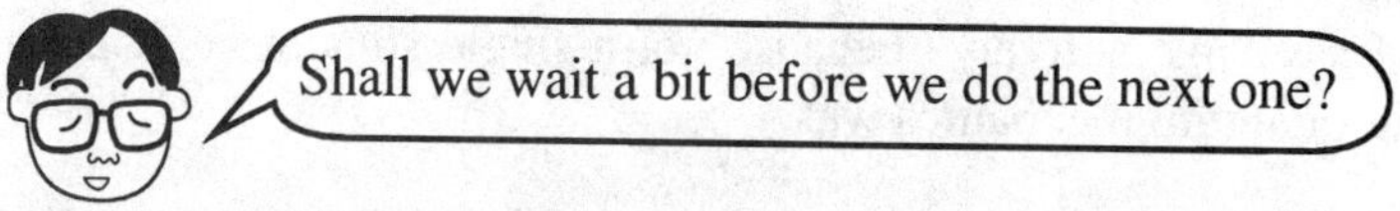

We talked and talked, and just as we were thinking maybe we should wait,

someone suddenly shouted.

It was, actually, the Dean of TCL. Everyone's eyes became sharp and their faces turned white. We all gulped, for just then, after two hours of debating it, we were on the verge of coming to that very decision.

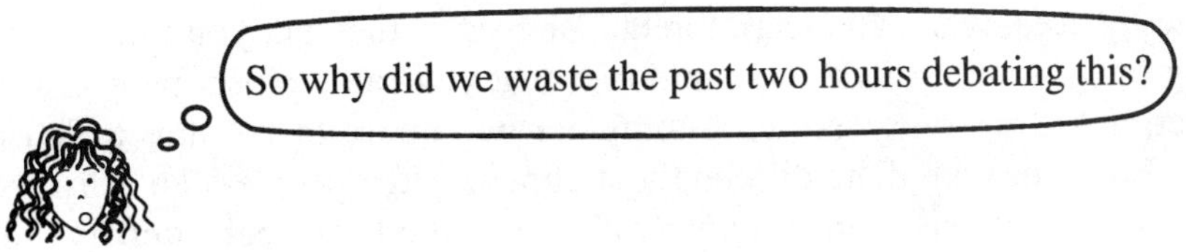

I can't have been the only one with that thought. Later we found out that the Dean had been catnapping through most of our discussion.

And so, with a single whoop of the crane, a single call from the Dean, it was decided we would go on to further adventure in quantum mechanics.

Anyone who has played computer games knows that as you clear one screen and go on to the next, new conditions enter in and it becomes increasingly difficult stage by stage. But that's what makes it interesting. When we came to the second stage of the adventure in quantum mechanics, there were new conditions for us, too.

First of all, we would aim at reaching more people than just TCL students. Our Hippo colleagues who knew nothing about quantum mechanics were to participate in our lectures and serve as our test group. We would teach the fathers, mothers and children of Hippo.

We had to cut down the time it took. In our first adventure, one lecture took almost ten hours. No one would be able to sit and listen for such a long time, except maybe TCL students. So we decided to put together two kinds of classes. They were:

Adventure in Quantum Mechanics —
    Monday, TCL Version (3:00-9:00 PM, ten meetings in all)
Adventure in Quantum Mechanics —
    Sunday Abridged Version (1:30-5:00 PM, four meetings in all)

The Monday version went into detail and was made up mostly of TCL students, while the Sunday version was a more general, "big wave" class aimed at Hippo friends and presented by all of our groups in units of an hour and a half. Some beginning TCL students joined us, moreover. They had just entered and didn't even understand Fourier. Anyone with common sense would have said that bringing in rank neophytes that way was a preposterous notion. But we couldn't have cared less.

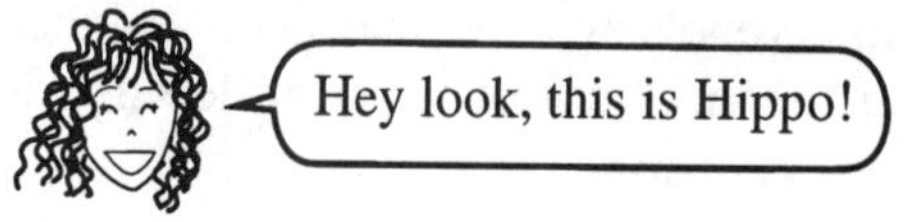

At most places, when you learn foreign languages, they put you into a class according to your ability. The assumption is that you can't expect people who have been at it for five years and complete beginners to be able to learn together. But things are done differently at Hippo. Here people aren't divided into classes. First-timers work together with those who have been attending for years. They do exactly the same things.

That's natural here, for the Hippo Family is really like a neighborhood park where many languages fly about and mingle. Over there you see Hanako, who has been coming to play for quite some time now, and Taro, who just moved into the neighborhood the day before yesterday, playing together. In the Hippo Family, just like the park, no one is ever sent to a beginner's corner. They join right in with everyone else.

When five-year-old Taro moved to America, he went out to the neighborhood parks and played happily with George and Mary. Just one year later, he is chattering away in English. And don't assume that after just a year Taro's English resembles a one-year-old's baby talk; he can speak English as fluently as an American child of six. Nature doesn't divide us into classes.

That's why we aren't divided into classes at Hippo Family or at TCL. People who have just joined our group can learn from those who have been members for some time, and vice versa. At TCL, we don't think twice about doing quantum mechanics together with new students who don't even know Fourier. To us, it's natural, and fun!

And so, together with our new companions, we set out on our second adventure in quantum mechanics.

INTRODUCTION

THE GENERAL FLOW

Now, before we put on the tapes of our adventure in quantum mechanics, let's go over our course. As your guide, I'll give you a broad idea of what we're getting into.

DON'T BE TENSE. ABOVE ALL, RELAX!!

Please think of this not so much as reading, but as viewing. While viewing, relax and enjoy yourself!

Since this is a Hippo school, I thought it would focus on literary topics. Hippo does mostly language-related activities, doesn't it? How did we ever get into math and physics? On top of that, how did we end up becoming involved in something as difficult as quantum mechanics!?

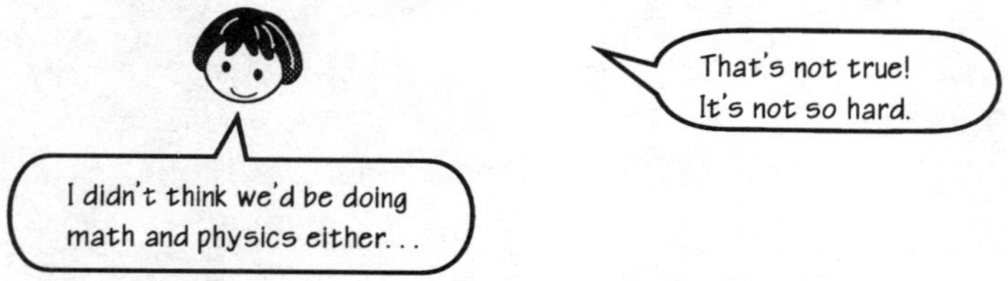

I was thinking I'd like to do research on language at TCL, but. . .

Oscilloscope

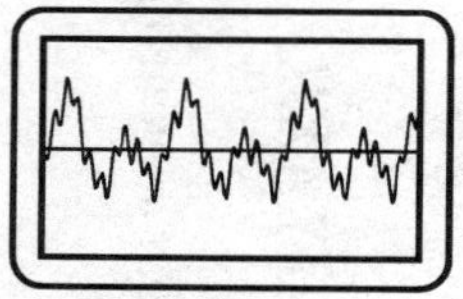

Looking at the wave patterns made by sound, you can actually see words and other vocal sounds with your own eyes.

Then came **the Fourier series.**
Complex waves are aggregates of simple waves.

Without using the Fourier series, it was impossible to break the waves up.

That's how things stood when we decided to do Fourier. And when we did. . .

Mathematics turned out to be a language, too.
Physics is another language that describes nature.

$f = ma$

That was a DISCOVERY!!

As a small child grows,
he or she learns to speak.

→ The natural way

At Hippo, we start speaking new languages like children do. That's why we can speak so many languages in our happy Hippo family.

If we observe  carefully, that little baby can show us how language is acquired naturally!!

At TCL, that's what we call the natural science approach to language acquisition.

Mathematics and physics are no big deal at TCL.

Right.

They're languages, too! And they're easy and fun!

And something else. . .

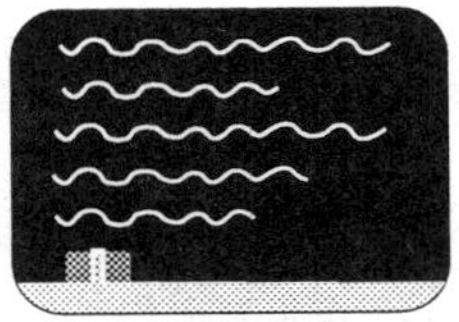

In the beginning, your head spins with all the equations on the blackboard,

But,

Quantum Mechanics

Math is a language, too. Think of the math you're learning as just another new Hippo language tape.

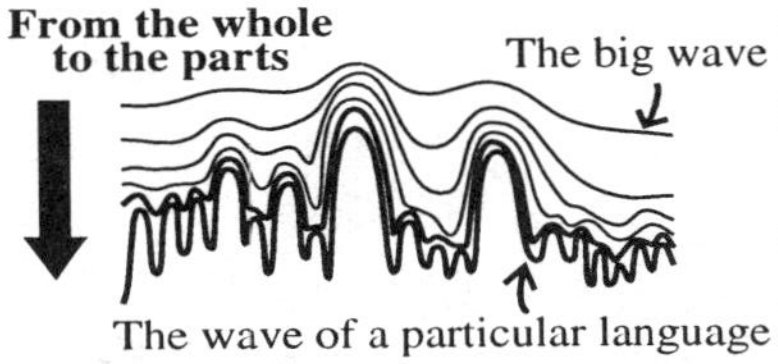

Even if you don't get all the finer points, it's enough if you absorb the general flow.

Gradually, as you listen again and again, you will pick up even the finer points.

Really, it's no different from learning by the other Hippo language tapes!!

Well, that may be so, but. . .

When you enter TCL, there's an assigned text called ***Physics and Beyond*** **by Werner Heisenberg.** You have to read it many times over.
Heisenberg was one of the stars in the world of physics.
We really wanted to know what Heisenberg had done. After we read his book, he felt like an old friend to us.

To enjoy
QUANTUM MECHANICS,
first listen to
THE OVERALL FLOW.
DON'T WORRY ABOUT THE DETAILS.

But, don't dismiss them entirely either.

It's important
to put quantum mechanics
together with everything
you've been doing at Hippo.

Nonetheless, it's  who's going to be giving a talk,

and so you can't expect too much!

Just relax and enjoy reading!

With that,

Vámonos!!

In Chapter 1

Around the end of the 19th century, there were two ways of speaking about things in the world of physics.

1. Particles

2. Waves

There were a number of different ways to explain the movement of things, but they all came down to two types of explanations — particle explanations and wave explanations.

Particles and waves are by definition different things.

Particle

You can throw it.

Wave

When you place your finger on the surface of water, a wave forms around it and gradually spreads.

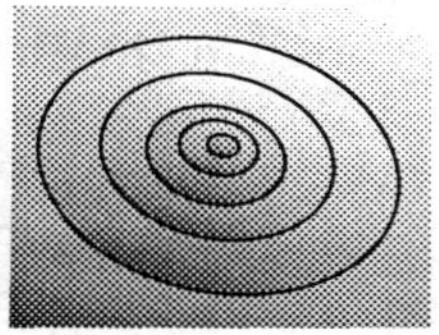

Waves are **continuous.**

Particles hop, and they are **discrete.**

I think waves are great. Which camp are you in, waves or particles?

Everything could be described in terms of one or the other. The descriptions were like two different languages. There were no problems and peace reigned in the world of waves and particles.

Happily, happily

A particle is a particle, and not a wave.
A wave is a wave, and not a particle.
The two were completely different.

The end

Now then. . .

was thought to be waves, not particles.

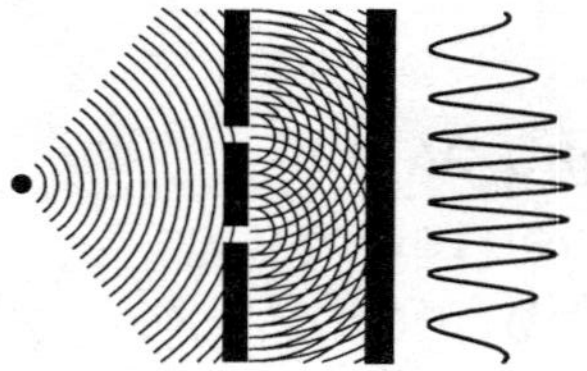

A characteristic of waves is that they expand and spread, and so if something interferes and leaves two openings, the waves pass through both openings and then come together again in a mixed pattern.

Wave Interference

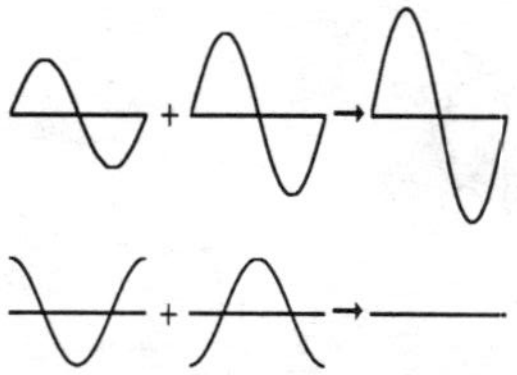

Waves are aggregates, the sum of a number of different waves. Some double when they combine. Others cancel each other out when combined, like the sum of a + and a −. The result is 0.

interfered, so one concluded that **LIGHT = WAVE**

About that time, some of the research being done on light involved a box made of iron or something similar.

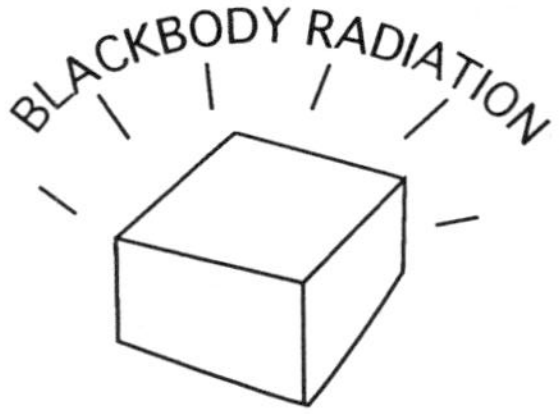

Inside, a vacuum was created, and the box was heated to a high temperature. As it got hotter, the inside of the box glowed. The energy of that light was investigated.

To investigate 

, you have to look at the **SPECTRUM.**

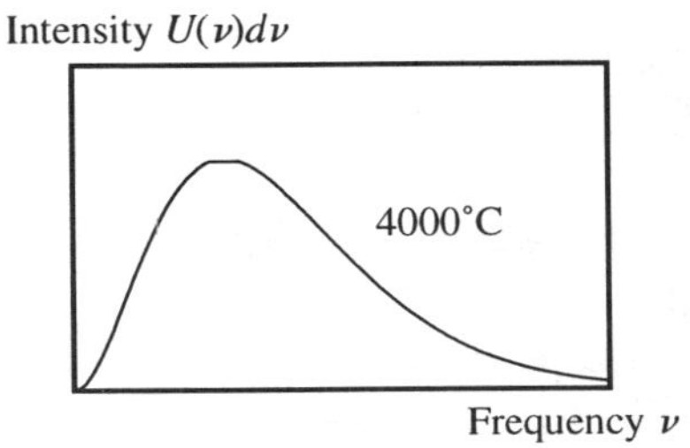

Do you know what a spectrum is?

When you use a prism, the light of the sun breaks up into colors. You can see the different colors that, mixed together, make up sunlight. A spectrum shows the proportions in which those colors are mixed.

Experiments were done, and spectra were identified.

↓ Next. . .

You struggle to find some sort of equation that matches your experimental results.

You see, in physics, you have to test ideas. So you do the experiments first, and the results suggest what laws might be at work.

First the experiments! Actually trying it is crucial! You can't do physics without testing!

Everyone went through much agony and frustration, and then Mr. M. Planck found:

$$U(\nu)d\nu = \frac{8\pi\nu^2}{c^3}\frac{h\nu}{e^{\frac{h\nu}{kT}}-1}d\nu$$

Don't get too intent on the equation. It's less intimidating if you look at it with one eye closed...

Wasn't that great?

But. . .

It's terrific that earnest Planck formulated this equation, but once he had it, even he wasn't sure what it really meant.

In other words, when he formulated the equation, he did not think too much about its deeper significance. His immediate concern was to match experimental results. The finer shades of meaning were less important at that point.

Somehow that reminds me of Hippo.

Night after night,
he thought about it.

I mean, he couldn't make an equation and let it go at that, without knowing what it really meant.

He concluded that. . .

The energy of light is measured in integral multiples of $h\nu$,
which is a specific number (h)
multiplied by the frequency (ν) of the wave.

That is, its energy jumps by
discrete amounts.

But if that is so, **a contradiction emerges.** Precisely because light is a wave (remember wave interference!), its energy should therefore be **continuous.**

A peculiarity of waves

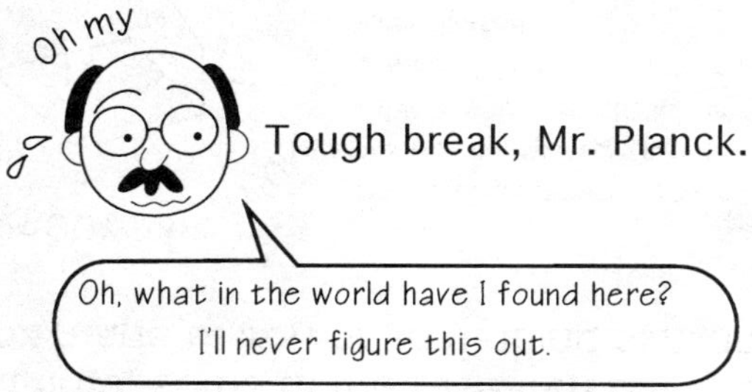

Tough break, Mr. Planck.

The problem was that even though light comes in waves, the values for its energy seemed to be an impossible thing — jumping, discrete values.

As a mathematical expression. . .

$$E = nh\nu \quad (n = 0, 1, 2, 3\cdots)$$

Energy

This is not simply a lowercase *h*.
It's called the **"Planck Constant."**
6.63×10^{-34} (joule·second)
Naturally, it's a value discovered by Planck.

If you can remember it, you'll really impress people!

And then. . .

THE GENIUS MADE HIS APPEARANCE!!

Mr. Einstein said:

"Light is a particle!"

A particle that has energy $h\nu$.

While everyone else was trying to figure it out, a genius spoke up, went beyond them all and settled everything. It was something so simple that no one had even thought of it. It's an incredible quality, and an important one.

Now that's what I call genius!

But simply making a claim about something is
NOT GOOD ENOUGH.

Unless you can actually show experiments where light is acting like a particle. . .

No matter how *good* it may sound, unless you can *prove* that really is the way nature acts, then we can't take it as truth.

Heh heh heh
There are such experiments. . .

PHOTOELECTRIC EFFECT
COMPTON EFFECT

You know, you *don't* have to understand all the details.

Something that could not be explained in terms of waves

could be explained if you used the language of particles.

The way we get sunburned is one case of the photon effect. Ultraviolet rays contained in sunlight are of high frequency (ν is large). When ν is large, $h\nu$ is also large, meaning that the energy ($E = nh\nu$) is high.

So when your face is struck by particles with high energy, you become sunburned.

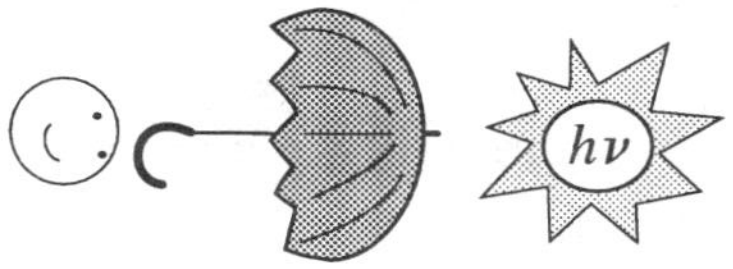

If you don't want to get sunburned, you should shade yourself using a parasol that ultraviolet rays cannot penetrate. How about that!

If  is a , **What Happens. . .?**

WHAT HAPPENS IS QUITE STRANGE.

Can you believe it, sometimes light is a particle; other times it's a wave. It's a pretty slippery notion.

Waves and particles are absolutely incompatible. No matter how much they grow to like one another, they can't be together.

What should we do. . .!?

Until now we have always used the language of particles and waves to talk about things,

But maybe that's simply not possible. . .

What should we do. . .!?

I wonder if we need a new language. . .

Ой, ничего не понимаю!
뭐가 뭔지 모르겠다.
I don't understand at all.

In Chapter 2

At the time of Einstein, there was another very peculiar discovery. **It concerned atoms.** When you break something up into smaller and smaller pieces, you end up with tiny particles.

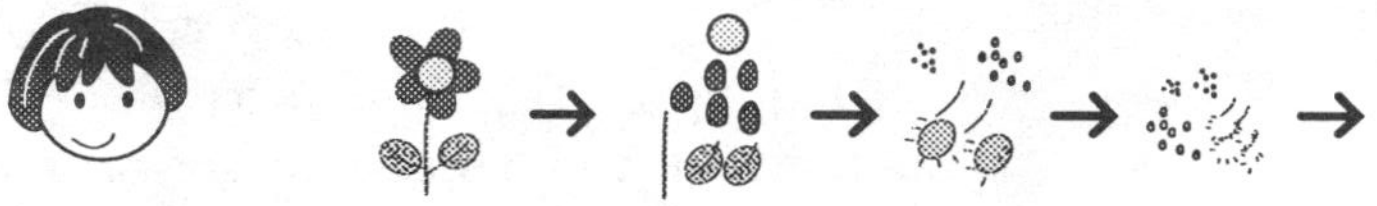

Then you reach a point where you cannot go any farther, and you are at the level of **the atom.**
Of course, it's a kind of particle.

But it was eventually found that the atom was made of yet smaller things.

But **because it was so small, it could not be seen,** and it was difficult to determine the structure of the atom.

When you can't see inside, what do you do?

You sniff it.
You try shaking it.
You test its weight.
You hold it up to the light.
Etc. etc.

You can do all sorts of things, can't you. . .

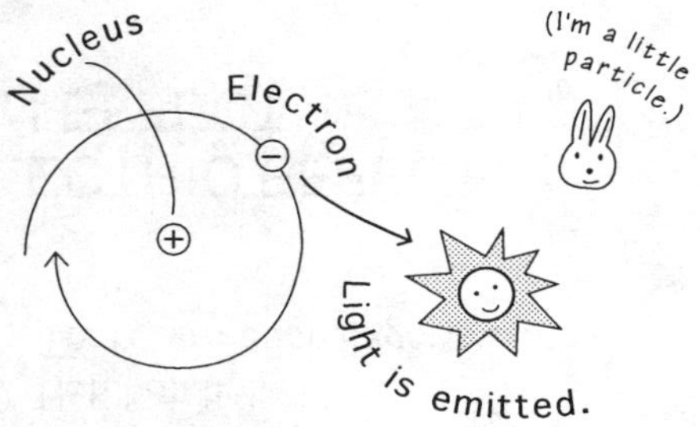

Probably. . .
There are electrons spinning around a nucleus.
When electrons move, they emit light.

That light can be observed.

Its spectrum can be analyzed.

Maybe the electrons and the nucleus behave like the planets rotating around the sun.

But if we continue this line of thought, an electron can give off light only if it works hard,

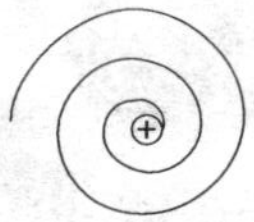

and that means that it uses up energy.

When that happens, the electron loses force. Because the charge of the electron is negative and the charge of the nucleus is positive, the electron is gradually attracted to the nucleus and the atom collapses.

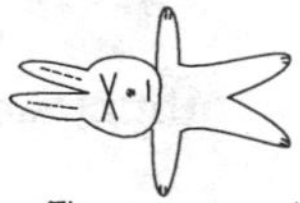

That means trouble.
After all, if that were so, even a person would suddenly become flatter than a pancake whenever energy ran out.
That never, ever happens!!

I think that's the wrong idea. . .

That's right.

It's a fact that atoms do not collapse, so let's revise our theory to show that they don't!

We need to make a substantive turnaround in our first premise, right?

I'm not really sure, but. . .
Let's just settle it!!

Electrons **rotate about the nucleus, but they do not emit light. . .**

Oh my, what a bold idea, but we all know that light has been actually observed.

- Bohr's hypothesis -

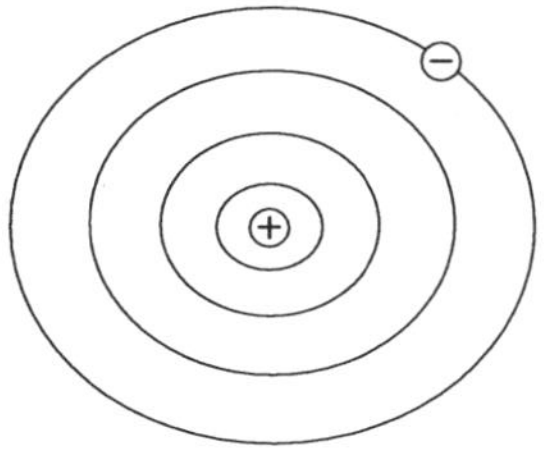

Inside an atom, there are orbits with fixed radii in which electrons rotate.

And when an electron jumps from one orbit to another, **it emits light.**

So if you think this way, our position is all right. We're into a new language for the atom.

Right! That's the bottom line. Rigid ideas are no good. Flexibility — that determines the power of thought.

Hey, wait a second.

I have a question. . .

Question 1. Why does an electron have to stay in a certain fixed orbit?
Question 2. When does an electron jump?

I don't know. . .
I noticed that too, and it puzzled me. . .
But in any case, an atom doesn't collapse into a pancake, and the light that is emitted from it has a certain fixed spectrum.

Taking that into consideration, this is what we end up with.

So you see, we need a special language for talking about atoms.

I'll have Heisenberg think about the rest.

Good idea.
It's easier to understand something you're having trouble with if you borrow everyone else's brains rather than grappling with it on your own.
Thinking together, all sorts of ideas come up.
Even listening to Hippo tapes, you get much more out of them when you listen with everyone else, instead of all by yourself.

At TCL, too, it's not about one person, but putting everyone's heads together.

That's why it's interesting.

At last. . .

In Chapter 3

Suddenly, the young Heisenberg makes his appearance.

A mi me gusta tocar el piano y la física.

No matter how long and hard you try, you can't see inside an atom. You can't know what's going on in there.

So, as for these notions about orbits, let's just forget about them!!

The problem is the spectrum of the light that the electrons give off. If I could only calculate and express it!

Building on the work of , he struggled forward.

A FORCED BREAKTHROUGH!!

At times, hammering away at a breakthrough is the best way. Hey look, sometimes you have to go at it hand and fist. Rah-rah!

Making skillful use of calculations done in physics thus far, Heisenberg was finally able to get his own calculations to work so he could express the spectrum of the atom.

Furthermore, he **formulated an equation** just for that purpose.

And how about this! There was actually a branch of mathematics called matrix theory, and Heisenberg, without knowing of it, ended up reconstructing it all on his own. AMAZING, isn't it?

I didn't know that mathematical theory was ever produced like that. But I suppose all of math actually was formulated in just the same way.

That's how it was. Really!

Mathematics is a drama too, isn't it. . .?

And then. . .

$$q = \sum_{\tau} Q(n; n-\tau) e^{i2\pi\nu(n; n-\tau)t}$$

$$H^{\circ}\xi - W\xi = 0$$

This expresses the electron jumping from n-th orbit to (n-τ)-th orbit.
tau

I'm thrilled!!

I did it!

With this, the spectra of the light emitted by the atom made perfect sense!

That's great, but there's no room at all to think about the orbits in the atom, right? So we're not supposed to think about the inside of the atom?

That is going too far.

No matter how perfectly you can discuss the spectra, that alone doesn't mean that you shouldn't consider the inside of the atom.

Hmm. . .

In Chapter 4

The nobleman de Broglie enters quietly on the scene.

Ladies and gentlemen,

We've thought of the electron as a particle.

Now, what if we thought of it as a wave ?

After all, light too was considered as particle. / wave.

Do you remember?

You see, if you think of it as a wave, then it is a matter of course that it can assume only fixed values.

That is to say. . .

With waves,

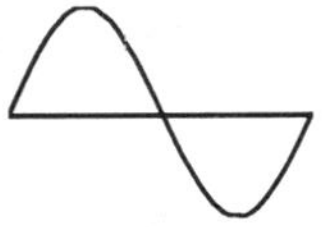

one cycle is always a complete cycle.

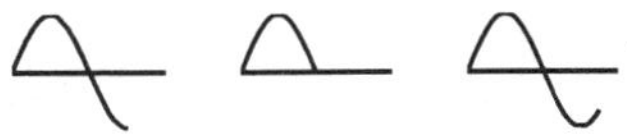

There are no in-betweens such as these,

and, no matter what, you get values constituted like this.

If you think of electrons as a wave, anything you say about orbits is totally unrelated.

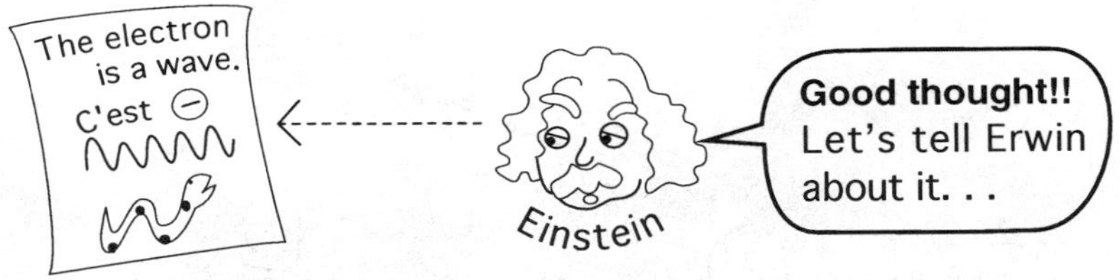

I, Erwin Schrödinger, was ticked off at Heisenberg's thinking.

What, is he kidding? What does he mean, saying, "Don't think about the inside of the atom"?

Don't be ridiculous!

Physics is about properly explaining things in nature. So if you tell me to give up midway and say okay, we'll just explain the spectra of light and let it go at that, we might as well give up on the whole thing right now.

I won't allow it.
I'm going to tell you precisely what's going on.
Like it or not, you'd better listen.

What great determination.

There you have it!

We'll start with that, that the **electron is a wave.**

Now, you can already imagine what a 

is, so you can imagine the inside of the atom.

Ha ha ha
Wow! I did it!

It's important to **be able to imagine** something.

And now,

Get ready. . .

Scribble scribble scribble

$$\nabla^2\phi + 8\pi^2\frac{m}{h}\left(\frac{E}{h}-\frac{V}{h}\right)\phi = 0$$

With this equation, you can talk about anything in the language of waves. Not just electrons, but everything else, too. .

So I can even talk about me, myself, using the language of waves.
My goodness!

In Chapter 5

The thing is,

Schrodinger's equation expressing the energy of an atom and Heisenberg's equation expressing the energy of an atom

AMOUNTED TO THE SAME THING.

That means you don't have to deal with Heisenberg's bothersome equation. It's unnecessary. If you stick to my equation, you won't need anything else.

Heisenberg's equation and my equation are the same thing.

In any event, Heisenberg's is sloppy. It doesn't give you an image of what's going on.

I'll ask Weyl to finish off the equation.

I'll give it a shot.

But as it turned out. . .

It's no good.
It won't work.

Hey, sorry about that.

Oh well, sigh.
I'll do it myself.

After all, if you really want something done, you've got to do it yourself. Right?

I'm going to do it!

Heisenberg's equation

$$\left(\frac{1}{2m}P^{\bigcirc 2}+\frac{k}{2}Q^{\bigcirc 2}\right)\xi - W\xi = 0$$

Schrodinger's equation

$$\frac{d^2}{dx^2}\phi(x)+8\pi^2\frac{m}{h}\left(\frac{E}{h}-\frac{k}{2h}x^2\right)\phi(x)=0$$

If we can neatly change the form of this

Clack clack bzzzzzz
(Actually, what we have to do is calculate everything.)

$$\left\{\frac{1}{2m}\left(\frac{h}{2\pi i}\frac{d}{dx}\right)^2+\frac{k}{2}x^2\right\}\phi(x)-E\phi(x)=0$$

If you take a close look,

$P^{\bigcirc}$ and $\frac{h}{2\pi i}\frac{d}{dx}$	
$Q^{\bigcirc}$ and x	
ξ and $\phi(x)$	
W and E	

These seem to correspond to one another.

Okay, I'll give it all I've got!

That's what I did. I threw myself into figuring out how to get rid of Heisenberg's equation. If I could use my equation to produce the values for every spectrum, in other words, to come up with what Heisenberg calculated by his equation, then my equation could stand alone, and my theory that the electron is a wave would have superseded Heisenberg's.

I struggled with it for a long time, and I finally got rid of the matrices that Heisenberg used.

What I finally arrived at was:

$$H\left(\frac{h}{2\pi i}\frac{d}{dx}, x\right)\phi - E\phi = 0$$

The Schrödinger equation

Perfected!!

That's **magnificent!**
The calculations were exasperating, but some interesting things came out of them.

They had to do with **the effects of language.**

In fact, in Schrödinger's equation,

the $\boxed{\frac{h}{2\pi i}\frac{d}{dx}}$ within a mathematical expression means

It's called an operator.

$\times$ or $+$ or $\div$ or $\int \bigcirc\triangle\square\, dx$

multiply — add — divide — find the area

In a word, do what's called for in a given operation. You can't do much with only this.

But with  stuck on, you can do such-and-such an operation and start calculating.

For example,

Operator ⟶ times 3

$= 3x^2$

When this happens, you can

calculate for all sorts of values of x, right?

At Hippo, **what this amounts to is,**

When you can say only the few things you know, language is still in the state of being an operator.

For example,
When you go to Mexico,

When a speaker successfully communicates to someone, then we can talk about meaning in language.

When a connection occurs between people, the real meaning in language comes to life.

That's how it is.

Therefore,

It's very important that there be a partner.

Language grows in the space between

one  **and the**  **.**

Don't forget, after all, that
the meaning of words has to do with the fact that they work.

Even though she didn't understand its meaning too well, when she used the word instinctively, it worked very well.

thinking that's what it meant,

How interesting it is that so many things are just like language!
I'm not afraid even of math now.

About that time,

Everything in the world is a wave, a wave!!
The electron is a wave.
It is. It is!
We don't need Heisenberg's equation at all, at all.
My equation compared to Heisenberg's is so easy, so easy.
Hurrah!!

WAIT A MINUTE!!

Cool eyes surveyed the situation. . .

Schrö

Hey, Schrö, since the wave $f(\phi)$ in your equation is a wave that can be imagined, one ought to be able to know where and when it occurs.
Nevertheless, when you try the various calculations, lo and behold, you end up with **6, 9 or even more dimensions!**

?

Darn!

So, after all this, we're back to the Heisenberg problem.
You can't maintain a visual image.

What in the world have I been doing up to now?

Wave was my starting point to be sure, but at some point, it turned into an incomprehensible monster.

I guess my equation is still **unfinished.**
However, it couldn't be entirely wrong!
Whichever one you choose, mine has got to be better than Heisenberg's. **Anyway, the problems in mine will be solved in no time.**

But the problems were not solved. Even with Schrödinger's equation, the electron, in the end, remained a mysterious, unknown thing.

In Chapter 6

Is light a particle or a wave?

Even if you start with a
particle ⟶ an image cannot be sustained.
wave ⟶ an image cannot be sustained.

Then what in the world is light ? is an electron ?

Look! Can you believe it? It's Olivia Newton-John's grandfather.

M. Born

This is not the behavior of waves and particles.

ordinary ordinary

In the end, I'd say this is about a wave of probability.

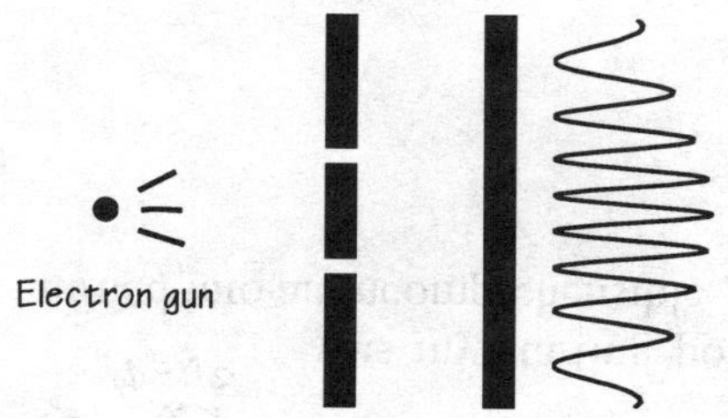

When you shoot off an electron gun at a wall through a screen with two holes, and then see where and in what quantity the electrons strike the wall, you find that they form an interference pattern.

This is a **wave**, isn't it?

But the electrons also display **particle**-like characteristics as in the Compton effect.

You really get the feeling that **they're both particle and wave.**

Still. . .

If you think of it as probability, a wave of probability, then you can neatly explain everything.

Probability? Is that when, for example, the chance of a six coming up on a die is $\frac{1}{6}$, kind of like a prediction?

That's right. That's right.

So far the theories have been expressed in terms of probability. That's why it's not a question here of particle or wave.

W. Heisenberg

Hey, I object to such a vague and uncertain method of resolving this!

It's true that when you apply the idea of probability, all of the numerical values and the phenomena are tied together. I don't dispute that.

We had thought it was wave interference, and if we think of it as the interference of a probability wave, it will look as if the problem has (perhaps) gone away.

It has been said that probability exhibits interference.

But probability is a matter of approximation. Is it all right to settle for something that has accidentally ended up becoming a matter of approximation?

Up until now, the question "Are light and electrons particles or waves?" has kept everyone in a quandary.

Now Born says that it's neither wave nor particle, but a (an ordinary) **PROBABILITY WAVE,** and that probability interferes and makes a wave-like interference pattern.

Somehow, I feel like I've been tricked.

Moreover, the electron can only be thought of as a particle. What's to become of the cloud chamber experiment?

The cloud chamber experiment?. . .

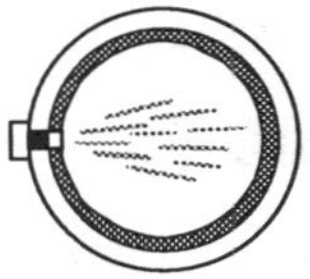

A box is prepared to allow fog to form inside. Things are set up so that electrons will be emitted. After a while, electrons spurt through the fog. At that time, tracks like the contrails of an airplane become visible.

This experiment was done to prove that the electron is a particle.

HMMMM. . .
THE YOUNG HEISENBERG THOUGHT AND THOUGHT.

As Einstein would say. . .

Absolutely!!

We thought we were seeing electrons flying around inside the cloud chamber.
Actually, we might have been looking at particles of fog formed by the passing electrons.

An ordinary wave

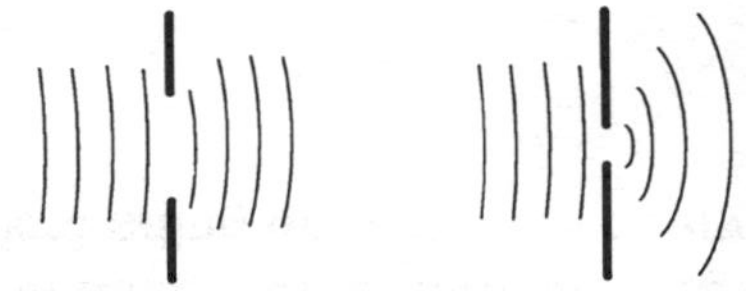

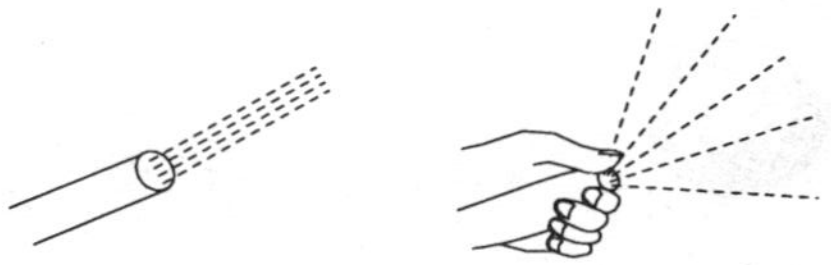

When you use a hose, if you don't squeeze it, the water flow as it comes out is about the breadth of the hose itself.

If you squeeze the end of the hose, the water goes shwee and spreads out.

When the hose width is large ⟶ the spread is small.
When the hose width is small ⟶ the spread is large.

It's an inverse relationship, isn't it?

That's true inside a cloud chamber, too.

Enlarge a cloud particle. . .

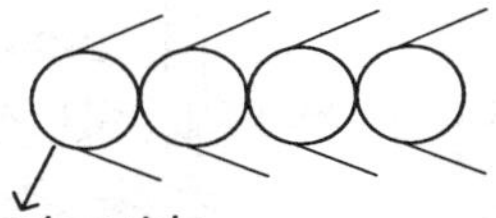

When the probability wave of the electron tries to spread, it strikes cloud particles. The width of the cloud particle is extremely large in comparison to the electron, and the spread is small.

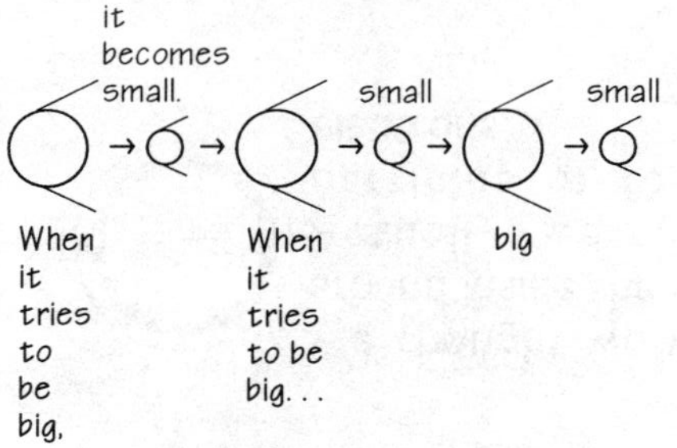

The end result is that it doesn't get very big. The spread doesn't fan out much.

That's why it came out looking like airplane contrails, right?

Although it's a wave, it turns out to be a wave that doesn't spread!!

This is. . .

the famous. . .

UNCERTAINTY PRINCIPLE

$$\Delta x \cdot \Delta p_x \approx h$$

It's the Planck constant!

Delta (a certain width)
Like a margin of error

If you try making this small — Δx — Δp_x — this gets bigger.

this grows bigger — Δx — Δp_x — If you make this smaller

Can't we get rid of one or both widths?

Light and Electron cannot be determined more precisely than within the width of *h*. Such light (Light) or electrons (electrons) are called QUANTA.

Whee!

Now that I think about it, and without even realizing it, I've set (foot) inside the world of **QUANTUM MECHANICS!**

It turned out to be even more momentous.

Until now,

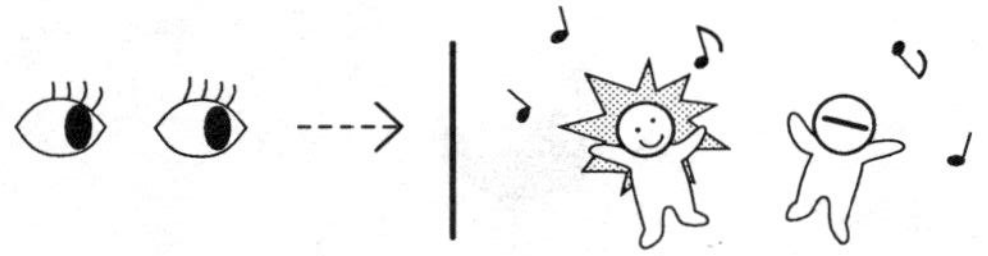

there was a clear **boundary** between the act of looking and things that could be seen.

It's the Berlin Wall!

Well, of course!

Even so. . . In the world of quanta,

The Berlin Wall crumbles!!

The condition of something appears differently depending on how it is observed.

In other words,
as it's a matter of probability,

A condition with several possibilities turns into a single condition.

And after having seen it, you can say with confidence,

"She's singing!"

In classical mechanics,

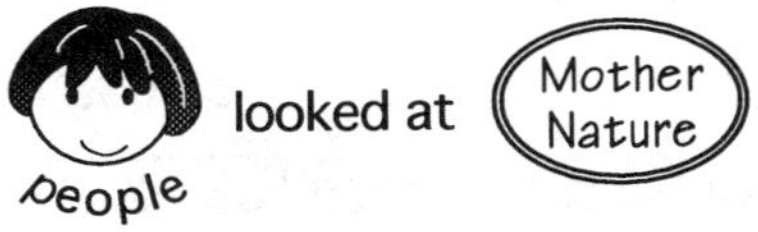

and tried to explain her from the standpoint of people looking in from the outside.

In quantum mechanics,

can be talked about from both inner and outer vantage points.

Nature that holds human beings within it

These two modes turned out to be decidedly different.

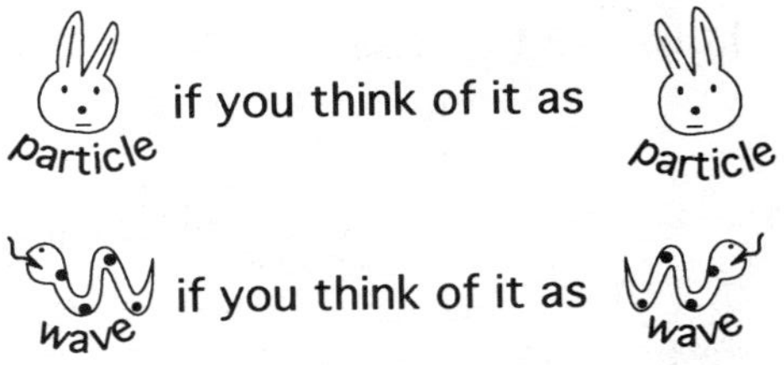

You can't think like that!

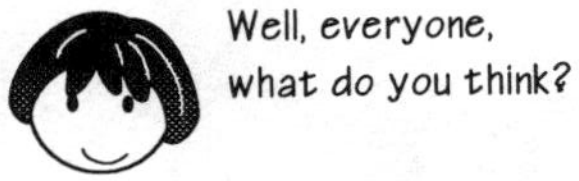

Well. . .

EINSTEIN was furious.

You say probability!!
The condition changes!!

A nature in which human beings are subsumed!!

You say that until you see it, it's a possibility, and when you see it, it's a fact!!

That's outrageous!
Nature is not fickle or vague.

There has to be an overall order to it,
completely apart from humans or anything else.
I'll prove it to you!

And so, he steadfastly refused to recognize the probability way of thinking.

Well, it sure is odd. . .

Even geniuses, when they get involved in new ways of thinking, sometimes don't understand exactly what they're doing.

Still, you have to admit that we can understand only the things that can be talked about and communicated through language.

But at Hippo. . .

grammar, spelling and pronunciation

Language **<u>isn't</u>** something that comes to us **<u>from outside</u>** ourselves.

Just like a baby
— the Natural Human if there ever was one —
we go by what's happening **within ourselves.**

Rather than classical mechanics,
don't you think this is quantum mechanics?

The world of quanta, considered in terms of our world,

isn't completely strange after all!

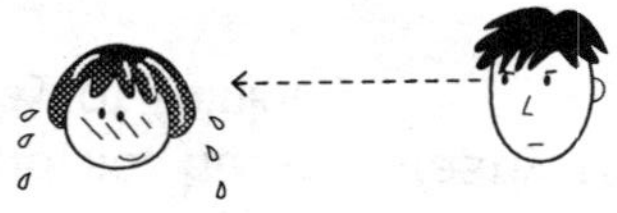

When you're riding on a train and feel someone's gaze on you, you become a bit startled and feel self-conscious.

Maybe a baby sings at home, but a baby wouldn't just sing out if other people were around.

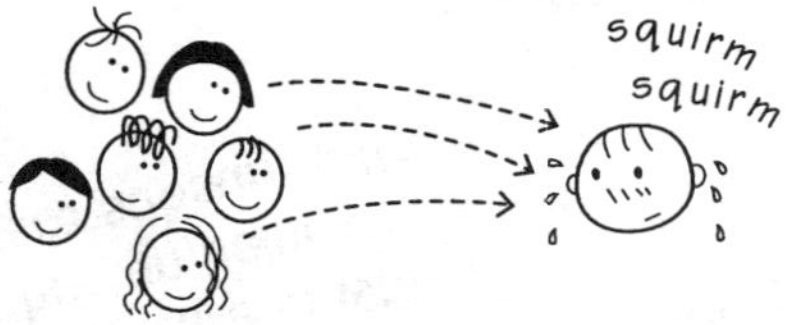

When many people are watching, a baby can't help but become tense and fidgety.

The act of watching changes the conditions.

It appears as if looking at something gives off some sort of energy.

The distinct sounds of each individual word and the BIG WAVE

If you try to zero in on each little sound, you won't pick up the big wave.

If you set your antennas only for the big wave, you won't pick up the little sounds.

THAT'S THE UNCERTAINTY PRINCIPLE!

It gets interesting when you think about and examine a variety of things. If you come across something interesting, think about it!

To conclude. . .

How was it?

We've touched on quantum mechanics. . .
I really want to know more about quantum mechanics. . .
Hippo is becoming more and more interesting. . .
I'm really beginning to think TCL is quite interesting. . .

It really gets interesting when you start to understand what you've striven to understand.

What do you think?

Actually, that's what I'm hoping for. Ha ha ha. . .

It's exactly the same as getting to know a language!!

Thanks for staying with us until the end.

Thank you!

CHAPTER 1

Max Planck and Albert Einstein

WHAT IS LIGHT?

It's time to set out on our adventure in quantum mechanics! The first clues to quantum mechanics were found in the strange behavior of light. For many years, light was described as a wave until new experiments began yielding results, time after time, that could only be explained if light was a particle. Was light a particle, or a wave?? Physicists were to be caught up in a heated theoretical debate over this question for more than thirty years.

1.1 GETTING STARTED

We're off!

It's time to set out on our adventure in quantum mechanics! Let's work together to make it an enjoyable one.

First, though, what do you each hope to get out of this adventure?

As for me, I'd like to know just what Heisenberg's *Physics and Beyond* is really talking about. I think it would be a really powerful experience to be able to read the Heisenberg-Schrödinger debates with an understanding of quantum mechanics.

Heisenberg, Werner Karl
[1901-1976]

Schrödinger, Erwin
[1887-1961]

I'd like to know how physicists discovered a language to describe quantum mechanics. One of our premises in our research at TCL is that human language is a natural phenomenon. Since language is a natural phenomenon, maybe it can be explained using the language of physics! After all, there must be some kind of order in it.

Gee, everybody is thinking about something different. In my case, I don't know a thing about quantum mechanics, and I'll be lucky to feel even a little comfortable with it by the end of our adventure.

This is really basic, but quantum mechanics is a part of physics, right? From the very start, I've never been able to understand physics. Beginning in high school, I wondered why in the world I had to study physics! But since entering TCL and working with all of you, I've begun to catch on. Physics makes much more sense to me now. Can I tell you about it?

WHAT IS PHYSICS?

High school physics uses mathematical formulas to explain things such as, "How does a spring with a weight attached to it move?" or "How does a ball fall?" or "How do the planets move?" But we don't have to know those things to play catch and see the stars, right? So I used to think, "Why do we have to go to all the trouble of studying physics?" and "Why do we even have physics?" But recently it hit me. Maybe physics began like this.

Once upon a time, there was fire. . .

1. Once upon a time, people came upon a fire that started by chance.
2. They warmed themselves by the fire, maybe roasted some fish, and found that the fire was useful.
3. But before long, it went out.
4. They just couldn't forget how useful that fire had been.

Starting another fire

1. Unable to put the wonderful fire out of their minds, people didn't want to just wait for nature to produce another one.
2. They tried to start their own fires.
3. Then while trying out different ideas, they were able to start a fire themselves.
4. So people could roast their fish again.

And they told everyone how.

Anyone would want to know about something so useful.

So, they showed other people how to start fires. They came, one after the other.

As they made more fires, they began to understand its properties better.

Gradually knowledge about fire spread and was passed on.

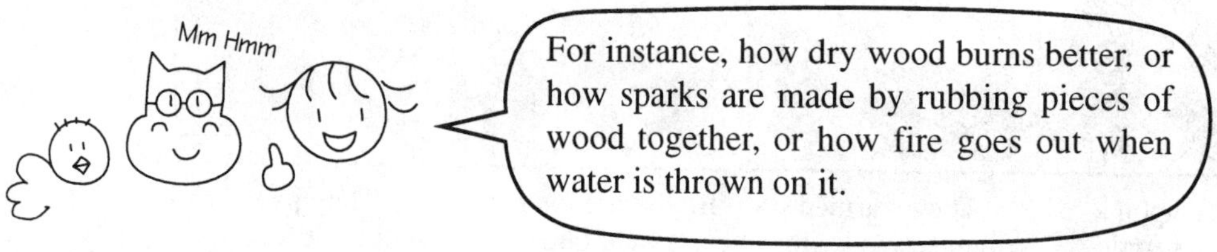

To us today, there is nothing mysterious about why fire burns, but long ago it was thought to be very strange. But because fire was so useful, people did their best to find out how to start it themselves. Through trial and error they discovered that, "If x and y are prepared, and z is done to them, then a fire will always start." It was a kind of natural law.

I bet physics started from trying to explain familiar but unexplained occurrences like this.

I realized that other natural phenomena, even if we don't pay much attention to them because we take them for granted, are also governed by natural laws. Today's physics must have come about as we gradually discovered and explained those laws. Physicists explain them using mathematical formulas instead of ordinary language. The formulas they use are a universal language that can be understood by people of all nations. When I realized this, I finally understood why, in high school physics, we studied the movement of a spring with a weight attached to it.

Since quantum mechanics is a part of physics, perhaps we can think of it in the same way as we regard starting fires. Quantum mechanics is the way physicists, using the vocabulary of mathematical expressions, describe and explain the strange physical phenomena arising from quanta, or subatomic particles.

Mathematical formulas are a universal language, after all.

All right! Let's get started on our adventure in quantum mechanics.

¡Si, Vamonos!

WHAT'S A QUANTUM?

When you hear the word "quantum" for the first time, you probably wonder, "quantum"?

"What's that?"

A quantum is the smallest unit of which all matter is composed.

If we take a substance and divide it into smaller and smaller parts, what happens?

This question was already being asked by the ancient Greeks. At the time, something called an atom was thought to be the smallest unit of all matter. In recent years, experiments have confirmed the existence of atoms, but scientists found that they could subdivide atoms into something even smaller. That smaller unit is a quantum.

Quantum does not refer to only one thing, however. Matter is made up of a number of tiny units, including electrons, photons, protons and so on. Quantum is a general term applied to all such units. They are so small that, even with today's technology, we still cannot see them.

Hey, you can't actually see quanta!

Quantum mechanics uses mathematical expressions to describe how these invisible quanta behave in nature.

But how can you describe something that you can't see? And how do we even know they exist, if we can't see them?

How can we say, "It's invisible, but it exists"?

DESCRIBE SOMETHING WE CAN'T SEE?!

Let's use an analogy to something familiar to get a general idea. Think about how someone can guess the contents of a gift package without opening the box.

You can infer several things from the box's size and weight.

Shake it and see what sound it makes!

Smell it.

We can hold it, shake it, and from the weight or the sound, imagine what the contents might be.

It's true that we can't see quanta directly, but through experiments we can observe phenomena that are affected by quanta, i.e. the way the movement of electrons affects the movement of an ammeter. By closely observing such phenomena, physicists tried to describe and understand what these invisible quanta were.

Actually, we often talk about things that we can't see and try to explain them. For example, when we are in a room and a door opens by itself, we say to ourselves, "It was the wind." Particularly in the areas of statistical mechanics and thermodynamics, physicists have made great discoveries by hypothesizing about tiny invisible particles or molecules.

So now we can begin to understand what it means to describe something that is invisible. Physics is more than explaining why clearly visible things react in a certain way under given conditions. Even when something is invisible, it is possible to manipulate it and then observe the resulting phenomena. In this way, we can explain quite a bit about something we can't see.

So that's how quantum mechanics explains things.

But what was it that got the whole field of quantum mechanics started? It must have been some strange, new phenomena that no one had ever observed before. . .

That must be it. And to explain them, physicists used the word "quanta." Through quanta, they were able to explain strange, new phenomena. Don't you think that is how they came to be explained?

Actually, that's not quite the way it happened. The original circumstances surrounding the advent of quantum mechanics concerned something that was already believed to be thoroughly understood.

WHAT IS THIS THING CALLED LIGHT?

We ordinarily live surrounded by light — sunlight, electric light, candlelight. We would not be able to see a thing without light, and a life without light is something that we cannot even imagine. That something so familiar should have been the beginning of quantum mechanics must be surprising to many people. For one thing, since we just said that quanta are invisible, you may be thinking, "Well, light is certainly visible, isn't it?" Of course we see light every day. But how many people can answer questions such as

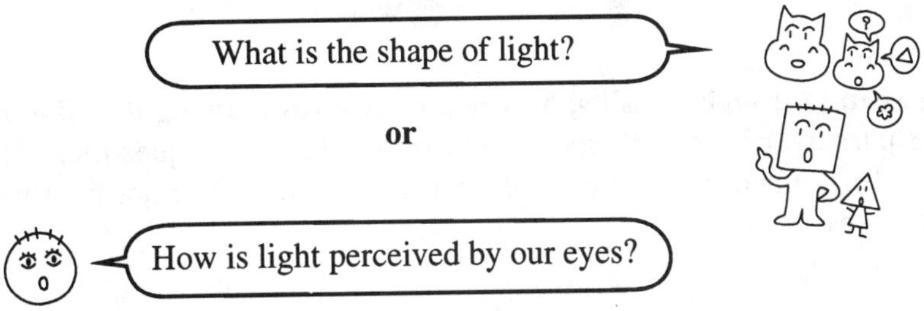

That's right! In fact, no one has seen the actual form of light. It is an odd thing; we see it and yet we don't see it. How was it explained by physicists before?

LIGHT IS WAVE MOTION

Before quantum mechanics was established, classical physics in the nineteenth century explained light as a wave.

They thought this because light **INTERFERES.** An example of interference that is familiar to everyone is the collision of two waves on the surface of water. We have said that the form of light itself cannot be directly observed. Nevertheless, by performing certain experiments, it is possible to observe signs that light is interfering. It has been shown that the manner in which light is transmitted follows the same patterns as waves in the sea. This was confirmed by the slit experiment, which was first performed in the early nineteenth century.

1. 2 THE SLIT EXPERIMENT

WHAT IS THE SLIT EXPERIMENT?

Young, Thomas
[1773-1829]

In 1807, an English physicist named Thomas Young performed the slit experiment. The equipment used in the experiment was something like this:

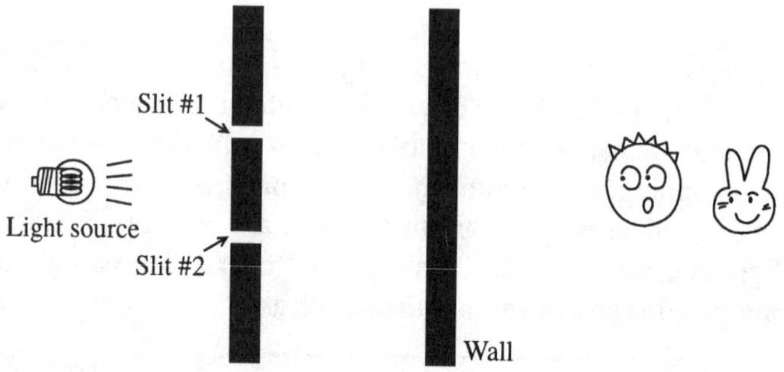

monochromatic light: light which oscillates at a certain frequency.

After passing through the slits, how will monochromatic light strike the wall? The purpose of the slit experiment was to study that question. The results of the experiment made it possible to confirm whether or not light was made up of waves.

WAVE INTERFERENCE

Before experimenting with light, let's first consider the phenomenon of wave interference using water waves, which we can see.

As shown in the illustration, a board with two slits is placed in a tank of water.

Next, a float in the water is vibrated at a fixed rate, forming waves.

The waves pass though the slits and strike the wall opposite.

What is the **intensity** of the waves as they strike this wall? The purpose of this experiment is to discover the answer.

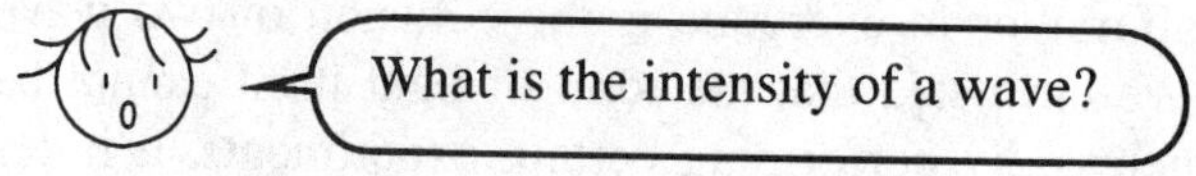

The intensity of a wave is its strength as measured by its amplitude, that is, its height. The intensity of a tall wave is high; that of a low wave is low.

I get it! After all, the higher a wave is in the ocean, the more destructive power it has!

To understand the results better, let's examine three separate cases.

1. Only slit #1 open
2. Only slit #2 open
3. Both slits open

1. Only slit #1 open

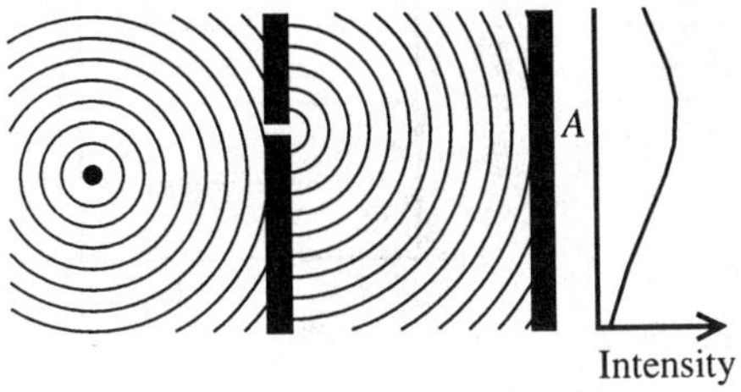

When a wave strikes the wall after passing through slit #1, its intensity is greatest at point *A*, directly opposite slit #1. This is because the farther a wave travels, the weaker it becomes. The intensity of the wave as it strikes the wall is shown in the graph on the left.

2. Only slit #2 open

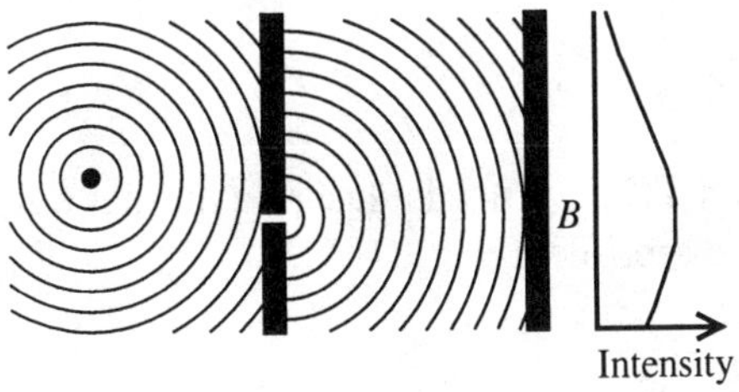

This is similar to case 1. This time the intensity of the wave is greatest at point *B*. As the distance from slit #2 increases, the wave becomes weaker.

3. Both slits open

Now what happens when we open both slits?

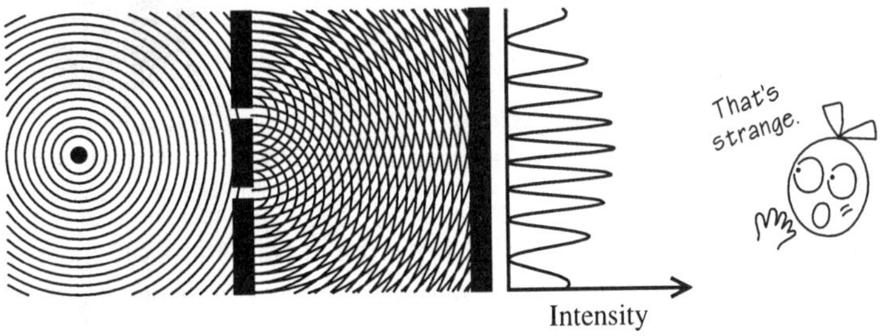

What? Look at that complicated graph. The waves passing through slit #1 and slit #2 are **INTERFERING**!

The radiating web of lines emerging from the slits is called an interference pattern. That pattern occurs because when two waves strike each other, there is a net effect. The waves either combine and grow stronger, or conversely, they cancel each other out.

For example. . .

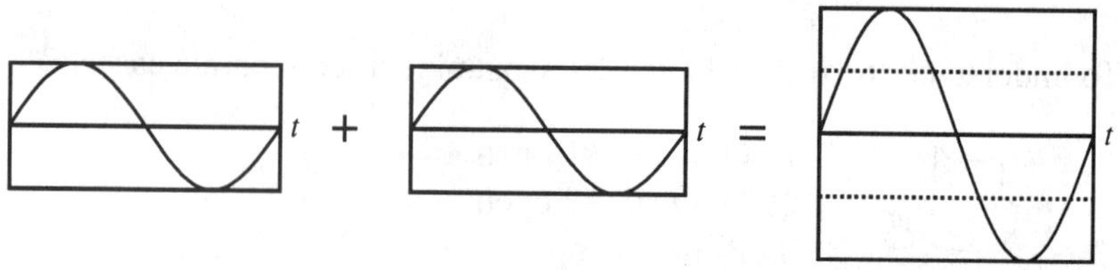

When the wave cycles coincide and are synchronous, their height (amplitude) is doubled.

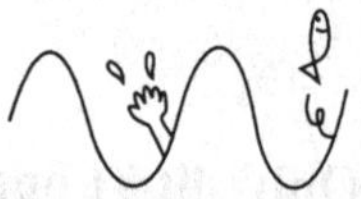

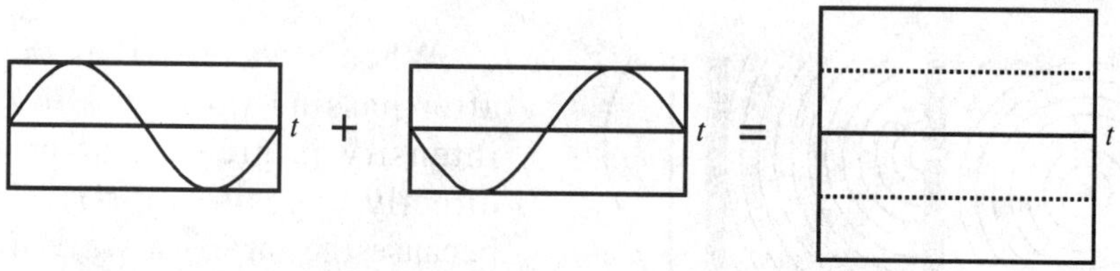

If the waves are half a cycle apart, they cancel each other out. The result is exactly the same as if there were no waves at all.

LET'S LOOK AT THE INTERFERENCE OF LIGHT!

Now let's look at light interference. At TCL we used a laser beam that emits monochromatic light to conduct the experiment.

The experiment using a laser beam

<Things to prepare>

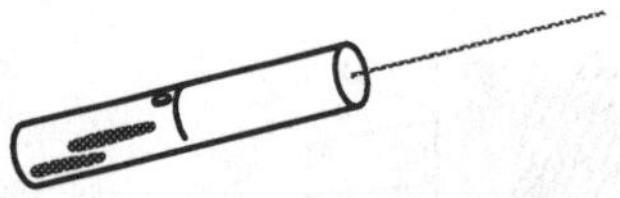

Laser beam projector
(Battery powered, hand-held device)

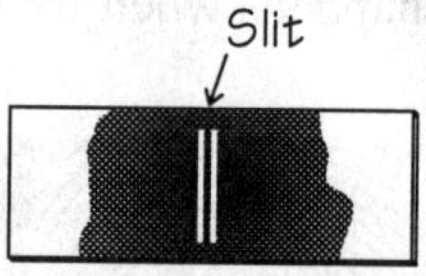

Glass slide with two slits
(Soot is applied using a lighter, and two slits are scraped out using an X-Acto knife.)

Okay, we're all set. Let's shine the laser beam on the glass slide! After passing through the two slits, how will the laser beam strike the wall?

<Experimental results>

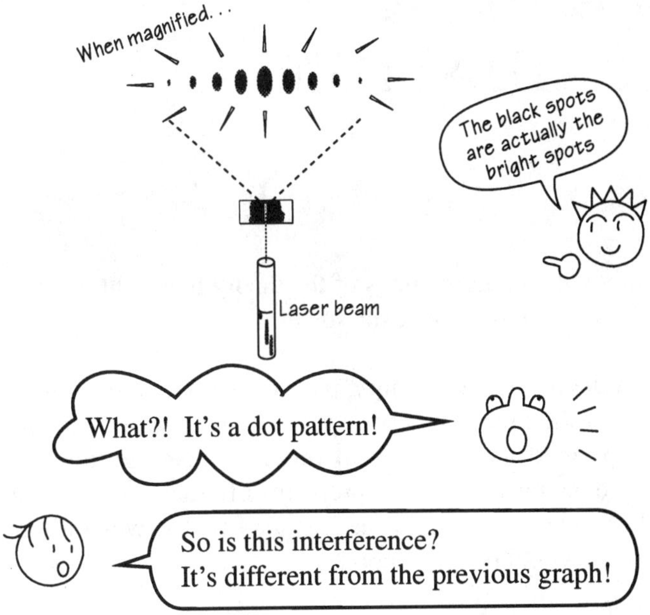

We can think of the brightness of light in the same way we thought of the intensity of water waves. If we express the dot pattern as a graph, the result is identical to the previous graph.

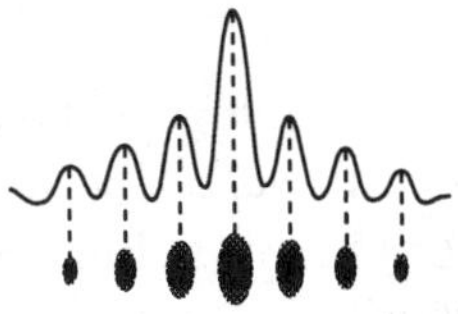

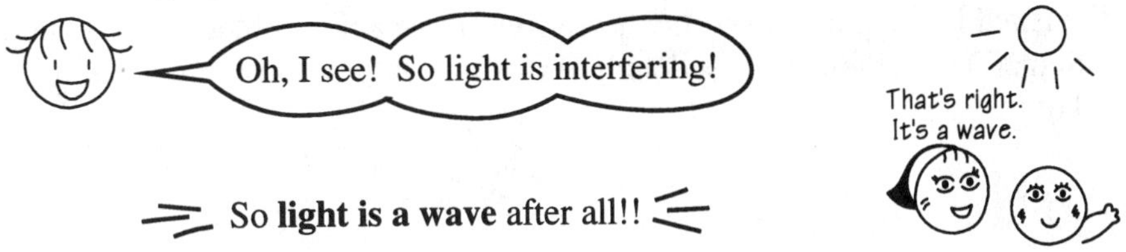

The results of the slit experiment confirmed that light is a wave. Following Young's experiment, this wave theory of light was not questioned for nearly a hundred years. The theory of electromagnetics, completed by James Maxwell at about the same time, was a culmination of the theory light = waves. The new theory of electromagnetics seemed to be further proof that light is a wave.

Maxwell, James Clerk
[1831-1879]

BUT! In December 1900, a single experiment shattered the seemingly unassailable argument that light is a wave. However, it was difficult to understand the meaning of the equations used to explain the experiment, since they had absolutely no connection with any theories known so far. With the results of this experiment in 1900, physicists had to go back to the drawing board and start over. This event was closely related to the birth of the quantum theory.

1. 3 BLACKBODY RADIATION

MAX PLANCK APPEARED ON THE SCENE

Just one test shook the underpinnings of the theory that light is a wave. It was called the "blackbody radiation" experiment.

By the end of the nineteenth century, physics seemed to be in its final stages of development. At the time it was believed that there were no phenomena that could not be explained using classical theory — Newtonian dynamics or Maxwell's electrodynamics. Only the problems of blackbody radiation and the atom remained unsolved, and everyone assumed that it was only a matter of time before they too would be understood.

Plank, Max Karl Ernst Ludwig
[1858-1947]

Max Planck, who spent four years studying blackbody radiation, was born in 1858 in Kiel, Germany. For generations his family had been lawyers and theologians, and so it was not surprising that he was brought up to be very proper and conservative. It was said that Planck, known to be an orthodox disciple of classical physics, was drawn to physics by the law of the conservation of energy.

After graduating from school with highest honors, the young Planck became a professor at Kiel University in 1885. He soon established himself as the leading authority on thermodynamics, but he had yet to make the great discovery that would set the world on edge. He plodded along in his research until, visited by fate, he solved the heretofore intractable problem of blackbody radiation. That achievement suddenly thrust him into the highest ranks of the world of physics.

Nevertheless, he was not satisfied with his results. The hypothesis he had constructed turned out to be an apparent anomaly that could not be explained by the classical theory that was the bedrock of his scientific assumptions. Disturbed by the implications of his work on blackbody radiation, he redid his calculations over and over again. Every time, the results pointed to the same hypothesis. It was the only possible explanation.

No one, not even Planck himself, could have imagined that this would open the door to quantum mechanics.

BLACKBODY RADIATION

The following experiment relates to blackbody radiation. A vacuum is created inside a box of iron or similar black metal. The box is then heated. The question is, can light be produced inside the box? If so, how? What kind of light will fill the box?

If the box is heated to 40°C (about 104°F), what will the temperature be inside the box?

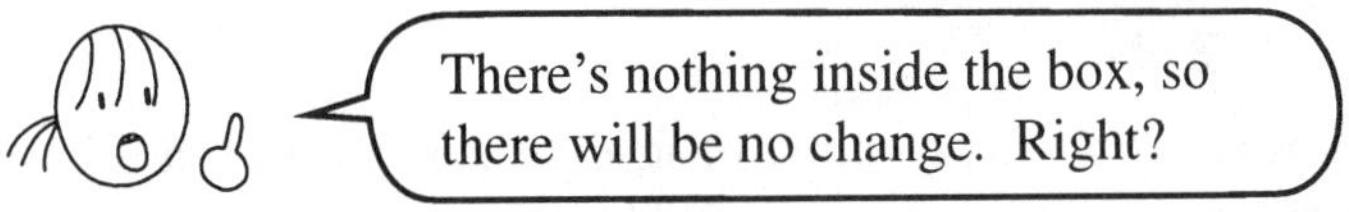

What if there is water in the box? The water will draw heat from the box and its temperature will rise to 40°C. In other words, heat is conducted to the water. You're wrong if you think heat is not transmitted in a vacuum because there is no medium of transmission. Even in a vacuum, heat is transmitted.

What transmits heat? **LIGHT.**

Consider sunbathing. Between a person sunbathing on the earth and the sun pouring forth its warm light, there are about 150 million kilometers (93 million miles) of empty vacuum in space. Nevertheless, the sun is able to send plenty of heat to the earth.

The blackbody radiation experiment may be better understood by thinking of an iron nail which glows when it is heated. At first, it will glow red. As the temperature is increased, the nail will begin to glow orange, gradually becoming "white hot."

In the blackbody radiation experiment, an iron box, rather than a nail, is used. When the box is heated, it glows the same way that the nail did. Now, what happens inside the box when it glows? That's it! The inside of the box is filled with light. Just like the nail, the light inside the box changes colors according to the temperature of the box. In dealing with blackbody radiation, we are concerned with this relationship of light and temperature. That is to say,

At various given temperatures, what sort of light will we find inside the box?

We will determine this, and then explain the result.

THE SPECTRUM

How can we precisely describe the light in the box? This can be simply done by measuring the spectrum.

What's a "spectrum"?

In a spectrum, we can find the characteristics of complicated light waves with one glance at a graph. Since a complicated light wave is made up of an accumulation of simple waves, by analyzing the quantities of the simple waves, it is possible to understand the larger, complicated wave.

Really? Come to think of it, light is a wave after all! Right? That's why its characteristics can be analyzed by measuring a spectrum.

But what kind of graph lets you see these characteristics at one glance?

Let's use the analogy of vegetable juice. (Some of you may have encountered this in our book *Who is Fourier? A Mathematical Adventure.*) Although companies *A*, *B* and *C* use exactly the same ingredients in their vegetable juice, their flavors are completely different. How does that happen?

I know! The proportions of the ingredients are different!

Exactly. Let us now look at the different quantities on a graph.

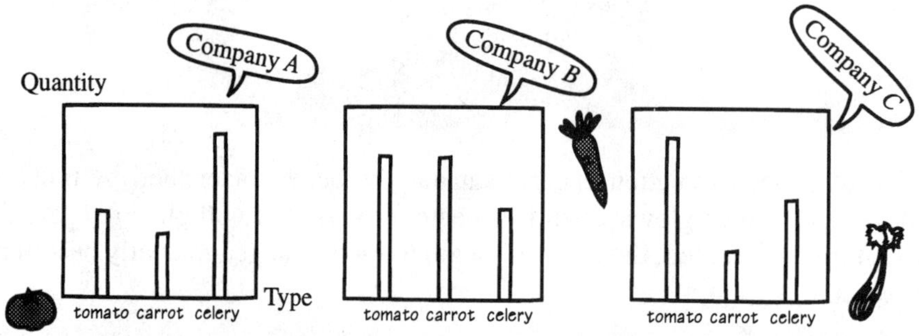

These are the graphs of spectrum. With this very useful technique, we can quickly see how all of the individual elements combine to form the whole.

Right! We can see what makes up the taste of the juice at one glance!

Okay, let's go back to the spectrum of light. Since light is made up of waves, we can show the distribution of the different kinds of waves in it with a graph recording the quantities of the various simple waves contained in that light.

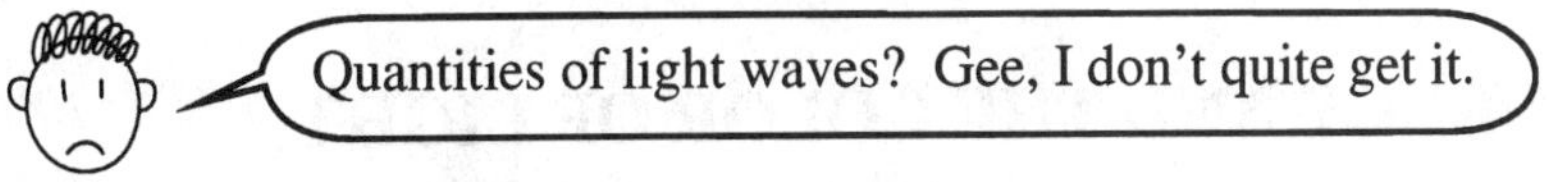

What we mean here by "light waves" is what we usually call color, and by "quantity" we mean the brightness of light. Normally light is made up of many different colors subtly mixed together so that they appear to us as one color. Therefore, when we wish to describe light by measuring a spectrum, **we show what colors and in what amounts they make up the light that we are examining.**

The way we do this is simple. We use a prism. Probably everyone has performed an experiment in grade school using a prism to break up light. When we pass sunlight through a prism, it breaks up into a pretty rainbow of seven colors: red, orange, yellow, green, blue, indigo and violet. The 'rainbows' are spectra of light.

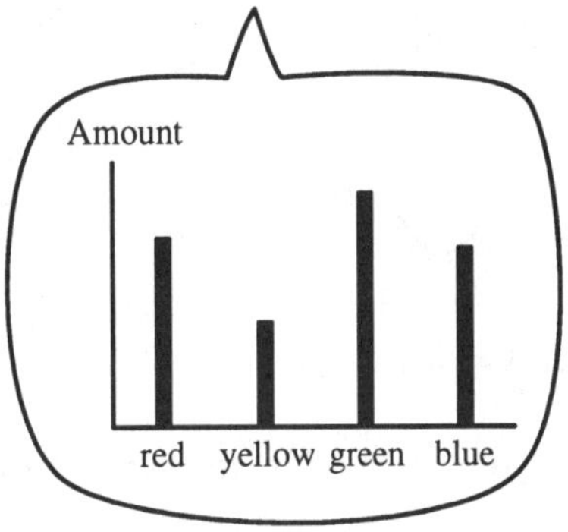

These beautiful gradations of color going from red to violet are, in a physical sense, the range of frequencies of individual light waves, and their brightness is related to the "intensity" of those frequencies. Although the sun's rays seem to be white, they are really composed of all the different colors mixed together in approximately equal proportions. Strictly speaking, the number of colors is infinite.

But to us, because of our limited visual perception, we can distinguish only seven colors of light.

Although we can observe spectra using only a prism, physicists use a device called a spectroscope to take more precise measurements. A spectroscope is not very complicated. In principle, it is identical to a prism, but it contains mechanisms that indicate the "frequency" and "instensity" of light in actual numbers.

WAVE FREQUENCY AND THE COLOR OF LIGHT

There are many different kinds of waves, such as "tight waves" and "loose waves." Physicists use wave frequency as one way of distinguishing them from each other.

Wave frequency is the number of cycles per second.

Let's see frequency in a diagram.

"Loose" or long waves = **low** frequency "Tight" or short waves = **high** frequency

Wave frequency is usually represented by the symbol ν (nu) in mathematical expressions.

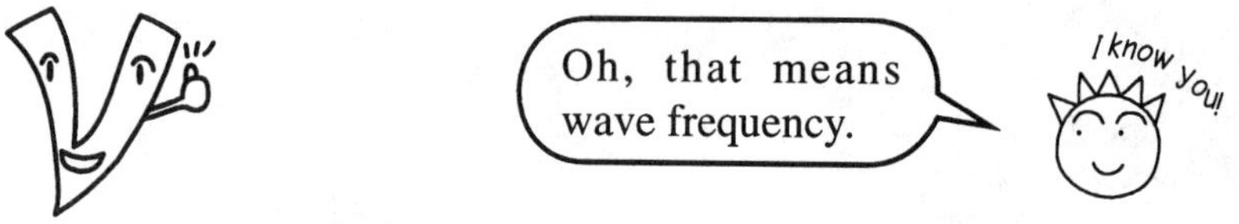

Now in the case of light waves, the frequency of the wave determines the color. We perceive differences in frequency as different colors. For instance, low-frequency light is reddish (ν = 400 trillion cycles per second) while high-frequency light is purplish (ν = 750 trillion cycles per second).

The visible spectrum, the range of colors that we normally see, is only a small fraction of all types of light. Some light is invisible to humans, such as X-rays and γ(gamma)-rays, or infrared light and ultraviolet light. Radio and television waves are also invisible forms of light, the frequency of these waves being very low. For example, FM radio waves are between 81.3MHz (megahertz) and 82.5 MHz (1 Herz [Hz] = 1 cycle per second), and oscillate about 80 million times per second. Red light, on the other hand, oscillates about 400 trillion times per second.

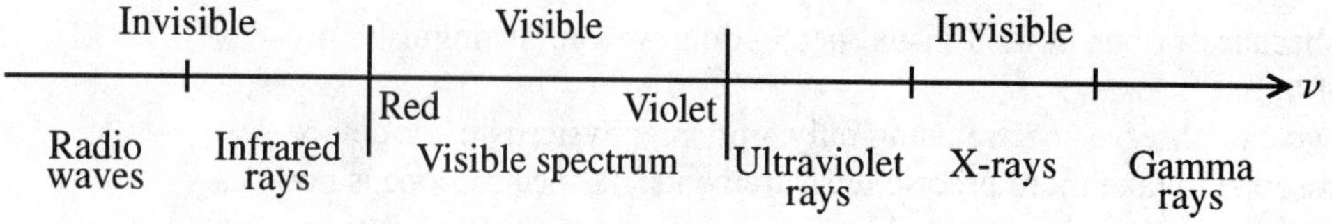

WHAT IS THE SPECTRUM OF THE LIGHT IN THE BOX?

What kind of light fills the box when we perform the blackbody radiation experiment? First let us examine the spectrum when the internal temperature is 4000°C.

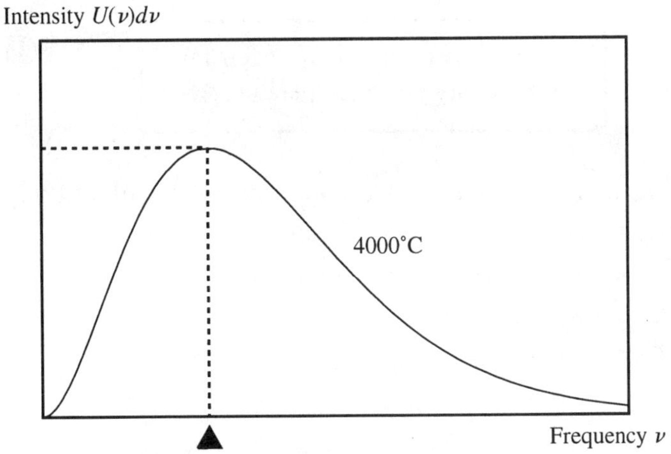

The horizontal axis of the graph shows frequency, while the vertical axis shows intensity. In this spectrum, we see that at 4000°C, the waves are strongest at the point marked by the arrow.

The frequencies with the highest intensities will determine the color. In other words, if the frequency marked by the arrow is that of blue light, then at 4000°C the light in the box will be bluish.

This graph illustrates the same point as the one of vegetable juice we looked at earlier. The only difference is that since the frequency of light is infinitely variable, the graph is continuous!

Because the light within the box changes according to temperature, its spectra also change.

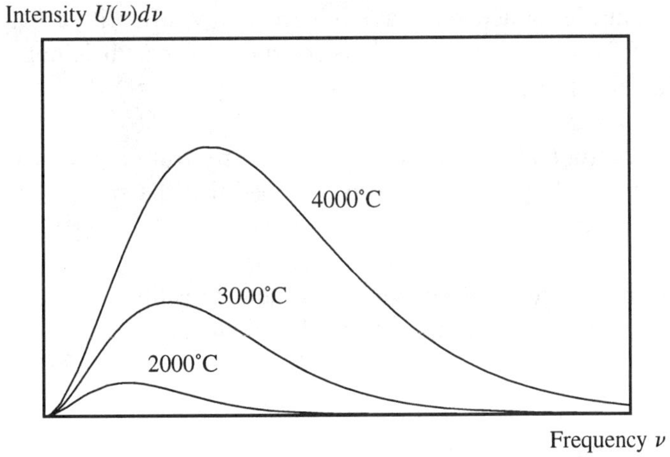

As we perform the blackbody radiation experiment, a number of different spectra may be observed by varying the temperature. The problem is finding words to explain our experimental results. That is,

Why does a particular spectrum exist at any given temperature?

When we can answer that, we can explain the blackbody radiation experiment.

THE RAYLEIGH-JEANS THEORY

Rayleigh, Lord John William Struff
[1842-1919]

Jeans, Sir James Hopwood
[1877-1946]

John Rayleigh and James Jeans, the stars of the physics world at the time, attempted to explain the experiment using classical theory. Because classical theory could explain the relationship of heat to light exceptionally well, they believed that it would work in this instance as well.

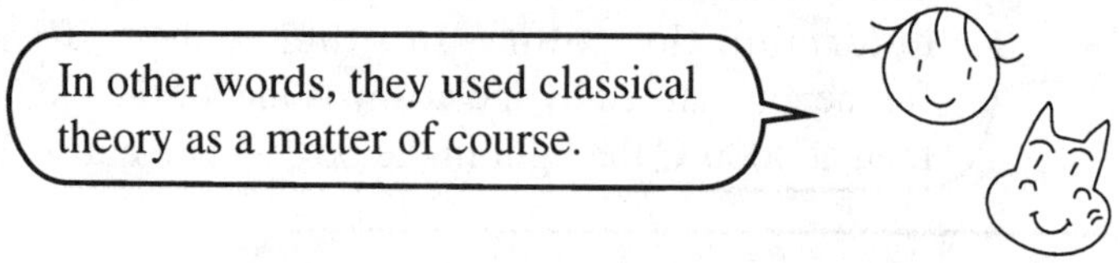

So, they derived the following mathematical formula to describe the spectra of the light in the box:

$$U(\nu)d\nu = \frac{8\pi\nu^2}{c^3} kT\, d\nu$$

This formula is named the Rayleigh-Jeans law after its creators. Don't worry if all of these unfamiliar symbols seem confusing. It is not necessary to go into the details immediately.

All this formula really describes is what the spectrum in the box will be at a given temperature. Rayleigh and Jeans assumed that the spectra obtained from the actual experiment would match this formula.

BUT! Disaster struck. When the experimental results were compared to the results predicted by this seemingly ironclad formula. . .

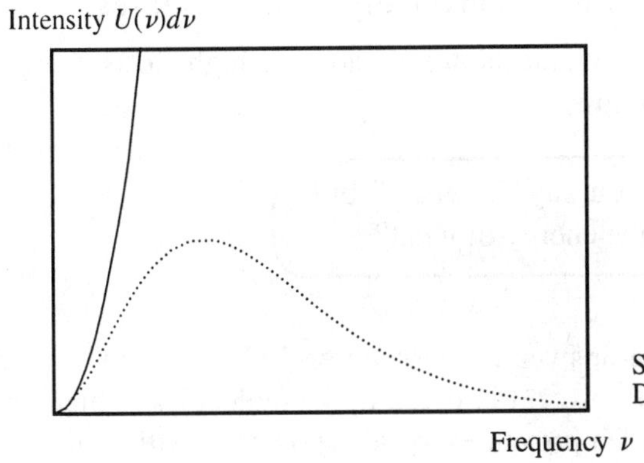

Solid line: Rayleigh-Jeans
Dotted line: Actual experimental results

What? There was no way to tell that these two graphs were describing the same thing. The physicists of the time were deeply troubled.

Classical theory had gone as far as anyone could take it, and so physicists naturally thought it would lead to perfect results. At the time, all other phenomena related to heat were explained by classical theory. Why didn't this one experiment fit?

THE LAW OF EQUAL DISTRIBUTION OF ENERGY

At this point, let's look at how Rayleigh and Jeans used classical rules to construct their formula. The classical law they used is expressed in the following equation:

$$\langle E \rangle = \frac{1}{2} kT$$

This law was discovered by the Austrian physicist, Ludwig Boltzmann, and is known as the law of equal distribution of energy. Let us look more closely at the symbols used in this equation.

Boltzmann, Ludwig Eduard
[1844-1906]

$\langle E \rangle$	. . .	Average energy over a period of time	
k	. . .	Constant	This constant is called Boltzmann's constant and is equal to 1.38×10^{-23} (joule / kelvin).
T	. . .	Temperature	

"joule" is a unit of energy.
"kelvin" is a unit of temperature.

Because $\frac{1}{2}$ and k are constants, this equation means that **energy $\langle E \rangle$ is determined by the temperature T.**

As T increases, $\frac{1}{2}kT$ increases. Conversely, as T decreases, $\frac{1}{2}kT$ decreases. Pretty simple, isn't it? When the temperature is high, so is energy. When it is low, then energy is also low.

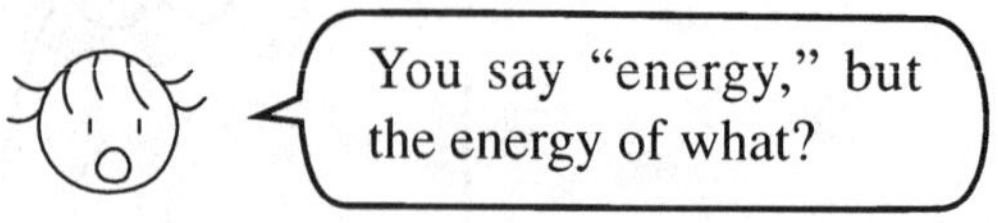

According to Boltzmann, the answer is "molecules." Boltzmann started from the idea that everything in the world is made up of molecules, which are clusters of small particles. This idea proved especially powerful with regard to heat. Boltzmann believed that heat varies according to the movement of molecules. He was right, and this clarified many unexplained phenomena.

The law of equal distribution of energy, however, was based on Newtonian dynamics. That is, in order to calculate the movement of molecules, Newtonian dynamics was applied to each molecule one by one. But there was a problem. The number of molecules in matter is absurdly large. It is not a matter of 100 million or even a trillion. The number is far, far greater.

How could the movements of such a huge number of molecules be dealt with one by one? You could spend a lifetime and still not get anywhere. Here is where **statistics**, the method used by Boltzmann, comes into play. Statistics is used to calculate such things as average test scores or the average height of students in a class.

Using statistics, Boltzmann was able to successfully describe the movements of huge numbers of molecules. This is called statistical dynamics. The result was Boltzmann's formula:

$$\langle E \rangle = \frac{1}{2}kT$$

The left side of this equation, $\langle E \rangle$, is **the molecular energy averaged** over a given period of time. Because molecular energy, when analyzed closely, varies in value from moment to moment, looking at each change individually would be too difficult. Statistics is therefore used to derive average values, and thence the energy of a molecule. Here we must be careful to note that the energy of a molecule $\langle E \rangle$ refers not to a single molecule, but rather to a single degree of freedom possessed by the molecule.

DEGREE OF FREEDOM

Degree of freedom is a number that describes how freely something can move in space.

To clarify this, let's consider the degree of freedom of a single-atom molecule as analogous to a moving ball. Let's see how many commands it would take to render a freely moving ball immobile, becoming immobile meaning the loss of freedom of movement. With a ball, it's easy to conceptualize, so let's try it.

To begin with, a ball is completely free and we can move it in any direction. Now, let's give the ball a command.

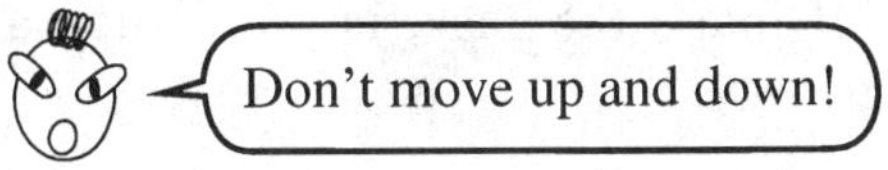

A ball that had been moving freely should now begin to move as if it were rolling on a flat surface such as a table.

The next command.

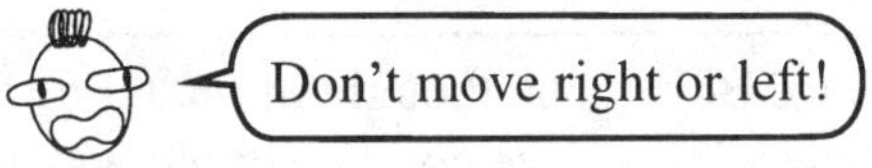

Now it can only move backward and forward.

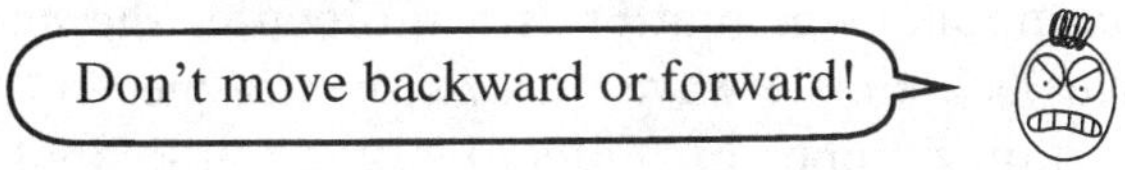

Now the ball cannot move at all.

Since these three commands caused the ball to stop moving, we can say that there were three directions of freedom.

That is, there were **three** degrees of freedom!

Configurations of molecules vary depending upon the number of atoms of which they are composed. For instance, biatomic molecules made up of two atoms are configured like iron alloys. When the number of atoms making up a molecule is three or more, the molecular configurations vary depending on how the atoms are linked together. A change in configuration causes a change in movement, and so it naturally follows that freedom of movement changes in value. Freedom of movement values are determined by the molecular configuration.

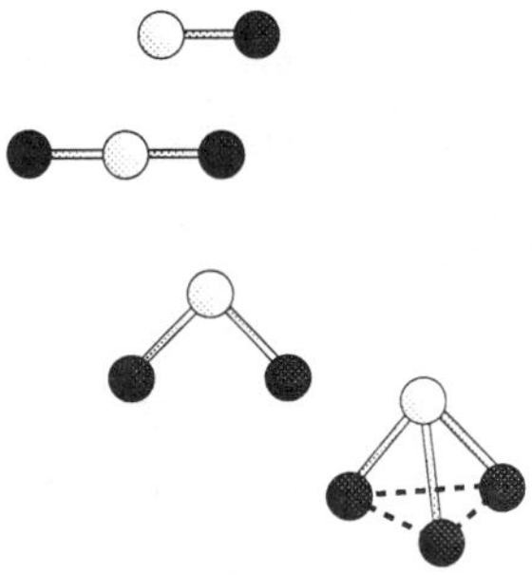

Since the law of equal distribution of energy says that $\frac{1}{2}kT$ of energy is applied to each degree of movement, it follows that in a molecule resembling the ball, $\frac{1}{2}kT$ of energy is applied to each of the three degrees of movement. The energy distributed is equal to:

$$\langle E \rangle = 3 \times \frac{1}{2}kT = \frac{3}{2}kT$$

DOES A WAVE HAVE DEGREES OF FREEDOM?

So, the law of equal distribution of energy has a lot to do with degrees of freedom! Understanding this is the key to understanding energy.

Yes, but we were talking about the degree of freedom, or freedom of movement, of single molecules, right? Light is a wave.

What!? If that's the case, is there such a thing as freedom of movement of a single wave?

In the case of waves, as opposed to wave cycles, we can't count them individually, and so we cannot use the same method of establishing degrees of freedom as we did with molecules. We need a new approach, one that is applicable to waves. But. . .what does a single molecule have to do with a wave?

Since Boltzmann thought of matter as an aggregate of molecules. . . I've got it! Simple waves, right?

If the basic component of matter is a molecule, the corresponding component in waves is a simple wave. Likewise, if a piece of matter is the aggregate of a certain number of molecules, a complicated wave is the aggregate of a number of simple waves.

I get it! Finding the degree of freedom of a wave means counting the degree of freedom of single waves!

With light, how many degrees of freedom does a single wave have?

The answer is **TWO.**

In the case of molecules, once they fly off, they're gone; but if a wave goes up, it must come down. That's what makes it a wave. Unlike molecules, a strong force operates on the matter which make up the waves to draw them back. That source comes from something known as **potential energy** (related to the position of matter). Although we could think of molecules, which just fly off, simply in terms of **kinetic energy** (related to the moment of matter), with waves we have to consider both potential and kinetic energy. Potential and kinetic energy each has its own direction, which means that waves have two degrees of freedom.

A force actively tries to pull waves back.

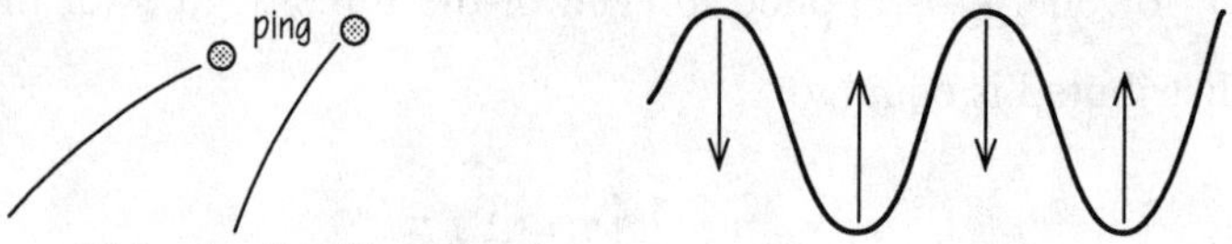

Molecules fly off.

So in the case of waves, the degree of freedom is always two.

That means the distribution of energy for simple waves is always:

$$\langle E \rangle = 2 \times \frac{1}{2} kT$$
$$= kT$$

NUMBER OF WAVES

Okay, but if kT units of energy are always distributed among simple waves, won't the result be strange? A spectograph is a graph that shows the intensity of the light of each simple wave, that is, the energy of each frequency. We should thus get something flat like this, shouldn't we?

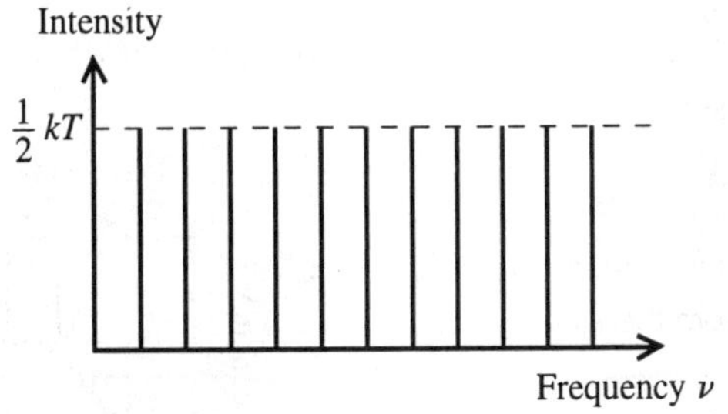

But that's not what really happens. In the case of one-dimensional waves, the result is in fact one straight line as shown above, but remember that light is a three-dimensional wave. Three-dimensional waves may be of the same intensity, but the frequencies vary so that there are places where they are more spread out and places where they are crowded or dense.

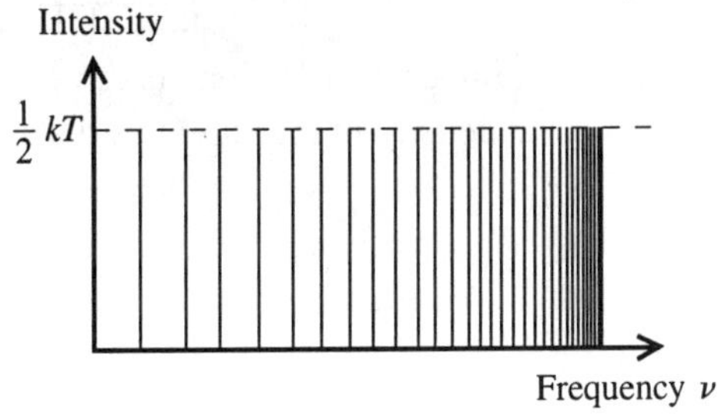

When we measure the energy of light using a spectroscope, the interval between waves is large enough so that we can measure the intensity of individual waves. Studying light in our black box, however, the interval between waves is very small. So instead of being able to measure the energy of each wave individually, we can only determine the cumulative energy of a number of waves that are close together.

In this case, when the waves are sparse, the energy measured by the spectroscope is low. When they are dense, the energy increases. So, we have to determine the "density" of waves of different frequencies.

How do you determine the density of waves?

That's easy. Just count the number of waves within a certain band.

But because the density of waves varies according to their frequencies, we need to keep the band narrow in order to count accurately.

That's right. Let the range equal $d\nu$. For each given frequency ν, count the number of waves between ν and $\nu + d\nu$. The density of one-dimensional waves does not vary with frequency; the oscillations come at equal intervals and so their spectrum is flat. But that is not true with three-dimensional waves, as we found in the blackbody radiation experiment. Instead of jumping ahead to three dimensions, it is simpler to start by looking at two dimensions.

When the number of directions is two, the number of wave patterns multiply as frequency increases.

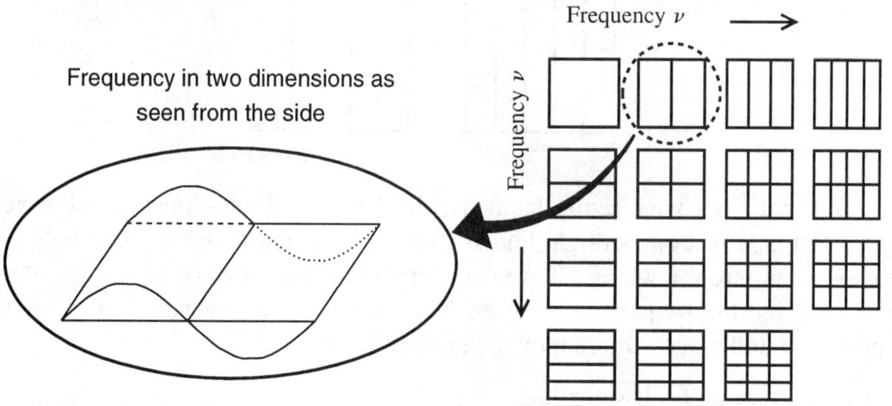

With three dimensions, the number of directions is three, greatly increasing the number of possible patterns. The density in this case has been calculated to be:

$$\frac{8\pi\nu^2}{c^3}\,d\nu$$

c is equal to the speed of light.

Let's see if I understand it. This means that within a certain narrow band $d\nu$, there are this number of simple waves, right?

This equation shows that as the frequency of a wave increases, the density increases to the frequency of ν to the power of two.

It's simple from here on. To find the energy as measured by a spectroscope, we simply do this:

(the density of the wave) × (the energy of a single wave)

We write the energy as measured by a spectroscope as $\boldsymbol{U(\nu)d\nu}$.

Because the energy of a single wave in classical theory is kT, if we write out the above formula as a mathematical expression we get:

$$U(\nu)d\nu = \frac{8\pi\nu^2}{c^3}kT\,d\nu$$

This describes the spectrum of light inside the box.

We did it! We derived the Rayleigh-Jeans law!

But wait a minute. When we used this formula, we arrived at something that barely resembled the spectra of blackbody radiation.

Oh, that's right. But why? Our calculations were so careful.

And there was no problem in our treatment of degrees of freedom. . .

Perhaps the law of equal distribution of energy was no good. Was there a problem with classical theory?

That couldn't be. Until now, classical theory could account for everything in nature.

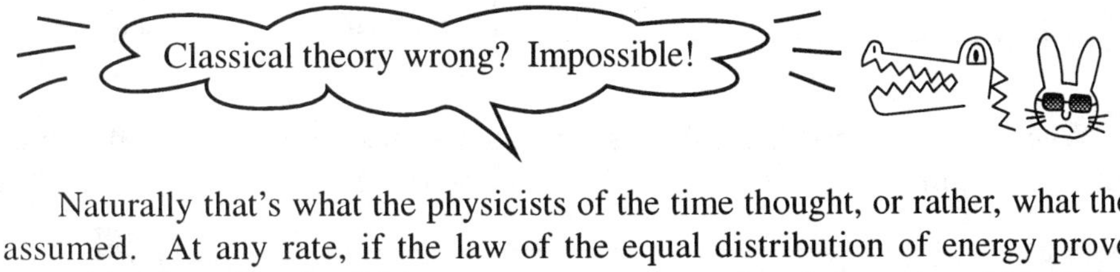

Naturally that's what the physicists of the time thought, or rather, what they assumed. At any rate, if the law of the equal distribution of energy proved unusable, then they would have no way to determine the spectra of blackbody radiation theoretically. They searched diligently for some delicate nuance in the workings of light that might have been overlooked. But that approach did not get them very far.

WIEN'S LAW

Wien, Wilhelm Carl Werner Otto Fritz Franz
[1864-1928]

It was then that the German physicist Wilhelm Wien came up with a new equation for expressing the spectra of the blackbody radiation experiment and used it to create a new theory. Wien's theory was based on a method of using spectra at a given temperature to predict spectra at any other temperature. Using this ingenious method, he was able to derive a formula that could accurately predict, at any temperature, the spectra obtained as actual experimental results. According to Wien's theory, energy $\langle E \rangle$ distributed according to degrees of freedom varies not only with temperature T, but also with frequency ν.

$$\langle E \rangle = \frac{1}{2} kT$$

(The equation accepted until then to express the law of the equal distribution of energy)

$$\langle E \rangle = \frac{k\beta\nu}{e^{\frac{\beta\nu}{T}}}$$

(Wien's law)

If we rewrite the equation for an actual spectrum $U(\nu)d\nu$ using his formula, we arrive at:

$$U(\nu)d\nu = \frac{8\pi\nu^2}{c^3}\frac{k\beta\nu}{e^{\frac{\beta\nu}{T}}}d\nu$$

In this equation β is a constant. By assigning it a suitable value, the result should match the spectrum obtained experimentally.

Now let's see if it agrees with the actual experimental results.

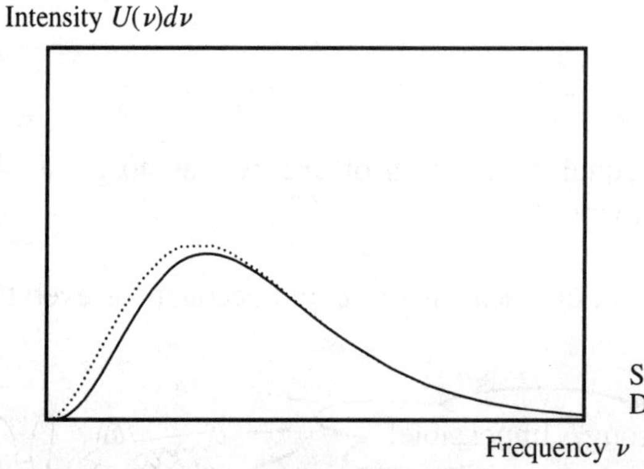

When frequency ν is high, Wien's formula matches the experimental results. But when the frequency ν is low, his formula is a bit off.

Unfortunately, Wien's theory did not completely solve the problem of blackbody radiation.

PLANCK COMES ON THE SCENE!

The Rayleigh-Jeans law, based on classical theory, did not match the experimental results, and even after devising his own theory, Wien's equation produced matching results only at high frequencies. Physicists were forced to find a new law to replace Wien's. Bring on the new star of our show, **MAX PLANCK!**

Planck had started working on the problem of blackbody radiation four years before. Though unconcerned with novel discoveries and new theories, the conscientious and industrious Planck hammered away at his research, always keeping in mind the failures of Rayleigh, Jeans and Wien. When looking at the spectra that resulted from work with the Rayleigh-Jeans and Wien's laws, Planck had an idea.

Rayleigh-Jeans

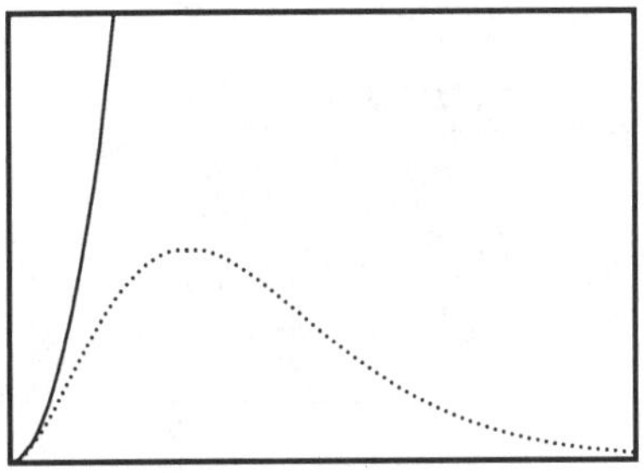

$$U(\nu)d\nu = \frac{8\pi\nu^2}{c^3} kT\, d\nu$$

Wien

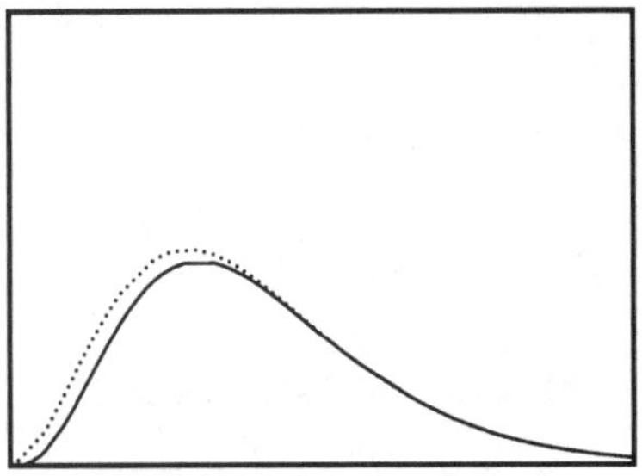

$$U(\nu)d\nu = \frac{8\pi\nu^2}{c^3} \frac{k\beta\nu}{e^{\frac{\beta\nu}{T}}} d\nu$$

What!? I thought the Rayleigh-Jeans's law made no sense, but look! When frequency ν is very low, then it perfectly matches the experimental results!

And the Wien's law works only when the frequency is high. Hmmm . . . . .yes! If I can somehow join these two equations together, there's a good chance I can explain the blackbody radiation spectra!

This was the beginning of Planck's great leap forward. He worked night and day to try to combine the two equations. Then, while he was adjusting Wien's law, he succeeded!

Here's the equation!!

$$\langle E \rangle = \frac{k\beta\nu}{e^{\frac{\beta\nu}{T}} - 1}$$

Planck discovered that the above equation could successfully predict distribution of energy with respect to degrees of freedom. By using this equation, the formula for spectra is as follows:

$$U(\nu)d\nu = \frac{8\pi\nu^2}{c^3}\frac{k\beta\nu}{e^{\frac{\beta\nu}{T}}-1}d\nu$$

Hey, didn't this equation come up before?

You're right. It's a lot like Wien's law. Let's have a look and compare the two.

Wien's law $\quad U(\nu)d\nu = \frac{8\pi\nu^2}{c^3}\frac{k\beta\nu}{e^{\frac{\beta\nu}{T}}}d\nu$

Planck's law $\quad U(\nu)d\nu = \frac{8\pi\nu^2}{c^3}\frac{k\beta\nu}{e^{\frac{\beta\nu}{T}}-1}d\nu$

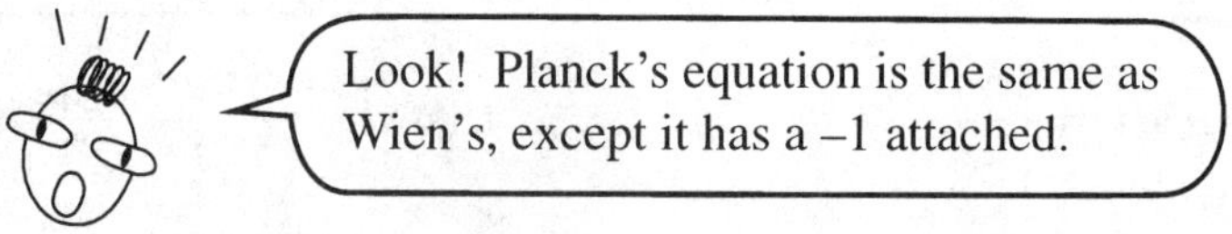

Does this really describe blackbody radiation spectra? Let's draw a graph and see.

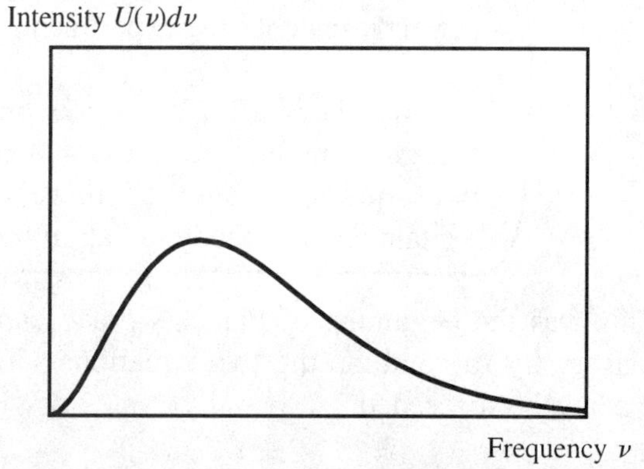

As it happened, by simply attaching a –1 to Wien's equation, Planck came up with a perfect solution. One story has it that a student of Planck's asked, **"Professor, won't it work if you just put a –1 in Wien's equation?"** And so when he tried it, it worked perfectly. Despite this story, it seems more likely that the answer emerged out of Planck's tireless, persistent calculations.

I made the calculations all by myself!

Putting the question of how the equation was derived aside for the moment, if the equation is correct it should have the following properties.

When the frequency is low, it transforms into the Rayleigh-Jeans law.
When the frequency is high, it transforms into the Wien law.

After all, when the frequency was low, the Rayleigh-Jeans law matched perfectly, and conversely when the frequency was high, the Wien law was perfect.

Now let's see how Planck's equation behaves at high and low frequencies.

DERIVING WIEN'S LAW FROM PLANCK'S LAW

Let's look at what happens to Planck's equation when the frequency is high. Will it really become the same as Wien's?

$$\langle E \rangle = \frac{k\beta\nu}{e^{\frac{\beta\nu}{T}} - 1} \quad \xrightarrow{\text{when } \nu \text{ is high}} \quad \langle E \rangle = \frac{k\beta\nu}{e^{\frac{\beta\nu}{T}}}$$

Planck's law — when ν is high — Wien's law

It shouldn't be difficult to turn it into Wien's law. After all, Planck's equation is nothing but Wien's law with a –1 attached.

The –1 is part of the denominator, so let's look only at the expression $e^{\frac{\beta\nu}{T}} - 1$. When $\frac{\beta\nu}{T}$ is very large, what happens to the value of the expression $e^{\frac{\beta\nu}{T}}$?

This is an exponential index, and so let's take 10^n as an example and see what happens.

For $10^n \cdots$

when $n = 1$, $10^1 = 10$
when $n = 2$, $10^2 = 100$
when $n = 5$, $10^5 = 100{,}000$

And when $n = 100$?

$1000000000000 \cdot \cdots\cdot$

You can't even write it! 

In $e^{\frac{\beta\nu}{T}} - 1$, when ν is very large, the quantity $e^{\frac{\beta\nu}{T}}$ is ridiculously big. With such a number, subtracting 1 makes almost no difference. So, when ν is very large, we can pretty much ignore the term -1, thus:

$$\langle E \rangle = \frac{k\beta\nu}{e^{\frac{\beta\nu}{T}}}$$

Planck's law has been transformed into Wien's law.

DERIVING THE RAYLEIGH-JEANS LAW FROM PLANCK'S LAW

Now let's look at what happens when frequency ν is low. Here, Planck's equation should become the Rayleigh-Jeans law.

Since the Rayleigh-Jeans law is a statistical law, we employ $\langle E \rangle = kT$, right? Can we really get this out of Planck's equation?

To transform it into the Rayleigh-Jeans law, we use a little trick. It's called the Taylor expansion. Most functions can be rewritten in the form of an infinite series. (See Chapter 4 for details.)

$$f(x) = C_0 + C_1x + C_2x^2 + C_3x^3 + \cdots$$

For example, if $f(x) = e^x$, using the Taylor expansion we get:

$$e^x = 1 + x + \frac{x^2}{2!} + \frac{x^3}{3!} + \cdots$$

Looking at $e^{\frac{\beta\nu}{T}}$ in Plank's equation, if we take $\frac{\beta\nu}{T}$ to be x, we can rewrite it in the following way.

$$e^{\frac{\beta\nu}{T}} = 1 + \frac{\beta\nu}{T} + \frac{\left(\frac{\beta\nu}{T}\right)^2}{2!} + \cdots\cdot$$

The Rayleigh-Jeans law only applies if ν is small. And if ν is small, each value from $\left(\frac{\beta\nu}{T}\right)^2 \Big/ 2!$ on, will be even smaller. Adding those values together would have almost no meaning. Therefore, they can be ignored and written in the following manner.

$$e^{\frac{\beta\nu}{T}} \fallingdotseq 1 + \frac{\beta\nu}{T}$$

$\fallingdotseq$: Nearly equal

Applying this to Planck's equation we get:

$$\langle E \rangle = \frac{k\beta\nu}{e^{\frac{\beta\nu}{T}} - 1} = \frac{k\beta\nu}{1 + \frac{\beta\nu}{T} - 1} = \frac{k\beta\nu}{\frac{\beta\nu}{T}}$$
$$= \frac{k\beta\nu T}{\beta\nu} = kT$$

Fantastic! It turned into the Rayleigh-Jeans law!

THE BIRTH OF PLANCK'S LAW

All right, now that we know the equation is correct, all we have to do is present it at a conference! Impatient as he was, Planck methodically continued his preparations.

First of all, let's try to write the equation a bit more elegantly.

At this point, Planck combined the terms k (the Boltzmann constant) and β (the constant obtained by Wien) in a single constant h. This was to become the **Planck constant** that was to play a vital role in the building of quantum mechanics. The actual number is:

$$\boldsymbol{h = 6.63 \times 10^{-34}\ (\text{joule} \cdot \text{second})}$$

Point

Now, let's rearrange Planck's equation using h!

$$\langle E \rangle = \frac{k\beta\nu}{e^{\frac{\beta\nu}{T}} - 1}$$

$\Downarrow$ If $h = k\beta$, then $\beta = \frac{h}{k}$

Point

$$\langle E \rangle = \frac{h\nu}{e^{\frac{h\nu}{kT}} - 1}$$

Planck announced his findings at a conference in the fall of 1900. Planck, an exceptionally late bloomer for a physicist, was forty-two years old when he made this great discovery. Afterward, this expression became widely used to explain the spectra of blackbody radiation, which it did extremely well, and it came to be known as Planck's law.

Great! You did it, Mr. Planck!

But not everything had been explained. There was still an important problem left for Planck to solve. This was:

Why does this equation describe blackbody radiation so well?

Although he had constructed an equation that explained the experimental results, there was still no essential theory behind it. Only half the mystery was solved. If he failed to pursue this further, his discovery would forever be attributed to luck. True to his nature as a physicist, Planck tirelessly searched for a solution to the problem. According to Planck, these were the most strained weeks of his life.

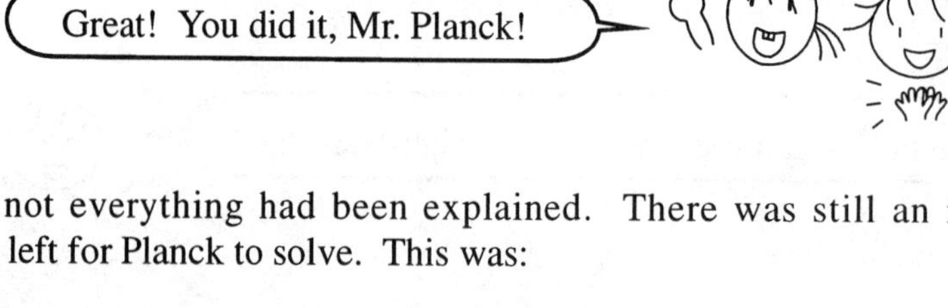

As he continued to make calculations, they all led to the same conclusion. It simply didn't fit with what he believed had to be true. No one, including himself, could quite understand this.

THE MEANING OF PLANCK'S FORMULA

Point

$$E = nh\nu \quad (n = 0, 1, 2, 3 \cdots)$$

That was his conclusion. It doesn't seem important, but its implications were beyond imagination. If one were to interpret it literally, then **the energy of light waves can only have certain fixed values.**

The left side E of the equation is the energy of light. The right side of the equation is an integral value which represents the various energy levels obtained by multiplying Planck's constant h by frequency ν. Thus, according to this equation, the energy of light changes in incremental values of $h\nu$ (0, $1h\nu$, $2h\nu$, $3h\nu$). . . and intermediate values such as $1.5h\nu$ or $0.2h\nu$ never arise under any circumstances.

Such fixed differences in energy are known as "**energy levels**"

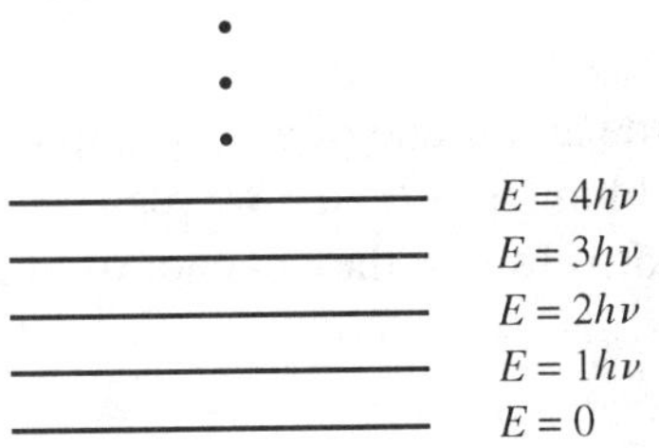

Energy levels

If we consider the characteristics of waves, this is definitely odd. One characteristic of waves is that

$$\text{Energy} \propto |\text{Amplitude}|^2$$

The energy of a wave is proportional to the square of the amplitude.

Because the amplitude of a wave is its height at the crest, if a wave is high, its energy is high. Likewise, if a wave is low, then its energy is low.

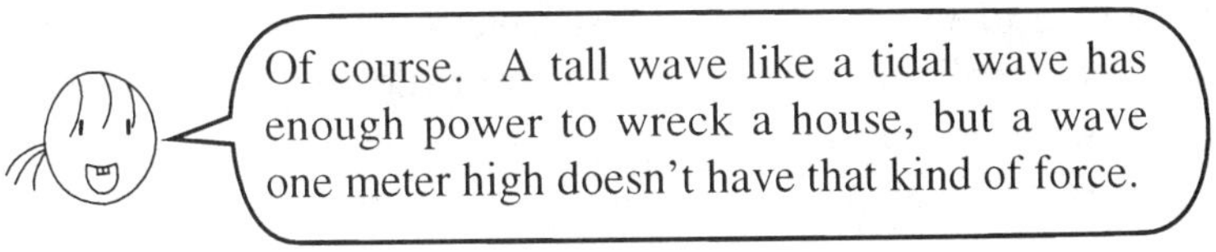

Let's consider this in terms of the equation derived by Planck, $E = nh\nu$. According to Planck's equation, the energy of light is $h\nu$ times an integer; in other words, it can only attain discrete and discontinuous values. In addition, the energy of a wave is determined by its amplitude. So. . . **FOR ENERGY LEVELS TO BE DISCRETE** it must follow that **THE AMPLITUDES OF WAVES MUST BE DISCRETE!**

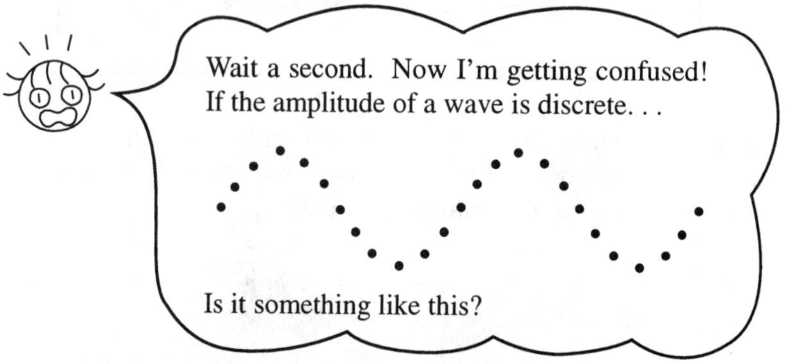

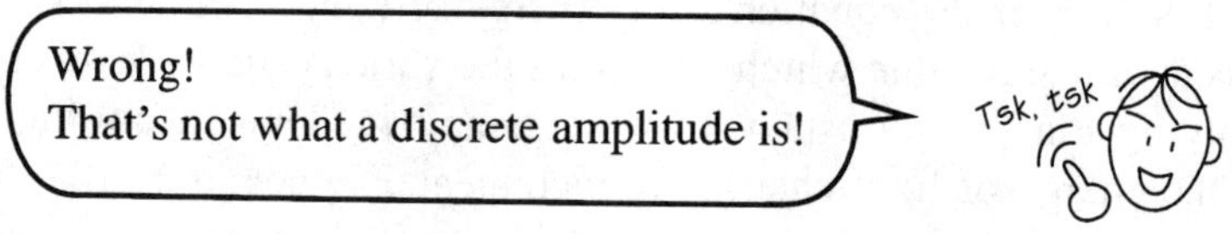

The amplitude is the height at the crest of an oscillating wave. So even though we're talking about light waves, it shouldn't be any more difficult to understand. Light waves oscillate up and down exactly like any other kind of wave.

The problem is that the amplitude of an oscillating light wave can only have certain given values. Although ordinary waves can have any amplitude, light waves alone cannot. That is to say, they cannot oscillate except at certain fixed amplitudes.

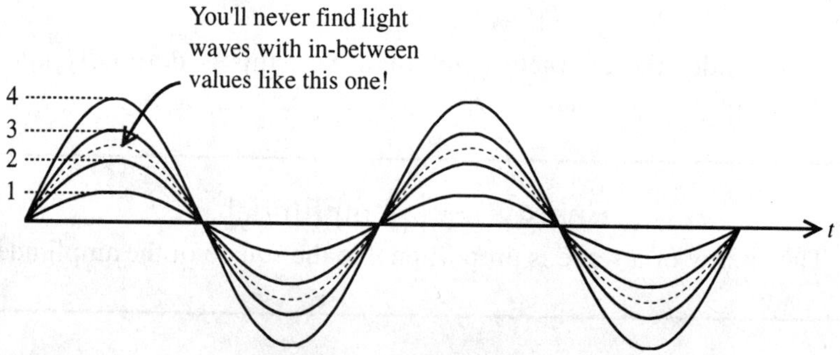

If the amplitude is really discrete like that, we'd be in trouble. But in the case of light waves, we just have to accept the notion of a discrete amplitude. If we don't, there is no way to explain blackbody radiation spectra.

DERIVING PLANCK'S FORMULA FROM $E = nh\nu$

So it was Planck's theory that gave birth to such incongruous results. Do we really have to use $E = nh\nu$ to explain Planck's formula? Let's take a closer look.

If $E = nh\nu$ is correct, then we ought to be able to derive Planck's formula from it.

$$\langle E \rangle = \frac{h\nu}{e^{\frac{h\nu}{kT}} - 1} \qquad \text{Planck's formula}$$

This equation shows average energy over a given interval of time per degree of freedom. Thus, if $E = nh\nu$ is really true, and if we use it to find the average values of a normally fluctuating source of energy, then we should arrive at Planck's formula.

Let's see if that's true!

Now, do you know how to find an average value? As an example, let's find the average number of cookies someone eats at tea time.

First, we record the number of cookies eaten at tea time every day for a week. If we take the total number of cookies eaten and divide that by the number of days in a week, seven, we arrive at the average number of cookies eaten per day.

Let's assume that the number of cookies eaten by Mr. Planck was as follows:

Sunday	:	2
Monday	:	3
Tuesday	:	2
Wednesday	:	2
Thursday	:	1
Friday	:	3
Saturday	:	1

Tabulating the number of cookies eaten that week, we find:

The number of days when 1 cookie was eaten	: 2
The number of days when 2 cookies were eaten	: 3
The number of days when 3 cookies were eaten	: 2

Now, let's find the average value!

$$\frac{1 \times 2 + 2 \times 3 + 3 \times 2}{2 + 3 + 2} = \frac{14}{7} = 2$$

In other words, he ate an average of two cookies per day.

When finding average values, we only need to know the total number of cookies eaten and the time frame in which they were eaten. It is not important to know on which days they were eaten.

We can obtain an average value for the energy of light waves in the same way.

To deal with light, all we need to know is the number of times a certain energy level occurs within a given period of time. This number has already been established using a statistical law, so we simply insert it into the equation. Then, all we need to do is add up the energy levels and divide by the time. Let's calculate this using the following formula.

First, using the statistical law discovered by L. Boltzmann, we find the number of occurrences of a given energy level using:

$$P(E) = A \cdot e^{-\frac{E}{kT}}$$

Translating this into a graph, we have the following:

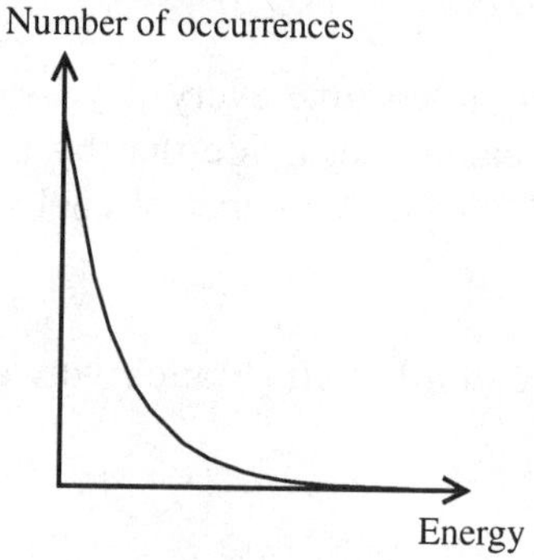

The horizontal axis of the graph is energy.

The vertical axis of the graph is number of occurrences of given energy levels.

The graph indicates that the higher the energy, the less frequently that level occurs.

This is almost the same thing as saying, the higher you go, the thinner the air becomes. Let's look at an example from statistical dynamics. If we consider air to be a collection of small particles, we see that their energy increases as their distance from the earth's surface increases. But the number of particles with high energy is small, so the higher one goes, the fewer the number of particles there are.

Using Boltzmann's expression, let's try adding up energy. First, remember that the energy of light is limited to the values 0, $h\nu$, $2h\nu$, $3h\nu$. . . Thus, the number of occurrences of given energy levels $h\nu$ or $2h\nu$ is as follows:

Energy	0	$1\ h\nu$	$2\ h\nu$	$3\ h\nu$
Number of occurrences	$P\ (0\ h\nu)$	$P\ (1\ h\nu)$	$P\ (2\ h\nu)$	$P\ (3\ h\nu)$

Thus, the sum of the energy levels is:

$$0h\nu \cdot P(0h\nu) + 1h\nu \cdot P(1h\nu) + 2h\nu \cdot P(2h\nu) + \cdots\cdots$$

Dividing this by the sum of the number of occurrences, we get:

$$\langle E \rangle = \frac{0h\nu \cdot P(0) + 1h\nu \cdot P(1h\nu) + 2h\nu \cdot P(2h\nu) + \cdots\cdot}{P(0) + P(1h\nu) + P(2h\nu) + \cdots\cdot}$$

Now, let's rewrite the equation.

$$\langle E \rangle = \frac{h\nu \left\{ P(h\nu) + 2P(2h\nu) + 3P(3h\nu) + \cdots\cdot \right\}}{P(0) + P(1h\nu) + P(2h\nu) + P(3h\nu) \cdots\cdot}$$

Since $P(h\nu) = A \cdot e^{-\frac{h\nu}{kT}}$

$$\langle E \rangle = \frac{h\nu \left(e^{-\frac{h\nu}{kT}} + 2e^{-\frac{2h\nu}{kT}} + 3e^{-\frac{3h\nu}{kT}} + \cdots\cdot \right)}{e^0 + e^{-\frac{h\nu}{kT}} + e^{-\frac{2h\nu}{kT}} + e^{-\frac{3h\nu}{kT}} + \cdots\cdot}$$

Since $e^{-\frac{h\nu}{kT}} = x$, we have $e^{-\frac{2h\nu}{kT}} = x^2$, $e^{-\frac{3h\nu}{kT}} = x^3$

$$\langle E \rangle = \frac{h\nu \left(x + 2x^2 + \cdots \right)}{1 + x + x^2 + \cdots} \quad \cdots\cdot\star$$

At this point, we use a little mathematical technique. This formula is useful in solving an infinite summation, or adding infinite numbers.

$$a + (a+d)x + (a+2d)x^2 + (a+3d)x^3 \cdots = \frac{a}{1-x} + \frac{xd}{(1-x)^2}$$

Using this, we rewrite the equation marked ★

Comparing ★ with the above equation, we see that in the numerator,

$$a = 0 \quad d = 1$$

and in the denominator,

$$a = 1 \quad d = 0$$

Now, we may rewrite ★ in the following way:

$$\langle E \rangle = \frac{h\nu \frac{x}{(1-x)^2}}{\frac{1}{1-x}} = h\nu \cdot \frac{x(1-x)}{(1-x)^2} = \frac{h\nu \cdot x}{1-x}$$

$$= \frac{h\nu \cdot x}{1-x}$$

Now, multiplying by $\frac{x^{-1}}{x^{-1}}$, we get

$$\langle E \rangle = \frac{h\nu x}{(1-x)} \frac{x^{-1}}{x^{-1}}$$

$$= \frac{h\nu}{x^{-1}-1}$$

Finally, we convert x back to $e^{-\frac{h\nu}{kT}}$:

$$\langle E \rangle = \frac{h\nu}{e^{\frac{h\nu}{kT}}-1}$$

And we obtain Planck's law.

Hey! We're back where we should be.

Just as Mr. Planck said, if we think of energy as $E = nh\nu$, we really can describe the spectra of blackbody radiation!

Looked at another way, the spectra of blackbody radiation take this form on the graph because the energy of light has fixed values and can be described as $E = nh\nu$.

In other words, the Rayleigh-Jeans law failed to explain the spectra of blackbody radiation not because it was based on the statistical dynamics law of equal distribution of energy, but because the energy of light took these discrete values.

The law of equal distribution of energy was originally based on the assumption that a body received energy continuously. It was not valid for discontinuous forms of energy such as light.

For the energy level of something to be discrete, it must receive energy in discrete bursts as well. So, there must be times when the energy being distributed is not all being received. For instance, let's consider energy at a level $200 \times h$, or $200h$, in a box whose temperature is such that the energy will be distributed by light of all frequencies. Light at frequencies $\nu = 1$, $\nu = 2$ will have energy levels equal to nh and $2nh$, respectively. The energy level $200h$ is divisible by either of these frequencies, and so all of the energy at the $200h$ level is distributed. But if frequency $\nu = 3$, it no longer divides evenly into $200h$; only $198h$ of that energy is divisible by $3h$, and so $198h$ is distributed while $2h$ remains. As the frequency increases, more energy tends to be wasted, and when the frequency ν of light exceeds 200 and the energy level is higher than $200h$, absolutely no energy is distributed.

This is what the spectrograph of the light from blackbody radiation shows. Beyond a certain frequency, the spectograph of that light suddenly becomes weak; for as the frequency increases, the graph approaches zero. This demonstrates that although energy is presumed to be evenly distributed, the energy of light, which can only have discrete values proportional to its frequency, approaches a condition where it cannot be received.

Thus, if we consider the energy of light as a discontinuous value ($E = nh\nu$), the spectra of light from blackbody radiation do not appear to agree with the statistical dynamics law of equal distribution of energy.

In fact, the fundamental discovery $E = nh\nu$ could not be explained by Newtonian dynamics or by any other established form of physics. In physical theory until then, the energy of light waves was assumed to vary continuously; it was unthinkable that it should have discrete values.

This is what Planck struggled with. He believed beyond a shadow of a doubt that

Newtonian dynamics had to be correct.

But he had arrived at conclusions that denied the apparent infallibility of Newtonian dynamics.

That can't be! There must be a mistake!

No matter how many times he redid his calculations, he found that the spectra for blackbody radiation could only be explained through the expression $E = nh\nu$.

$$E = nh\nu$$

"The energy of light can only have discrete values."

Planck had no choice but to publish these results in a paper. At the end of it he added wistfully, "I hope, nevertheless, that we will find a solution using Newtonian dynamics."

Planck was not alone; just about every physicist hoped the same thing. This problem was particularly unwelcome because it appeared just as physics theory appeared to be virtually complete. Partly because physicists resisted the implications, Planck's paper seemed to be largely ignored when it was published. That is, everyone saw but pretended not to see.

BUT. . .

In 1905, an unknown young man found an entirely new approach to the situation. Twenty-six-year-old Albert Einstein had appeared on the physics scene, and the physicists who had been ignoring Planck's discoveries found their escape routes blocked. They could no longer deny Planck's findings.

Einstein, Albert
[1879-1955]

1. 4 LIGHT IS A PARTICLE!?

EINSTEIN MAKES HIS APPEARANCE

It was about the time that Planck made the remarkably odd discovery that $E = nh\nu$, or that the energy of light had discontinuous values, when in a corner of the Swiss countryside, there was a young man employed at a patent office who was doing research in physics on the side.

That man was **Albert Einstein.**

There is probably no one who has not heard the name Einstein. Even among well-known physicists, his name stands apart from the rest.

Why does the needle of a compass always point in the same direction?

Although it is said that this question led Einstein into the world of physics, it was the study of light that drew his interest. Not especially fond of school, nor favored with outstanding teachers, Einstein carried out his research completely on his own. Planck's paper with the astonishing discovery $E = nh\nu$ caught his attention. Although other physicists ignored these findings, Einstein took a look and instantly realized,

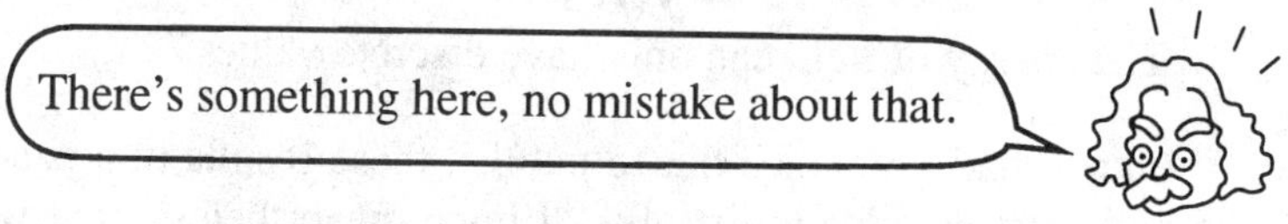

And so, in 1905 Einstein took everyone's breath away with a daring yet simple revelation that plainly explained just what Planck's discovery meant. It was written up in the paper, "The Photon Hypothesis," which ultimately led to a Nobel Prize.

What is truly amazing is that in the same year, Einstein also published his "Special Theory of Relativity" and the "Theory of Brownian Motion," bringing to a total three papers of Nobel Prize caliber. His "Special Theory of Relativity" is particularly well-known, and is practically synonymous with his name. Everyone, even grade school students, has at least heard of it. With these three papers, the name Einstein immediately became known the world over. Overnight he rose from the status of an unknown young man to that of a great physicist.

Yes, yes, that's fine, but what was this bold revelation that took everyone's breath away?

From the beginning we have assumed that since light produces interference patterns, it must be a wave. But Planck's explanation of the blackbody radiation experiment has shown that light waves are not like the ordinary waves that we know so well.

The energy levels of light have discrete values!

That must mean, then, that if light is a wave, the energy level of waves are discrete. At this point, Einstein began to think.

> The energy levels of waves only have discrete values!? Well, if light really is a wave, then something is wrong here.

From there Einstein went back and examined things from square one.

THE ENERGY OF WAVES

Once again Einstein tried to determine whether the energy of light really had the properties of a wave. As we saw earlier when discussing Planck's work, the energy of waves is determined by their amplitude. Written as a mathematical expression, this means

$$\textbf{Wave Energy} \propto |\textbf{Amplitude}|^2$$

Logically, since the energy increases as the amplitude increases, if the wave energy is discrete, then the amplitude must be discrete as well.

Planck was troubled by the fact that the equation he had discovered, $E = nh\nu$, suggested that the amplitude of light waves could only have discrete values. He couldn't understand how wave amplitudes could have anything other than continuous values. Thus, the light waves predicted by Planck's theory seemed strange — waves whose amplitudes could only have certain values.

If light is no more than an odd kind of wave, then, for the time being, we should have no trouble considering it as a sort of cousin to a wave. But when Einstein reexamined the question carefully, it became evident that this was not the only problem. The new problem was related to **THE TRANSMISSION OF ENERGY.** If we think of how energy is transmitted, then the idea that light is a wave becomes truly nonsensical.

EXPERIMENT OF THE LITTLE BOX

To analyze the way in which energy is transmitted, Einstein tried a little mental test, based upon the blackbody radiation experiment.

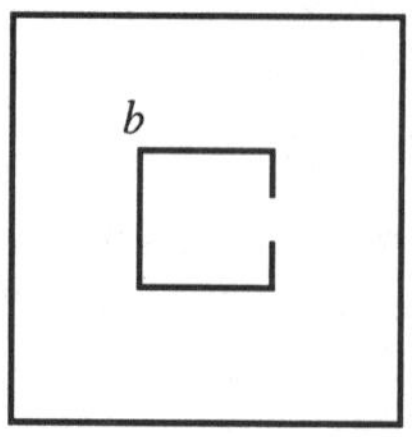

Let's insert a little box b with a window inside the iron box B that we used in the blackbody radiation experiment. As B is gradually heated, light fills its interior. Because there are many different frequencies of light waves and they are interfering wildly, the energy level in the box is constantly fluctuating. In addition, waves are probably passing in and out through the window of little box b.

How does the energy of light waves in the smaller box behave now? If they were ordinary waves, the energy level should vary continuously, along with the continually fluctuating wave amplitudes, gradually increasing and decreasing one step at a time.

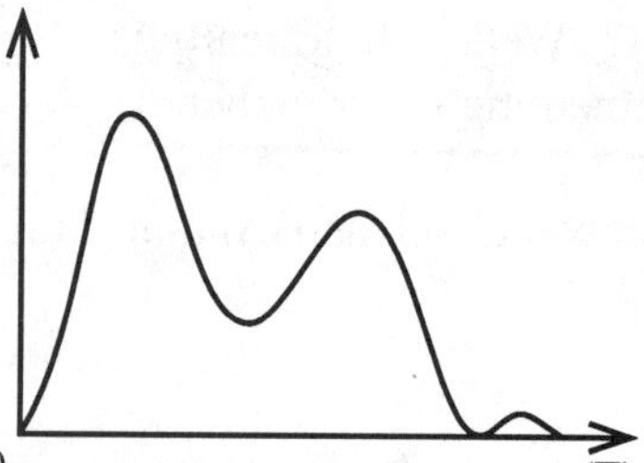

The energy should fluctuate in gradual curves as shown above. But as Planck discovered, according to $E = nh\nu$, the energy of light waves could have only discontinuous values. Moreover, these discontinuous values took on $h\nu$ values in integral multiples.

This meant that the energy inside small box b fluctuated according to integral multiples of $h\nu$; it never assumed intermediate values. At one instant, the value might be $h\nu$; at the next, $3h\nu$; and an instant later, zero. Therefore, the value must be changing at every instant. This being the case, the fluctuation of the energy in small box b

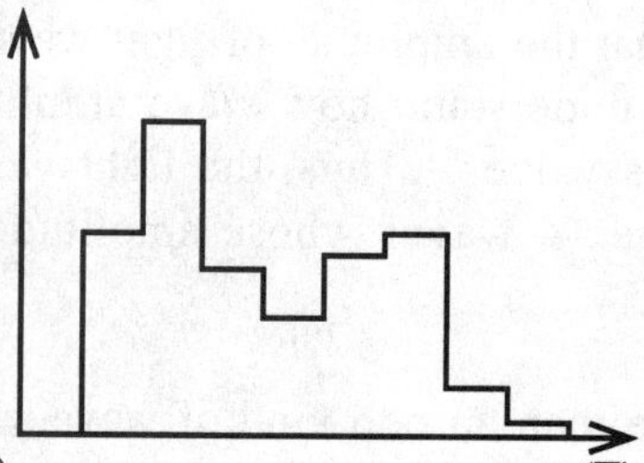

must be described by a stepped, rectilinear graph such as this.

THIS IS REALLY STRANGE!!

At this time an eight-letter word that had been rolling around in the back of Einstein's brain popped up.

If light isn't a wave. . .

LIGHT ISN'T A WAVE!?

For the transmission of light to have such an angular graph, the actual transfer of energy must take place in an instant. This means that light's energy must have a transfer vehicle in the form of a ball. What does that mean, a ball of energy?

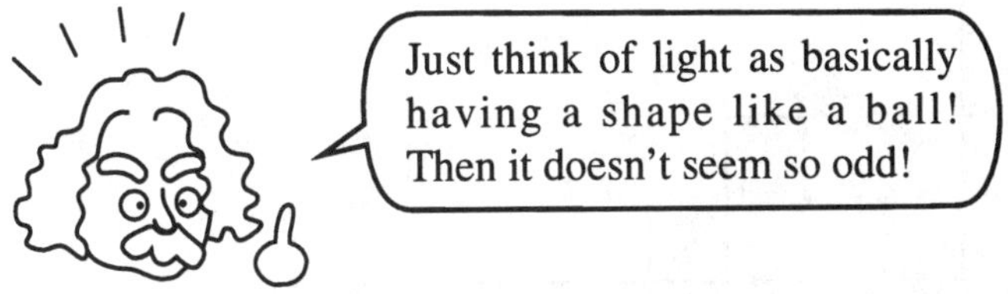

LIGHT IS NOT A WAVE. IT IS A PARTICLE THAT HAS ENERGY $E = h\nu$!

Point

Einstein had thought up something that shook the world of contemporary physics to its very roots. This idea fully explained Planck's discovery, and the fact that energy has discrete values becomes a matter of course. We just need to conceptualize the n in $E = nh\nu$ as the number of "balls," or light particles.

If we think of particles of light going in and out, it is clearer why, in the experiment with the small box, it was only natural that the energy in small box b fluctuated discontinuously. Because light particles are too small to see, we cannot say that only a portion of the particles went in at a time; the discrete jumping, in and out, occurred in an instant. Let's say that the energy of one light particle leaping into small box b is $h\nu$; of two particles, $2h\nu$; of three particles, $3h\nu$; and so on. When no particles leap in, the energy is zero. Stated simply, the fluctuation of light's energy takes a jumping form, its fluctuation being the effect of particles jumping in discrete amounts.

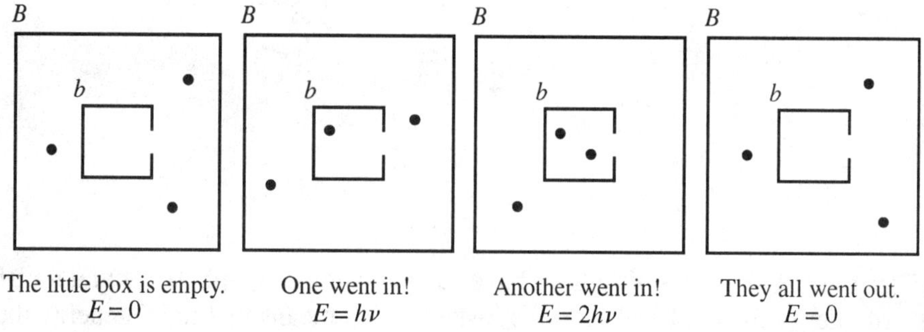

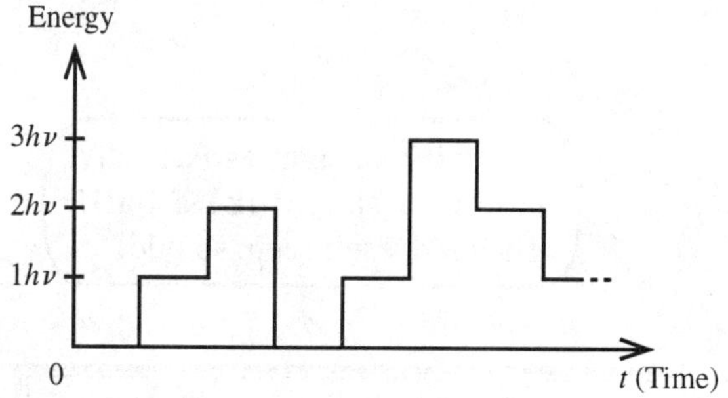

When we thought of $E = nh\nu$ in terms of a wave, it just didn't make sense. If we think of it as a particle, however, it all becomes clear.

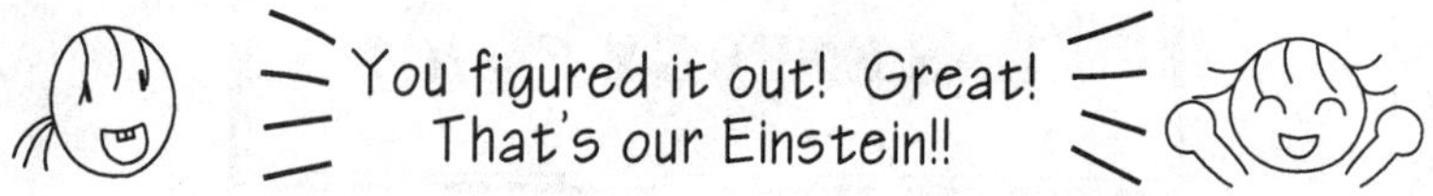

This is the famous **Photon Hypothesis**, "Light is not a wave. It is a particle that has energy $E = h\nu$". Still, it was only a hypothesis that had not yet been tested experimentally. The small box experiment was just a mental exercise performed in Einstein's head. With nothing more than that to go on, it would be hard to convince anyone of the idea that light was a particle. Such a claim would seem to lack common sense. In order to prove that light was a particle, it was necessary to obtain facts, namely experimental results that could only be explained in terms of the particle hypothesis. At this point, Einstein began to look at all sorts of experiments concerning light.

1. 5 THE PHOTOELECTRIC EFFECT

LENARD'S EXPERIMENT

And then Einstein discovered an experiment whose conclusions could not be explained unless light was a particle! It was the test of the photoelectric effect and was designed to examine this phenomenon. It demonstrated that:

"When high-frequency light hits a metallic substance, electrons fly off."

The phenomenon was already known through experimentation, but no one could explain yet why it happened. It was the German physicist Philipp Lenard who thoroughly studied the photoelectric effect, and the results of his experiment were compiled and reported. First, let's see what this experiment involved.

Lenard, Philipp Eduard Anton
[1862-1947]

We're about to see why light is a particle.

Experimental method

1. As shown below, an apparatus is constructed with two metal plates placed facing each other. Through the action of the battery, electrons flow from the negative pole to the positive pole. The path ends, and the electrons stop at plate *A*.

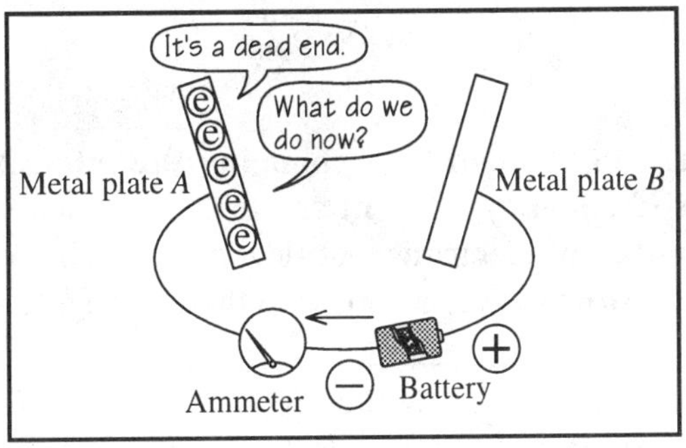

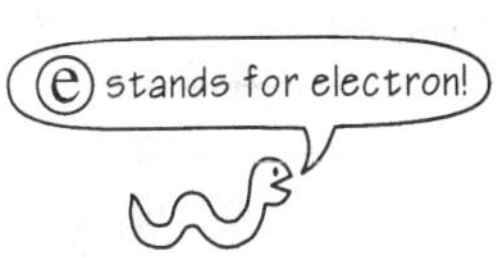

2. Now, if we shine light on metal plate *A*, electrons receive energy from the light and begin to fly off from the surface.

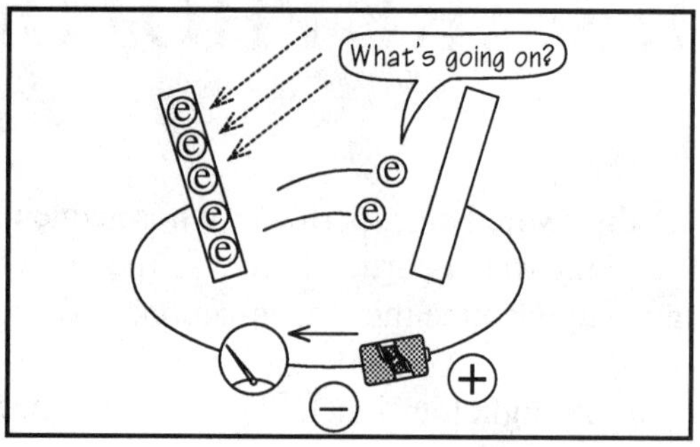

 That's the photoelectric effect! 

3. The electrons that fly off are attracted to metal plate *B*. And then. . . hey! Even though the plates are not connected, electrical current ends up flowing!

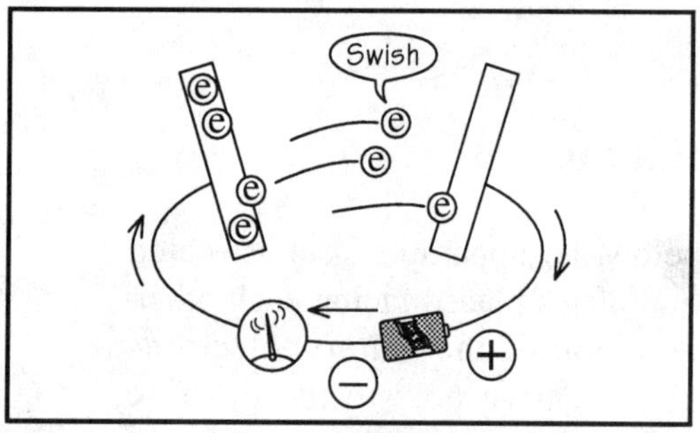

4. In this experiment Lenard tried **changing the intensity (amplitude)** or **the color (frequency) of light** and then examined very thoroughly **how the number of electrons** that flew off, and **the force (energy of a single electron)** varied in response to these changes.

Because we know the electrical charge (amount of electricity) of a single electron, we can find the number of electrons from the amount of electric current.

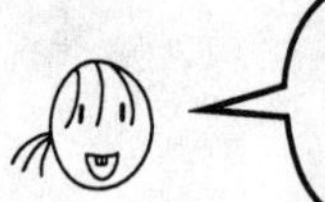

The energy of one electron can be found by measuring the ability of an electron to pass between metal plates *A* and *B* against an electric potential difference.

Let's now look at the experimental results! 

The data was compiled into the table below.

	Number of electrons escaping	Energy of a single escaping electron
When the light is intensified. . .	it increases!	there is no change.
When the frequency is increased. . .	there is no change.	it gets bigger!

I can't really understand what the experimental results mean just by looking at this table.

I bet no one was able to explain it until Einstein figured it out. After all, if you think of light as a wave, these results seem very peculiar!

PHOTOELECTRIC EFFECT IF LIGHT IS A WAVE

First, let's see what problems the physicists of the time ran into when they looked at the experimental results.

The photoelectric effect, when light was thought to be a wave

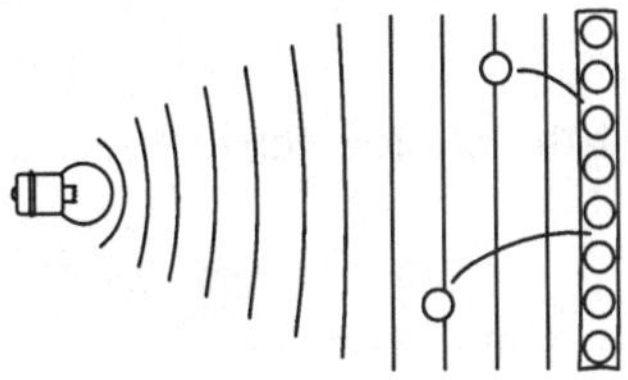

The electrons on a metal surface gain excess energy from being bounced around by light waves and fly off.

Since we are thinking of light as a wave,

The brightness (intensity) of light → The height of wave amplitude

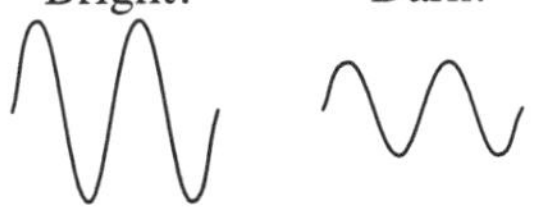

Frequency level → The number of times a wave oscillates per unit of time

the brightness of light and its frequency have a given relationship as shown above.

With that in mind, let's see if we can explain the photoelectric effect. A wave of light may be difficult to imagine, but it is easy to understand if we think of an ocean wave instead.

Photoelectric effect comics

<Scenario 1> A giant wave rolls in, but it's all right!
(As light is made brighter → the number of electrons breaking away increases)

The waves are gentle, and a number of people are floating on the surface.	The waves are getting bigger! Some people are sent flying!	An even bigger wave comes, and now many people are sent flying! Hey, but isn't the energy of the people who were thrown off the same as it was before?!

<Scenario 2> People are sent flying by little ripples!
(As frequency is increased → they're tossed off with greater force)

Many people are floating in the sea.	A gentle but enormously high wave comes along. No one is sent flying.	Here come some fine ripples. Huh?! A number of people are sent flying with great force!

Is this what happens if we think of the photoelectric effect experiment in terms of waves?

This would never happen with waves in the ocean.

Because the energy of a wave is proportional to its $|\text{amplitude}|^2$, one would normally expect that if a big wave came along, the people (electrons) floating about would be tossed in the air with great force. In the photoelectric effect, however, no matter how strong the light becomes, the energy of the electrons that are thrown off is the same. Not only that, there is no way that people would be thrown forcefully into the air if many little ripples came along! The frequency should do no more than determine wave type, or color, and have no relationship to energy.

Beginning with Lenard himself, no one could explain these results. No one doubted the idea that light was a wave. They thought that if they continued their research, eventually they would come up with a good explanation.

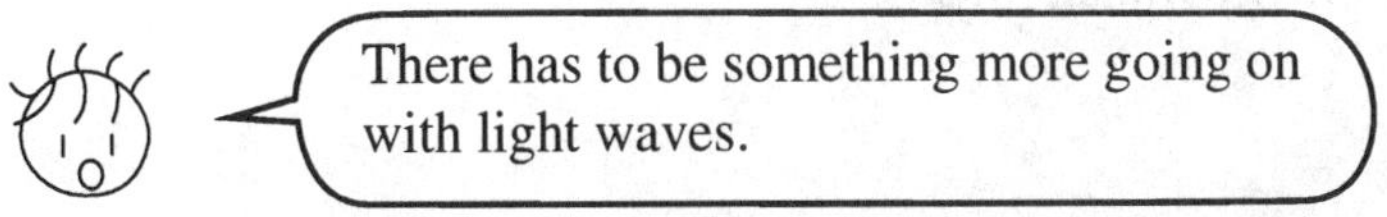

But then, along came Einstein. He worked his way toward a solution by reconsidering light and finding that **LIGHT IS A PARTICLE!**

LOOKING AT LIGHT AS A PARTICLE

Let's look at the experimental results one more time, with the same assumption that underlay the little box experiment. That is, $E = h\nu$: light is made up of particles, each one having energy $h\nu$.

Photoelectric effect if light is a particle

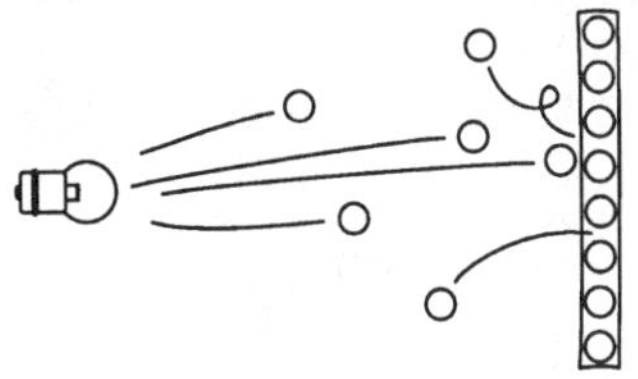

Particles of light come flying along and collide with electrons on the surface of a substance. This bombardment eventually causes electrons to break away.

Looking at it this way, the strength or intensity of light (in the case of light waves, its amplitude) is determined by **the number of light particles.**

Because the energy of a single particle of light is determined by $h\nu$, as the number of particles increases, light becomes stronger. In that case, the experimental results make sense; the number of electrons that fly off increases as the light grows brighter, but the energy of each electron does not change!

If many light particles come flying along, then many electrons get hit, **and the number of electrons that fly off increases!**

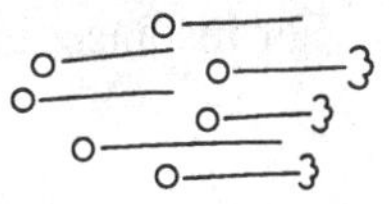

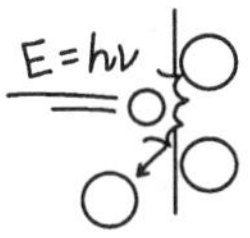

But in this case, since the energy of each light particle is fixed at $h\nu$, regardless of their number, **the energy of each electron does not change!**

Also, since the energy of this light is equal to $h\nu$, the energy levels are determined by its frequency ν (h is Planck's constant and is a fixed value). That is to say, if ν becomes large, then the energy of each light particle also increases.

And so, there is nothing peculiar about the experimental result that suggests when we increase frequency ν of the bombarding light, the number of electrons that fly off does not increase, whereas the energy of each electron increases. When a light particle with a great deal of energy hits, it follows that an electron will fly off with much force.

So if you think of light as a particle, it all makes perfect sense. Why didn't anyone think of this before?

It just goes to show how hard it is to reject what has been established as common sense. I think Einstein's greatness lies in his ability to think in new ways.

This idea did more than just allow us to roughly determine what the energy would be; it let us precisely predict experimental results.

The energy of the bombarding light is $E = h\nu$, ν varying with the color of light. The electrons, having received all of this energy, fly off. However, since a small amount of that energy is spent in breaking away from the surface of the material, the energy of the electron actually is

$$E = h\nu - \phi$$

(ϕ is the energy spent in breaking away)

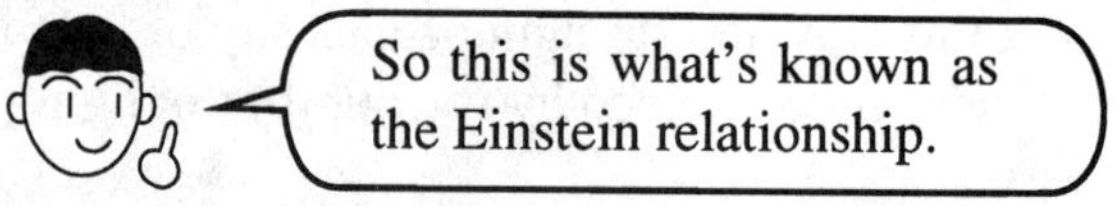

With this, Einstein was able to explain Lenard's experimental results beautifully!

For instance, in the case of violet light, the frequency of the color violet

$$\nu = 0.8 \times 10^{15} \text{ (1/sec)}$$

As Planck's constant is

$$h = 6.63 \times 10^{-34} \text{ (joule} \cdot \text{ second)}$$

in this case, the energy E of light is

$$E = h\nu = 6.63 \times 10^{-34} \times 0.8 \times 10^{15}$$
$$= 5.3 \times 10^{-19} \text{ (joule)}$$

We know from experiments that the energy E of escaping electrons is

$$5 \times 10^{-19} \text{ (joule)}$$

which is in agreement with the experimental results!

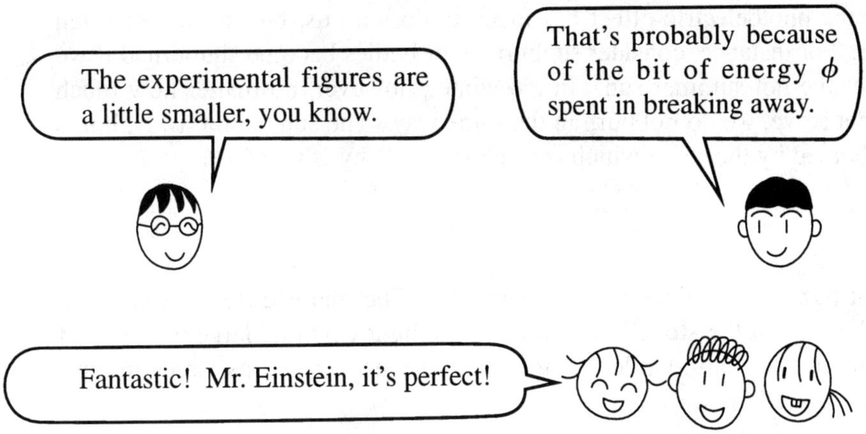

Thus, the photoelectric effect is much better described by using Einstein's $E = h\nu$.

So we can't think of light as a wave! Light is a particle!

PHOTOELECTRIC EFFECTS AROUND US

It is hard to believe that the photoelectric effect has much to do with us, but in fact we often experience it in everyday life. For instance, consider sunburn. Our bodies become sunburned if we spend even ten minutes under the hot summer sun. In the winter, however, no matter how much time we spend before a red-hot stove, we do not burn in the same way. The sun, so far away, burns our skin, and yet we are not burned by the stove which is so close by. Why is that?

Consider the premise that light is a particle having energy $h\nu$. The major difference between the light of the sun and the light from the stove is frequency. Sunlight contains large amounts of high-frequency light, called ultraviolet light, while the light from the stove contains large amounts of low-frequency light, called infrared light.

When we think of $E = h\nu$ in terms of sunlight, with its large amounts of high-frequency ultraviolet light, we see that the energy level of each light particle is extremely high. When light particles with such high energy hit the atoms of our skin, the considerable energy transmitted to them causes the electrons in the atoms to break off with great force. When electrons fly out of our skin, a violent chemical reaction occurs; that is what we know as sunburn.

On the other hand, the light from the stove contains large amounts of low-frequency infrared light, and the energy of each light particle is small. When this light strikes the atoms of our skin, the energy is too low to cause electrons to fly off, regardless of how many particles there are. That is why, no matter how much we warm ourselves by a hot stove, we never get sunburned.

The photoelectric effect demonstrates the particle nature of light, and is something that concerns us all, not just physicists. It is the explanation for some of the phenomena occurring around us every day.

1.6 THE COMPTON EFFECT

In 1923, eighteen years after the experiment on the photoelectric effect, another experiment was done that again confirmed the particle theory of light. This was called the Compton effect experiment.

How do X-rays scatter after striking something?

The American physicist Arthur Compton was able to answer this question by assuming that the particles of light were involved in spherical collisions.

Compton, Arthur Holly
[1892-1962]

Just like the experiment on the photoelectric effect, this one was already known, but because light had been considered to be a wave, it had remained unexplained for a long time. Compton thought about the photoelectric effect and wondered if the same thing would apply here in this experiment. He reexamined it with the assumption that light was a particle.

 Really! Light collides spherically. That's interesting.

 But what are X-rays again? Do they have something to do with light?

 Come on, don't you remember? They came up when we were discussing Planck's work. There are many different kinds of light. X-rays, ultraviolet rays and infrared rays are all invisible rays. X-rays have an even higher frequency than ultraviolet rays.

 Oh, right.

 Okay, now let's get to the Compton effect.

It was already known that when X-rays strike something, they scatter in every direction. The fact that they scatter is not strange, but the problem is

what happens to the frequency of the X-rays after they are dispersed?

Using monochromatic X-rays of a single frequency (that is, simple waves), we measure the frequency of the dispersed X-rays at various locations. We then compare these frequencies with the frequency of the X-rays at the time they were emitted. Surprisingly, we find that

when they scatter after striking a surface, depending on their location, the X-rays have a lower frequency than they had when they were emitted!

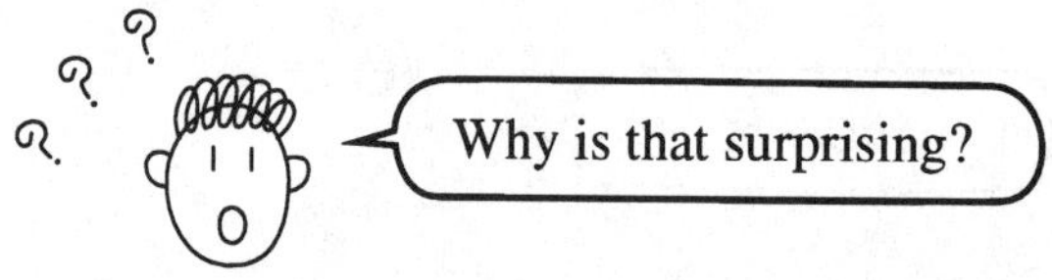

At the time, it appeared that light had been perfectly explained using Maxwell's electromagnetics. The trouble was that there was no way Maxwell's theory could explain this experiment with X-rays. Going by the assumption that light is a wave, it would be absolutely impossible for the X-rays' frequency to decrease after being dispersed.

X-RAY DISPERSION IN THE WAVE THEORY OF LIGHT

Let's look at X-ray dispersion from the perspective of the wave theory of light.

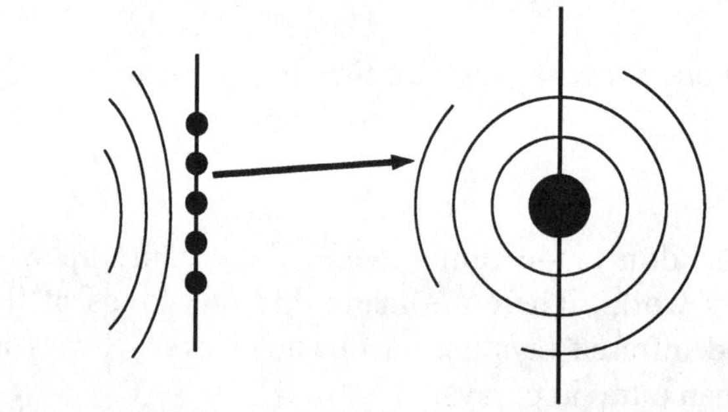

1. A wave of X-rays comes along.
2. It strikes a substance.
3. The electrons in the substance are shaken about and are emitted as spherical waves.

This is X-ray dispersion as explained by Maxwell's electromagnetics. Since electrons emit light as their movement becomes more rapid, it follows that the electrons disturbed in this experiment ought to emit light as well. When the light spreads out into space in the form of spherical waves, these waves represent the dispersed X-rays.

To visualize these spherical waves spreading out into space, we need only recall the waves that were created when we moved a float up and down in a tank of water.

Thinking about dispersed X-rays in this manner,

1. The electrons that become agitated oscillate at the same frequency as the X-rays did at the time they were emitted.

2. Because the X-rays are monochromatic, the electrons should naturally all have the same period of oscillation.

3. Therefore, the spherical waves should always have the same frequency as the original X-rays.

Thus, the experimental outcome that the frequency of dispersed X-rays is less than when the X-rays were emitted cannot be explained by the wave theory of light.

You're right. It doesn't seem to make sense.

In the end, it was simply left unexplained.

But then Einstein announced his photoelectron hypothesis, and Compton realized that if he used it in relation to the X-ray experiment, the problem might be solved.

Okay, now let's examine the experiment on X-ray dispersion assuming, as did Compton, that light is a particle having the energy equal to $h\nu$. If we assume light is a particle, what happens to the X-rays as they scatter?

X-RAY DISPERSION IN THE PARTICLE THEORY OF LIGHT

Assuming light to be a particle, let's look at X-ray dispersion.

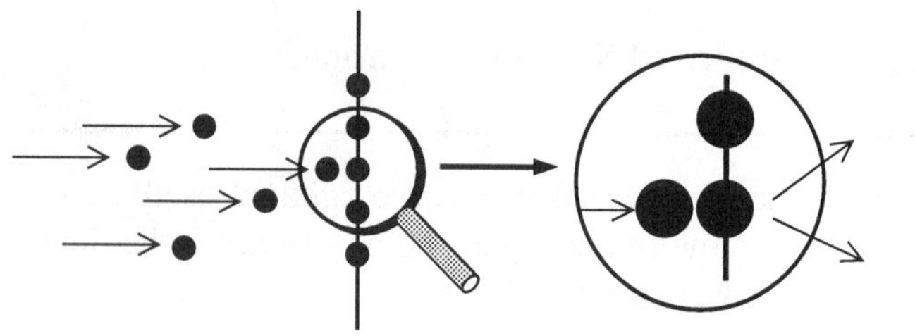

1. Many particles of light come flying along.
2. They strike a substance.
3. The particles of light strike electrons, which then fly off in all directions.

This is X-ray dispersion assuming light is a particle. Put briefly, these are "spherical collisions," just like in billiards. Spherical collisions are explained by Newtonian dynamics, so in this case we can proceed as we did before. The only small difference is that the energy of a particle of light is $\boldsymbol{E = h\nu}$.

First of all, let's look at what happens if a light particle with energy $h\nu$ strikes an electron.

A particle with energy $h\nu$ strikes an electron and sends it flying.

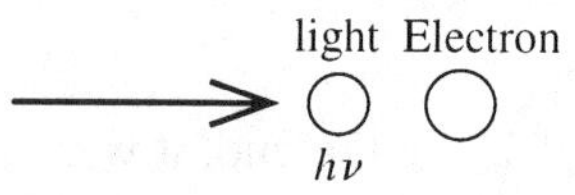

As a result of this collision, the particle of light loses just the amount of energy that was gained by the electron when it was struck.

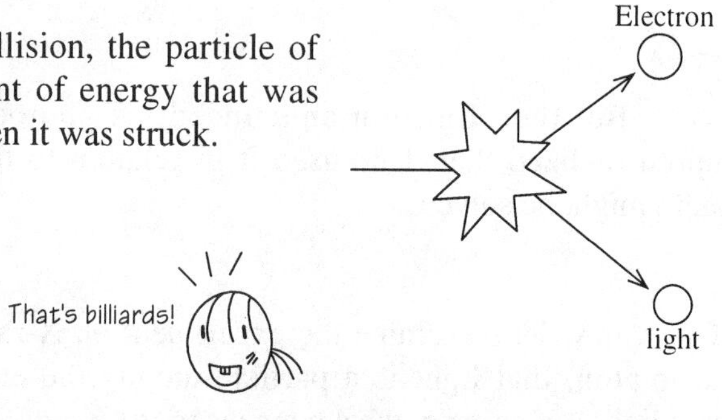

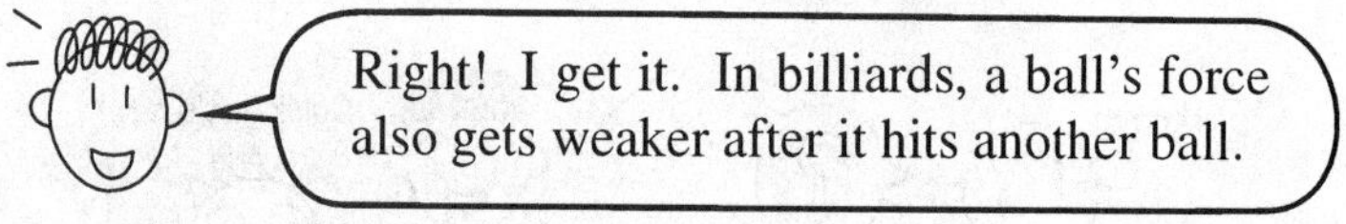

The bombarded electrons move because they have received energy from the light particles. In this case, the energy gained by the electrons is the same as the energy lost by the light particles. Expressing this as an equation, we get:

original light energy	=	energy of light after impact	+	energy imparted to electron

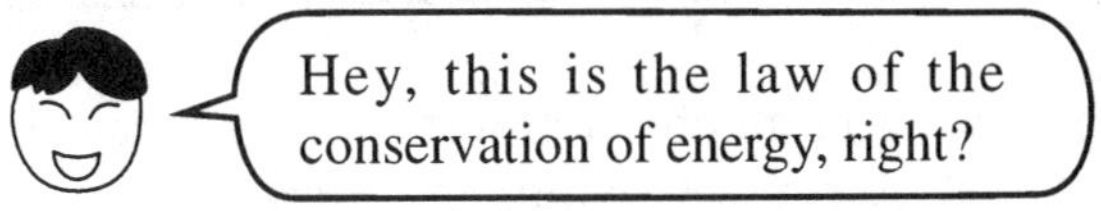

Because the energy of a light particle is $h\nu$, let's apply it to the law of the conservation of energy. Because h is a constant, the energy of light can change only when its frequency ν also changes. Thus, if we let ν_1 equal the original frequency, and ν_2 equal the frequency after collision, we may rewrite the law of the conservation of energy like this:

$$h\nu_1 = h\nu_2 + \text{(the energy of the electron)}$$

This means that,

$$\not{h}\nu_1 \geqq \not{h}\nu_2$$

$$\nu_1 \geqq \nu_2$$

In other words, the frequency of light's energy after impact is less than its frequency before impact.

and we can derive this relationship.

So, if we assume light to be a particle, it makes sense that the frequency of the dispersed X-rays would be lower than when they were emitted.

At this point, however, we have only proven that the reduction in frequency is to be expected if we assume light to be a particle. In fact, the experiment goes on to record that the frequency of the dispersed X-rays varies depending on their location. We must still make calculations and show that the results match up with actual experimental results. Only then can we say with certainty that the impact behavior of light is spherical, like balls.

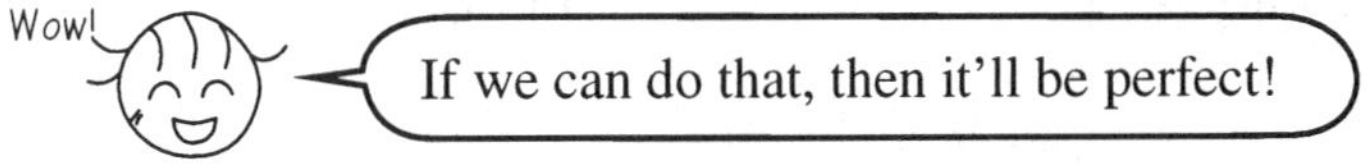

MOMENTUM OF LIGHT

In order to explain the phenomenon of spherical collisions, we first need to understand the concept of "**momentum**". Momentum, as it relates to particles, is shown by the following equation:

$$p = mv$$

momentum = mass × velocity

Mass is the weight of an object at rest. Velocity describes how fast and in what direction that object is moving. Newton defined motion as an object (particle) moving at a given velocity. But the term "object" includes objects of varying weight, that is to say, mass. Therefore, although two objects may be traveling at the same velocity, if their masses are different, the force of their movement will differ as well. This "force of movement" is momentum. Momentum is determined by the relationship between a moving object's mass and its velocity.

In spherical collisions, classical theory can determine the momenta of the balls after collision by knowing their momenta prior to collision and their angle of rebound. In other words, we are easily able to determine the direction and speed of the two balls after impact.

I get it! So in this experiment, we need to find the momentum of light, right?

And then, after we make the calculations and they agree with the experimental results, we will have proven indisputably that light is a particle and that light particles really do behave like spheres when they collide.

Let's find the momentum of light!

Okay, we just need to use the equation "momentum p equals mass m multiplied by velocity v," right?

What? Hold on a minute. The speed of light is 300,000 km/sec (186,000 miles/sec), but what is the mass of light?

Exactly. For light, mass is a problem. Momentum, in Newtonian mechanics, is

$$p = mv$$

However, mass m is the "**stationary mass**", that is, the mass of something when it is at rest. One of the properties of light is that its velocity does not change, no matter where or when we measure it. Light always travels at 300,000 km/sec. If its velocity drops even a tiny amount, then it is no longer light. This means that no matter how sophisticated our instruments are, we will never be able to measure the mass of light at rest.

According to Einstein's theory of relativity, the stationary mass of light is zero!

Come to think of it, the spherical collisions described by classical theory referred to the velocity of two balls after impact, whereas the Compton effect experiment observed the frequency of dispersed light. In other words, we have to describe the momentum of light in terms of frequency.

According to classical theory, momentum is expressed by $p = mv$, which is in terms of **mass** and **velocity**, right?

In the case of light, we cannot find its momentum using established classical theory. We need a different method of determining it.

You mean we're going to describe momentum as something other than $p = mv$?

Is that possible??

As a matter of fact, the **momentum of light** was described in relation to energy by Einstein in the following equation:

$$p = \frac{E}{c}$$

In this famous equation, which appears in "The Theory of Relativity," E represents the energy of light, and c is the speed of light. In his theory of relativity, Einstein discovered that the momentum of light must be related to its energy.

Now, there is one more equation that we must bring in when we deal with the energy of light. Here it is:

$$E = h\nu$$

Because both of these equations contain E, the energy of light, all we have to do is substitute $h\nu$ for E. By doing this, we can express the momentum of light in the following way:

Point

$$p = \frac{h\nu}{c}$$

THE MOMENTUM OF LIGHT IS ITS ENERGY ($h\nu$) DIVIDED BY ITS VELOCITY (c)!

Now we can see the relationship between the momentum of light and its frequency. If we use this relationship in our calculations and find that the frequencies of the dispersed X-rays match the experimental results, then we've got our answer. Let's compare the observed values and the theoretical values for X-rays when the angle of rebound is 90 degrees.

Frequency observed experimentally · · · · 4.5×10^{11} (1/sec)

Frequency obtained through calculation · · · 4.2×10^{11} (1/sec)

Wow! They're almost the same!

So this means we've proven that light collides spherically.

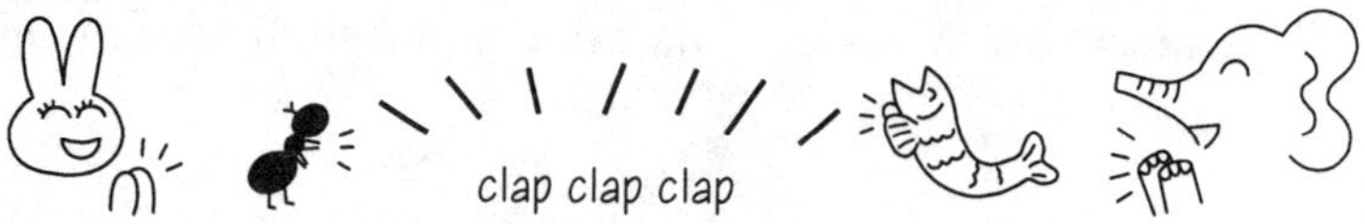

After Compton explained the results of his experiment, Einstein's photoelectron hypothesis became more than just a hypothesis; it became a reality. Up until then, though light appeared to be a particle, all physicists could say with certainty was that

"The exchange of energy is discontinuous."

No one could say with absolute certainty that light was a particle. But this experiment, which explained the momentum of light particles, erased all traces of remaining doubt.

LIGHT HAS BEEN PROVEN CONCLUSIVELY TO BE A PARTICLE!

ANOTHER WAY OF DESCRIBING THE MOMENTUM OF LIGHT

We just represented the momentum p of light in the form

$$p = \frac{h\nu}{c} \qquad \text{Equation (1)}$$

Just for the record, let's represent it in another form. It is possible to rewrite this equation using wavelength λ (lambda). Wavelength is,

"the distance a wave travels in the space of one cycle."

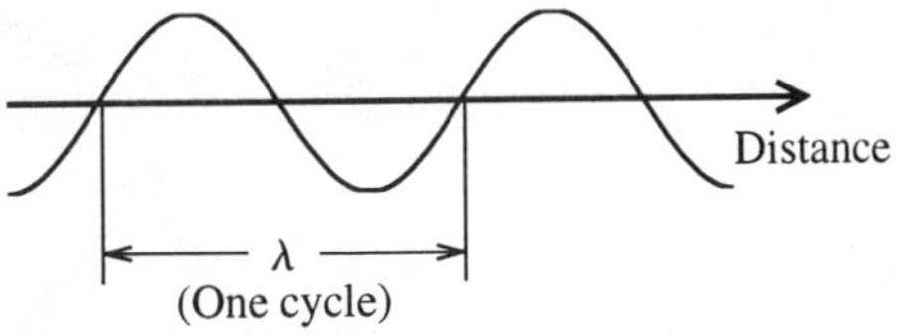

To find wavelength λ for light, we divide the distance light travels in one second, 300,000 kilometers, by the number of cycles per second. Written as a mathematical expression, we obtain:

$$\lambda = \frac{\text{speed of light } c}{\text{frequency } \nu}$$

Recall that we defined frequency as the number of times a wave oscillates per second. For example, if $\nu = 5$, that means that in one second the wave oscillates five times, and 300,000km/5 is the length of the wave. In short, this is how wavelength λ can be determined.

Because the term $\frac{\nu}{c}$ in Equation (1) is the inverse of wavelength λ,

$$\frac{\nu}{c} = \frac{1}{\lambda}$$

Placing it in Equation (1), we find we may rewrite Equation (1) as

$$p = \frac{h}{\lambda}$$

The momentum of light p is equal to Planck's constant h divided by wavelength λ.

1. 7 CLOUD CHAMBER EXPERIMENT

We have learned that the Compton effect can be explained using the same theory of spherical collisions that applies to objects we know such as billiard balls. According to this law, if we know the momentum of one of the two balls that collide, we can determine the momentum of the other ball. The Compton effect focused on the change in frequency of X-rays; the electrons that broke away were not considered. However, if we have information about the rebounding X-rays, we can find both the direction and velocity of the electron.

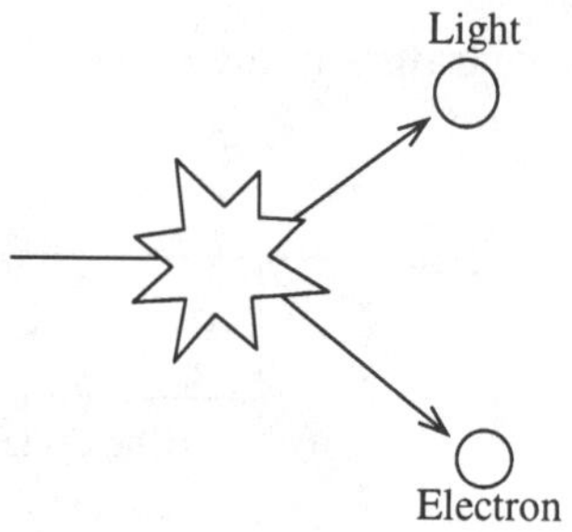

If we could somehow observe the leaping electrons, and then show that their paths agree with those predicted by the Compton effect, that would be like gilding the lily. Compton's theory would be even more complete. Electrons are extremely small and cannot be observed directly. Since no one could see electrons when Compton announced his theory, he did not touch upon the electrons that broke off. But a few months later, two physicists, Charles Wilson and Walther Bothe, independently devised a method to perceive the movement of electrons with the naked eye! The results were amazing! They confirmed that electrons broke off exactly as Compton's theory had predicted.

Wilson, Charles Thomson Rees [1869-1959]

Bothe, Walther Wilhelm Georg [1891-1957]

Fantastic! So Compton was perfectly correct.

But just how were electrons observed? As for light, all we need to do is observe frequency, but how can you see the movement of a single electron?

In order to "see" electrons that cannot be observed per se, we use a **CLOUD CHAMBER.**

This procedure was worked out by cleverly using the properties of fog.

What do you mean by the "properties of fog"? Fog is that wet, hazy thing that you often run into high up in the mountains, right?

That's right. Fog occurs when air of high humidity is suddenly cooled, and the water vapor in the air condenses into little droplets of water. They form around particles of dust in the air.

I see. A cloud chamber is a box filled with fog, right? But how can you see anything, let alone an electron, in fog?

Well, you don't actually see the electrons in the box. Normally what you see are the tracks left by the electrons in the fog, but in some instances ions (atoms to which electricity has been applied) play the part of dust.

Here is how the cloud chamber works. A box that contains no dust is filled with water vapor and then suddenly chilled. In this supersaturated state, fog wants to form, but because there is no dust to form a core, there is no way it can. Now we let an electron fly. As the electron collides with atoms in the air, it strips electrons from the atoms, forming ions. Fog then forms around the ions, becoming a line of fog created by the ions (electrons) as they travel through the chamber. Their paths are thus clearly visible.

In this way, Wilson and Bothe were able to observe in detail electrons thrown off during the Compton effect. If the electrons are thrown off with much force, their energy is high and their tracks are long; when there is little force, their tracks are short. By knowing how far an electron traveled, it is possible to calculate the energy with which it started. These calculations yielded results that closely agreed with Compton's.

Hey, that's interesting. So you can observe an electron's tracks. That I want to see!

You know, we actually tried the experiment at TCL. Let's take a look.

LET'S DO AN EXPERIMENT USING THE CLOUD CHAMBER!

One day, students performed the cloud chamber experiment in the Hippo classroom at TCL. Finally we would be able to confirm the motion of electrons in the Compton effect with our own eyes!

At TCL, we used a simple cloud chamber from a set of educational materials. The "cloud chamber" was a round container that could be held in the palms of two hands. As shown in the drawing below, instead of electrons, this set contained an alpha ray generator that emitted alpha particles. Since electrons and alpha particles are both quanta (particles smaller than atoms), they will appear to be almost identical.

First, we drip alcohol on the upper part of a sponge that is inside the container. Because it vaporizes much more easily than water, it forms fog more readily.

At the same time, we pack the bottom of the container with dry ice to cool it.

When we shut the lid and wait, the alcohol vaporizes and steadily falls downwards. The bottom of the container is cooled, and the vapor tries to return to a liquid state. After a while, a fog of alcohol forms with dust as the core, and the fog subsides to the bottom. The container is then full of alcohol that cannot form a fog.

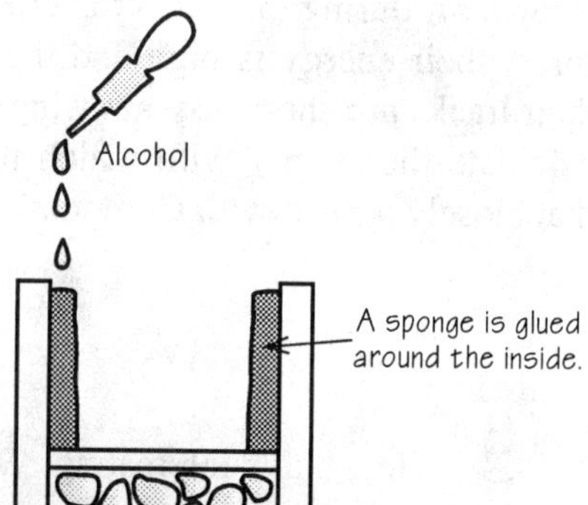

Now let's try emitting some alpha particles into the container! Put the outlet of the alpha ray source into the hole in the box. All right, here we go!

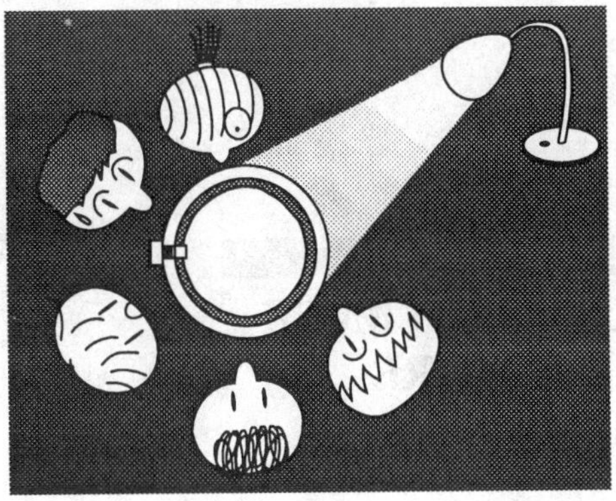

It's easy to see if we turn off the lights in the room and shine a single spotlight on the cloud chamber.

Because we weren't using the correct amount of alcohol, we had failure after failure at TCL.

Just as we were about to give up. . .we **SAW** it!

We could clearly see the tracks of the alpha particles spurting with plenty of force, looking like the contrails left by airplanes.

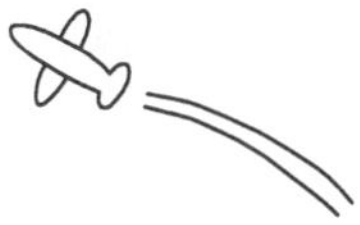

After so many failures, the room exploded with excitement when we finally saw them.

So that's how you can see the tracks of electrons. Then you just have to observe the direction and the speed of the tracks. Whoever thought up this experiment was brilliant.

The cloud chamber was the only way that the movement of electrons could be observed. Later, it was to play an indispensable role in nuclear physics research.

1. 8 SO, WHAT IS LIGHT!?

LET'S GO BACK ONE MORE TIME!

Well, I guess no matter how you look at it, light is a particle.

Yes, and that cloud chamber experiment was really interesting. When I saw the tracks, which looked like airplane contrails, I got really excited.

It was Compton's theory that enabled such a solid explanation. Now, no matter what anyone thinks, light is indisputably a particle.

Light particles are so small we can't see them, but they move in exactly the same way as a rolling ball.

So now nobody has any objections to saying light is a particle.

Is that so? Have you all forgotten what we learned at the very beginning? Let's retrace our steps.

Our point of departure was the question, **"WHAT IS LIGHT?"**

↓

Initially, physicists had described it as a **wave** because light was known to **INTERFERE.**

↓

↓

Let's confirm it with
the SLIT EXPERIMENT.

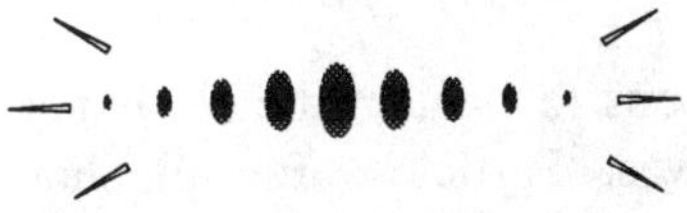

Light is a **wave,** after all!

↓

BUT! Through the blackbody radiation experiment, Planck discovered that light could not be explained if it were approached as an ordinary wave.

$$\boldsymbol{E = nh\nu} \quad (\nu = 0, 1, 2, 3 \cdots)$$

The energy of light can only have discontinuous values!

↓

Einstein arrived on the scene!

He discovered in a little mental exercise called the little box experiment that the results of the blackbody radiation test could be nicely explained by assuming that light is a particle! Following that, he brilliantly demonstrated with the experiment on the photoelectric effect that

$$\boldsymbol{E = h\nu}$$

He demonstrated that **light is composed of particles, each having energy $h\nu$.**

↓

And then in the Compton effect experiment, we found that,

$$p = \frac{h\nu}{c} = \frac{h}{\lambda}$$

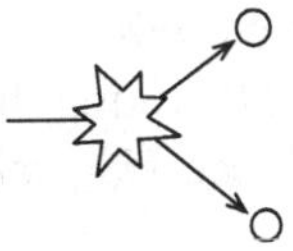

How about that! We were even able to find the **MOMENTUM** involved in the particle theory of light.

See! No matter how many times we examine it, it appears in the end that light is composed of particles.

But what happens to light in the slit experiment? This showed that light is composed of waves. Particles, after all, shouldn't display interference. Right?

Yes, but in the experiments on the photoelectric effect and the Compton effect, there is no choice but to think of light as a particle.

So what approach should we take now?

I've got it! How about rethinking the slit experiment for particles? Then if we end up with the same patterns, we'll have to conclude that light is a particle.

That's right. Let's try it!

SLIT EXPERIMENT FOR PARTICLES

As we saw at the very beginning, when waves pass through two slits at the same time, the intensity of the waves when they arrive at the wall can be shown in the following diagram.

If we try this using particles, what will result? In the case of waves, we examined their force at the time of striking the wall. Since a particle cannot be split into two, we will shoot them in succession using something like a machine gun.

The procedure is the same as it was for waves. We observe the three resulting patterns based on the following:

1. Only slit #1 open
2. Only slit #2 open
3. Both slits open

1. Only slit #1 open

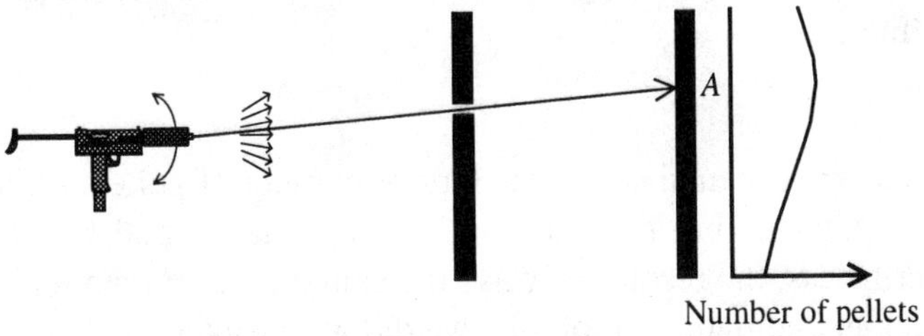

Although pellets strike the edges of slit #1 and substantially change course at times, most of them pass through the slit in a straight line from where they were fired, arriving at the wall in the vicinity of point A, as shown in the diagram.

2. Only slit #2 open

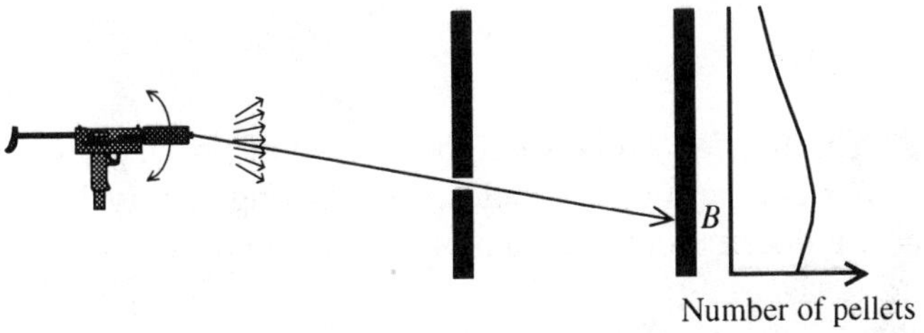

As in case 1, the most number of pellets arrive near point B, as shown in the diagram.

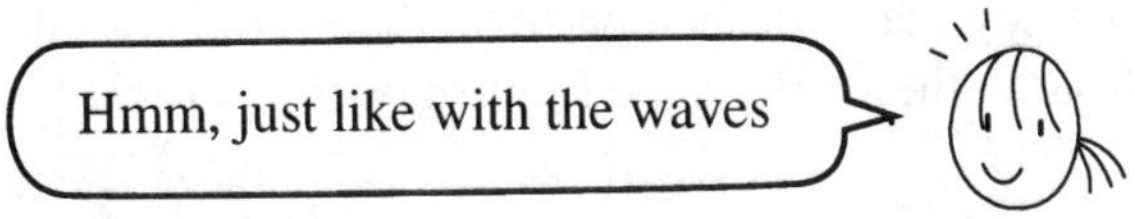

3. Both slits open

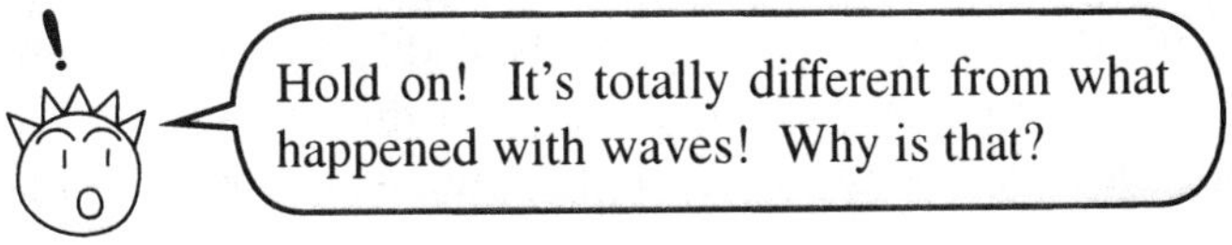

When both slits are opened, cases 1 and 2 occur at the same time, so the result is a simple addition of graph 1 and graph 2.

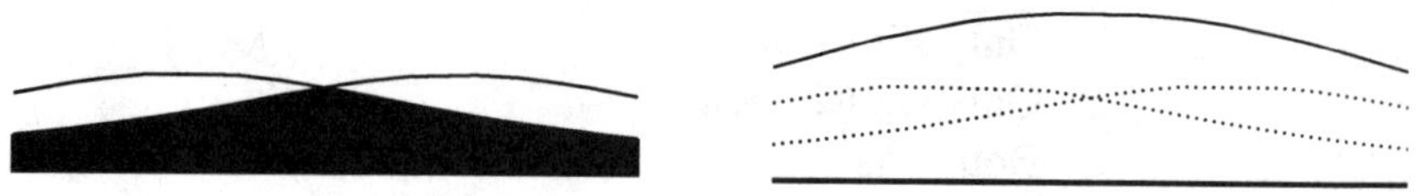

Think of it as adding the darkened portion of the graph to the dotted lines.

With this experimental setup, the largest number of pellets arrive right in the middle near point C, but that can change depending upon the location of the slits. Nevertheless, the result is always the sum of 1+2; no matter what happens, we never get an undulating graph like we did with waves.

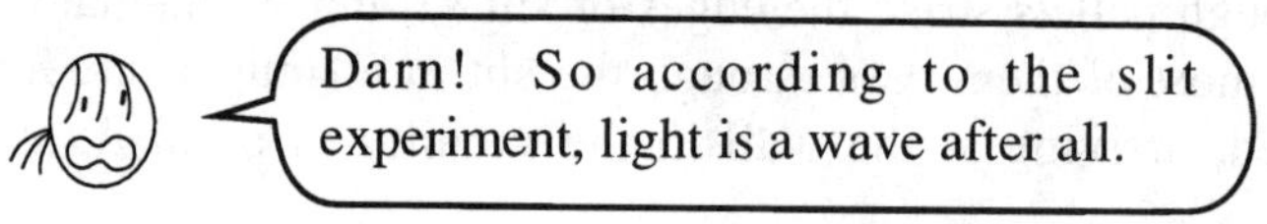

DEPARTURE TO A NEW THEORY

Oh, my. We went to all the trouble of proving so neatly that light is composed of particles, each having energy E equal to $h\nu$, and now it doesn't look like our conclusion holds up anymore.

Look, don't you think it's strange when we really look at "$E = h\nu$"? I mean, while we say that light is a particle, there's a "ν" in there. That ν means frequency. What in the world is the frequency of a particle?

You're right. If that's the case, even if we assume that light is a particle, we have absolutely no idea what kind of particle.

SO WHAT IS LIGHT!?

The physicists of the time were in a fix, just like we are now. In the slit experiment, the light that created interference patterns could not be thought of as anything other than a wave. However, Planck found that light waves could have only discontinuous energy levels, and Einstein and then Compton went on to prove that light could be nothing other than a particle. The Compton Effect experiment even went so far as to determine the momentum of light particles.

So light pops up in one experiment as a wave, and as a particle in another experiment. But light never appears at the same time as both a wave and a particle.

These terms "wave" and "particle" had very specific meanings in the world of physics. The reason is that physics up to then described everything in the world in broad terms of either particles or waves.

The two had absolutely opposite properties, and so they were mutually incompatible. A particle could never act like a wave, and a wave could never behave like a particle.

Physicists were troubled by these odd characteristics of light. At this time, when experiments on light were being carried out all the time, the famous Swiss physicist Max Born quipped,

Born, Max
[1882-1970]

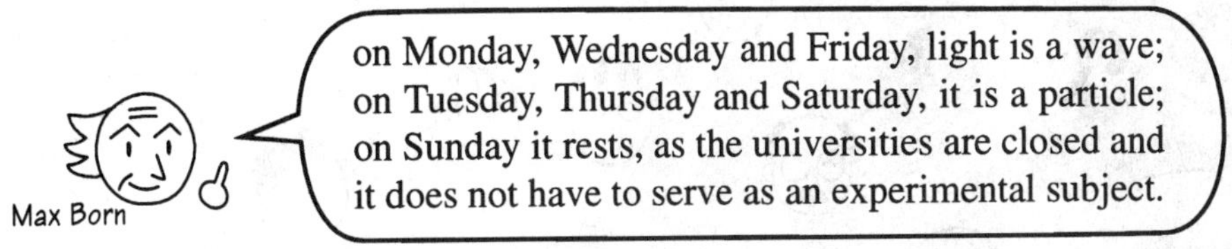

Up until then, physicists explained the physical world using Newtonian dynamics and electromagnetics, but neither set of theories could explain the particle and wave aspects of light. Later, however, it was found that phenomena other than light were also unexplained by classical theory. There was the blackbody radiation problem, as well as **the problem of the atom.**

Atoms were considered the smallest units of matter, but it was discovered that even atoms could be analyzed and separated into parts, namely electrons and atomic nuclei. The new questions concerned electrons and atomic nuclei, and their properties with regard to the atom. Yet no amount of investigation in these areas based on classical theory could yield consistent results.

Then Niels Bohr appeared on the scene. In connection with the problem of the atom, he applied the term to describe the energy of light, $E = h\nu$, and was successful. With Bohr's discovery, physics entered a whole new phase.

Bohr, Niels Henrik David
[1885-1962]

It was the birth of early quantum theory.

In this, Planck's constant played a significant role.

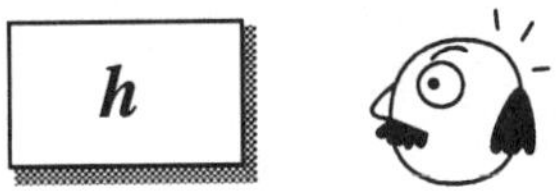

In fact, this constant h would become indispensable in understanding the quantum. At this stage, we still have not discussed the impact that the constant h was to have. It will become clear as we go along. What was in store was a

different sort of conclusion that could by no means have been understood in terms of the theories that dominated physics of the time.

It became clear that Newtonian dynamics and electromagnetism were unable to explain quanta, and they eventually came to be known as something outdated called "classical physics." The new physics, quantum mechanics, was to become something to which many young, talented physicists would dedicate their lives. Just how will this new theory, quantum mechanics, which explains both light and the atom, unfold?

CHAPTER 2

Niels Bohr

EARLY QUANTUM THEORY

Planck and Einstein opened the door to quantum theory. With others, they made it possible to study the electron, one of the parts that make up the atom. The behavior of electrons seemed very odd at first. Since it could not be explained by classical mechanics, it defied scientific understanding until someone was able to drive a wedge into the problem. That person was Niels Bohr. Let's take Bohr's bold and brilliant concept and see how it helped to unravel the perplexities of one strange phenomenon after another.

2.1 SETTING OFF ON THE ADVENTURE

Quantum mechanics? What's that?

Ugh! It sounds complicated.

Some people have never heard of quantum mechanics before this, and others have heard of it but assume it has nothing to do with them. There are many levels of familiarity among us. A few probably have studied it but found it so difficult that they understood practically nothing. But that doesn't matter at all. If you are able to understand language, then you can participate in this adventure.

In particular, if you have even once thought, "Just what is this world that we live in?" or "How amazing that people learn to speak a language!" that is enough. The term quantum mechanics is a guide word made up by natural scientists who set out on this journey a step ahead of us. They, too, wondered about the world, asking themselves, "What makes up the natural world?" When it comes to adventure, they have a lot of experience!

But many mathematical expressions come up, right? I'm no good at math!

I won't be able to follow along.

Don't worry. Mathematical expressions are a magnificent language that can express what makes up the natural world.

Math — a language that expresses nature?

Really?

This was a surprising new idea to me. I had never thought of math that way before. But having been told, I saw it was really true. Math is above all a language of international communication that people from any country can understand. Now does it seem a little more approachable?

Natural scientists are the same human beings we are.
"That's right. What one person can understand, anyone can understand."

We love learning languages, and math is a language, too. It's true!

We think it's perfectly natural that children learn to talk; the math of quantum mechanics is also a natural phenomenon. At Hippo Family Club, we try to absorb language by learning the way small children do. As for finding out what makes up the natural world, we approach it like a treasure hunt!

Doing quantum mechanics, you get the same feeling as when you are discovering a language, or when you meet people from other countries and begin to feel, "Hey, we're all on the same treasure hunt!" Although our lives and languages differ, we are all human beings. At first glance things may look totally different, yet they behave in the same way.

"Same" — it's a warm, comfortable word. Don't you agree?

If we're all on a treasure hunt looking for the same thing, I guess we can do it together.

I agree.

Right! We can go any time.
Let's set off on our adventure together!

2. 2 THE STRANGE BEHAVIOR OF ATOMS

From here we enter the invisible world of **ATOMS** and **ELECTRONS.** The stage is set for Niels Bohr, who built the foundation for quantum mechanics. This foundation was later to be called early quantum theory.

Until then physicists believed that they understood the laws governing the physical world. But when it came to light, they were puzzled. Light sometimes behaved like a wave, and at other times like a particle. Many physicists simply could not believe that this problem was beyond the reach of classical theory. Research by Planck and Einstein then opened the door to quantum mechanics. No one knew what kind of world would begin to unfold. Scientists later came to realize that a great event had occurred, one that would affect our entire way of thinking. Just what was about to happen?

Gleeful expectation

Before introducing Bohr's work, let's go over the problems that remained unsolved while the atom was being studied.

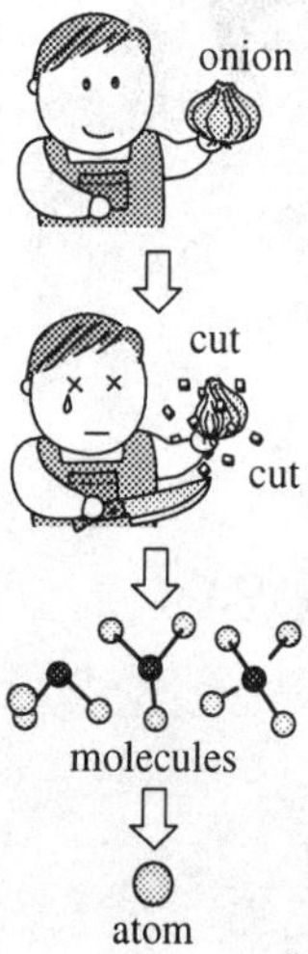

When a substance is broken down into smaller parts, there comes a point when it cannot be broken down any further. The ancient Greeks called the smallest unit they perceived an **"ATOM."** It took a great deal of research, but it was found that all known substances appeared to be composed of only several dozen different kinds of atoms. Moreover, it was known that when something is heated (when energy is applied), light is emitted. It was thus clear that **ATOMS EMIT LIGHT.** However, there was something very odd about it.

As we saw before, after sunlight passes through a prism, a very pretty banded spectrum like a rainbow appears.

This is a band spectrum. 

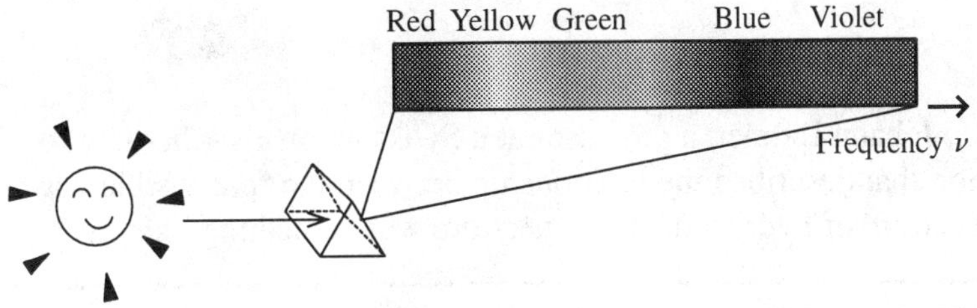

The differences in frequency appear as differences in color, right? 

 A prism separates the components of mixed light. It's a very useful thing.

When a substance (atom) is heated, however, it was found that it emits only **CERTAIN FREQUENCIES OF LIGHT.**

This is a line spectrum. 

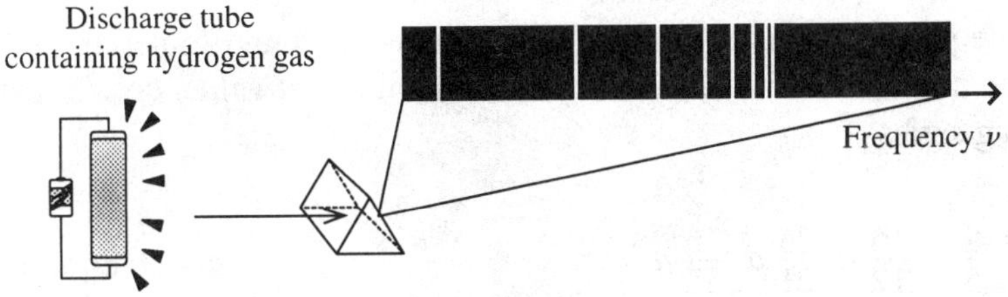

 In other words, the colors that are mixed together into light differ depending on the kind of atom.

Right. For example, sodium is orange, hydrogen is pink, and so on. You are already familiar with some of them, such as the orange highway lights which are the light of sodium atoms.

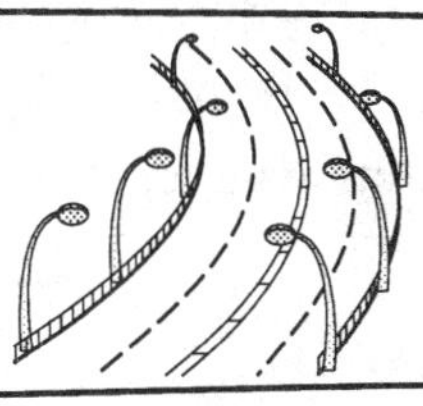

 Gee.

The light that is produced is determined by the atom, and the same atom will always produce the same frequencies of light. Through a great deal of research, physicists were able to determine what kinds of light were produced by each atom, but it was not known why or how only certain frequencies of light were produced.

LIGHT EMITTED BY ATOMS

Balmer, Johann Jakob [1825-1898]

In 1885, Johann Balmer, a professor at a Swiss women's school, worked out an equation that described the relationship between the four visible wave lengths in the spectrum of hydrogen. That spectrum was something like this.

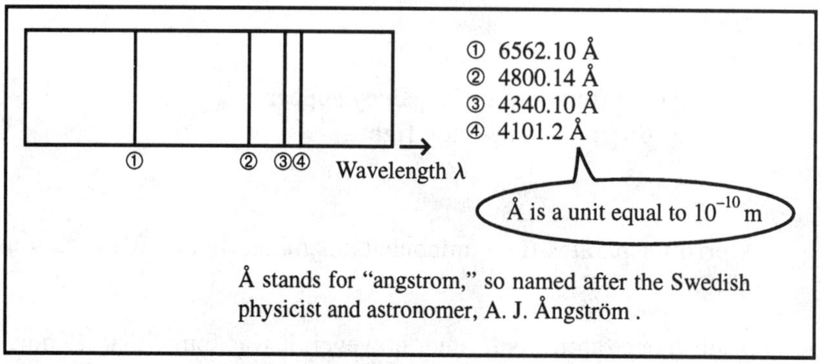

Balmer liked to amuse himself by taking four numbers and then finding an equation describing their relationship.

While playing around with his four numbers, he found something interesting about the number 3645.6 Å. Giving the symbol a that value, he worked out the following series:

$$\frac{9}{5}a,\ \frac{16}{12}a,\ \frac{25}{21}a,\ \frac{36}{32}a \qquad (a = 3645.6\text{Å})$$

If we analyze them further, we can find this rule:

$$\frac{3^2}{3^2-4}a,\ \frac{4^2}{4^2-4}a,\ \frac{5^2}{5^2-4}a,\ \frac{6^2}{6^2-4}a \qquad (a = 3645.6\text{Å})$$

Putting it all together, we have Balmer's equation:

$$\lambda = \frac{n^2}{n^2-4}a \qquad \begin{matrix}(n = 3, 4, 5, 6)\\(a = 3645.6\text{Å})\end{matrix}$$

This was the initial discovery that there is a regularity in the spectra emitted by atoms!

So a hobby of playing with numbers developed into a great discovery.

Balmer's equation, however, only described the spectrum of hydrogen. Shortly thereafter, Johannes Rydberg found that Balmer's equation could also be expressed neatly in terms of frequency rather than wavelength, and he came up with an equation that matched the spectra of all atoms.

Rydberg, Johannes Robert
[1854-1919]

Rydberg's Equation

$$\nu = \frac{Rc}{(m+a)^2} - \frac{Rc}{(n+b)^2}$$

$R = 1.0973 \times 10^5\ \text{cm}^{-1}$ is a constant found by Rydberg. By using this constant, the equation matches the experimental results perfectly.

In this equation, n and m are constants, and $n > m$. The values a and b are constants that are determined by the type of atom. By putting together m, n, a, and b, one can identify all the spectra that are given off by an atom. For instance, although only four of the hydrogen spectra are visible, this equation lets us know that there are many, many more. Isn't that astounding? It's an equation that predicts things we can't even see! When a and b are both zero, the equation describes the spectra of hydrogen.

The equation for the spectra of hydrogen

$$\nu = \frac{Rc}{m^2} - \frac{Rc}{n^2} \quad (n > m)$$

Point

When $m = 2$, this equation matches Balmer's equation perfectly.

Those who want to calculate this for themselves, please go ahead.

Just as Rydberg's equation predicted, more and more invisible spectra were found as experimental technology improved.

Let's look at the spectra of hydrogen as an example.

Lyman, Theodore
[1874-1954]

Paschen, Louis Carl Heinrich Friedrich
[1865-1947]

Blackett, Patric Maynard Stuart
[1897-1974]

The *m* in Rydberg's equation is an integer. The part corresponding to $m = 1$ (ultraviolet series) was discovered by Theodore Lyman in 1906, and the part corresponding to $m = 3$ (infrared series) by Louis Paschen in 1908. That corresponding to $m = 4$ was found in 1922 by Patric Blackett. Not surprisingly, they are called the Lyman series, Paschen series and Blackett series.

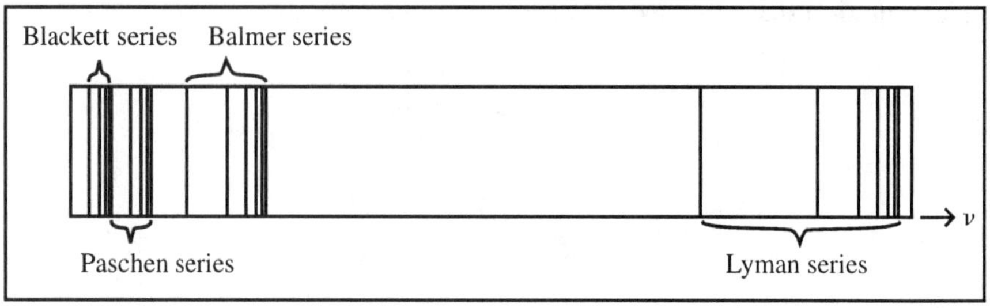

But, but, but. . .
How do these spectra come up?
Just what is this?

Although they could predict the spectra of atoms, neither Balmer nor Rydberg could explain why they occurred.

In physics, if questions like "Why?" and "By what means?" cannot be answered, it means that the phenomenon has not been explained.

Because Rydberg's equation perfectly described the spectra of light from atoms, it ought to have been an important clue to understanding the atom. But actually it didn't work quite so well.

In general, it was not known how or why the spectra emitted by atoms are line spectra, nor why they only appeared in certain predetermined places in relation to each other. Fourier had described light in terms of complicated waves (complicated waves are summations of simple waves, and the frequency of complicated waves is an integral multiple of fundamental frequencies), but his and Rydberg's equations looked very different.

It takes the form of ❑ – ❑
something minus something.

Now, physicists could not account for the light emitted by atoms. Where did it come from? How was it emitted? They began to study it in earnest.

FIND THE STRUCTURE OF THE ATOM! One after another, difficulties arose

For hundreds of years the atom was thought to be the smallest unit that made up all matter. But around 1900, it was discovered that atoms were constructed of yet smaller particles, one of which was called the **ELECTRON.**

I'm the one who discovered the electron, Joseph Thomson. Among other places, electrons are found in atoms. What is more, when electrons move, they emit light. In other words, the spectra of atoms are the light given off by electrons.

Thomson, Sir Joseph John
[1856-1940]

But exactly how are electrons contained within atoms?

Starting with me, physicists asked those questions and began to think about the structure of the atom.

Known facts about the hydrogen atom

Atomic	Mass: 1.673×10^{-24} g
	Charge: neutral
	Size: 10^{-8} cm
Electron	Mass: 9.109×10^{-28} g
	Charge: $-e$ (negative charge)
	$(e^2 = 23.04 \times 10^{-20}\ \mathrm{g \cdot cm^3 \cdot sec^{-2}})$

We use 'electrostatic system of units', (whose basic units are 'cm', 'g', 'sec') to make the formulas simple.

The size of the atom was determined by scientists. And the weight of an electron was calculated to be about 1/2000 of an atom — a great deal lighter.

Since the charge of an electron is negative, does the fact that an atom is neutral mean that there must be something that is positively charged inside an atom?

Right! That is exactly what physicists were thinking. They believed that atoms must be composed of:

⊖ A very light electron with a negative charge	+	⊕ A substance with a positive charge that constitutes the remaining weight	=	? Atom

They thought it had to be like that.

At that point, several physicists published models predicting the structure of the atom. Among them were two models that became particularly well known.

Thomson model

watermelon model

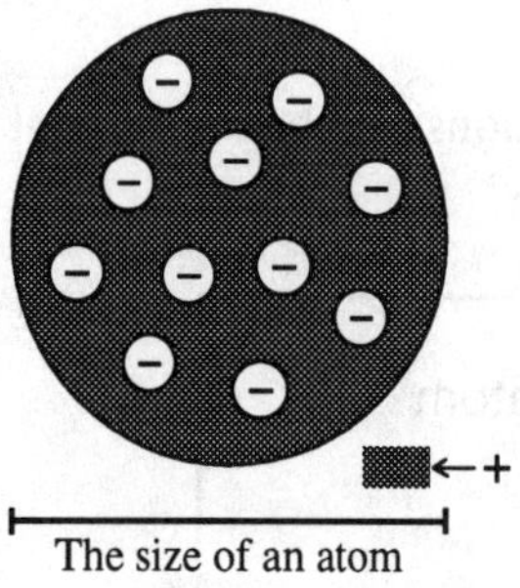

Thomson thought up a model like this:

Electrons are scattered about inside a substance with a positive charge. The whole resembles a watermelon. The reason for this arrangement of the electrons is that because they have a negative charge, if they are too close to one another, they repel each other. Thus, they are at rest in electrically balanced positions, buried within a positively charged substance and held in stable positions. The positive substance, furthermore, extends to become the size of the atom (10^{-8}cm).

Nagaoka, Hantaro
[1865-1950]

Another model was formulated by Hantaro Nagaoka.

Nagaoka model

Saturn model

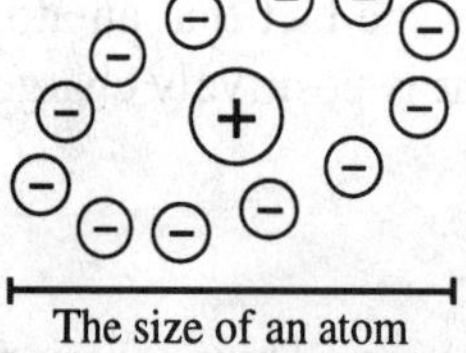

Nagaoka thought the structure of an atom was something like Saturn. In his model, the positively charged substance is concentrated in the center, and the negatively charged electrons are arranged around it.

Because the Thomson model defined the size of the atom more clearly and agreed with Maxwell's electromagnetics, it was generally accepted. Nevertheless, it was still only a hypothesis that had not yet been experimentally confirmed.

Then, in 1911, Thomson's pupil Ernest Rutherford appeared on the scene.

Rutherford, Sir Ernest
[1871-1937]

Rutherford performed an experiment to prove that the model of his teacher Thomson was correct. The experiment consisted of striking gold foil with alpha particles emitted by radium (which possesses a positive charge and a great deal of energy) and predicting the internal structure of the atom from the reactions of the alpha particles.

Let's try to imagine what happened.

In the Thomson model, because the positively charged substance extends throughout the dimensions of the atom, the positive charge is somewhat thinly spread. That is, the density of the charge is low. If you strike the positively charged substance with alpha particles, they should be able to pass through easily, but some of them may be deflected off their course. Because the mass of an alpha particle is approximately 7,000 times that of an electron, here we may ignore the influence of the electrons.

Let's say the positively charged substance in an atom is sugar, and we want to discover whether the sugar is cotton candy or hard candy. We'll make our alpha particles peas from a pea-shooter. If they pass through, it's cotton candy. But if they are deflected, then we suppose that it is hard candy.

Okay, let's try the experiment.

Rutherford's experiment on the scattering of alpha particles

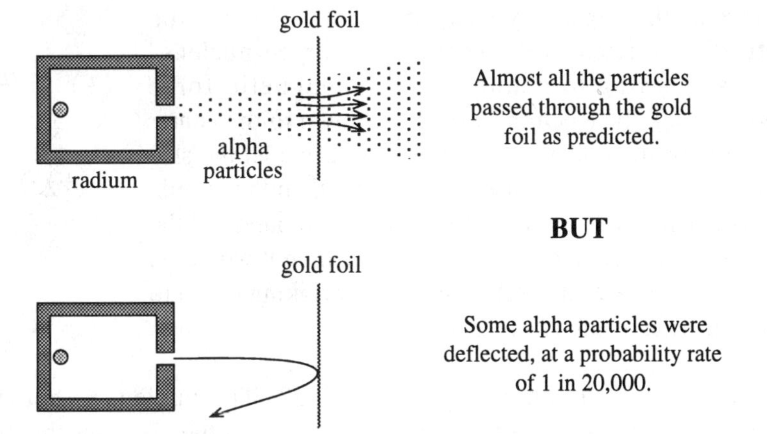

What? Alpha particles were being deflected at a probability rate of 1 in 20,000?!

Rutherford, who was convinced of the accuracy of the Thomson model, said about the experiment:

> "It was quite the most incredible event that had ever happened to me in my life. It was almost as incredible as if you fired a fifteen-inch shell at a piece of tissue paper and it came back and hit you."
>
> — From *Ernest Rutherford* by P. Kelman and A. H. Stone

The supporters of Thomson's model were truly astonished. Going by the Thomson model, the probability of an alpha particle being deflected was so low as to completely rule out the possibility of its occurrence.

The Thomson model was wrong!

To account for the deflection of alpha particles, there had to be something in the center of the atom that was positively charged, into which almost the entire mass of the atom was squeezed. Rutherford called this the **ATOMIC NUCLEUS.**

He was Thomson's pupil, but he ended up discovering his teacher's mistakes.

Well, these things happen.

Now, an atom is made up of a nucleus and electrons. But what prevents the negatively charged electrons from being magnetically attracted to the positively charged nucleus? Without something to counteract this magnetic force (Coulomb force), the electrons would be drawn to the center and the atom would collapse. For instance, if we let the size of an atom be the size of a baseball stadium, then the atomic nucleus is smaller than a grain of sand on the mound. If the electrons are attracted to the atomic nucleus, then it would be like an atom the size of a baseball stadium shrinking down to the size of a grain of sand (Appendix 2).

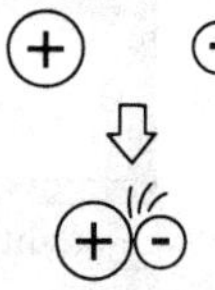

So, what keeps an atom from collapsing? The nucleus is heavy, and probably less mobile than the electrons. Therefore it's the electrons that have to be doing something. If the electrons had some force that counteracted the Coulomb force, they wouldn't be drawn to the nucleus, and the atom would maintain its size.

Yes, but how?

If you put a pinball in a bowl and tried to keep it from falling to the bottom, it would work if you just kept rotating the bowl, right? It's something like that. Whenever something revolves around something else a force operates to pull it inward. That force is called a "centripetal force." At the same time we can presume that another apparent force, a "centrifugal force" is pushing the object outward. Furthermore, we may presume that the balancing of these two forces assures that the object will revolve around the center in a stable orbit. In the case of an electron, the "centrifugal force" is the Coulomb force. The "centrifugal force" can be determined by the mass of the electron, its angular velocity, and the radius of its orbit. The size of the atom is determined by this path traced by the rotating electron. This path, and therefore the size of the atom, is determined by the Coulomb force as centripetal force and centrifugal forces (Appendix 1).

Following that line of thought, Rutherford created a model in which the electron rotated round and round at a distance where Coulomb force as centripetal force $\boxed{-\frac{e^2}{r^2}}$ and centrifugal force $\boxed{mr\omega^2}$ balanced out.

RUTHERFORD'S ATOMIC MODEL

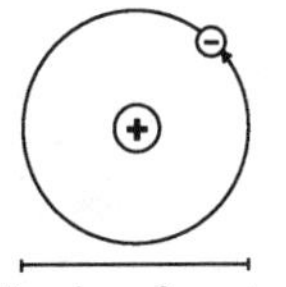

A positively charged nucleus that holds almost all the weight of an atom is squeezed into the center of the atom, while the negatively charged electrons revolve around it.

Point

Rutherford finally hit upon what was going on inside the atom!

Scientists could not see anything smaller than the atom, and so they created models, which they used in attempting to explain invisible phenomena.

The model is complete! It would seem that we have established the structure of an atom, but this model has many features that do not make sense when it comes to explaining phenomena that we know.

What do you mean? Didn't everything go well just now? What happened?

Everything in our world — human beings, chairs, desks— is made up of atoms. And atoms always maintain their size. Can you imagine waking up to find yourself reduced to 1mm in height? That could only happen in a science fiction movie!

Rutherford's model could not explain obvious phenomena like that. Maxwell's electromagnetics confirmed, both in theory and through experiments, that **when electrons accelerate, light is emitted**. Circular movement also involves acceleration. (Appendix 1)

In the Rutherford model, therefore, electrons would have to give forth light as they rotated. Since light was considered to be a wave according to Maxwell's electromagnetics, it was thought that the path of an electron as it rotated about the nucleus was transmitted as light.

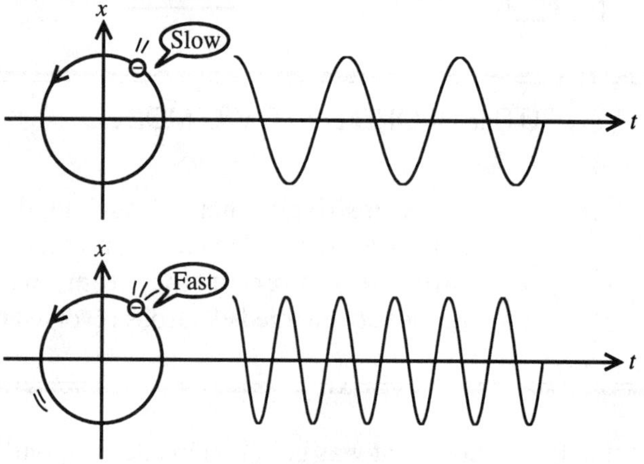

But energy is lost as the electron rotates and gives off light, causing an imbalance in the Coulomb force and centrifugal force in the atom. The electron is pulled closer to the nucleus and is finally unable to rotate. In other words, the size of the atom is preserved by the rotation of the electron; without its rotation, the structure of the atom cannot be maintained. In fact, the principal reason that Nagaoka's model was not adopted was related to that point.

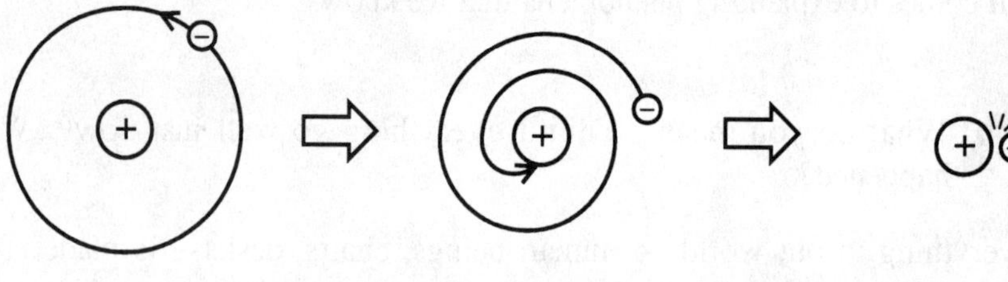

PROBLEM 1: THE SIZE OF THE ATOM CANNOT BE MAINTAINED

How strange to imagine an atom collapsing!

We'd all be tired too, if we were running continuously. We'd run out of energy.

When energy is supplied, an atom gives off light. But the frequencies of light that are emitted are fixed, depending on the type of atom. This is a fact we cannot explain.

In Maxwell's electromagnetics, the light emitted by the rotating electrons appears as fixed line spectra.

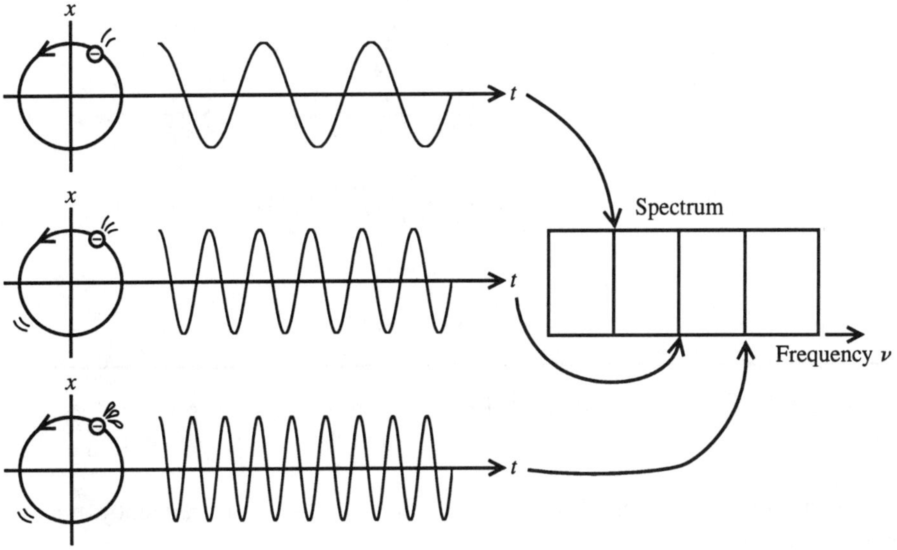

But if the size of the atom shrinks because of the emission of light by the electrons, the light emitted in that case

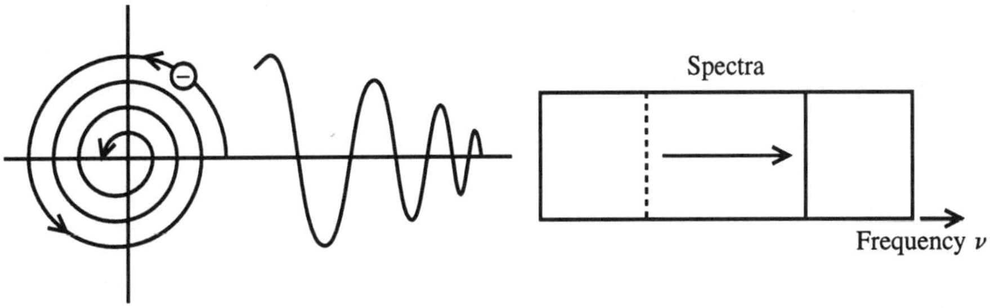

would gradually change in frequency, as shown above. The spectra would move and could not form line spectra.

PROBLEM 2: THE SPECTRA EMITTED BY THE ATOM ARE INEXPLICABLE

At this point let's admit defeat and, putting aside problems 1 and 2, let's assume that electrons continue to rotate, and that their spectra do not change. Still, we simply cannot get away from problem 3.

PROBLEM 3: THE FREQUENCY OF THE LIGHT FROM ATOMS CANNOT BE EXPRESSED THROUGH FOURIER SERIES

If we look at Rydberg's equation, which describes the line-up of frequencies, we see that it is not a Fourier equation as we know it.

<u>Fourier Series</u>

"Any repetitive wave, no matter how complex, is the sum of waves that are composed of integral multiples of fundamental frequencies."

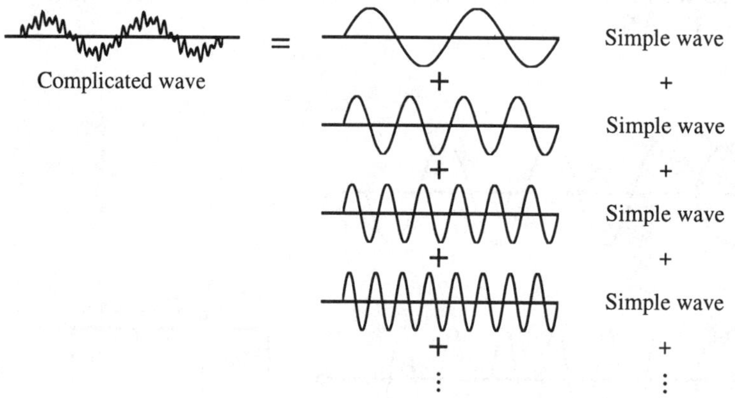

$$q = \sum_{\tau} Q(n, \tau)\, e^{i2\pi\nu(n, \tau)t}$$

Unlike the Fourier equation, this has the form of □ − □
something minus something.

It is not based on integral multiples of some fundamental frequency, nor is it an equation involving addition.

To this point we have described waves entirely through Fourier math, but the frequency of light emitted by atoms has odd, discrete values and cannot be expressed using Fourier. Therefore this could not be explained by the physics in Rutherford's time.

They didn't know why this happens.

There was yet another problem. The size of the atom was determined experimentally. But in the Rutherford model, the only fixed quantities were electrical charge e^2 (g · cm^3 · sec^{-2}) and mass m (g). No matter how you approached it, it was impossible to derive theoretically a simple value in centimeters that expressed the size of the atom.

PROBLEM 4: A FIGURE IN CENTIMETERS EXPRESSING SIZE CANNOT BE DERIVED

Thus numerous problems arose concerning the Rutherford model, causing Rutherford and other physicists to struggle for answers. They were trying to neatly explain the spectra produced by rotating electrons and why atoms do not collapse. It seemed that answers to both questions would explain the makeup of the atom once and for all, but it just didn't work out that way.

What Rutherford discovered through experimentation did not agree with mechanics as it was understood at the time.

Incidentally, Rutherford later gave up work on the structure of the atom and threw himself into research on the nucleus.

So what in the world is going on inside the atom???

Prior to the appearance of Bohr, this had been the tale of the physicists' adventure.

2. 3 BOHR MAKES HIS APPEARANCE

BOHR'S HYPOTHESIS

The hero Bohr makes his appearance. Niels Bohr, a Danish physicist, was then 26. He was also conducting research on the atom in the same laboratory where Rutherford had studied. Bohr made important contributions to the description of the invisible world, and to full development of quantum mechanics. We cannot speak of quantum mechanics without mentioning him.

Bohr always started by trying to see the workings of the natural world. That approach enabled him not only to build the foundations of quantum mechanics, but also to revolutionize science itself and the ways of thinking by which people describe the natural world. With Bohr as the pathfinder for Heisenberg and other young physicists, physics itself made great leaps forward.

Bohr was thinking all the time, and was very involved in discussions of the problem areas of the Rutherford model. What was the biggest problem?

The biggest problem was explaining why atoms do not collapse. Since this self-evident fact could not be explained, it became apparent that perhaps there were problems with Newton's mechanics and Maxwell's electromagnetics. Perhaps classical theory was not definitive, after all!

Physics and Beyond

> My starting point was rather the stability of matter, a pure miracle when considered from the standpoint of classical physics. This cannot be explained by the principles of classical mechanics.

In Newton's mechanics, an electron was considered a particle. Maxwell's electromagnetics theory regarded light as a wave. Neither of these theories gave an adequate explanation as to why the atom does not collapse.

To think that they couldn't explain something so obvious!

About that time, Bohr encountered the quantum theory of Einstein and Planck, who were gradually identifying the elements in that perplexing problem.

> Planck's energy quantum hypothesis
>
> **The energy of light has discrete values.**
>
> $\boldsymbol{E = nh\nu \quad (\nu = 0, 1, 2, 3 \ldots)}$

> Einstein's light quantum hypothesis
>
> **Light is a particle with energy $\boldsymbol{h\nu}$.**
>
> $\boldsymbol{E = h\nu}$

In Einstein's quantum theory, light could not be thought of as a wave; instead, it was taken to be at times a wave, and at other times a particle. Further, this theory identified light as not just a particle but as a quantum. This theory could also explain the results of the blackbody radiation experiment, the photon effect and the Compton effect. These experiments indicated that Maxwell's electromagnetics, in which light is considered to be a wave, was not accurate. Here is where Bohr turned his attention.

If the difficulties with Rutherford's model are to be resolved, then light cannot be thought of as a wave, can it?

TO UNRAVEL THE MYSTERY OF THE ATOM BOHR DECIDED TO ADOPT QUANTUM THEORY.

Bohr considered what would happen to the structure of the atom if light was treated as a quantum.

BOHR'S ATOMIC MODEL

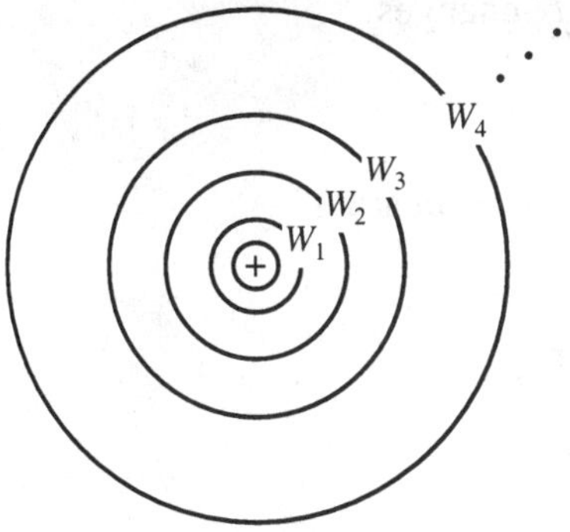

W_n: Energy

Applying Planck's formula $E = nh\nu$ (the energy of light can attain only certain predetermined discrete values) to the atomic model, it follows that the energy of an atom can have only discrete values.

According to classical theory, the energy of an atom is determined by the distance of the orbits of the electrons from the atomic nucleus. The fact that the energy of the atom can only have discrete values means that **THE ORBITS OF THE ELECTRONS HAVE DISCRETE VALUES.**

As the distance of the electron's orbits from the nucleus increases, the energy of the atom increases proportionately.

I get it. If the orbits are discrete, then the energy values are discrete also.

When electrons follow a certain orbit, a certain fixed energy state exists. Let us refer to this state as a "stationary state." According to classical theory, when an electron moves it emits light. But in a stationary state no energy is spent, and the electron can keep rotating in the same orbit indefinitely. In that case, the electron will not be drawn to the nucleus, and the atom's size will be maintained. Thus, the fact that the atom does not collapse can be explained.

This lets us solve the first problem; we can now understand how the size of the atom can be maintained.

Yes, but it's also true that electrons emit light, right? When and how do they do it?

The light emitted is composed of **PHOTONS!**

Let us recall Einstein's photon hypothesis.

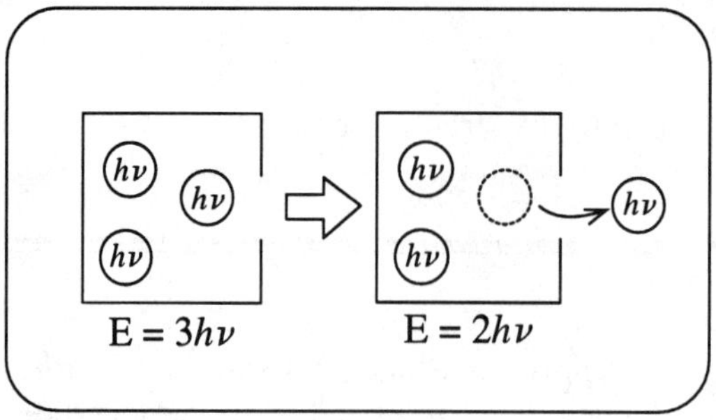

Units of light are quanta having energy of $h\nu$. The energy in the little box has discrete values. As photons go in and out of the little box, the energy in the little box changes.

So it's all right to think of this little box as an atom?

Right. Let's think about this together.

If you replace the little box with the atom. . .

When the electrons inside the atom move from one orbit to another, or undergo transition, it is like photons moving in and out.

When the electrons are in the outer orbits, the energy is greater. Then, when the electrons undergo transition to an inner, smaller orbit and the energy decreases, the excess energy is used and expended in the form of the photon's energy $h\nu$. Conversely, when an atom absorbs photons with energy $h\nu$, the electrons undergo transition to the outer orbits.

With each transition, photons are either emitted or absorbed. At that time, a spectrum with frequency ν, that is to say a line spectrum, appears. When we adapt Einstein's equation to Bohr's theory, we get this.

$$W_n - W_m = h\nu \ (n > m)$$

n :	n^{th} orbit (integer)
m :	m^{th} orbit (integer)
w_n :	the energy in the atom at orbit number n

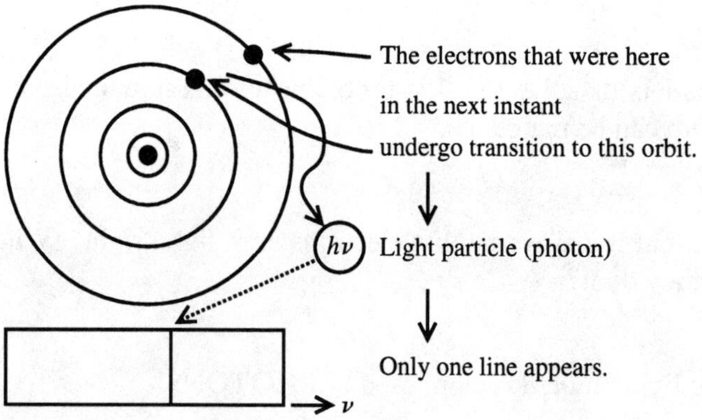

To find the frequency, we solve for ν.

$$\nu = \frac{W_n - W_m}{h}$$

$$\nu = \frac{W_n}{h} - \frac{W_m}{h}$$

This is called Bohr's **FREQUENCY RELATIONSHIP** equation.

I see. According to Maxwell's electromagnetics **electrons emit light as they rotate.**

But according to Bohr's theory **electrons emit light when they undergo transition from one orbit to another.**

That is to say, the basic concept itself has changed.

But how does the transition itself work?

Even I don't know that! Ha ha ha.

But didn't we explain the problems with Rutherford's model — the stability of the atom and the appearance of predetermined, fixed spectra — by applying quantum theory? You see, the important thing is to explain known facts. After all, we can't see inside the atom. Isn't it enough that we can explain those facts with this new atomic model?

Let's summarize the Bohr hypothesis.

Hypothesis 1

The atom has certain **STEPPED ORBITS,** in which electrons rotate. At constant rotation, they do not emit light. We call such a state of energy a **STATIONARY STATE.**

Hypothesis 2

Electrons can undergo **TRANSITIONS** from one orbit to another by absorbing or emitting **PHOTONS.**

SOLVING THE PROBLEM

Bohr composed these two hypotheses with the idea that light is a quantum, but in doing so he appeared to have resolved all of the problems with the Rutherford model.

The first problem with the Rutherford model, that the atom would not maintain its size if it were giving off light, was resolved by the statement that when the electrons remain in their orbits, no light is emitted.

The second problem, that the spectra of atomic light could not be explained, was resolved by positing that when electrons undergo transition from one orbit to another, photons with energy $h\nu$ are emitted, resulting in line spectra.

The fourth problem was that the size of the atom in meters could not be derived. But Bohr adopted Planck's $E = nh\nu$. By virtue of the units of Planck's constant h ($[h] = \text{kg m}^2 \text{ sec}^{-1}$), it became possible to determine the size of the atom.

In the ways described above, three out of four problems were solved.

Then what about the third problem, that the frequencies of atomic light cannot be expressed through Fourier math?

Since the emission of light could now be explained by quantum theory, Fourier math was no longer necessary. Bohr's frequency relationship became a new language for describing the light of the atom.

Thus, Bohr ended up formulating an equation to express the light of an atom using quantum theory. But then, Bohr came across Rydberg's equation expressing the spectra of atomic light!

Rydberg's equation

$$\nu = \frac{Rc}{m^2} - \frac{Rc}{n^2} \quad (n > m)$$

This expression describes the spectra of hydrogen.

Bohr's frequency relationship equation

$$\nu = \frac{W_n}{h} - \frac{W_m}{h}$$

The two equations have exactly the same form. Rydberg's equation neatly described the frequency distributions of the spectra of an atom. And Bohr's equation was the frequency relationship that he had derived from his own theory. It is said that this was the point when Bohr became convinced that his theory was valid.

Fantastic! It's so dramatic.

If Bohr's theory was correct, then these equations should be equivalent. Bohr immediately took the two equations to see if they were equal.

Both equations are in a form where ν is determined by integers n and m. If we make the terms containing n equal to one another, we may find the energy W_n.

If we change this into an = format, we obtain the following.

$$\frac{W_n}{h} = -\frac{Rc}{n^2}$$

Equation describing the energy levels of the hydrogen atom

$$W_n = -\frac{Rhc}{n^2}$$

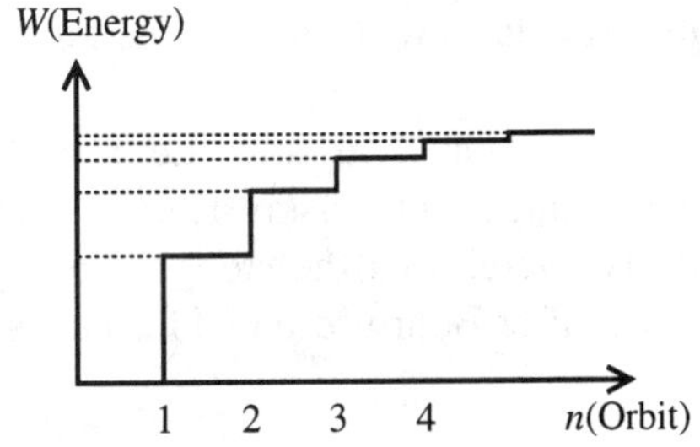

This equation expresses the energy in the hydrogen atom at orbit number n. It appears that the energy level of the hydrogen atom works in a discontinuous, stepped form as shown in the diagram.

Energy levels increase in the outer orbits, but the differences in energy between adjacent orbits decrease.

WE'VE DISCOVERED THE MEANING OF THE SERIES!

The spectral series was determined by setting the value of m in Rydberg's formula. Considering m in terms of Bohr's theory, it then means the orbit to which the electron undergoes transition. Putting this into a diagram, we obtain the following.

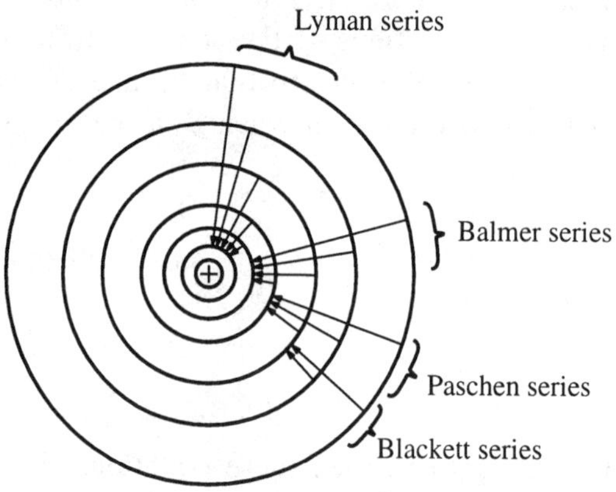

The movement of the electrons has become very concrete. We've taken one step into the world of the atom!

But wait a minute. Bohr used quantum theory in working out his ideas. Then he just went ahead and took his own hypothesis as a basis for adjusting Rydberg's equation and deriving the energies of electrons in a stationary state. But we do not yet know whether or not there are such stationary states with stepped values.

Franck, James
[1882-1964]

Hertz, Gustav Ludwig
[1887-1975]

Two people thought, "Let's try and confirm it right away!" They were James Franck and Gustav Hertz. They immediately performed an experiment and discovered that the stepped energy form was a reality. That was in 1914, the year after Bohr presented his atomic model.

TCL Experiment Log

Let us now tell you about Franck and Hertz's experiment which we performed at TCL. Professor Minami, a well liked senior fellow at TCL, normally pursues research on Electromagnetics, on topics such as auroras and plasma. Whenever he comes to TCL, he brings along some experimental equipment and performs experiments for us. His lectures are always delightful and interesting.

On that day too, he taught the TCL students a new experiment, as he usually does. Without realizing it, we performed Franck and Hertz's experiment! This experiment involved shooting electrons into a glass pipe filled with hydrogen gas.

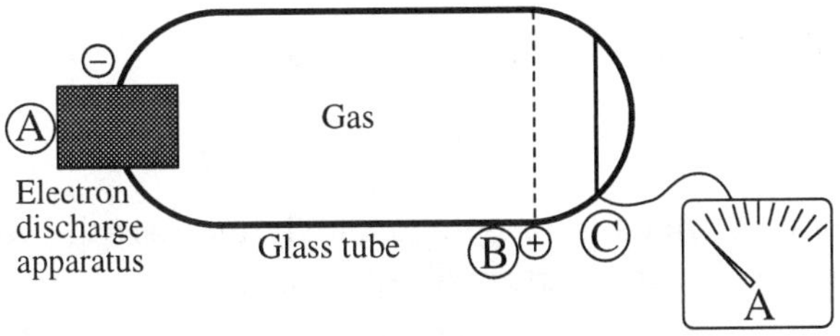

The hydrogen atom has several discrete energy levels W_1, W_2, W_3. . . Let us assume that the atom is now at its lowest energy state.

If the electron has just enough energy to raise the energy state of the hydrogen atom by one level when striking it, the electron will pass that energy on to the atom, and will then leave with a lower level of energy than it had before striking.

If the energy of the electron is not enough to raise the energy level of the hydrogen atom, the electron should not pass any energy on to the atom and the energy of the electron will remain unchanged.

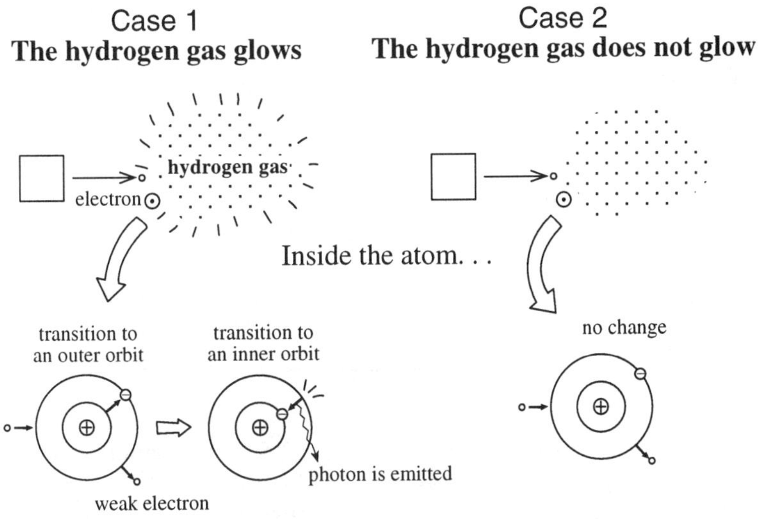

The actual experiment is set up so that by changing the voltage between Ⓐ and Ⓑ, it is possible to regulate the speed of the electrons. When the speed of the electron is high, its energy is also high.

When an electron, having left from Ⓐ, arrives at Ⓒ, the needle of the ammeter will quiver. Since Ⓑ is charged with +0.5 volts, unless the electron has enough energy to pass through Ⓑ, it will be seized by Ⓑ and the ammeter will not move.

All right! Let's begin the experiment.

We release electrons from Ⓐ and slowly increase the voltage. At a certain point the ammeter starts gradually rising.

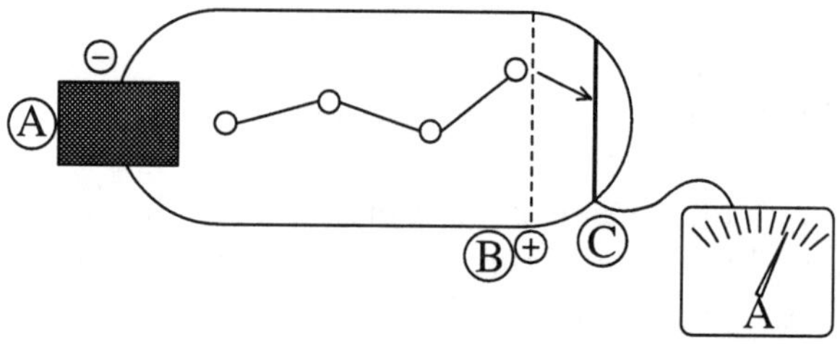

At this point, the electrons do not have enough energy to raise the energy level of the atom, and they strike the atom without releasing any energy, passing through Ⓑ to arrive at Ⓒ.

We raise the voltage again. At the instant a certain voltage is attained, the current suddenly drops.

We did it! That's just what we predicted.

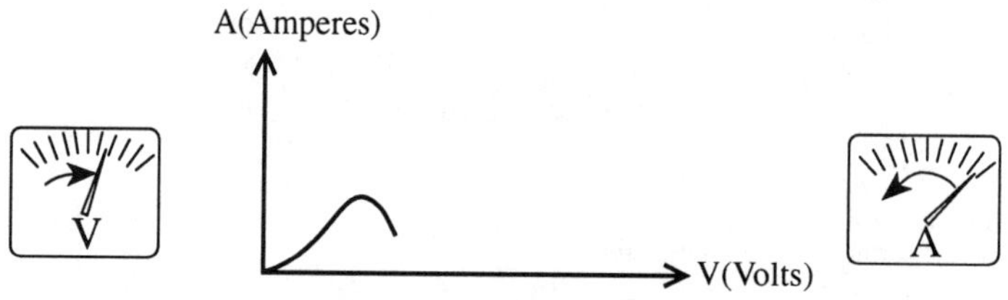

An electron with a great deal of energy strikes the atom, passing on its energy and changing the atom's energy level from W_1 to W_2. The electron loses energy and is seized by Ⓑ, and current can no longer flow. (Because some electrons reach Ⓒ without striking any atoms, the current does not become zero.)

Let's raise the voltage some more. The current is starting to rise again.

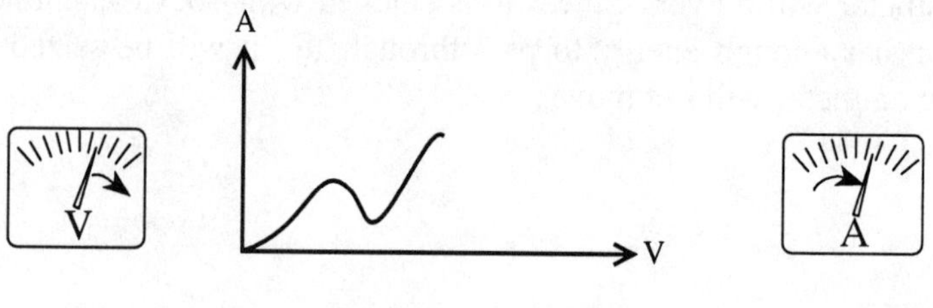

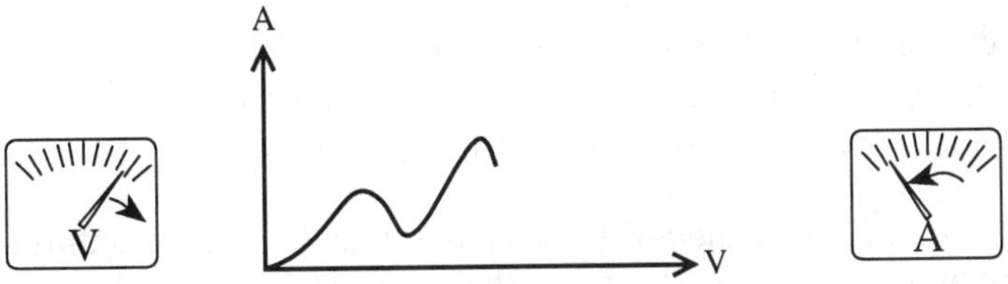

Look! The current really can't flow when the voltage reaches a certain, predetermined level.

The energy level of the atom was raised again. And with the excess energy, electrons are able to break through Ⓑ and arrive at Ⓒ. As we continued the experiment, we found our results could be graphed.

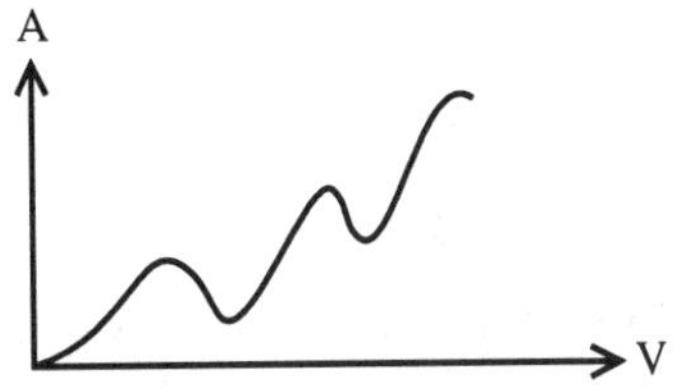

It really is just as Mr. Bohr said. The energy levels of the atom are discontinuous and stepped. If we are this happy at our results, imagine the jubilant feelings of those who first performed the experiment. They won the Nobel Prize in 1925. Franck and Hertz were satisfied with the results which demonstrated that the energy level of the electron in the atom was, as predicted, stepped. And their results matched the energy levels derived by Bohr.

One is reminded of Einstein's saying: "When one has a theory, one must first establish what can be observed."

Physics and Beyond

2. 4 EARLY QUANTUM THEORY

THE CORRESPON-DENCE PRINCIPLE

Nothing was left to daunt Bohr. There was no doubt that by hypothetically applying quantum theory, the nature of matter could be explained. Bohr worked on perfecting his theory. His research involved the equation expressing the energy levels of hydrogen atoms.

$$W_n = -\frac{Rhc}{n^2}$$

Let us focus on the term R in this equation.

R is a constant that was used by Rydberg in constructing his equation. It does not change regardless of the type of atom. This constant was derived experimentally, but it had not been explained theoretically. It would be useful to find out the identity of R. How can we find out what R is?

At this point Bohr made a discovery that was to be a breakthrough in later enabling quantum mechanics to move ahead. When n is very large, the electron rotates in an orbit at the extreme outer edge. Since energy levels are proportional to $-\frac{1}{n^2}$, when n is very large, the difference in energy from one orbit to the next nearly disappears.

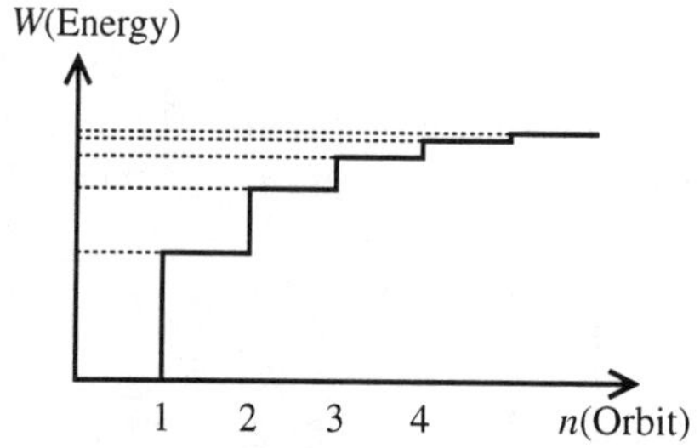

When the difference in energy all but disappears, the energy levels are virtually continuous. In that case, although the electrons are in fact emitting light as they undergo transition from one orbit to the next, one could think as in classical theory that the electrons are emitting light as they rotate. This idea led to other possibilities. Classical theory posited integral values for the frequencies of light. When n is large, both Bohr's theory and classical theory give the same answers, even though the mechanisms they propose for emitting light are completely different. Using this fact, it was a matter of trying to derive R when n was very large.

All right, let's see what happens to the frequencies in Rydberg's equation when n is very large!

Rydberg's equation

$$\nu = -\frac{Rc}{n^2} + \frac{Rc}{m^2}$$

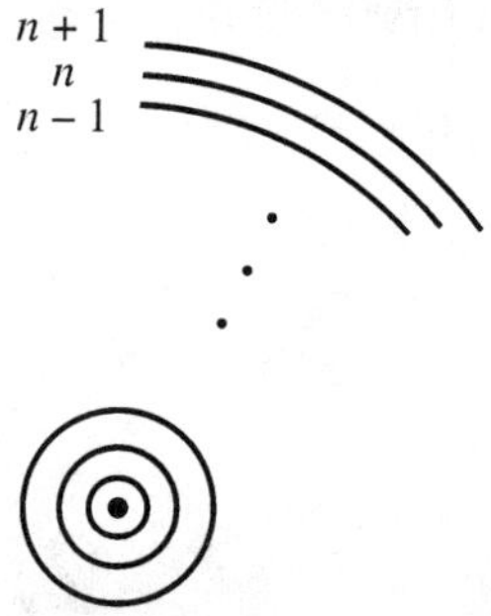

When the electrons are rotating in the extreme outer orbits as shown in the drawing, what happens to the frequencies of light that are emitted when electrons undergo transition from those orbits to orbits a little closer in?

First, let us define m as referring to an orbit that is τ (tau) levels inward from the orbit at level n. We can write it as $m = n - \tau$ $(n = 1, 2, 3...)$. For example, when m is two levels inwards from n, then $\tau = 2$ and $m = n - 2$. By rewriting Rydberg's equation using $n - \tau$ in place of m, we can derive an equation that expresses the frequency ν in terms of the stepped orbits τ.

$$\nu = -\frac{Rc}{n^2} + \frac{Rc}{(n-\tau)^2}$$

We set it so that $\boldsymbol{m = n - \tau}$.

$$= \frac{-Rc\left(n^2 - 2n\tau + \tau^2\right) + Rcn^2}{n^2\left(n^2 - 2n\tau + \tau^2\right)}$$

$$= \frac{-Rcn^2 + 2n\tau Rc - Rc\tau^2 + Rcn^2}{n^4 - 2n^3\tau + n^2\tau^2}$$

$$= \frac{2Rc\tau - \frac{\tau^2}{n}Rc}{n^3 - 2n^2\tau + n\tau^2}$$

We factored out $\boldsymbol{n}$.

$$= \frac{2Rc\tau\left(1 - \boxed{\frac{\tau}{2n}}\right)}{n^3\left(1 - \boxed{\frac{2\tau}{n}} + \boxed{\frac{\tau^2}{n^2}}\right)}$$

Now, as n is very large, (this part) and (these parts) have no overall effect, as the numerator is very small compared to the denominator. Thus, they may be ignored. We then obtain the following.

$$\nu = \frac{2Rc}{n^3}\tau \qquad (\tau = 1, 2, 3, \cdots)$$

We got it!

How about that! This equation shows us that we actually obtain frequencies that are τ multiples (integral multiples) of the fundamental frequency $\frac{2Rc}{n^3}$ as per classical theory.

In other words, Bohr's results do match classical theory when n is large. In cases when n is large, the value of frequency ν is equal to the value of frequency ν obtained in the classical theory. Let's think about how we can obtain frequency ν using the classical theory.

Frequency can be obtained by using the equation "Coulomb force = centifugal force" as mentioned in the beginning of this chapter.

$$\frac{e^2}{r^2} = mr\omega^2 \quad \text{(Coulomb force as centripetal force = centrifugal force)}$$

The angular velocity ω (omega) being $\omega = 2\pi\nu$, we use this relationship to find the frequency ν and obtain the following.

$$\nu^2 = \frac{e^2}{4\pi^2 m r^3}$$

$$\nu = \sqrt{\frac{e^2}{4\pi^2 m r^3}}$$

This is the fundamental frequency ν of classical theory from which we obtain multiples of τ.

Rydberg's equation for ν when n is large	The classical equation for ν
$\nu = \frac{2Rc}{n^3}\tau \quad (\tau = 1,2,3 \cdots)$	$\nu = \sqrt{\frac{e^2}{4\pi^2 m r^3}}\,\tau$

We have now completed the first step in finding R and found 2 equations that produce the same values for frequency ν, although the method in which light was applied was completely different. Now, all that needs to be done to find R is to make them equal.

But it won't work this way.

Looking at the quantities in the two equations that are known and leaving out R, we have the integral constants 2, c, e, 4, π, m and τ. In other words, the frequency is determined in the Bohr theory by **ORBIT n,** and in classical theory by **RADIUS r.** Size is respectively determined by the differing properties n and r, respectively. Even if we make a simple equivalence, we cannot find R. We need to rewrite n and r in separate ways to find a corresponding factor. So, how should they be rewritten? The key to that lies in energy. n(ORBIT) and r(RADIUS) are determined by the amount of energy the electrons hold. If we rewrite portions of n and r to reflect the amount of energy, we can then make the two equations equal and find the value of R.

Let's try it.

When we rewrite the two equations with n and r in the form of energy, we get this.

Energy as derived from Bohr's theory	Energy according to classical theory
$W_n = -\frac{Rhc}{n^2}$	$W = -\frac{e^2}{2r}$
↓	↓
$n = \sqrt{\frac{Rhc}{\lvert W_n \rvert}}$	$r = \frac{e^2}{2\lvert W \rvert}$

Now, we're ready. Let's place the n from Bohr's theory into Rydberg's equation for ν when n is large and the r from classical theory into the classical equation for ν. Equalizing them we get:

Bohr's equation = Classical theory equation

$$\frac{2Rc}{\left(\sqrt{\frac{Rhc}{W_n}}\right)^3}\tau = \sqrt{\frac{e^2}{4\pi^2 m\left(\frac{e^2}{2|W|}\right)^3}}\,\tau$$

We rearrange and take out τ.

$$\frac{2Rc}{\left(\sqrt{Rhc}\right)^3}\left(\sqrt{|W_n|}\right)^3 = \sqrt{\frac{e^2}{4\pi^2 m\frac{e^6}{8|W|^3}}}$$

$(\sqrt{x})^3 = x^{\frac{3}{2}}$

$$\frac{2Rc}{Rhc\sqrt{Rhc}}|W_n|^{\frac{3}{2}} = \sqrt{\frac{e^2}{4\pi^2 me^6}8|W|^3}$$

$$\frac{2}{\sqrt{Rh^3c}}|W_n|^{\frac{3}{2}} = \sqrt{\frac{2}{\pi^2 me^4}|W|^3}$$

$$\frac{2}{\sqrt{Rh^3c}}|W_n|^{\frac{3}{2}} = \sqrt{\frac{2}{\pi^2 me^4}}\,|W|^{\frac{3}{2}}$$

Factoring out $|W_n|^{\frac{3}{2}}$

$$\frac{2}{\sqrt{Rh^3c}} = \sqrt{\frac{2}{\pi^2 me^4}}$$

We square and remove $\sqrt{\ }$.

$$\frac{4}{Rh^3c} = \frac{2}{\pi^2 me^4}$$

$$R = \frac{4}{h^3c}\frac{\pi^2 me^4}{2}$$

$$\boxed{R = \frac{2\pi^2 me^4}{ch^3}}$$

Got it!

If we do the calculating, we obtain the same value as the Rydberg constant.

Try working it out for yourself!

Circumference ratio : π = 3.142

Electron mass : $m = 9.109 \times 10^{-28}$ g

Electrical charge : $e^2 = 23.04 \times 10^{-20}$ g cm^3 sec^{-2}

Planck's constant : $h = 6.626 \times 10^{-27}$ g cm^2 sec^{-1}

Speed of light : $c = 2.998 \times 10^{10}$ cm sec^{-1}

Calculation area

$R =$ [ ] cm^{-1}

Have you completed your calculations? Is your answer correct? $R = 1.095 \times 10^5\,\text{cm}^{-1}$ (exact value is $1.0973 \times 10^5\,\text{cm}^{-1}$)

We've found that when we insert actual values, it works out, doesn't it? With this, the contents of the constant R, which had been a mystery, was revealed. Now let's try inserting the R derived from Bohr's theory into the equation for the energy level of the hydrogen atom.

$$W_n = -\frac{Rhc}{n^2}$$

$$= -\frac{\dfrac{2\pi^2 me^4}{ch^3}hc}{n^2}$$

$$= -\frac{2\pi^2 me^4}{h^2}\frac{1}{n^2}$$

Equation for energy levels

$$W_n = -\frac{2\pi^2 me^4}{h^2}\frac{1}{n^2}$$

We did it! We've actually managed to express the energy levels for the hydrogen atom perfectly using Bohr's theory! Fantastic!

At this point, we must not forget that although we have created an equivalence between classical theory and Bohr's theory, their interpretations of the mechanisms of light production are completely different. And even though he understood that an atom could not be described using classical theory, Bohr happened to notice that the results corresponded for large values of n. In this way, he **BORROWED THE LANGUAGE OF CLASSICAL THEORY** and it worked. Bohr's approach may appear impetuous, but all of us take an "impetuous approach" when attempting to explain something completely new to people.

When we try to describe the taste of something that we are eating for the first time, most of us instinctively use comparisons. For example, "It's like chocolate, but it isn't sweet and it smells like roses. . ." It is difficult to communicate in a way that others will understand if we don't use familiar references. Even if the taste of the thing is not conveyed very well, by offering them some clues people will form their own images and get some idea of the real thing.

Bohr used classical theory as his familiar reference, incorporating its terms as he forged ahead into the unknown, newly unfolding quantum theory. The use of such references describes what was called the **CORRESPONDENCE PRINCIPLE**, which would assume a very important role in the development of quantum mechanics. With the condition that n is large, the answers yielded by Bohr's quantum theory and classical theory agreed, serving to affirm the place of the new theory. Bohr's quantum theory was not something that was completely apart from classical theory; it incorporated classical theory and in effect expanded the boundaries of what could be explained.

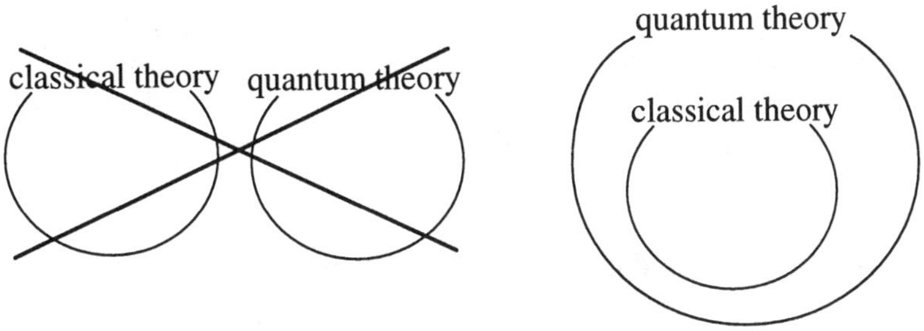

Because of Bohr's Correspondence Principle, the boundaries of what could be explained would expand yet further, opening up great, new possibilities.

Full of spirit and bursting with energy, Bohr would continue to bound ahead in the research of quantum mechanics. (In particular Bohr's institute in Copenhagen, Denmark became the place where all young physicists went to try out new ideas.)

THE ROAD TO THE QUANTUM CONDITION

By then, not only had Bohr extracted a body of facts concerning energy levels and frequencies from theory, he had also confirmed them experimentally. From there, drawing more and more information from his theory, he progressed toward the discovery of the quantum condition. Bohr wanted to investigate many, many other things. But by itself, the approach he used to that point was not adequate. So, Bohr constructed his third hypothesis.

> **Hypothesis 3**
>
> When electrons are rotating in their orbits (stationary state), they behave as classical theory predicts.

But Mr. Bohr, you did say at the beginning that classical theory was wrong.

If we don't leave well enough alone, we may find ourselves on the wrong road. So far the results have agreed with the experiments, but the pitcher can go to the well one time too many.

No, no, what happens twice will happen again. I'm sure everything will be fine.

Are you all aware that this hypothesis indicated some change in Bohr's thinking? Until now, when n was large, energy and frequency were the same in classical theory and quantum theory. But this hypothesis proposed that when electrons are rotating in their orbits without emitting any light, energy and frequency are the same as in classical theory, whether n is large or small.

Let's try and find the size of the atom by determining its radius!

Radius? That's something new!

That's true. Previously Bohr was dealing with orbit number n, but just now we made a correspondence between the orbits of Bohr's theory and the radii of classical theory, and we haven't yet explained anything about the radius according to quantum theory. Let's give it a try.

When an atom is in a stationary state, the energy is the same in both classical and quantum theory, so we may equate the two equations. Let's modify them and find radius r.

Equation that expresses energy in quantum theory	Equation that expresses energy in classical theory
$W_n = -\frac{2\pi^2 me^4}{h^2}\frac{1}{n^2}$	$W = -\frac{e^2}{2r}$ (See Appendix 4)

We can make these two equations equal to each other and express them in terms of r. Let's try it!

$$-\frac{2\pi^2 me^4}{h^2}\frac{1}{n^2} = -\frac{e^2}{2r}$$

$$\frac{h^2n^2}{2\pi^2 me^4} = \frac{2r}{e^2}$$

$$\frac{e^2}{2}\frac{h^2n^2}{2\pi^2 me^4} = \frac{2r}{e^2}\frac{e^2}{2}$$

$$\frac{h^2}{4\pi^2 me^2}n^2 = r$$

We got it! This is the radius of the atom!

When $n = 1$, this equation is known as the Bohr radius.

Bohr radius equation

$$a = \frac{h^2}{4\pi^2 me^2}$$

Point

What this means is that, as in the diagram of the orbits of an atom, as n grows larger, the intervals between orbits grow larger in turn.

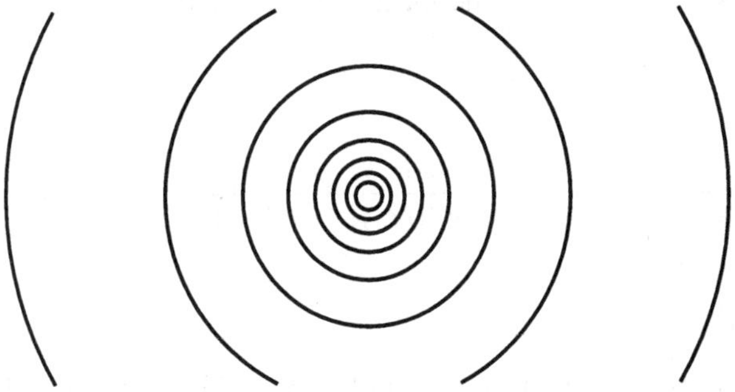

When we make n in this equation equal to 1, the most stable condition, we can take that as the size of the atom. Let's try working it out!

From experiments we found that the diameter of an atom is about 10^{-8} cm!

Will we really get that? If we do, then Hypothesis 3 must be true also.

First, let's just do our units!

$$[h] = \text{g cm}^2 \text{ sec}^{-1}$$

$$[m] = \text{g}$$

$$[e^2] = \text{g cm}^3 \text{ sec}^{-2}$$

$$\frac{\text{g}^2 \cdot \text{cm}^4 \cdot \text{sec}^{-2}}{\text{g} \cdot \text{g} \cdot \text{cm}^3 \cdot \text{sec}^{-2}} = cm$$

So the units agreed nicely, didn't they?
What you said before about finding out the number of centimeters by putting in Planck's constant h was really true, wasn't it?

Okay, let's do the quantities as well!

$$h = 6.626 \times 10^{-27} \text{ g cm}^2 \text{ sec}^{-1}$$

$$\pi = 3.142$$

$$m = 9.109 \times 10^{-28} \text{ g}$$

$$e^2 = 23.04 \times 10^{-20} \text{ g cm}^3 \text{ sec}^{-2}$$

Let's try it for $n = 1$, the most stable condition.

$$\frac{(6.626 \times 10^{-27})^2}{4 \times (3.142)^2 \times 9.109 \times 10^{-28} \times 23.04 \times 10^{-20}} = 0.5298 \times 10^{-8}$$

The radius of an atom is found to be 0.53×10^{-8} cm. The diameter is 1.06×10^{-8} cm.

That's it, we got 10^{-8} cm! That matches the experimental value perfectly. This means Hypothesis 3 was right also, doesn't it?

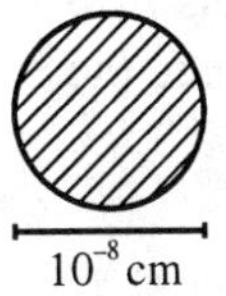

Hmm. . .

What are you thinking?

At the beginning there was the problem of size — it seemed that an atom's size could not be maintained. I can understand that the size of an atom is the size when it is the most stable. But since atoms have all kinds of orbits, doesn't it mean then, that there can be many different sizes? It still seems very strange to me.

Yes, it's strange. But when n is equal to 1, it matches the experimental value. I think that's good enough. It's all right, certainly for now.

By using Hypothesis 3, the radius could also be determined.

At this point, Bohr realized that he could easily find the angular momentum as well.

Here I go again with calculations!

DISCOVERY OF THE QUANTUM CONDITION

He did say we could find the angular momentum easily, but. . .

What's angular momentum anyway?

The angular momentum is the momentum of something rotating in a circle or an ellipse. In the case of a circle, the usual momentum mv is multiplied by radius r. (See Appendix 3)

Angular momentum

$$M = mvr$$

$$M = mr^2\omega$$

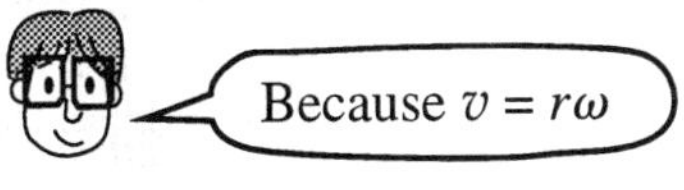

This time let's proceed in the same way by making the equation for energy levels in Bohr's theory equal to the equation for energy in classical theory, and deduce the answer!

Bohr's theory = classical theory

$$-\frac{2\pi^2 m e^4}{h^2}\frac{1}{n^2} = -\frac{e^2}{2r}$$

What!? This time there isn't any M or mr^2v. It was easy last time because there was an r. Oh, dear! What are we going to do?

Here's a good place to use the "Coulomb force as centripetal force = centrifugal force" formula that we used in making the model of an atom. That way we can gather all the components — m, r and ω — that we need to find the angular momentum, so we're sure to get M.

$$mr\omega^2 = \frac{e^2}{r^2} \quad \text{(centrifugal force = Coulomb force as centripetal force)}$$

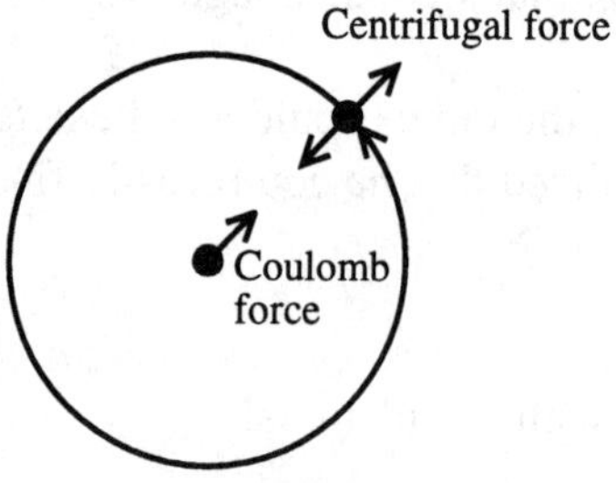

We modify this slightly.

$$e^2 = mr^3\omega^2$$

If we place this term in the "Bohr's theory = classical theory" equation, we can easily obtain M.

$$-\frac{2\pi^2 m e^4}{h^2}\frac{1}{n^2} = -\frac{mr^3\omega^2}{2r}$$

Now the numerator on the right side resembles $mr^2\omega$, which equals M, right? So let's try rewriting it using M. Since $M^2 = m^2r^4\omega^2$.

right side

$$= -\frac{M^2}{2mr^2}$$

There were too many m's and r's, so they went into the denominator, right?

Okay, now we can use the form M^2. Let's try it!

$$-\frac{2\pi^2 me^4}{h^2}\frac{1}{n^2} = -\frac{M^2}{2mr^2}$$

$$\frac{2\pi^2 m\,e^4}{h^2}\frac{1}{n^2}\times 2mr^2 = \frac{M^2}{2mr^2}\times 2mr^2$$

Multiply both sides by $2mr^2$.

$$\frac{2\pi^2 m\,e^4}{h^2}\frac{2mr^2}{n^2} = M^2$$

Then we substitute the term we found earlier

$$r = \frac{h^2}{4\pi^2 m\,e^2}n^2$$

into the equation

$$\frac{4\pi^2 m^2 e^4\left(\dfrac{h^2}{4\pi^2 m\,e^2}n^2\right)^2}{h^2}\frac{1}{n^2} = M^2$$

$$M^2 = \frac{\cancel{4}\cancel{\pi^2}\cancel{m^2}\cancel{e^4}\dfrac{h^{\cancel{4}\,2}}{4\,\cancel{16}\,\pi^{\cancel{4}\,2}\cancel{m^2}\cancel{e^4}}n^{\cancel{4}\,2}}{\cancel{h^2}}\frac{1}{\cancel{n^2}}$$

Just keep on eliminating the numbers!

$$= \frac{h^2}{4\pi^2}n^2$$

$$M = \frac{h}{2\pi}n$$

We got it! The calculations were a bit long and bothersome, but what came out was so simple!

I was amazed too when I first saw this. Even though we obtained the energy and the frequency and the radius before, it was astounding to see it come out so neat and clean this time.

This equation contains no special number like m that changes depending on the type of atom. That meant it had to be a law that would apply to all phenomena relating to quanta. Thinking this, Bohr was **OVERJOYED.**

All atoms behave according to the law

$$M = \frac{h}{2\pi} n$$

Bohr gave a name to this principle. It is

BOHR'S QUANTUM CONDITION

Up until this point Bohr had been building up his new theory by himself. Eventually, it was demonstrated that his theory corresponded with experimental findings. One more very important fact can be learned from this equation. That is that Planck's constant h is expressed in the simple form of angular momentum M multiplied by 2π, and that it has the same units as the angular momentum. If one knows that the constant h, which determines the discrete energy state of the atom, and the angular momentum are expressed in the same units, one also knows that the angular momentum helps determine the discrete energy state. Bohr was absolutely elated about what he had accomplished so far, and he went to show Arnold Sommerfeld. After looking it over, Sommerfeld said simply,

Sommerfeld, Arnold Johannes Wilhelm
[1868-1951]

Bohr, you're still pretty green.

What is it? Why do you say that?

Sommerfeld noticed that the equation $M = \frac{h}{2\pi} n$ described angular momentum, and so it could only be applied to things moving in a circle or an ellipse. That's what was wrong. If the quantum condition was going to be a general physical law, it would have to be applicable to quanta moving in any manner.

After all, quanta don't only move in circles or ellipses.

Bohr and Sommerfeld tried to think of something based on $E = nh\nu$ that would allow for more and different kinds of movements. However, the equation they came up with could only be used for simple harmonic oscillation.

E: energy of light with simple harmonic oscillation
ν: frequency of light with simple harmonic oscillation

Wanting to write ν and E in a different form, the form of the relationship $E = nh\nu$ was altered to obtain:

$$\frac{E}{\nu} = nh$$

Okay, let's express $\frac{E}{\nu}$ in a different form. That way we can use it for any kind of motion.

From here on, both equations and unfamiliar words will come up often, but if you look closely at them, you'll find that they're rather simple. So let's all do our best!

All right, let's get to it!

At this point Sommerfeld looked in his manual, which contained all sorts of equations, and found one that looked as if it might work.

What is it? What is it?

It's the **PHASE PLANE.**

What's that?

Even if a difficult word comes up, don't worry about it. Sometimes you hear a word you don't know when you're listening to the news. But if you listen to the whole news broadcast, you at least get the general idea, right? It's the same thing with quantum mechanics.

Keep at it! Keep at it!

Put simply, the phase plane describes the momentum and the position in one plane. Using the phase plane, simple harmonic oscillation will be expressed as ellipses.

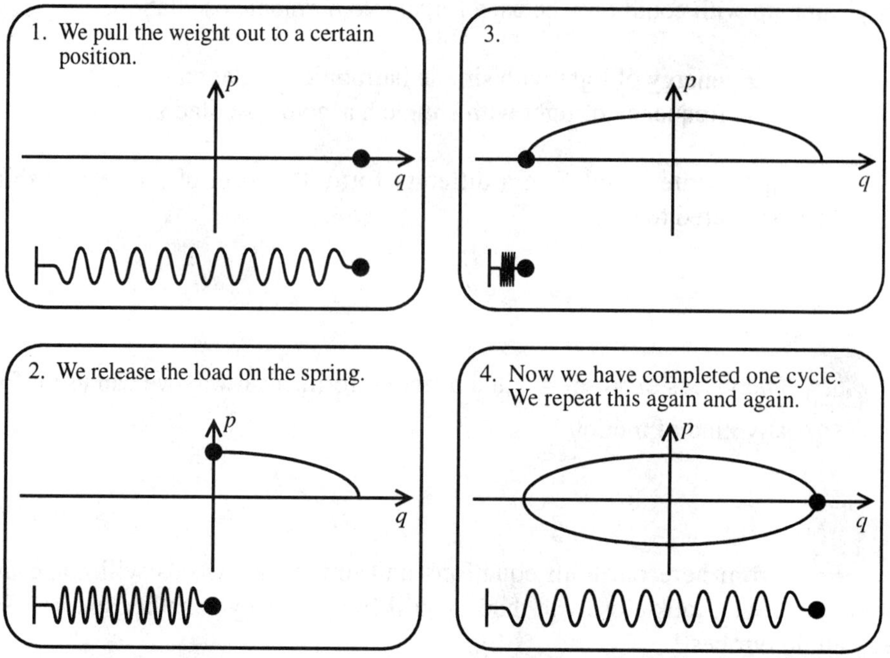

Sommerfeld noticed that $\frac{E}{\nu}$ became the same as area J of the ellipse, and by equating the two he was able to describe the quantum condition for any type of movement.

Is that true?

All right, let's see if J really becomes $\frac{E}{\nu}$ in the case of harmonic oscillation.

To begin, here is your basic information about ellipses.

Equation describing an ellipse $\frac{x^2}{a^2} + \frac{y^2}{b^2} = 1$
Area of an ellipse $J = \pi ab$

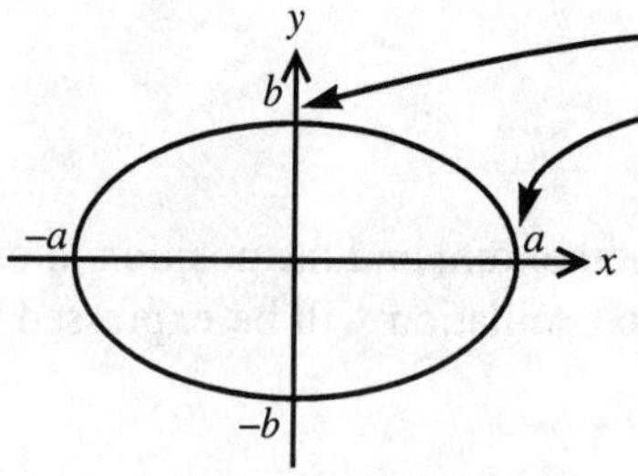

To find the area of an ellipse, we need to know this and this on the phase plane. But right now we do not know what a and b in the equation for area are, so let's try and find them from the equation describing the ellipse above. If we put momentum and position in the places of x and y, we can form the equation for an ellipse. Let's try using momentum and position.

Now, first of all, the equation for energy for harmonic oscillation is:

$$E(p,q) = \frac{p^2}{2m} + \frac{k}{2} q^2$$

If we use this equation, momentum and position are included in it. Let's rearrange the equation to make the formula describing an ellipse, and then find the parts that correspond to a and b.

$$E(p,q) = \frac{p^2}{2m} + \frac{k}{2} q^2$$

$$1 = \frac{p^2}{2mE} + \frac{k}{2E} q^2$$

$$1 = \frac{p^2}{\left(\sqrt{2mE}\right)^2} + \frac{q^2}{\frac{2E}{k}}$$

$$\frac{k}{2E} \times q^2 = q^2 \div \frac{2E}{k} = \frac{q^2}{\frac{2E}{k}}$$

$$1 = \frac{p^2}{\left(\sqrt{2mE}\right)^2} + \frac{q^2}{\left(\sqrt{\frac{2E}{k}}\right)^2}$$

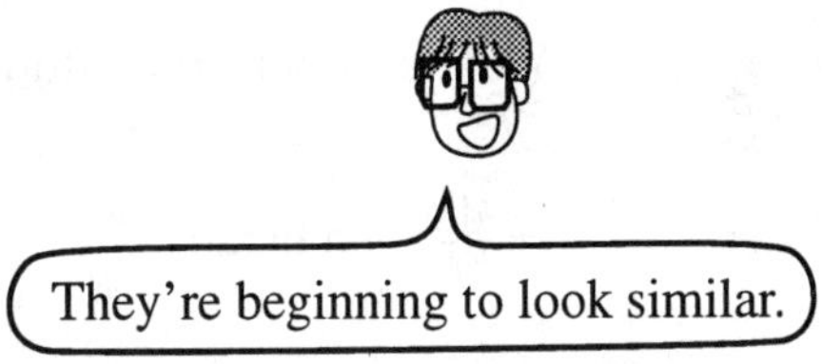

 We did it! They're exactly alike! That is, we came up with

$$a = \sqrt{2mE}$$

$$b = \sqrt{\frac{2E}{k}}$$

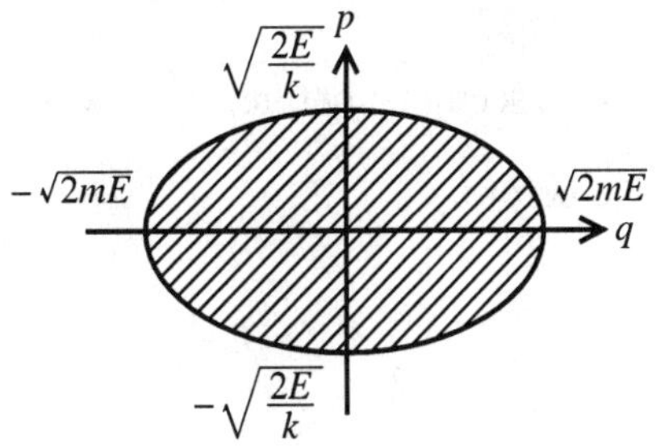

 Now that we know this, the rest is simple. All we do now is insert it into the equation for the area of an ellipse. So let's try it!

Area of an ellipse
$J = \pi ab$

So, we get

$$J = \sqrt{2mE}\sqrt{\frac{2E}{k}}\,\pi$$
$$= 2\pi E\sqrt{\frac{m}{k}}$$

The term $\sqrt{\frac{m}{k}}$ in this equation is very similar to the ω of harmonic oscillation. ω is the angular velocity and the speed of something when it goes around and around.

But wasn't $\omega = \sqrt{\frac{k}{m}}$?

Exactly! That means that $\sqrt{\frac{m}{k}} = \frac{1}{\omega}$.

I see. Well, then, let's try putting in $\frac{1}{\omega}$.

We insert $\sqrt{\frac{m}{k}} = \frac{1}{\omega}$ and obtain

$$J = 2\pi E\frac{1}{\omega}$$
$$J = E\frac{2\pi}{\omega}$$

Oh! I've seen that before. $\frac{\omega}{2\pi}$ was ν, so all we have to do is invert it and put it in like before.

$$J = E\frac{1}{\nu}$$

We got it! We actually got $J = \frac{E}{\nu}$!

Just now we took the $\frac{E}{\nu}$ in the equation $\frac{E}{\nu} = nh$ and expressed it in the form of J, writing

$$J = nh$$

By crossing out E and ν from the equation $E = nh\nu$, we tried to create a quantum condition that could be used in a wider variety of cases. Now we've finished that equation! With this, the motion can be any motion, not just circular!

We did it! It's a new quantum condition.

But don't we want a term that's a bit better looking than "J"?

Well, then, let's dress it up!

J was found by isolating one cycle of a repetitive movement and finding its area, and so. . .

$$\oint [\quad] dq = nh$$

What are we doing? We want to find momentum, so we insert p and obtain

$$\oint p \, dq = nh \quad (n = 1, 2, 3, 4 \cdots\cdot)$$

PERFECTED EDITION OF THE QUANTUM CONDITION!!

The quantum condition must be satisified by all quantum-related phenomena. It is, however, limited to iterative motion.

Instead of using classical theory, by using the quantum theory principle that **"the energy of light is discrete"** as the basis for his hypothesis and atomic model, Bohr discovered a language that thoroughly explained the spectra of atomic light, the stability of the atom, and even the hitherto inexplicable discrete energy condition.

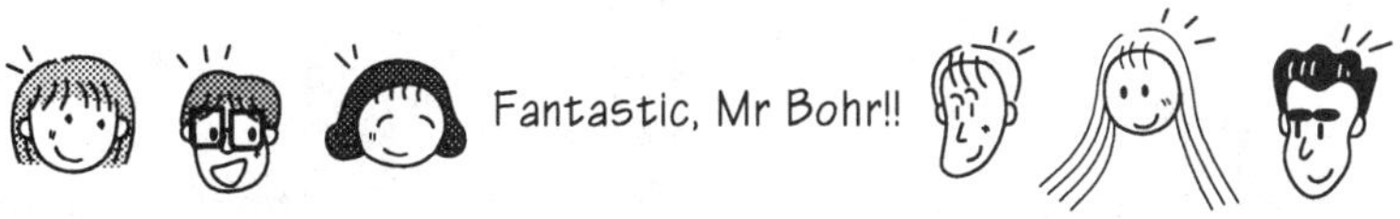

And yet Bohr's new theory, quantum theory, was something anyone could handle, just by taking the old language of classical theory plus the quantum condition.

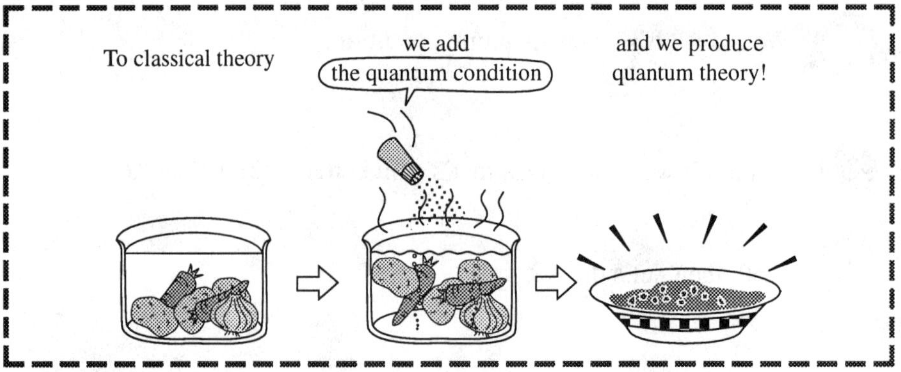

How wonderful! Now we are able to explain things we cannot even see. Just when it looked like peace had returned to the world of physics. . .

A spectrum is not just a matter of frequencies; it is also important to know how much light of each frequency is present, right?

We can determine how much light of a given frequency is contained in a spectrum by reading the intensity of individual colors in a line spectrum. If a color in the line spectrum is deep, then it contains a large portion of light of that frequency (meaning the light is strong). Conversely, if the color is faint, the portion of light of that frequency is small (meaning the light is weak).

Oh! That's right. . .

Even if we know the components, it doesn't mean anything unless we know their quantities.

When you make a curry, if you use the standard ingredients — meat, potatoes, carrots and curry powder — but you don't use standard quantities,

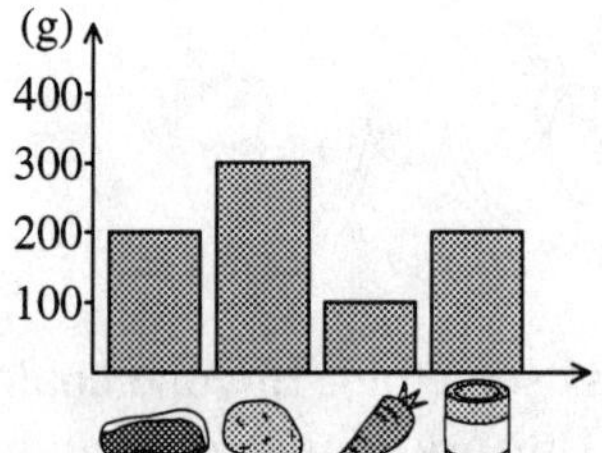

this much

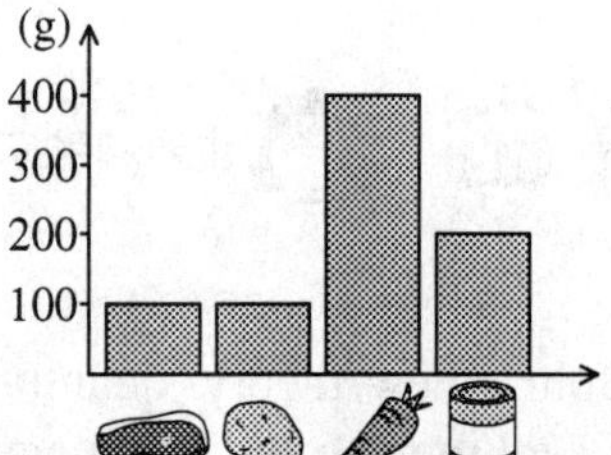

or that much

the result is totally different from what it usually is. That's right, we have to remember quantities. Bohr's new language only accounted for spectral frequencies.

2. 5 THEORETICAL INCONSISTENCIES AND METHODS OF SOLVING THEM

THE INTENSITY OF LIGHT

So, all we've been doing up to now is making classifications. . .

There's no need to feel discouraged. Let's think. How can we find the intensity of light?

I know!
The intensity of light = $|\text{amplitude}|^2$

Fantastic!

Absolutely. But think again. What was intensity? It was the height of the light waves. That was an equation used in classical theory, where light was thought to be composed of waves. But light is. . .

A quantum particle!

We can't use the language of light waves anymore because we are now thinking in quantum terms. According to classical theory, electrons gave off light waves simply by rotating in their orbits. It was thought that the motion of the electrons could be determined from the light waves, and that it was possible to find the amplitude of the light waves from the motion of the electrons. But electrons give off light quanta when they undergo transition inside the atom, so we cannot find the movement of the electrons in the same way we would using classical theory. Therefore, we cannot find the amplitude.

What are we going to do?

Well, since we know that a single light particle (photon) has energy $h\nu$, can't we count up the number of light quanta of a given frequency ν that emerge, that is to say, the number of transition cycles?

That's right! If we can determine how many particles emerge in a given unit of time, then we can find the intensity.

intensity of light = number of transitions

That's right. But we know nothing at all of the mechanism of transition. When, where and how transition takes place and light is emitted are anybody's guess.

So we can't figure it out after all.

In general, transition occurs when the electrons inside the atom move instantaneously from one stepped orbit to the other. No one understood how that could happen. As long as Bohr's theory contained this kind of nonsensical assumption, physicists thought, it couldn't possibly be very useful. One of his colleagues, physicist Paul Ehrenfest, wrote to another, Hendrik Lorentz: "I was disappointed with Bohr's Balmer formula. If he can achieve his purposes with that kind of work, I'll have to give up physics."

Ehrenfest, Paul [1880-1933]

Lorentz, Hendrik Antoon [1853-1928]

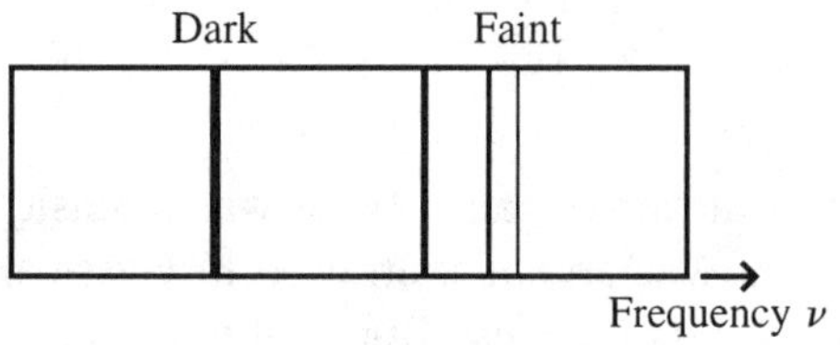

Looking at a spectrum, physicists could tell whether the colors of the lines were dark or faint. But without understanding how electrons undergo transition, it was impossible to express the intensity of light. Then Bohr thought of using probability to express the intensity of light — to describe it in terms of how easily an electron can undergo transition from one orbit to another. Then the intensity of light would be decided according to how high the level of probability of transition was.

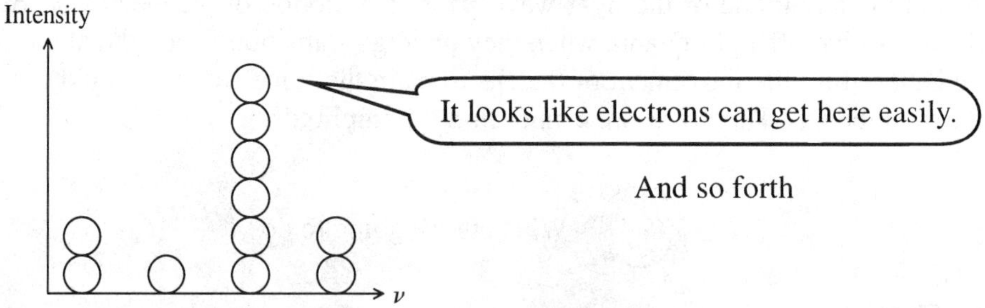

Somehow this feels a bit shaky.

Well, it couldn't be helped. There was no other method to understand it. In any case, what matters is that the method produced results. Bohr reasoned that there might be a "certain quantity" that, if squared as in measuring the intensity of waves, would equal the probability of transition.

Classical theory

intensity of light = |amplitude|^2

Quantum theory

intensity of light = probability of transition = |a certain quantity|^2

To think that the intensity of light can only be expressed in terms of probability. . .

Other physicists were not satisfied at all. Some were convinced that if only the mechanism of transition were understood, other answers would fall into place. They threw themselves into their research, wondering if there were some secret escape route from one orbit to another. But the mechanism of transition remained a mystery.

But can't we just use the Correspondence Principle, like we've done up till now?

Right! We're not empty-handed. We can find an answer using Bohr's Correspondence Principle. When the n in Bohr's theory is large, that is, when the electrons are rotating in the extreme outer orbits and their energy is very high, they expend some energy undergoing transition and emitting light, but this energy loss is very low. We can consider them to be giving off light as they rotate, with energy values comparable to those we get using classical theory.

According to classical theory, light is composed of waves. Because a light wave goes around and around, it is a cyclical wave. Of course. . .

This can be expressed through Fourier math!

Right! Now here's the Fourier series.

$$q = \sum_{\tau} \underbrace{Q(n, \tau)}_{\text{amplitude}} e^{i2\pi \overbrace{\nu(n, \tau)}^{\text{frequency}} t}$$

A complicated wave is the sum of τ (integral) multiples of simple waves.

By placing the equation for simple waves in correspondence with the equation for light emitted during a single transition, we can find the amplitude and the frequency. We can then deduce intensity by squaring the amplitude. That result will agree with Bohr's result for the times when n is large! That's how we'll do it!

But it will only work when n is large, right?

Well, that's true. When n is small we do not have integral multiples, and as was discovered, the results do not match at all. But by forcing the situation, the answers do match to some extent, even when n is small.

Like when?

It seems to come out that way only when the amplitude is zero, that is when absolutely no transitions take place from one orbit to another. Maybe it's a pattern of transition.

I dislike using terms like "more or less." They make me nervous. But I guess we can't describe everything.

Though we've come this far, from here on the problem might be too much, even for Bohr's Correspondence Principle.

ROAD TO A TRUE THEORY Pushing ahead with the Correspondence Principle

The physicists in Copenhagen, with Bohr at the center, were thinking hard. How were they to find a language to describe the new world of quanta? Let's go back to the beginning and retrace our steps. Bohr wanted to construct a language that could express the fact that the **ATOM IS STABLE.** As long as one thought in terms of classical theory, this could not be done. Then came the new quantum theory. It let physicists explain things about light that classical theory could not.

Planck Einstein

We adopted Planck's "The energy of light is an integral multiple of $h\nu$" and Einstein's "Light is a particle (photon) with energy $h\nu$."

And then we agreed that inside the atom were **STEPPED ORBITS,** and that the energy of the electron changed in discrete intervals. Thus, we could explain why the atom does not collapse.

Furthermore, when n was large, the answers were exactly the same as in classical theory! On the basis of that fact, new mechanisms that were absolutely unknown before were successfully described using the language of classical theory. This process was called the **CORRESPONDENCE PRINCIPLE**, and supplied the parts that were missing in Bohr's theory. The results achieved matched experimental results again and again. Thus we have been guided this far by the Correspondence Principle.

But there are still some things we don't know.

> Why do we get only discrete energy?
> What are the mechanisms of transition?

We've come this far without knowing anything about these two things.

Bohr too had come this far, aware that he didn't have the answers.

The quantum theory that Bohr introduced was derived from experiments, and so it was reliable. Nevertheless, it could not explain the workings of the atom. Without taking classical theory apart piece by piece, and producing an explanation through trial and error, nothing could be described. Worse, if we didn't proceed with quantum theory, we would not be able to produce a viable image of the atom.

By attaching the quantum condition to classical theory as a sort of provisional measure, we have been content so far to express the new quantum theory in the language of classical theory.

Classical theory		Quantum condition	
$F = m\ddot{q}$	$+$	$\oint p\,dq = nh$	$=$ quantum theory
continuous		discrete	discrete

Bohr often spoke of the time when he realized, "When I say 'what people will understand,' I mean the same thing as what I know myself!" For Bohr, the most important thing was to describe the structure of the invisible atom using a language which was already known. It wasn't that Bohr was convinced that atoms have orbits, or even that he believed that transitions in a literal sense occurred.

By describing the atom as having stepped orbits, Bohr provided us with the image of the atom familiar to us today.

> I hope that they describe the structure of the atoms as well, but only as well, as is possible in the descriptive language of classical physics. We must be clear that, when it comes to atoms, language can be used only as in poetry. The poet, too, is not nearly so concerned with describing facts as with creating images and establishing mental connections.

Physics and Beyond

At this point we have two choices:

1. Continue trying to discover a quantum theory that clearly describes the mechanisms of transition without using the quantum condition discovered by Bohr. That is, we will have found the answer when we can mentally picture the internal structure of the atom.

2. Continue using the Correspondence Principle, since it has worked so well until now. In other words, rather than trying to discover the structure of the atom, continue trying to find the frequency and amplitude from the known spectra of an atom using Fourier math.

I like the first choice. It seems neat and clear.

There may be people who think that way. But in that case, do the mechanisms of transition adhere to laws that we can understand?

I don't know.

Indeed, nobody knows. Of course it's all right to keep thinking and trying. However, it may be that to try and understand is pushing things too far. It may be like trying to understand how Taro could be in Tokyo one moment, and in Mexico the next instant.

While some physicists continued their research on the mechanisms of transition, Bohr and the Copenhagen group pressed on with the Correspondence Principle; that is, they came to believe that the only road to a true theory was to use the only language available for finding the intensity of light — Fourier math — to find the amplitudes and frequencies of the spectra.

Classical theory considered something to be known only when the logical path leading to the conclusion could be described. But from here on, something was considered known if the body of experimental results could be perfectly described, even if the path to the conclusion could not be described.

One begins to wonder just what the word "know" means.

Bohr's young friend Heisenberg, upon learning about Bohr's thinking, asked a question that must have been on everyone's mind.

> "If the inner structure of the atom is as closed to descriptive accounts as you say, if we really lack a language for dealing with it, how can we ever hope to understand atoms?"
>
> Bohr hesitated for a moment, and then said: "I think we may yet be able to do so. But in the process we may have to learn what the word 'understanding' really means."

Physics and Beyond

Now that we've stopped trying to disclose the workings of transition, we no longer have to think about what is happening inside the atom. We just have to find the intensity of light, solving things just as we perceive them using a correspondence to Fourier's |amplitude|^2 in the following form.

The probability of transition when an electron emits light = |a certain quantity|^2
Let's start calculating and figure it out!

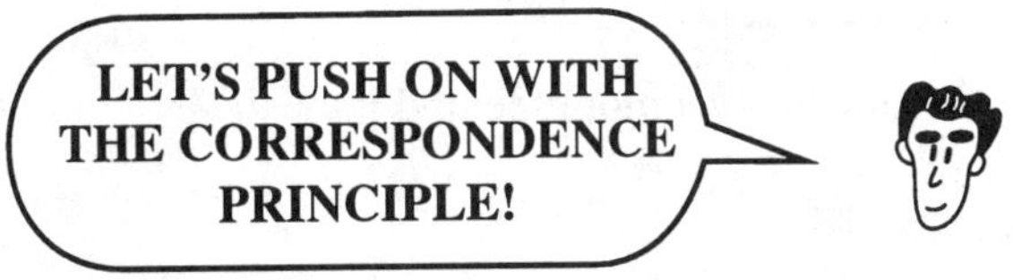

You may wonder if this was a wise decision. At any rate, as Bohr was pushing on with the Correspondence Principle he became aware of something significant. It will become clear as we proceed. But first, let's work at making a correspondence between classical theory and quantum theory.

Okay, I'm ready to begin!

First, let's look once again at the corresponding classical theory.

MECHANISMS BY WHICH ATOMS EMIT LIGHT IN CLASSICAL THEORY

Electrons emit light **AS THEY REVOLVE!** But they use up their energy in giving off light and are drawn to the nucleus. When the electrons are revolving in the extreme outer orbits, however, their energy is great, and even when they expend energy in emitting light, they have enough energy left to sustain a slightly smaller orbit of which the difference from the former orbit is hardly noticeable. Thus it seems that electrons emit light as they rotate.

The light that emerges in this case would be a periodic **WAVE.** Of course we can express that using Fourier.

The Fourier equation in classical theory

Any periodic complicated wave is the sum of waves with wave cycles that are integer multiples of fundamental frequencies.

$$q = \sum_{\tau} Q(n, \tau)\, e^{i2\pi\nu(n,\tau)t}$$

q: position of the electron

$Q(n, \tau)$: the amplitude of the τth simple wave which is included in the complicated wave generated in the nth orbit.

$e^{i2\pi\nu(n,\tau)t}$: the τth simple wave which is included in the complicated wave generated in the nth orbit.

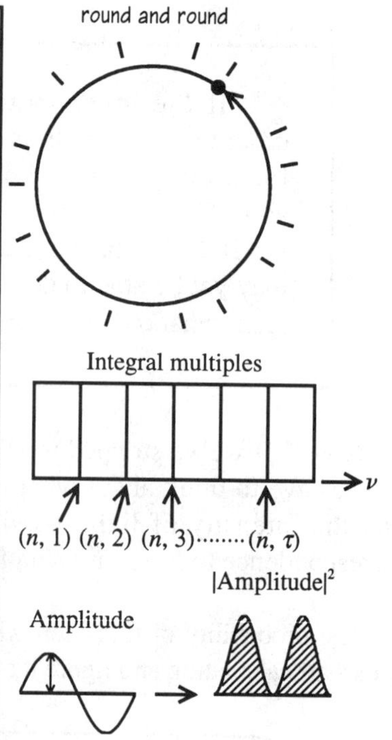

This neatly describes the frequency, amplitude and intensity.

Intensity of light = |amplitude|^2

The sum q of simple waves according to the Fourier equation shows the position of the electron, which means that the direction in which the electron moved can be determined.

That calls for Newton's equation of motion

$$F = m\ddot{q} \qquad (q : \text{position})$$

$\ddot{q}$: second-order differentiation of position q with respect to time. This is the same as acceleration a.

With this equation, all the movements of the electron could be described.

Up until now we have been casually talking about the "old, classical" way of thinking, but in fact Newton's mechanics was truly spectacular. For three hundred years it described the movements of everything.

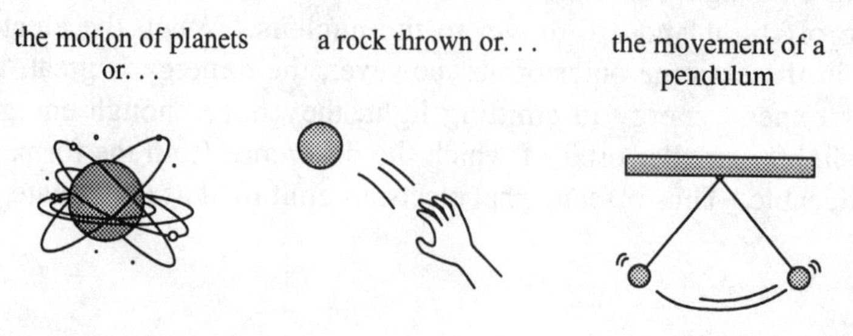

It was Sir Isaac Newton who discovered that although these movements appear at first glance to be totally different, they are essentially the same phenomenon.

Newton, Sir Isaac [1643-1727]

Force = mass × acceleration

$F = m \times \ddot{q}$

derivative with respect to time — derivative with respect to time

position q ⟶ velocity $\dot{q}$ derivative ⟶ acceleration $\ddot{q}$

As Newton thought about this force, he perceived ordered regularity in the motion of all things. If its position and velocity are known, the movement of any given thing can be described completely. Of course this law is still valid (that is, except when describing what goes on inside the atom). It is even used when we send rockets flying into space.

MECHANISMS BY WHICH ATOMS EMIT LIGHT IN QUANTUM THEORY

$$\nu = \frac{W_n - W_{n-\tau}}{h}$$

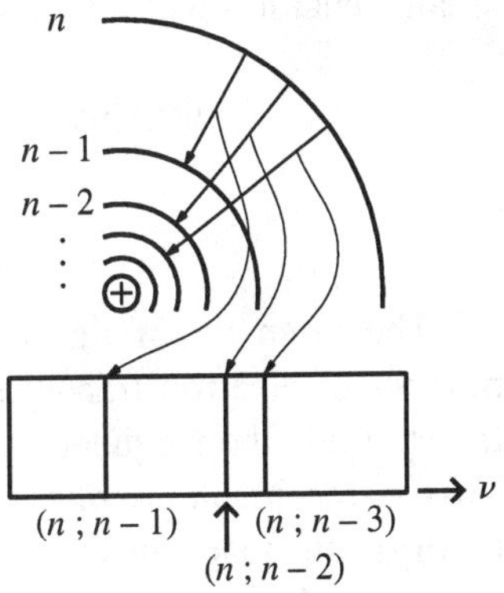

When an atom undergoes a **TRANSITION,** it gives off **PARTICLES** of light! When a transition occurs from orbit n to orbit $n - \tau$, a certain fixed frequency of light is emitted. Those frequencies describe a discrete spectrum peculiar to the type of atom in which it occurs.

The alignment of frequencies is shown by Rydberg's equation:

$$\nu = -\frac{Rc}{n^2} + \frac{Rc}{m^2} \text{ (in the case of hydrogen atoms)}$$

Now the frequency is clear, but we don't know the intensity.

But when n is large

$$\nu = \frac{2Rc}{n^3}\tau$$

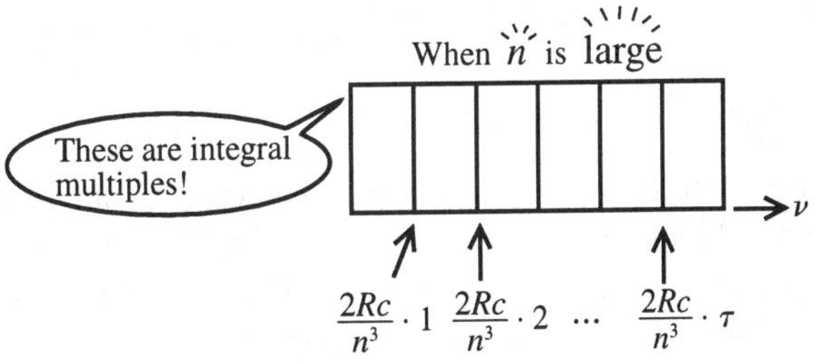

So we get discrete frequencies in (integral) multiples of τ! Let's make a correspondence between this and Fourier. Using the mechanisms of classical theory alone, we could not express this when n was small. So now let's rewrite the Fourier equation so that it relates to quantum theory.

The Fourier equation for quantum theory

Transition component = $Q(n; n-\tau)e^{i2\pi\nu(n;\, n-\tau)t}$

$(n; n-\tau)$: when there is transition from level n to level $n-\tau$

In classical theory, the light emitted by an electron was described as the sum of τ (integral) multiples of simple waves, but in quantum theory only one frequency of light is emitted for a single transition. Therefore, the lineup of the spectrum does not need to follow integral multiples. We can make the correspondence with Fourier this way:

"A single simple wave in classical theory" and "A single line spectrum from a given transition".

Now we have an equation that will work when n is large and also when it is small. That lets us find the intensity as well as the frequency.

intensity of light = number of transitions
= probability of transition
= |a certain quantity|^2

The intensity of light according to quantum theory rules — that is, the number of electron transitions — can be found in the same way that classical theory finds the frequencies of simple waves, one by one, using Fourier math. This is the mechanism for the spectrum of the atom according to quantum theory! In quantum theory, the frequency of each individual line spectrum corresponds to a particular transition, so to sum them up has no meaning. However, if we try to use the Fourier equation in order to make the best of the Correspondence Principle, the resulting equation will not tell us anything about the position of the electron. In that event, the formula to describe the movement of something on the basis of knowing its position

$$F = m\ddot{q}$$

ENDS UP BEING UNUSABLE!

Bohr came to think of orbit ***n*** as something that described the position of an electron. That idea led him to describe the energy of an electron by using correspondence with energy that could be described using $F = m\ddot{q}$. In this way, he was also able to describe the frequency of light. At that time, he worked under the assumption that classical theory would be usable. But if the q found from the Fourier equation could not describe the position, then nothing could be said about its energy or frequency. Would this mean that everything we've done up to now has ended up being meaningless?

Without considering orbits, we cannot find the energy. 

That must have been why Bohr brought orbits into his theory.

"If the spectra of atomic light can be expressed using Fourier math, by which we can find frequency as well as amplitude, let us be satisified that we have understood the atom, even if we can't envision its structure."

It appears that Bohr actually felt this way. But this would mean the $F = m\ddot{q}$ that he relied on so much would be useless.

But hold on a second. 

Come to think of it, we've been finding the intensity when n is large by taking the $|\text{amplitude}|^2$ straight from the Fourier form as it was conceived in classical theory.

$$q = \sum_{\tau} \underbrace{Q(n,\tau)}_{\text{amplitude}}\, e^{i2\pi \overbrace{\nu(n,\tau)}^{\text{frequency}} t}$$

With this equation, $F = m\ddot{q}$ is right on target! 

In quantum theory this becomes

$$q = \sum_{\tau} Q(n; n-\tau)\, e^{i2\pi\nu(n;\, n-\tau)t}$$

Then $F = m\ddot{q}$ is being used. 

 What? What does that mean?

When Fourier was considered in terms of classical theory, the position was a sum of integral multiples, and the movement of an electron was expressed by $F = m\ddot{q}$. When we thought of Fourier in terms of quantum theory, since the light given off by the atom was emitted during transition, we found that the Fourier equation would not work when describing the position of the electron. But for some reason, we could use it to find frequencies and amplitudes when n was large.

Newtonian mechanics was never able to describe them when n was small, so Newton's mechanics was incomplete. But Newton's mechanics works well when n is large, so just as we rewrote the Fourier equation according to the mechanisms of quantum theory, we must also rewrite $F = m\ddot{q}$ according to quantum theory.

WHAT! WON'T THE VERY MEANING OF $F = m\ddot{q}$ CHANGE?

To this point it seemed that we could not use $F = m\ddot{q}$ without considering the orbits that corresponded to position. But, if the thing we describe using the Fourier equation has a separate meaning with no connection to the position of the electron, then we can proceed by changing the meaning of $F = m\ddot{q}$ to correspond to the version of Fourier that we are now using.

But we have **ABSOLUTELY NO ASSURANCE** that it is correct.

In order to explain the workings of the atom, Bohr changed the form of the question.

In the invisible world, things we don't understand occur.

Although classical theory could not describe what was inside the atom, it provided us with the only language we had to describe the physical world. So we borrowed the language of classical theory and described the inner workings of the atom as well as we could. Even if it couldn't describe the inside of the atom, classical theory (Newtonian mechanics) described the movements of everything else. It will probably continue to do so, for it is perfect as a theory. It is hard to believe that if some phenomenon comes along that doesn't fit into a theory, it is possible to add on just a few changes to solve the problem. But isn't it better to change our way of thinking itself, rather than adding on amendments bit by bit?

The word "mechanics" refers to the new quantum theory, a theory that describes a world invisible to the naked eye. Is this really a completely new way of thinking?

What if we could translate Newton's mechanics itself into the language of quantum theory? The foundations that we thought were crumbling might instead develop into something bigger and better. We simply don't know whether it will or not. After all is said and done, we can't see inside the atom. But wait. . .there is a way, right before our eyes. Shall we do it or not? That is the only question to consider.

> If I were asked what was Christopher Columbus' greatest achievement in discovering America, my answer would not be that he took advantage of the spherical shape of the earth to get to India by the western route - this idea had occurred to others before him - or that he prepared his expedition meticulously and rigged his ships most expertly - that, too, others could have done equally well. His most remarkable feat was the decision to leave the known regions of the world and to sail westward, far beyond the point from which his provisions could have got him back home again.

Columbus, Christopher
[1451-1506]

Physics and Beyond

The adventure is gradually approaching a new climax. And the hero of this adventure, Bohr, is about to pass the baton to his young friend, Werner Heisenberg! We'd like you to stay and see what he presents.

The Strange Adventure of Quantum Kid

APPENDIX
The mechanics used by Bohr

Bohr tried to explain the atom using classical mechanics. Let us look closely at the tools he used when making a theoretical model of the atom.

APPENDIX 1. CENTRIFUGAL FORCE AND CENTRIPETAL FORCE

If you fill a bucket with water and spin it around hard enough, no water will spill out even when the bucket is sideways or upside down. When spinning the bucket, you need to hold on tightly to the handle. If you don't, the bucket will fly out of your hand. The circular movement of the bucket is caused by the pulling inward of the arm and is called the "centripetal" force. At the same time, there is an apparent outward force at work on the water within the bucket. This is called the "centrifugal" force. We may therefore presume that the two forces are equally balanced resulting in a stable circular orbit. There are two equal forces working in opposite directions!

The force we apply by pulling is called centripetal force and the force that holds the water down toward the bottom of the bucket is called centrifugal force. First let's look at centripetal force. When we want to find a force, we can use the basic equation of Newtonian mechanics:

$$F = m\,a$$

Force Mass Acceleration

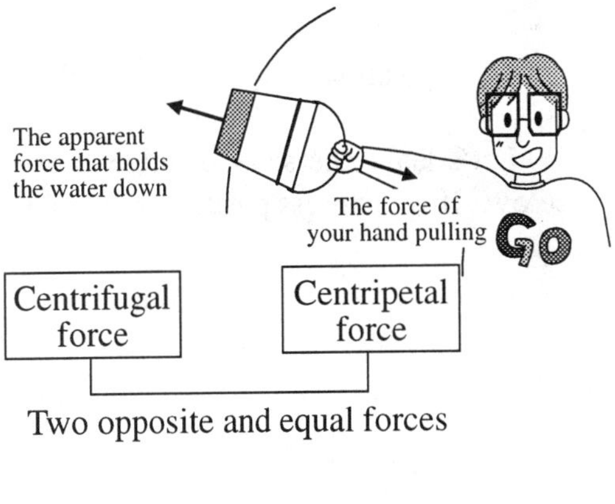

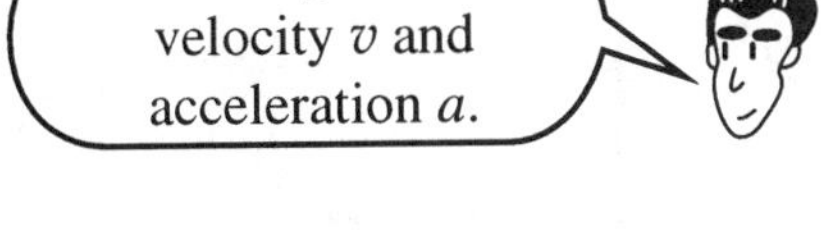

This means that when there is acceleration, there is also force. But when something spins around at a steady speed, can there be acceleration? For example, sometimes you go around on the exit ramp at an expressway interchange. What happens when you're in the car?

Acceleration is a change in velocity. Typically, velocity is expressed in terms of speed and direction. For example, "Our present velocity is southward at 50 kilometers an hour (about 30 miles per hour)." As the car follows the curve on the exit ramp, it changes direction while running at the same speed. Since velocity is determined by direction and speed, in this case, although the speed does not change, the direction does, and so does the velocity. A change in velocity in this case is acceleration; in other words, acceleration does occur.

Acceleration a is a differential of velocity v with respect to time t, and is written: $a = \frac{dv}{dt}$

Velocity v is a differential of position x against time t, and is written: $v = \frac{dx}{dt}$

If we know the where's and when's, from those positions we can find the velocity, and from the velocity we can find the acceleration. Further, if the mass is known, then we can also determine the force.

x	$\rightarrow$	v	$\rightarrow$	a
position		velocity		acceleration

Let's leave the story of the expressway and continue with an example such as in the drawing below. If we express position x, y in terms of radius r and angle θ, we come up with:

$$x = r\cos\theta$$
$$y = r\sin\theta$$

The angle θ is:

θ	=	ω	$\times$	t
angle	=	angular velocity	$\times$	time

(The angular velocity describes how much an angle changes in one second.)

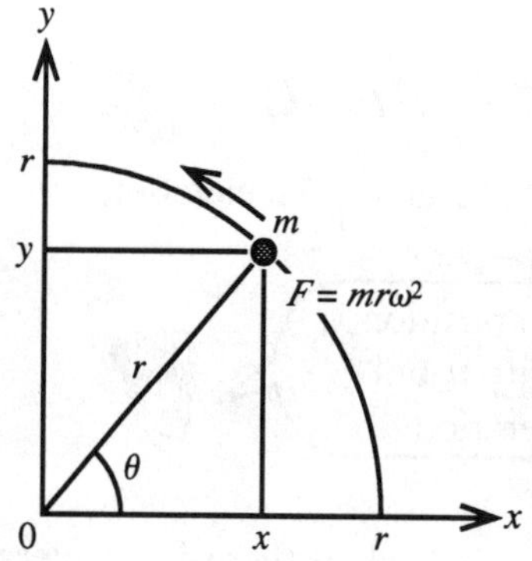

The position x, y is: $x = r\cos\omega t$, $y = r\sin\omega t$

First, let's **FIND THE VELOCITY.**

Velocity v_x in direction x is a differential of position x with respect to time t:

$$v_x = \frac{dx}{dt} = -r\omega \sin\omega t$$

In the same way, in direction y, we make a differential of position y with respect to time t:

$$v_y = \frac{dy}{dt} = r\omega \cos\omega t$$

Next, let's **FIND THE ACCELERATION.**

Acceleration a is a differential of the velocity with respect to time t:

$$a_x = \frac{dv_x}{dt} = -r\omega^2 \cos\omega t$$

$$a_y = \frac{dv_y}{dt} = -r\omega^2 \sin\omega t$$

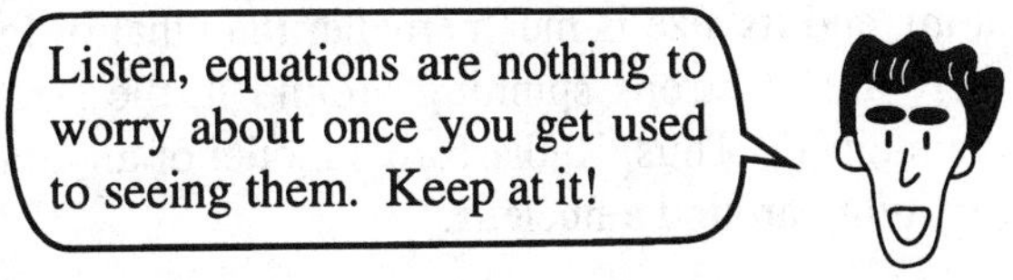

If the acceleration can be found, force F can also be found.
For force F_x in direction x and force F_y in direction y, we use $F = ma$:

$$F_x = ma_x = -mr\omega^2 \cos\omega t$$
$$F_y = ma_y = -mr\omega^2 \sin\omega t$$

We put these two forces together using the Pythagorean theorem:

$$F^2 = F_x^{\ 2} + F_y^{\ 2}$$
$$= m^2r^2\omega^4 \cos^2\omega t + m^2r^2\omega^4 \sin^2\omega t$$

Factoring out $m^2r^2\omega^4$, we get:

$$= m^2r^2\omega^4\left(\cos^2\omega t + \sin^2\omega t\right)$$

$\cos^2\omega t + \sin^2\omega t = 1$

$$F^2 = m^2r^2\omega^4$$
$$F = mr\omega^2$$

This is the centripetal force that pulls on the bucket. The centrifugal force is of equal magnitude and is directed outward. To the object in orbit, the inward centripetal force and the apparent outward centrifugal force seem to be in an equilibrium.

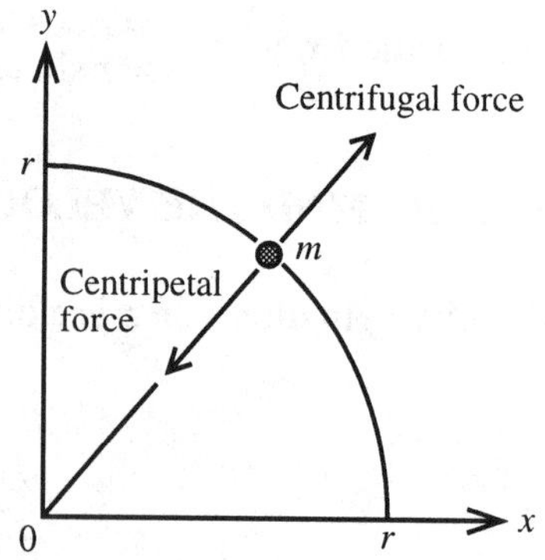

APPENDIX 2. ELECTRONS ROTATE AROUND THE NUCLEUS

Through experimentation, Rutherford proved the existence of a nucleus at the center of the atom. The nucleus is at the center of the atom, and its size is much smaller than that of the entire atom, so unless there are electrons spinning around it, the size of the atom cannot be maintained. Thus, Rutherford's model of an atom consisted of electrons revolving around a nucleus.

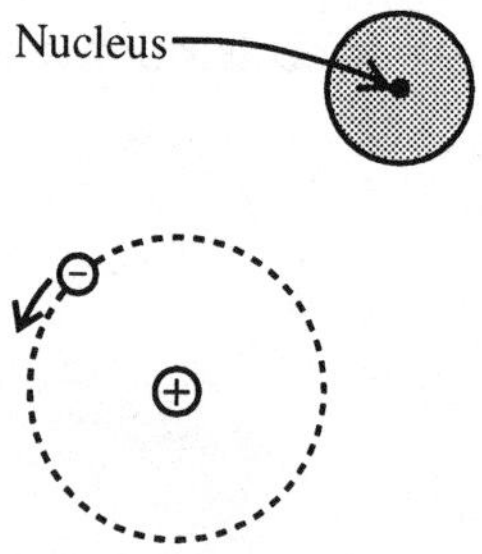

Could something firm with a strong positive charge somehow exist?

In the example of the spinning bucket, the bucket corresponds to a rotating electron, and the circular path it traces corresponds to the size of the atom. The fact that it is revolving means that to the electron in orbit, there seems to be an apparent centrifugal force. But since there is nothing tying the electron to the nucleus, wouldn't the electron end up flying off? What is pulling on the electron? Well, they're actually being drawn by this electrical force that we call Coulomb force. Having said that, it's time to talk about the Coulomb force.

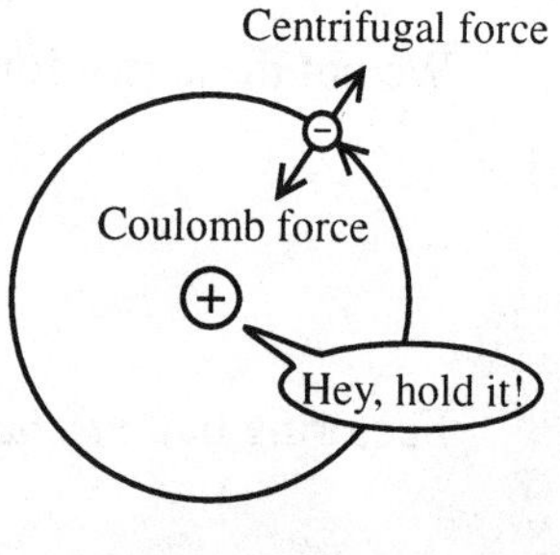

See, it'll work if the Coulomb force as centripetal force and centrifugal force match up like this.

COULOMB FORCE is electrical force.

If you rub a sheet of plastic and place it close to the top of your head, your hair will be drawn toward it even though there is nothing between your hair and this sheet. Your hair is being drawn up by electrical force. Things can have either a positive or negative electrical charge. Positive and negative attract, so something with a positive charge will be attracted to something with a negative charge. Between things with like charges — positive and positive, or negative and negative — a repelling force is at work. Because the hair is drawn to the plastic sheet, that means that one has a positive charge and the other has a negative charge.

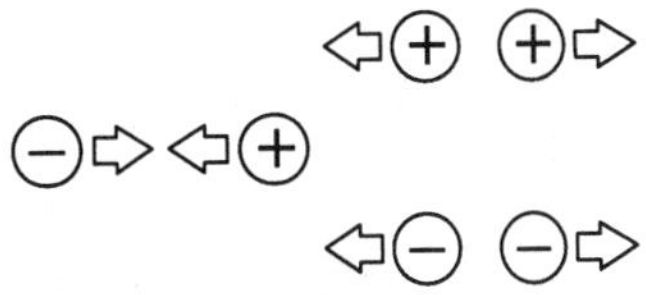

It's like a magnet, isn't it?

It was Coulomb who researched this electrical force. As a result, he discovered an equation that was able to describe the force of electrical attraction:

$$F = -\frac{q_1 q_2}{r^2}$$

(Note : 'electrostatic system of units' is used.)

q describes the magnitude of the positive or negative charge, and r describes how far apart they are.

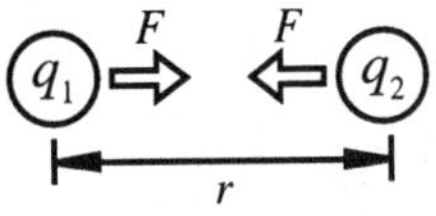

In the case of the model of the hydrogen atom, the nucleus has a positive charge of $+e$, and the electron has a negative charge of $-e$. So placing them this way,

$$q_1 = e\,,\quad q_2 = -e$$

and inserting them into the Coulomb equation, we get:

$$F = -\frac{e \cdot -e}{r^2} = -\frac{-e^2}{r^2}$$

Model of the hydrogen atom

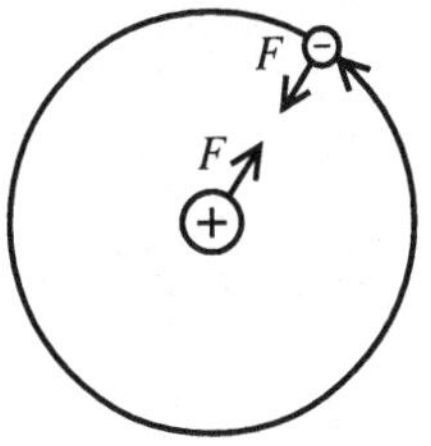

They are being attracted with a force of $F = \frac{e^2}{r^2}$

This is the force that the nucleus exerts to pull electrons.

That is, the nucleus is pulling the electron with a force equal to

$$F = \frac{e^2}{r^2}$$

When the force that tries to make the electrons fly away (centrifugal force) is matched with the force that tries to hold them back (Coulomb force), the atom can maintain a particular size. We did it! We've now figured out one part of the atomic structure!

But. . .there's a trap door under our feet.

According to Maxwell's electromagnetics, an electron (something that has an electrical charge) gives off light when it revolves around the nucleus. By emitting light, the electron expends energy and loses vitality, causing an imbalance in the Coulomb force and centrifugal force in the atom. As a result, the electron is drawn toward the nucleus.

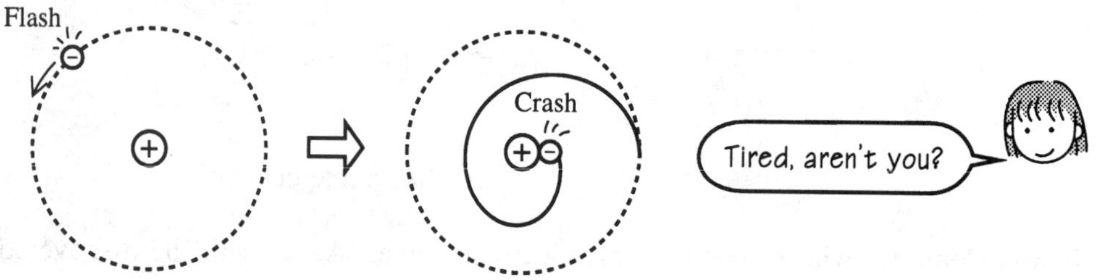

The atom can't maintain its size like this, which means that the Rutherford model is no good anymore.

Rutherford's pupil, Bohr, thought up a method to resolve this problem. It seemed preposterous, but Bohr decided to ignore Maxwell's electromagnetics and propose that no light was emitted even if there was rotation! Yet his preposterous idea enabled Bohr to explain various things about the workings of the atom.

APPENDIX 3. ANGULAR MOMENTUM

The Bohr-Sommerfeld quantum condition was in the form of the equation

$$\oint p\, dq = nh$$

This equation was an extension of the equation

$$\text{angular momentum } M = \frac{h}{2\pi} n$$

discovered by Bohr. The equation did not contain a single constant, such as e or m, that described the structure of a particular atom. Thus it can be considered an equation for a general condition that determines the discrete energy state of all types of atoms. In the equation discovered by Bohr, the discrete state was described by angular momentum M.

Now, before we discuss angular momentum, let's start by discussing simple momentum. First, let's rewrite $F = ma$, a basic equation of Newton's mechanics.

$$F = ma = m\frac{dv}{dt} = \frac{d}{dt}(mv)$$

mv is the momentum, and the change in momentum over time is the force F. Angular momentum is angular, that is, when something is moving in a circle, it's the momentum of the angle, right? If that is the case, if we take a force suitable for circular motion and take a differential of it with respect to time, then we should have the momentum of circular movement or angular momentum.

LINEAR AND CIRCULAR MOTION

For linear motion, if we know location x at a certain time t, then we can find velocity v, acceleration a and force F. In the case of rotating motion, if we can find something that is equivalent to position x of linear motion, we should be able to find the angular momentum through correspondence. What corresponds to position x is angle θ. Similarly we let angular velocity ω correspond to velocity v, and angular acceleration a_θ correspond to acceleration a. Putting it all together, we have the following:

	Linear motion	Rotating motion	
Position	x	θ	Angle
Velocity	$v = \frac{dx}{dt}$ 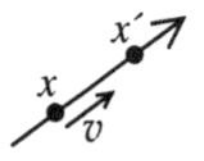	$\omega = \frac{d\theta}{dt}$ 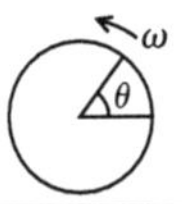	Angular velocity
Acceleration	$a = \frac{dv}{dt} = \frac{d^2x}{dt^2}$	$a_\theta = \frac{d\omega}{dt} = \frac{d^2\theta}{dt^2}$	Angular acceleration

While we're at it, let's find out what we can substitute for force F and momentum p that we know from linear motion.

TORQUE

Placing θ in correspondence with x, let's try to find force F for circular motion that corresponds to force F for linear motion. That force is called torque. Let us assume that an object with mass m shifts from point P to point Q within time Δt on a circle with radius r.

When it is at point P,
time is t
position is x, y
angle is θ

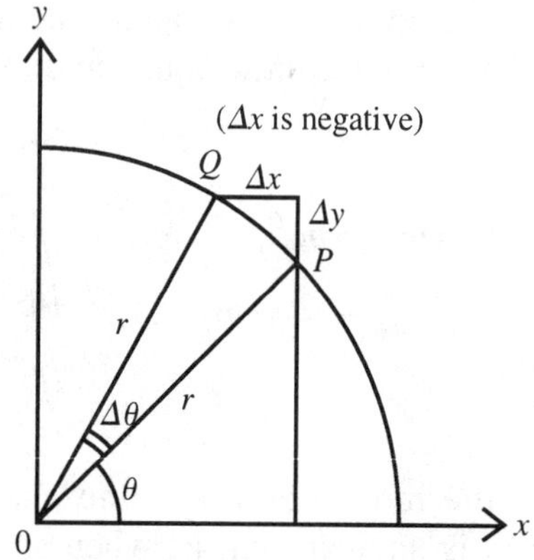

When it shifts from the point P to point Q, the time increases by exactly Δt, so the time at point Q is $t + \Delta t$. As for the position, the respective coordinates increase by Δx and Δy, so the position of point Q is $x + \Delta x$, $y + \Delta y$. The angle is $\theta + \Delta\theta$.

And, as the time interval of the movement Δt becomes very small, $\angle QPO$ gradually approaches a right angle. What happens if $\angle QPO$ is a right angle? What happens is that this angle becomes θ. Thus, we may write Δx and Δy in the following manner using length PQ and angle θ.

$$\Delta x = -PQ \sin\theta$$
$$\Delta y = PQ \cos\theta$$

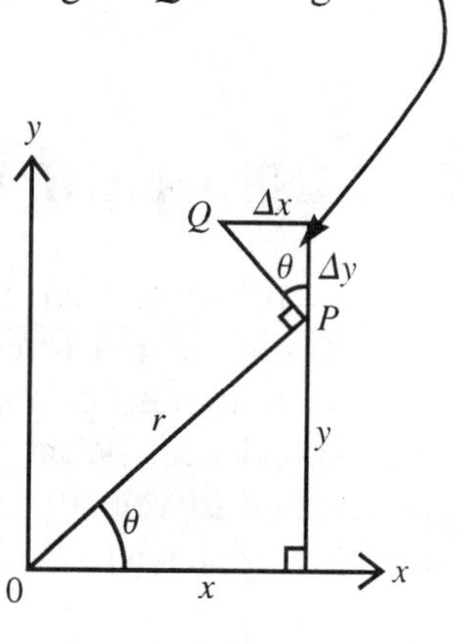

At this point, we may write length PQ using radius r and the change in $\Delta\theta$ as

$$PQ = r \cdot \Delta\theta$$

We then obtain

$$\Delta x = -r\Delta\theta \sin\theta$$
$$\Delta y = r\Delta\theta \cos\theta$$

We also know

$$\sin\theta = \frac{y}{r}$$
$$\cos\theta = \frac{x}{r}$$

And putting this into the equation for Δx and Δy, we get

$$\Delta x = -r\Delta\theta \frac{y}{r} = -\Delta\theta\, y$$
$$\Delta y = r\Delta\theta \frac{x}{r} = \Delta\theta\, x$$

Now let's finally use this to find the force in the case of circular motion. At this point, let's also apply the idea of "work." Work can be described as

work = force × distance.

For circular motion, it corresponds to

work = (something corresponding to force) × angle.

Let's pin down this thing that corresponds to force.

Work, which acts with force F over the distance PQ is the sum of work that acts with force F_x over the distance Δx and work that acts with force F_y over the distance Δy.

Putting this in an equation, we get

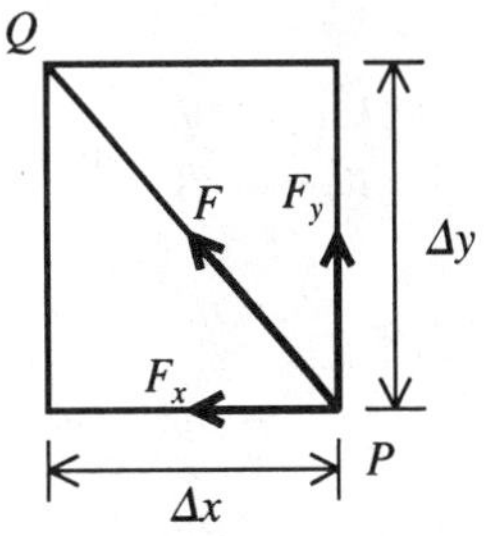

$$F \times PQ = F_y \Delta\, y + F_x \Delta\, x$$

Rewriting Δx and Δy, we get

$$F \times PQ = F_y \Delta\theta\, x + F_x(-\Delta\theta\, y)$$

Extracting $\Delta\theta$, we obtain

$$F \times PQ = \left(F_y\, x - F_x\, y\right) \times \Delta\theta$$

Let's take a close look at this equation.

$$\underset{\text{linear force}}{F} \times \underset{\text{distance}}{PQ} = \underset{\text{circular force}}{\left(F_y\, x - F_x\, y\right)} \times \underset{\text{angle}}{\Delta\theta}$$

Thus we were able to determine work for circular motion. That is to say, $(F_y\, x - F_x\, y)$ is the force in the case of circular motion. This force is called torque.

ANGULAR MOMENTUM

If we can find the force in the case of circular motion, the rest is simple. That's because the angular momentum has a correspondence to Newton's equation.

$$F = \frac{d}{dt} p$$

$$\text{torque} = \frac{d}{dt} \text{(angular momentum)}$$

If we can find a formula whose derivative turns out to be torque, we have found angular momentum.

Let's try, $M = mv_y\, x - mv_x\, y$

Taking the derivative of M with respect to time, we get

$$\begin{aligned}
\frac{d}{dt} M &= \frac{d}{dt}\left(mv_y\, x - mv_x\, y\right) \\
&= m\frac{dv_y}{dt} x + mv_y \frac{dx}{dt} - m\frac{dv_x}{dt} y - mv_x \frac{dy}{dt} \\
&= ma_y\, x + mv_y v_x - ma_x\, y - mv_x v_y \\
&= ma_y\, x - ma_x\, y \\
&= F_y\, x - F_x\, y
\end{aligned}$$

The derivative of M here is torque. Therefore M must be the angular momentum.

angular momentum $M = mv_y x - mv_x y$

Since the angular momentum changes over time relative to the torque (force in circular motion), when the torque is zero, the angular momentum is constant. That is, unless torque is applied, the angular momentum is maintained at a constant value. This is called the law of the conservation of the angular momentum.

THE ANGULAR MOMENTUM IN THE CASE OF CIRCULAR MOTION

The angular momentum that we just found is applied in general cases, and can naturally be used for elliptical orbits. Since Bohr believed that the electrons of a hydrogen atom rotated in a circular orbit, let's find the angular momentum for circular motion.

Expressing the circular orbit in terms of radius r of the circle and angle θ, in terms of x and y, we get

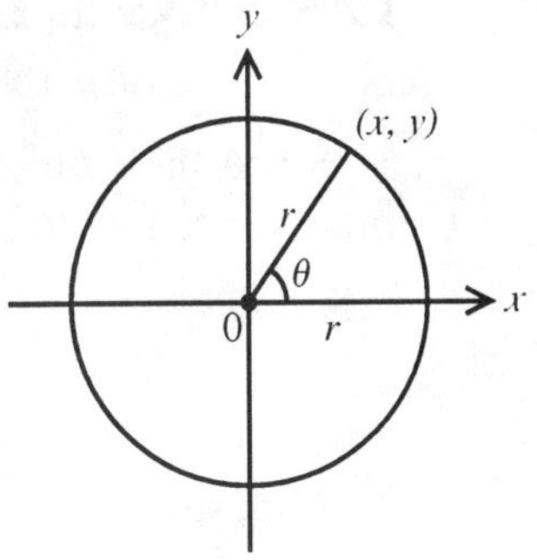

$$x = r\cos\theta$$
$$y = r\sin\theta$$

Because there is rotating motion in a circular orbit, angle θ changes relative to time t. Assuming that the rotation is at a constant angular velocity ω, we rewrite it as

$$\underset{\text{angle}}{\theta} = \underset{\text{angular velocity}}{\omega} \times \underset{\text{time}}{t}$$

and we get

$$x = r\cos\omega t$$
$$y = r\sin\omega t$$

Velocities v_x and v_y are

$$v_x = \frac{dx}{dt} = -r\omega\sin\omega t$$
$$= -v\sin\omega t$$
$$v_y = \frac{dy}{dt} = r\omega\cos\omega t$$
$$= v\cos\omega t$$

Using these in the equation for angular momentum,

$$\text{angular momentum } M = mv_y x - mv_x y$$
$$= m(v\cos\omega t)(r\cos\omega t) - m(-v\sin\omega t)(r\sin\omega t)$$
$$= mvr\cos^2\omega t + mvr\sin^2\omega t$$
$$= mvr\left(\cos^2\omega t + \sin^2\omega t\right)$$

Velocity for circular orbits

The length of an arc is found by using $s = r\theta$. But what happens when angle θ changes relative to time? Let's describe the velocity along a circular orbit.

$$v = \frac{ds}{dt}$$

In this equation

$$v = \frac{d}{dt}(r\theta)$$

r is constant and has no relation to time, so

$$v = r\frac{d\theta}{dt}$$

However, $\frac{d\theta}{dt}$ expresses the change in angle θ relative to time, and so it describes angular velocity ω.

We obtain the equation

$$v = r\omega$$

which means that the velocity along the circular orbit is the angular velocity multiplied by the radius.

In other words, angular momentum can be expressed as $M = mvr$. Because mv is momentum p, the angular momentum for a circular orbit takes the form of momentum p multiplied by radius r.

APPENDIX 4. FINDING THE TOTAL ENERGY IN CLASSICAL THEORY

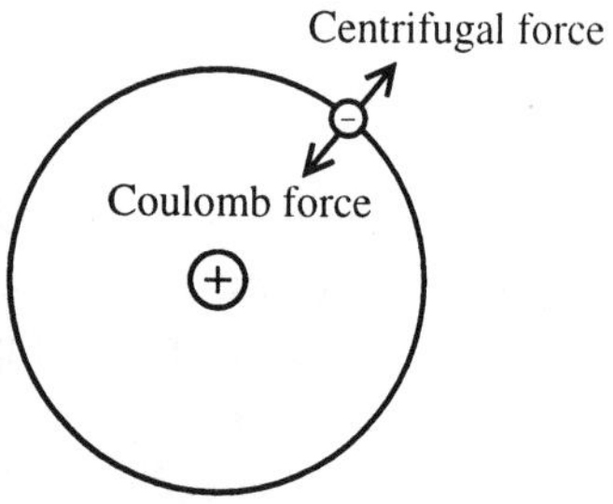

Since the Coulomb force as centripetal force is equal to centrifugal force, we can write

$$\frac{e^2}{r^2} = mr\omega^2$$

And, since $\omega = \frac{v}{r}$, we can rewrite this as

$$\frac{e^2}{r^2} = m\frac{v^2}{r}$$

Now, let's find the energy from this equation!!

There are two kinds of energy, kinetic and potential, and total energy is the sum of the two.

$$W\text{(total energy)} = K\text{(kinetic energy)} + V\text{(potential energy)}$$

The formula for potential energy is

$$V = -\int^{x} F\,dx$$

Here force F is a Coulomb force, so inserting $-\frac{e^2}{r^2}$ for F, we come up with

Because the Coulomb force and the centrifugal force act in mutually opposing directions, we place a minus sign in front of the Coulomb force. (See Appendix 1)

$$V = -\int_{\infty}^{r} -\frac{e^2}{r^2}\,dr = -\left[e^2\frac{1}{r}\right]_{\infty}^{r} = -e^2\frac{1}{r}$$

The potential energy is now $V = -\frac{e^2}{r}$

While kinetic energy is expressed as $K = \frac{1}{2}mv^2$

the equation for the Coulomb force is $\frac{e^2}{r^2} = m\frac{v^2}{r}$

Insofar as this resembles the expression for kinetic energy, let's rewrite the equation for the Coulomb force.

$$\frac{e^2}{r^2} = \frac{1}{2} mv^2 \frac{2}{r}$$

Now put it in the same form!

$$\frac{1}{2} mv^2 = \frac{e^2}{2r}$$

We did it! We got kinetic energy. Once we have this, it's simple. Now all we have to do is add the two up. The total energy W is

$$W = -\frac{e^2}{r} + \frac{e^2}{2r} = -\frac{e^2}{2r}$$

This is the total energy!

Then, giving it an absolute value, we obtain

$$|W| = \frac{e^2}{2r}$$

This is the total energy in classical theory.

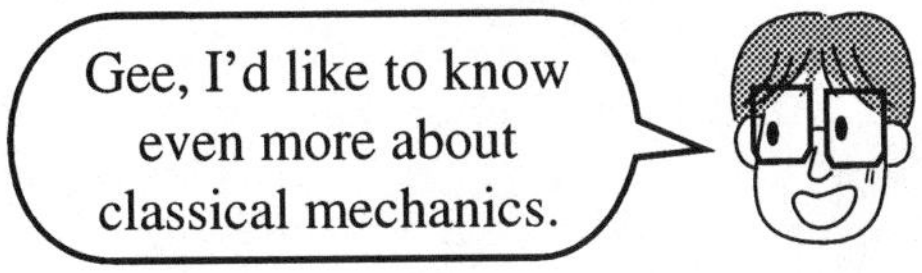

CHAPTER 3

Werner Heisenberg

THE BIRTH OF QUANTUM MECHANICS

Bohr had discovered a method for finding the frequency of atomic spectra, but no one had yet found a way to determine its intensity. Physicists were all keyed up, hoping for a breakthrough. At this point, it was the young Heisenberg who took the first steps that stretched the boundaries of knowledge; it was Heisenberg who sought out new possibilities for Newton's equation for motion $F = m\ddot{q}$*. In this chapter, we are going to look at how matrix mechanics was developed.*

Introducing the Cast
THE HEISENBERG ADVENTURE
Let's get the general idea.
San
Ricky
Ban
Yuko
Manatsu
Hyon
Pero
¡Hola!

All right, let's get started on our Heisenberg adventure! We'll begin as usual. Okay, what's the Heisenberg squad's objective? Let's say it all together on the count of three! One, two. . .
Let's get the general idea!
clap clap
Well done! You, too, Hyon. Say something!
z z z

3.1 LET'S REVIEW

GETTING MENTALLY PREPARED FOR QUANTUM MECHANICS!

"Quanta" refer to light or electrons that are invisible and behave strangely. So what are their mechanics? The field of quantum mechanics is on the leading edge of the physical sciences.

Natural science unveils the unchanging order of things that occur regularly in nature. At TCL, we consider language to have the same kind of underlying regularity. So we look at language, too, in terms of natural science. If we speak of an unchanging order in language, it means those rules of natural order that science tries to pin down.

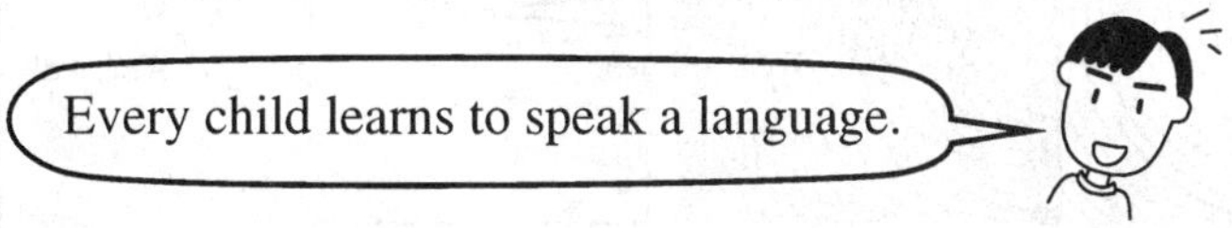

At TCL we are trying to find the mechanisms that push us to acquire language.

This is something I learned only recently. Until now, when someone talked about the order of language, I thought it meant that if it was Japanese, then it was the order of Japanese; if it was French, then it was the order of French. I thought the order of each language was different. After all, even the Japanese spoken in the 17th and 18th centuries during the Edo period is different from that of today. And almost nothing has been preserved exactly as it was from the speech of still earlier periods.

I remember a time when, thinking along these lines, I couldn't understand what they were doing at TCL, but then I began to understand what "people acquire language" really meant. It is a rule of human life, and it doesn't change. When I realized this, I felt a wonderful sense of happiness.

Now within the natural sciences, physics looks for the order in the movement of things. For example,

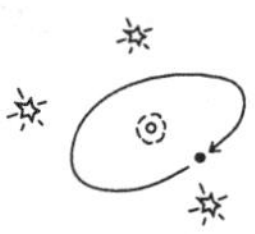

The movement of planets

The movement of coffee molecules in a cup

It tries to find the laws governing order in the movement of things. Previously it was thought that the laws or rules in the movement of all things could be described using classical mechanics — Newtonian mechanics, Maxwell's electromagnetism. There was peace in the world of physics.

But it eventually became clear that classical mechanics could not describe the movement of those particles too small to be seen, such as photons and atoms.

CONCERNING LIGHT

Since the ancient past, light had always been a puzzling phenomenon. As no one had actually been able to see the form of light, no one could really know what it was. Then in 1807 the British physicist Thomas Young tried the "slit experiment" with light.

What's the slit experiment?

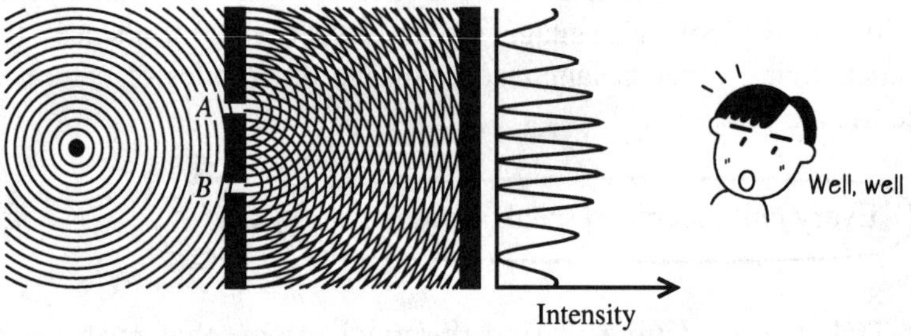

It is an experiment that shows when a wave passes through two slits, it exhibits interference patterns!

Based on that knowledge, Young tried it with light.

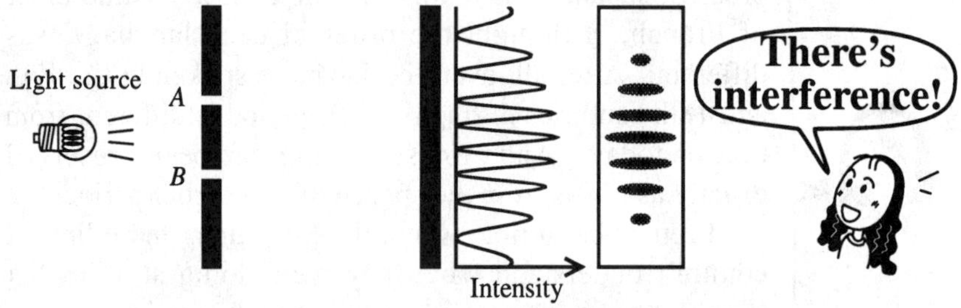

That's why light came to be thought of as something like a **wave**.

But in 1900, Planck discovered that the energy of light only took values that were integral multiples of $h\nu$.

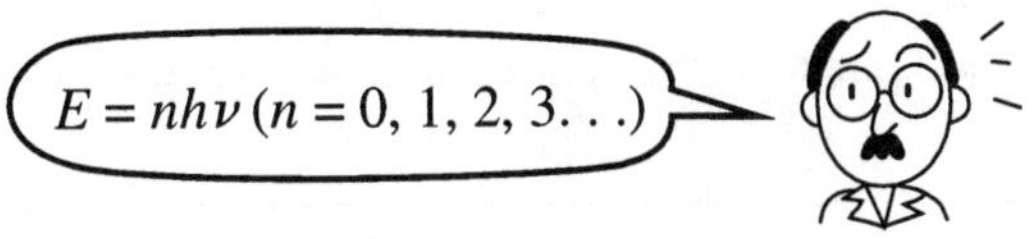

As long as light was thought to be a wave, there was no way this could be explained.

For instance. . .

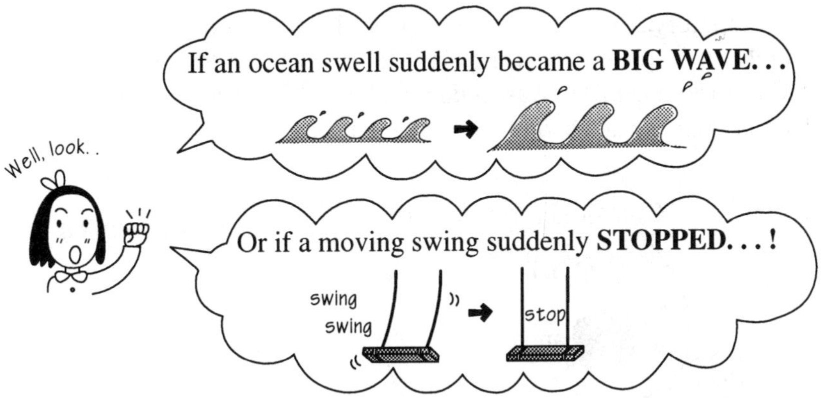

It would be odd, no matter how you looked at it. The people around thought,

with Planck's discovery.

Next on the scene was Einstein, who looked at Planck's discovery and said, "Light is a **particle**-like thing that has energy equal to $h\nu$."

Various experiments, like the ones for the photoelectric effect and the Compton effect, could not be explained unless light was thought of as being composed of particles. Experiments showed that light could sometimes be thought of as being composed of waves, and sometimes as being composed of particles. That much seemed undeniable, because the experiments had to be true.

But it still didn't tell people what light really was.

LIGHT	wave.........interference
	particle......photoelectric effect, Compton effect

Can something really be thought of as being both a wave and a particle?

Unfortunately, that didn't seem possible to us. It was regarded as an impossibility to explain light using classical mechanics. Physicists began to call light, whose true character was unknown, "quanta". They excluded light from classical mechanics and tried to find other ways to describe it.

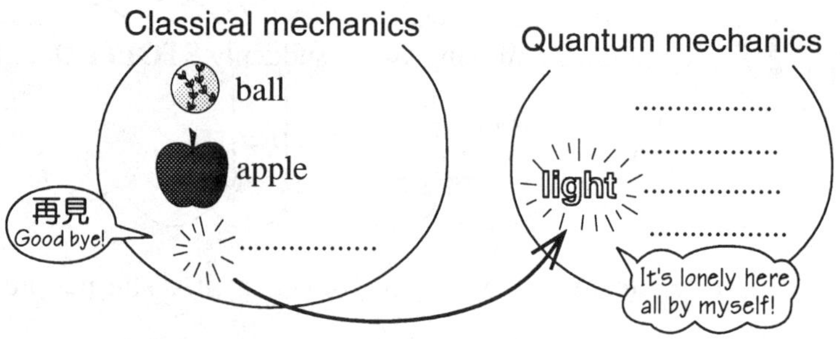

If you think about it, Einstein's equation $E = h\nu$ is strange as well! Since the energy of a particle is tied with an equal sign to the frequency of a wave... is a particle a wave??

ABOUT ATOMS

I. The makeup of an atom

At the time, an atom was thought to be the "smallest unit of matter," and research on it was being conducted parallel to the research on light.

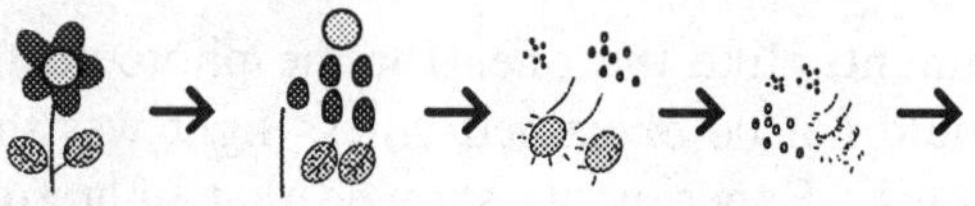

When you break something up into smaller and smaller pieces, you end up with an atom.

In the course of this research, however, certain experiments showed that atoms were made up of still smaller particles:

> • A heavy nucleus with a positive electrical charge
> • Light electrons with a negative electrical charge
>
> In addition, the size of an entire atom (about one angstrom = 10^{-10} m) was comparatively a great deal bigger than the nucleus and electron.

Different atoms had different numbers of electrons inside.

Number of electrons	1	2	3	4	5	6	7	8	9	10	...
Chemical symbol	H	He	Li	Be	B	C	N	O	F	Ne	...
Type of atom	hydrogen	helium	lithium	beryllium	boron	carbon	nitrogen	oxygen	fluorine	neon	...

Taking all these things into consideration, let's think about the makeup of the atom. From here on we will be looking at the most simple kind of atom, the hydrogen atom. Normally ⊕ and ⊖ attract each other, so that the negatively charged electrons are pulled toward the positively charged nucleus, drawing together as ⊕⊖, and the size of the atom collapses. In order for the atom to maintain a size of about one angstrom, the electrons have to rotate around the nucleus.

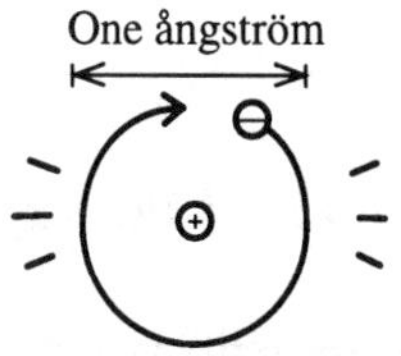

Rutherford's atomic model

Experimental Corner!

Okay, now let's try a little experiment! First, we take a ball from a pinball machine and a deep bowl. The pinball is the electron, and the bottom of the bowl is the nucleus. Now what can we do to keep the ball from veering toward the bottom of the bowl?

If you use cement glue to stick the ball to the side of the bowl away from the bottom, that should do the trick!

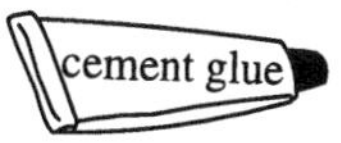

Yup, that would work here, but suppose there wasn't any cement glue?

I know! Let's turn the bowl around and around! That's it, right?

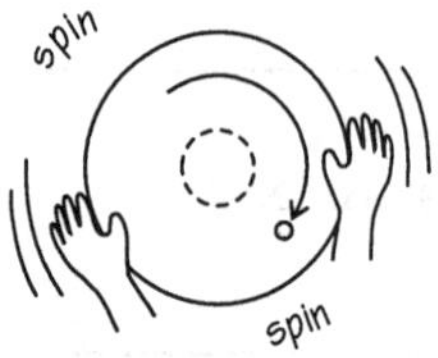

Very good! Bull's eye! That's exactly like an atom. As long as there is this rotating movement, the ⊕ and the ⊖ won't stick to each other and the size of the atom can be maintained at about one angstrom.

Right. . .

II. The key to the search for the atom

Scientists couldn't look inside the atom, but they found the crucial key to the makeup of the atom in. . .**THE SPECTRUM!**

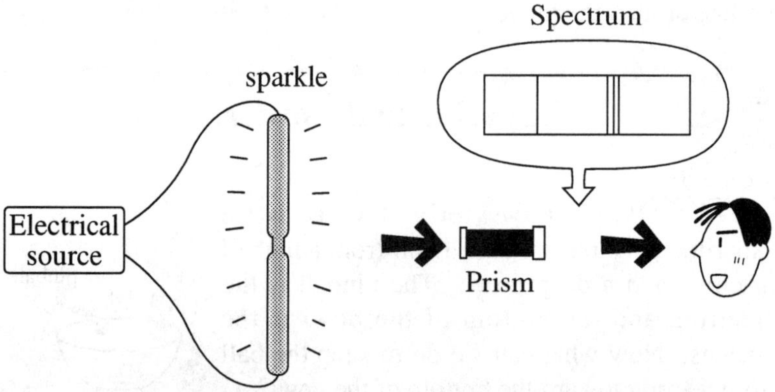

When you put atoms inside a glass tube and apply energy by passing electricity through it, it glows. The color of this light, or spectrum, differs with each type of atom.

About Spectra!

☆ The spectra of a mixed fruit drink

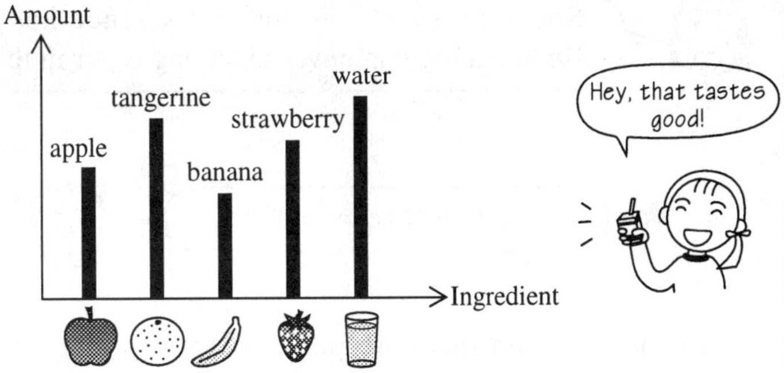

The flavor of a mixed fruit drink is determined by the types of fruits used and the quantities of each kind of juice mixed in. A spectrograph is something that shows the proportional quantities. You can see it laid out at a single glance.

☆ Spectra of light

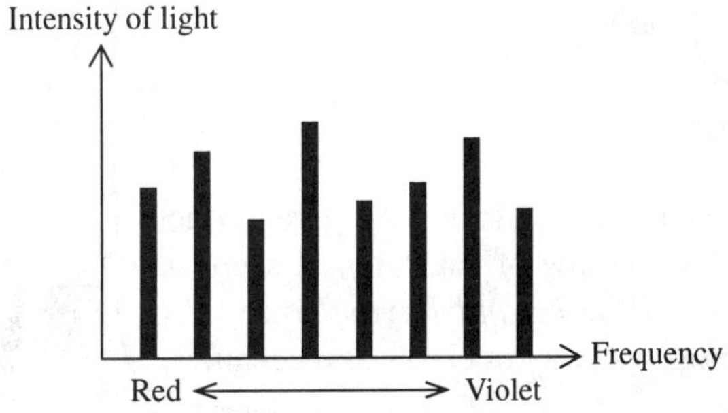

We perceive light as colors. Different frequencies of light appear as different colors. With respect to the amount of light, when the light is strong it is bright, and when it is weak it is dim. This is described in terms of intensity. The characteristics of light are determined by both frequency and intensity.

The spectrum of the hydrogen atom

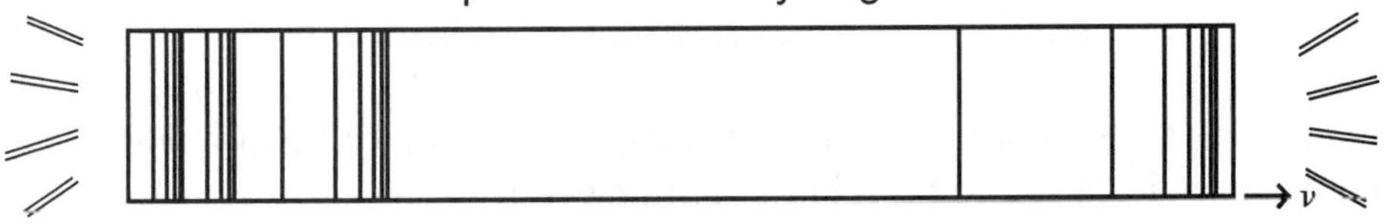

Now there are two reasons why spectra may be considered the crucial key in the search for the atom.

1. A given atom will always produce a fixed spectrum; hydrogen atoms produce a hydrogen spectrum, helium atoms produce a helium spectrum, and so on.

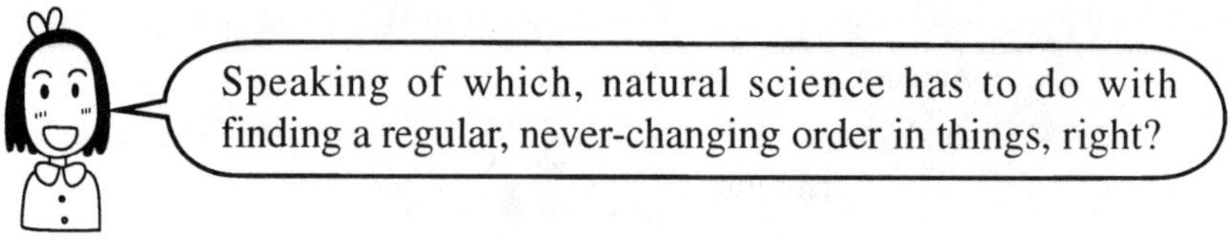

2. Inside the atom there are only electrons and a nucleus. Because the nucleus is much heavier compared to the electrons, it is the electrons that are thought to move. Since the electrons produce the spectra, by investigating the spectra, one can discover the movements of the electrons.

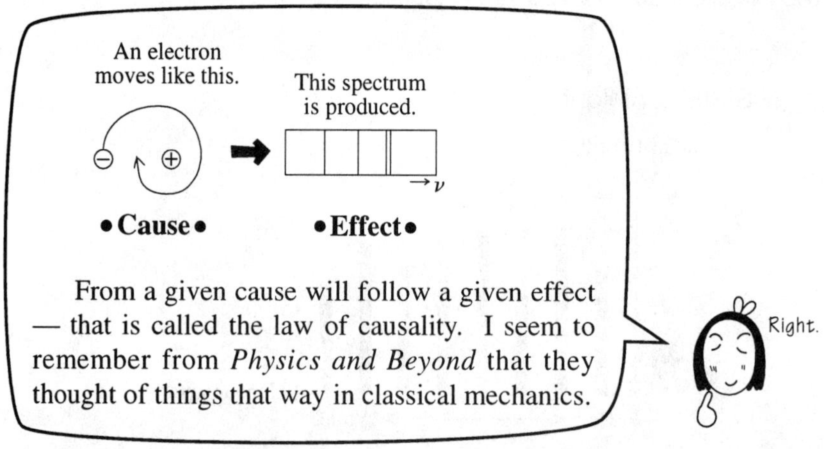

It was Rydberg who succeeded in mathematically expressing the frequencies of these spectra.

Frequency of the hydrogen spectrum

$$\nu = \frac{Rc}{m^2} - \frac{Rc}{n^2} \qquad m, n \text{ are integers } (n > m)$$

At that time no one, including Rydberg himself, knew the meaning of this equation, which matched the actual spectrum perfectly.

III. Problems in Rutherford's atomic model

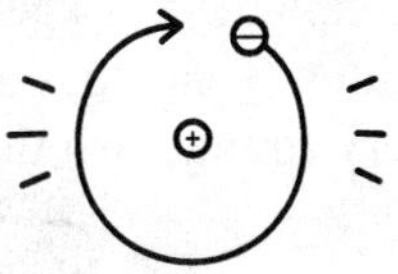

Rutherford's atomic model

Now it was found that in order to consider the makeup of atoms, it was necessary to explain their spectra. Physicists tried to do this using Rutherford's model.

There is a general law of classical mechanics that can properly explain both experiments and theory.

> **Maxwell's Electromagnetics**
>
> When something with an electrical charge moves in a circle, it gives off light.

An electron, which has a negative charge ⊖ , gives off light as it rotates. What this means is:

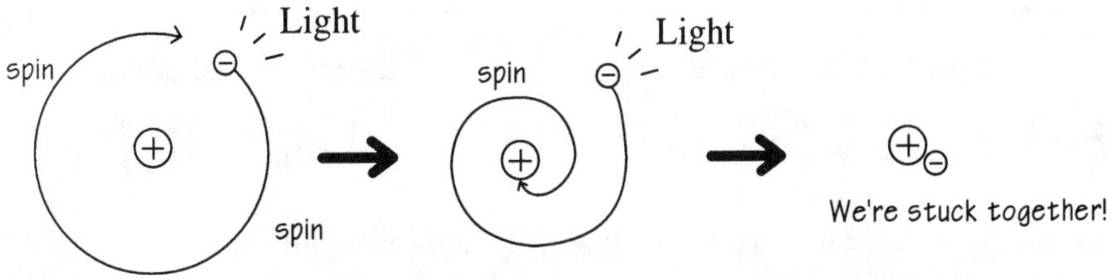

Therefore by rotating, the electrons lose energy and finally end up stuck to the nucleus. Although the electrons have to be rotating **to keep the size of the atom constant,** according to Maxwell's electromagnetics, if the electrons rotate, the atom winds up being unable to maintain its size! In this instance, the spectrum changes:

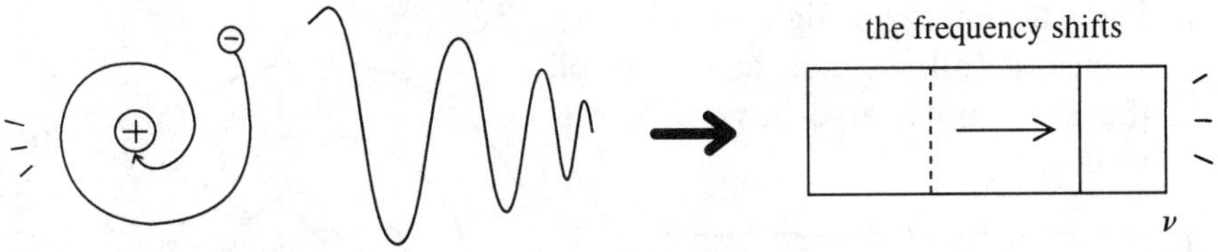

When this happens, the spectrum shifts moving toward the higher frequencies, which doesn't match the spectrum from experiments.

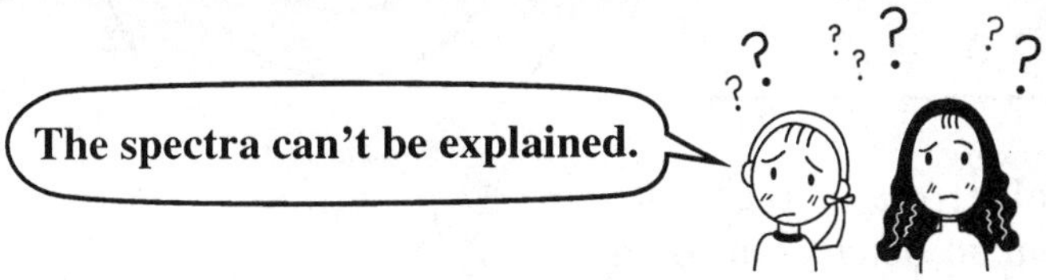

BOHR SHOWS UP

If the Rutherford model was correct, then the atom's spectra could not be explained. Experiments had confirmed both "the spectra" and that "the atom, with a ⊕ nucleus and a ⊖ electron, maintains a certain size." So Bohr found it very strange that they could not be explained.

It's not the experimental facts that are wrong, it's that Maxwell's electrodynamics can't be applied here. Maxwell's theory is based on the assumption that light is a wave. That's why it doesn't work for the spectrum.

According to Einstein and Planck, you could account for light only by thinking of it as being sometimes a wave, sometimes a particle. Such an idea was unprecedented; they finally decided light was a "quantum" of unknown character and excluded it from classical mechanics. Bohr decided to see what would happen to the makeup of the atom if he tried thinking of light as a quantum.

Planck's discovery

$E = nh\nu$ $(n = 0, 1, 2, 3 \ldots)$

The energy of light has discrete values.

Einstein's discovery

$E = h\nu$

Light is a particle with energy $h\nu$.

If we apply these to the inside of an atom. . .

1. Since the energy of light has discrete values, it follows that the energy of the atom must also have discrete values.

Quantum condition

$$\oint p\, dq = nh$$

$(n = 1, 2, 3, \cdots)$

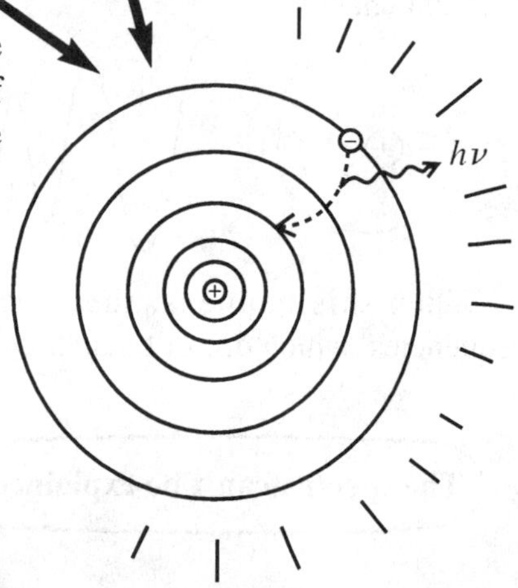

2. When an electron makes the transition from an outer orbit to an inner orbit, the excess energy $h\nu$ is emitted as light.

Bohr's frequency relation

$$\nu = \frac{W_n}{h} - \frac{W_m}{h} \quad (n > m)$$

Lo and behold, by thinking of light as a quantum, Bohr found it was possible to perfectly explain the conservation of the atom's size and the frequencies of its spectra.

Shortly afterward something happened to fall into the lap of the happy Bohr.

> **Rydberg's equation for the spectrum of the hydrogen atom**
>
> $$\nu = \frac{Rc}{m^2} - \frac{Rc}{n^2}$$

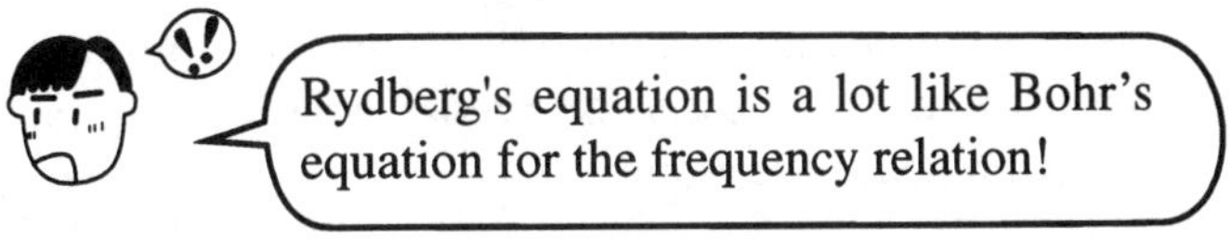

They are both in the form of "ν (frequency) equals something," and both are stated in terms of the difference in value between two things (subtraction). The instant Bohr saw this equation, he was convinced that his theory was valid.

Afterwards Bohr worked away steadily and finalized his theory, and met with great success.

PROBLEMS WITH BOHR'S THEORY

Bohr's theory was able to resolve previously problematic points, but two new ones arose.

1. The mechanisms of electron transition were unknown.
2. The intensity of the spectrum could not be explained.

CONCERNING PROBLEM 1: TRANSITION

On Transition

Transition, in simple terms, is instantaneous relocation. Put more simply, it's a warp.

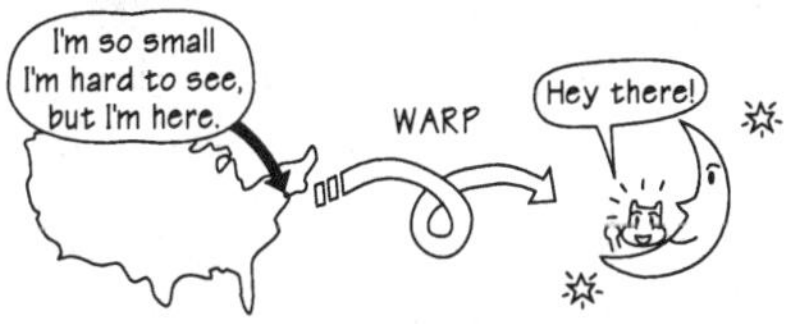

A hippopotamoid (a character from the Hippo Tapes) who is in New York in the next instant suddenly finds himself on the moon! How in the world did he get there?

In other words, the route the electrons took when they underwent transition was unknown. It had been thought that if spectra could be explained, then the way electrons worked within an atom would be understood. But no matter how well Bohr's transition theory could explain spectra, the movements of the electron were still not known.

What are we going to do?
Don't we understand anything about the atom?

Bohr, however, stood firm.

It's not as if we don't know anything about the atom any more! Its just that now we ***can't imagine*** what's going on with the electron inside the atom!

In this way, the electron joined the company of quanta. No one knew what their real nature was.

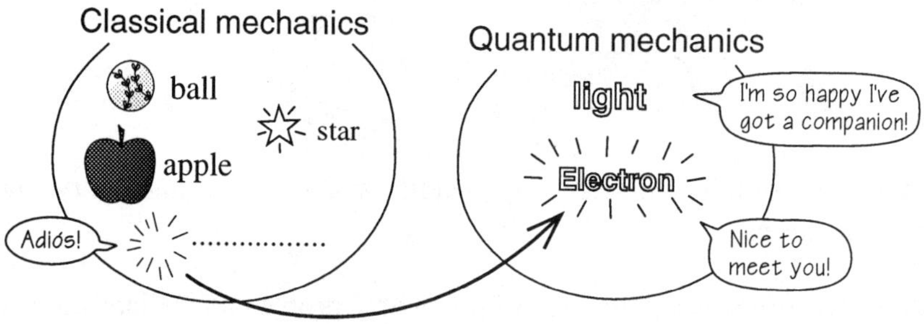

CONCERNING PROBLEM 2: SPECTRAL INTENSITY

Bohr's theory was flawless with respect to spectral frequencies. However, there was no way to determine the intensity of those spectra. At the time, the rallying cry among Bohr's supporters was this:

$$\oint p\,dq = nh$$

$$\nu = \frac{W_n}{h} - \frac{W_m}{h}$$

LET'S FIND THE SPECTRAL INTENSITY!

But the truth was that no matter how much they may have wanted to determine spectral intensity, they could not come up with a method for doing so.

When you're in trouble, play INNOCENT!

Thinking along the lines of classical mechanics, if n were small (as in the case of the inner orbits), the electron would ultimately be drawn into the nucleus, and the atom would remain unexplained. Bohr, however, realized that when n was large (as in the case of the outer orbits), the atom could be explained nicely by either classical mechanics or by his own theory.

◆Thinking In Terms Of Classical Mechanics When n Is Large

CORRESPONDENCE PRINCIPLE

According to Maxwell's electromagnetics, the electron emits light waves as it rotates. This thinking was not feasible when n was small, as the atom would end up collapsing. However, when n was large, one could suppose that the rotating electron would not be drawn into the nucleus even though it was losing energy.

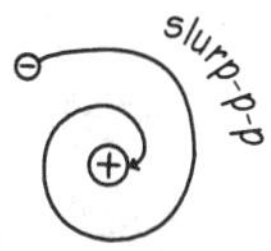

When n is small, the electron is rotating in an inner orbit and its energy is small. Therefore, if it loses even a bit of energy by giving off light, it will end up falling inwards. When n is large, however, the electron is rotating in an outer orbit, and its energy is great. So even if it loses some energy while giving off light, it seems logical that it wouldn't fall inwards.

What? I don't quite get it.

Isn't it something like this? Let's think of the energy consumed in giving off light as spending 1 dollar. Let's say then, when n is large, the energy of the electron is 1 million dollars; and when it is small, 1 dollar. One day, Hyon goes out to buy a 1 dollar can of soda.

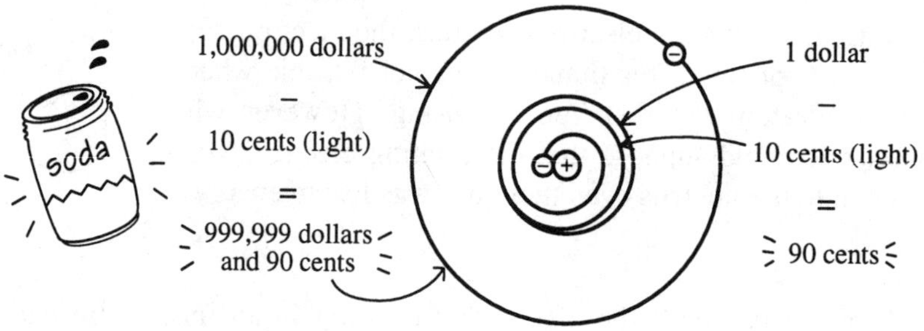

Oh, I see. That's how it is.

Hey, listen, isn't that like dirt in a bathtub? When you pull the stopper out of a tub, you get a whirlpool, right? And then the dirt floating in the tub goes round and round with it. When the dirt is some distance from the center of the whirlpool, it circulates slowly and doesn't get swallowed up as quickly. But when the dirt is near the vortex, it gets swallowed up—swish, swish—before you know it.

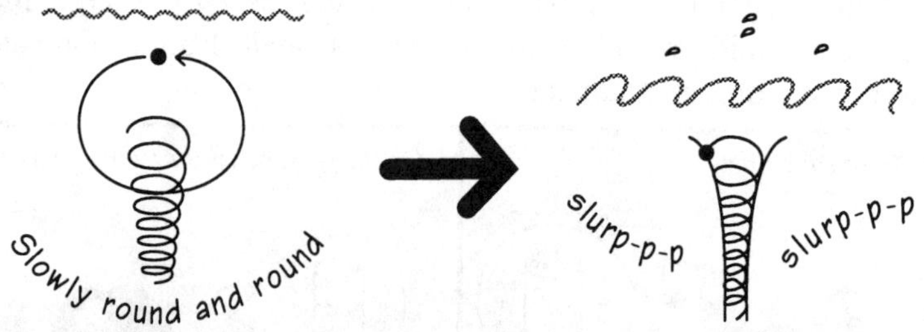

I see, though it's a bit dirty!

If you don't get it, try experimenting for yourself!

When n is large, we can think of the electron as spinning around in the same place. With this kind of movement, light waves become complex, iterative waves.

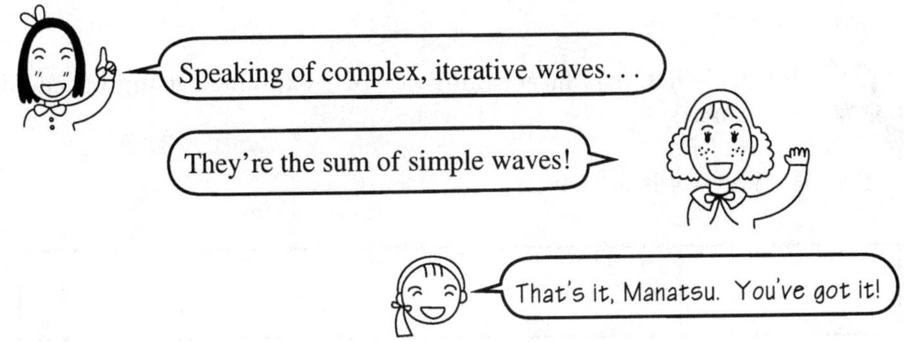

Exactly! That's **Fourier Series!**

The most important feature in Fourier series theory is that frequencies are integral multiples.

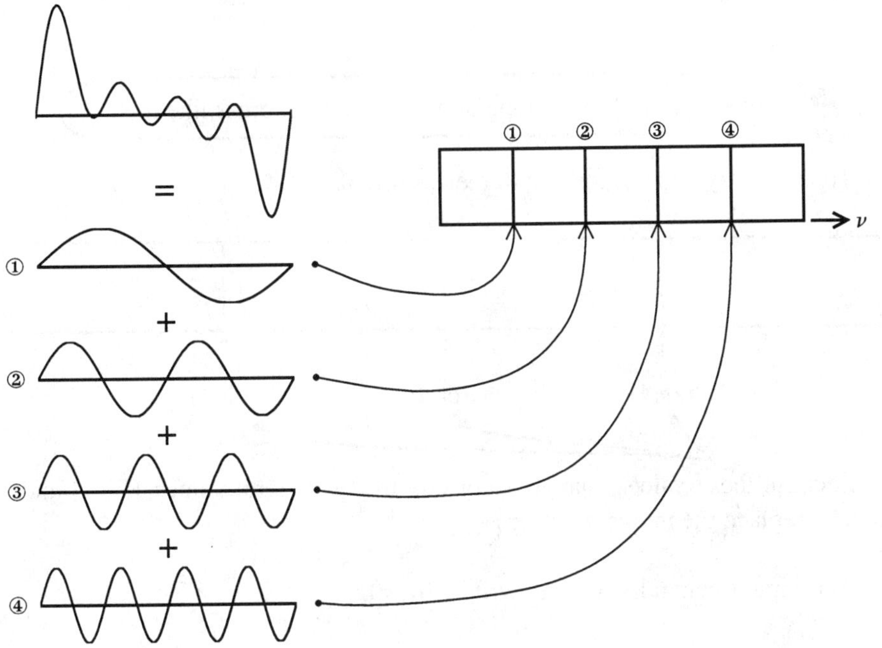

Now what about the spectra that experiments produced?

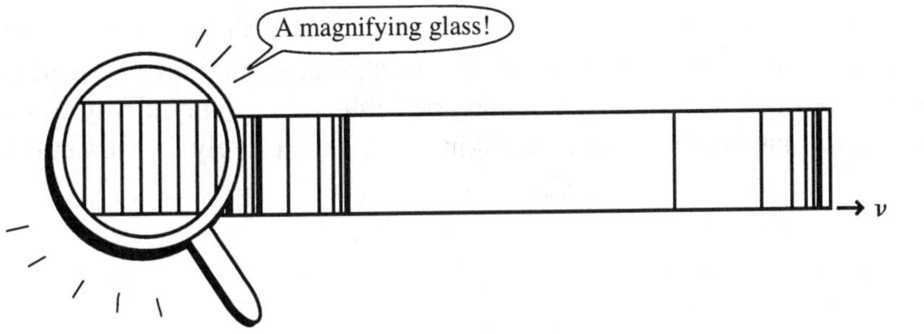

How about that! When n is large, we have integral multiples!

I see. When n is large, things can be explained using classical mechanics!

Putting it into words, we get this:

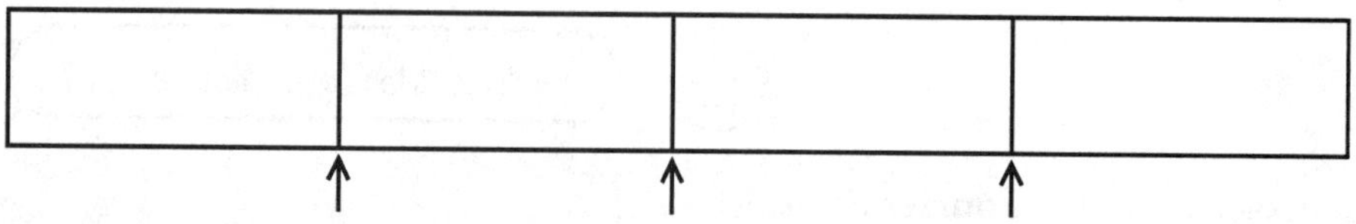

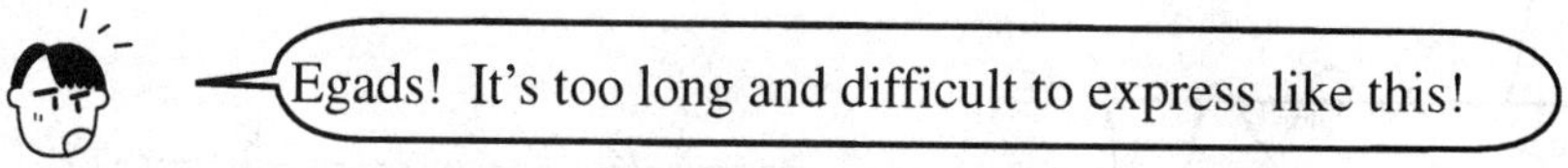

Then let's try expressing it with these symbols:

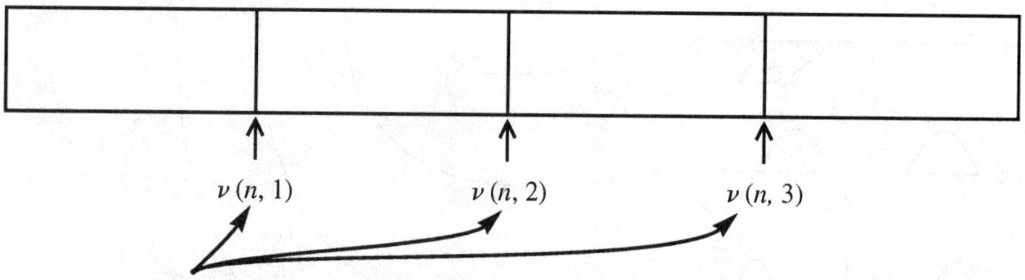

Because these values change according to the integral values 1, 2, 3 and so on, let's replace the integers with τ.

Applying it generally, we can write $\boldsymbol{\nu(n, \tau)}$.

◆ Thinking In Terms Of Bohr's Theory When *n* Is Large

When the electron makes a transition from one orbit to another, it emits a light quantum that has an energy $h\nu$. When n is large, the difference in energy between one orbit and another is in stepped intervals, giving a way to explain the integral values in the spectra. Looking at it more closely, it's something like this.

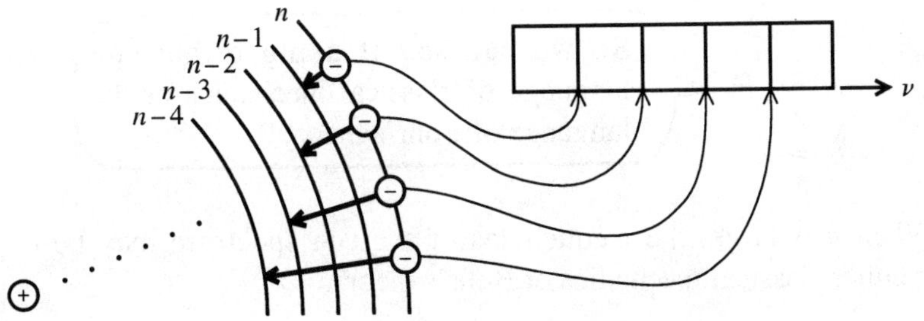

Putting it into words, we get the following:

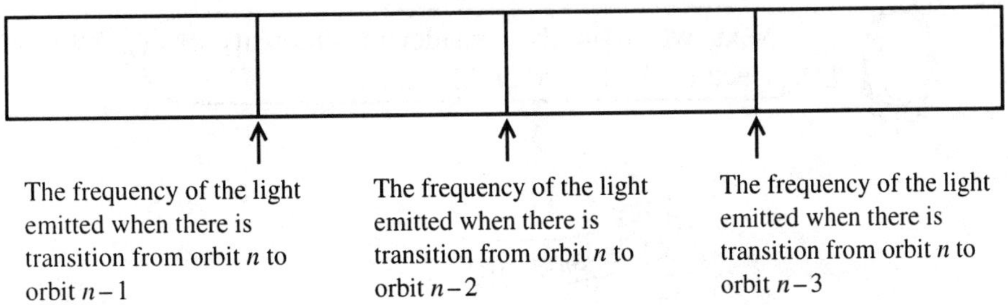

This is even longer! Now let's express it using symbols.

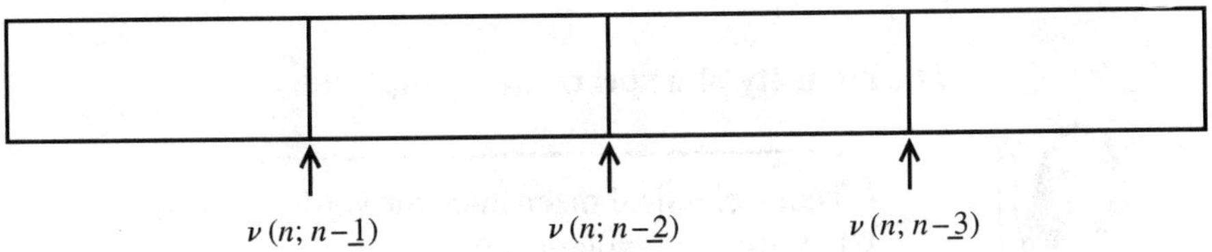

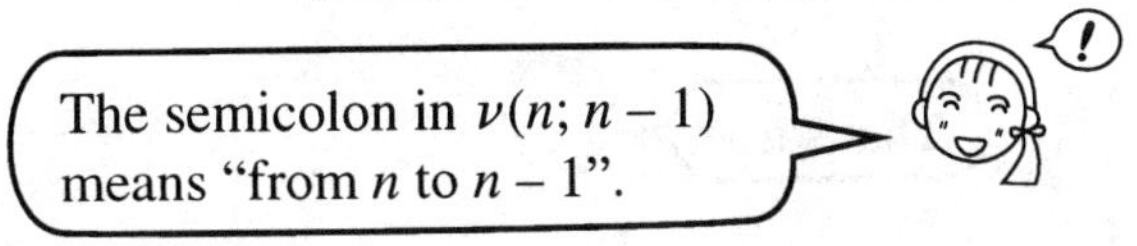

Because these values change according to the integral values 1, 2, 3 and so on, let's replace them with τ here too.

Applying it generally we write ν **(*n*; *n* – τ).**

Since we can use symbols to express both Bohr's theory and classical mechanics, let's write them together.

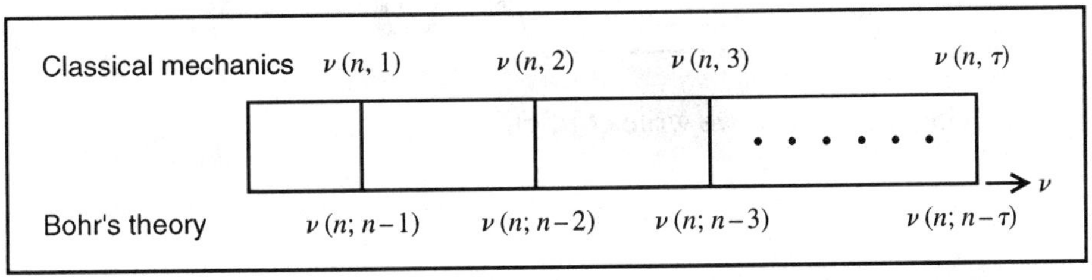

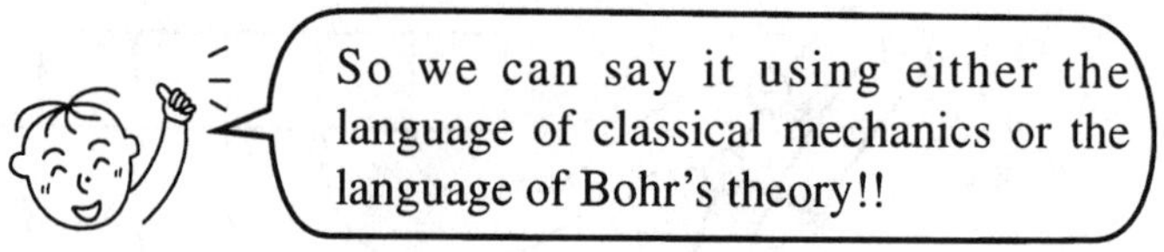

When n is large, the frequencies of a given spectrum may be explained using either classical mechanics or Bohr's theory.

◆ Thinking About the Intensity of Spectra

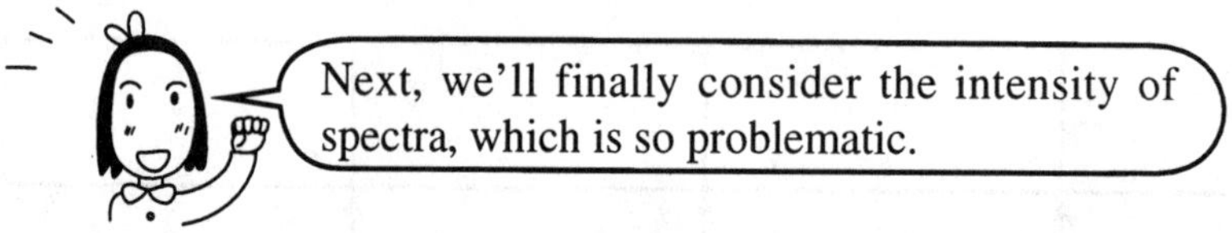

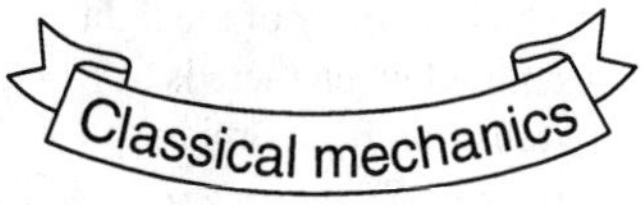

When n is large, we can use classical mechanics to find the amplitudes of simple waves, one by one. For the intensity of the spectrum, all we have to do is square those amplitudes.

The intensity of a spectrum = $|\text{amplitude}|^2$

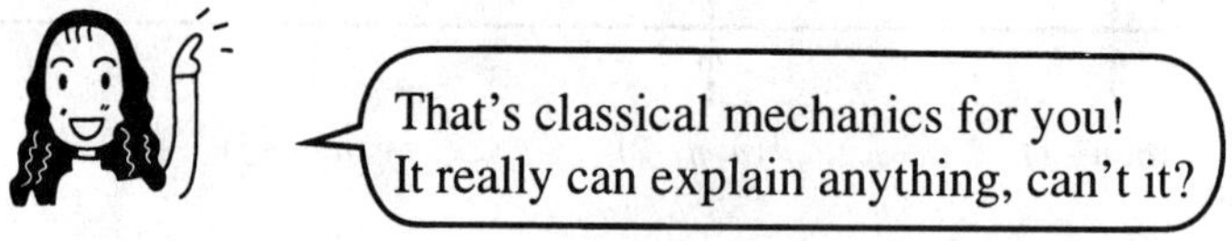

While we're at it, let's also express the amplitude as a symbol! Let's let the symbol for amplitude be $\boldsymbol{Q}$.

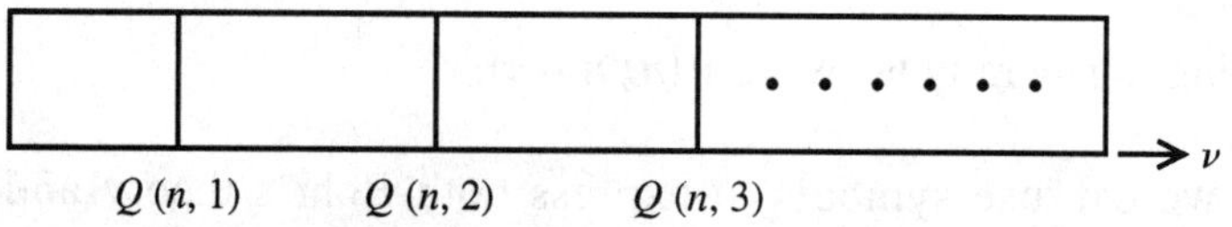

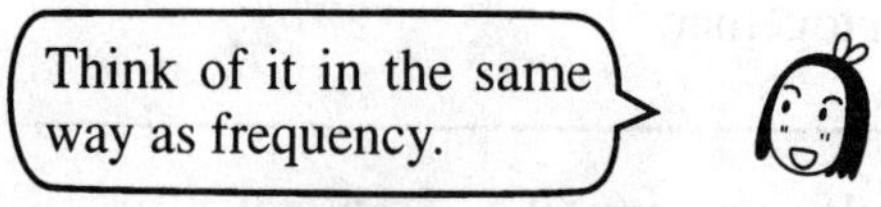

Applying it generally, we write $\boldsymbol{Q(n, \tau)}$.

Bohr's Thinking

Now I really want to find out what will happen to the intensity of the spectrum using Bohr's theory!

Come to think of it, in the "photon effect experiment," Einstein discovered that **if light is strong, that means there are many light particles; if it is weak, there are few light particles.**

One light particle is emitted for each transition that takes place, so that the number of light particles is related to the number of transitions.

So, if we put it all together, it looks like this, right?

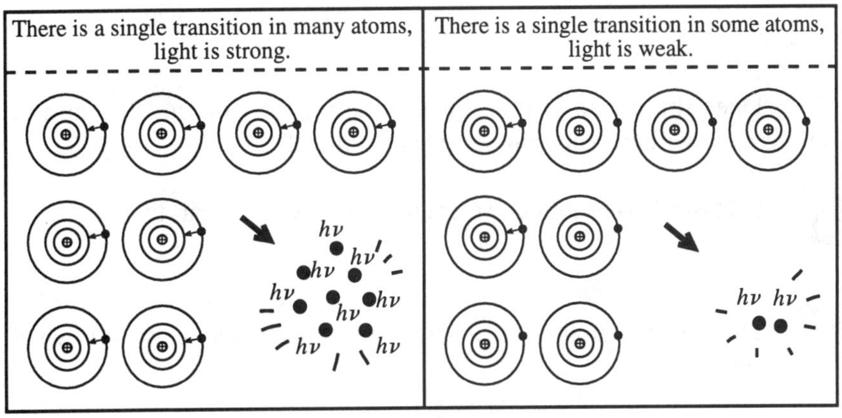

But the problem is that we don't have a clue why transitions take place. If we don't know why transitions take place, there's no way we can know the number of transitions.

In other words, we can't find spectral intensity!

Since there's nothing we can do about that, for the time being let's review the pros and cons of classical mechanics and Bohr's theory, and arrange them in an easy-to-understand table!

	frequency		intensity of light
	n is small	n is large	
classical mechanics	NO	OK	OK
Bohr's theory	OK	OK	NO

According to this table, when n is large spectral intensity can be found by classical theory as the square of the amplitude of simple waves. But since light isn't composed of waves, what in fact was being found was the number of light particles.

Does this mean that when n is large, we can find the number of transitions even without knowing what causes them?

Fantastic! We thought we couldn't, but we can, can't we?

That's right. Bohr's theory is able to find frequencies even when n is small.

In that case, if we take classical mechanics in a broader sense and apply Bohr's theory to it, then won't we be able to find frequencies, as well as spectral intensities, when n is small?

That's right. Let's try it!

Let's try it. Let's try it!

If it works, then we'd have a theory of mechanics that can explain the quantum — a quantum mechanics!

The following sign was posted in Bohr's research institute:

> **METHOD FOR CONSTRUCTING**
> **A NEW QUANTUM MECHANICS!**
>
> Using classical mechanics, we were able to find the number of transitions (spectral intensity) when n was big. By expanding classical mechanics and fiddling with it a bit, we look for a method of finding the number of transitions when n is small. This method is "quantum mechanics."

Upon seeing this sign, the young physicists in Bohr's institute were inspired to work night and day. One of them was Heisenberg. But his great discovery would not follow until later.

Since we're broadening classical mechanics, our new quantum mechanics should incorporate classical mechanics, not be completely separate from it.

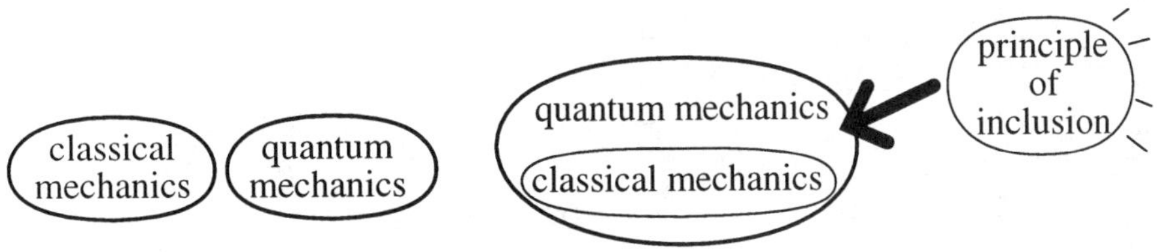

I love things like the principle of inclusion and it all looked pretty good to me. But I couldn't quite understand what it meant to make quantum mechanics by broadening classical mechanics. Then one day I ran across this sentence in a book that had absolutely nothing to do with quantum mechanics: "Although new ideas generally look new at first glance, they are in fact based on old things." I thought, "That's it!" If you think about it, everything's like that. New car models are based on old models. You can't just go and make something completely new with nothing behind it.

One reason for building the theory of quantum mechanics within the broad frame of classical mechanics is that we have to know how to use the classical mechanics paradigm to find the number of transitions when n is large. Otherwise we won't get anywhere. So, keeping this in mind, let's proceed!

3. 2 SOLVING HARMONIC OSCILLATION WITH CLASSICAL MECHANICS!

But if we use classical mechanics to find the number of transitions when n is large for the spectrum of the hydrogen atom, the calculations are very difficult. Instead, let's just try solving for simple harmonic oscillation.

But first, a word to those who are worried about doing this.

What is a simple harmonic oscillation?

Let's start with a spring, to which a weight is then attached. We pull it downwards in the direction of the arrows, let it go, and observe the way it bounces.

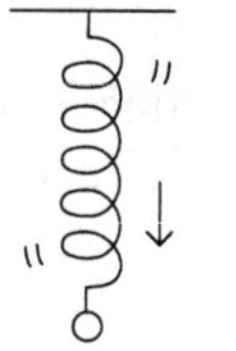

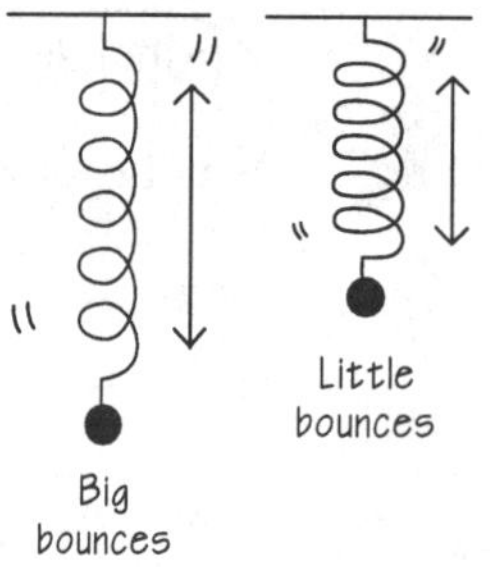

A spring can make big bounces or little bounces.

This is just like the way electrons in a hydrogen atom behave, rotating now in a small orbit, now in a large orbit.

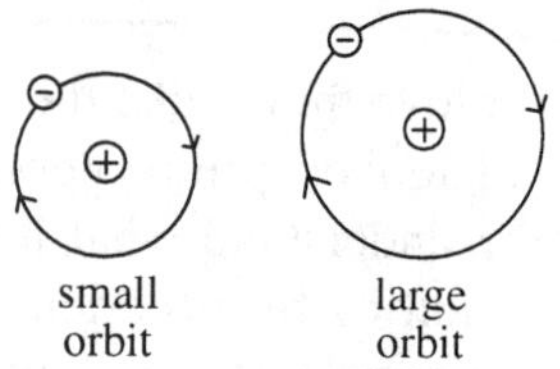

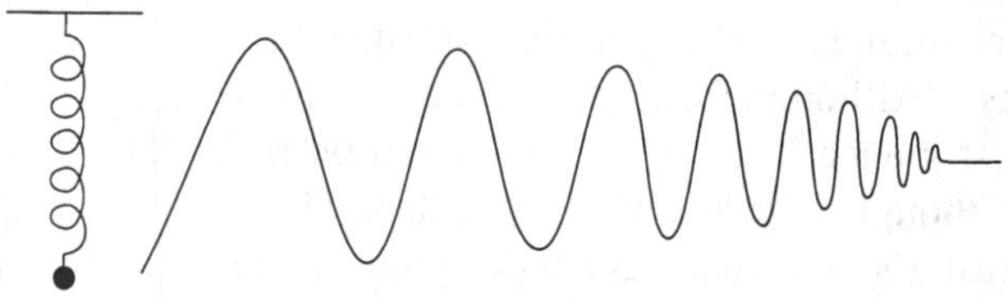

In a hydrogen atom, the electron's loss of energy and its subsequent transitions into smaller orbits correspond to the bounces of the spring as they gradually diminish in size.

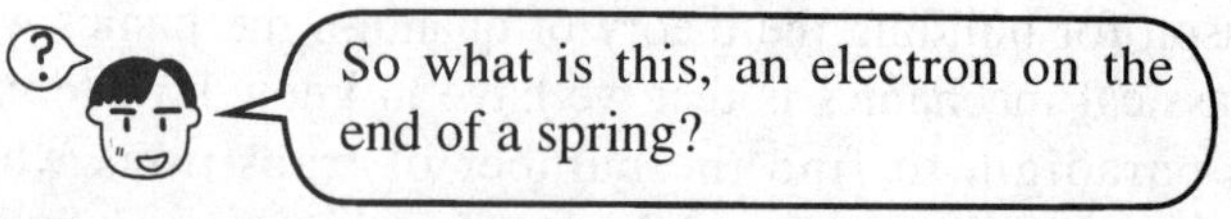

Well, it's actually not a spring. A force similar to the force of a spring is acting on the electron.

I see. So the hydrogen atom and harmonic oscillation act basically the same. The important thing is how things behave. In this case, harmonic oscillation is enough for us to illustrate how electrons in the hydrogen atom behave.

Let's get to our calculations!

You usually won't hear wild cheering when the word "calculation" comes up. Most people would think, "Yuk!" Even I don't like them much. But let me tell you something. The equations here are long and sometimes a pain, but not so difficult. When you can work through them, you feel great, like you're really smart. These equations are long, but once you've learned one the rest can be learned easily, because they have similar forms. Even if you skip over the calculations for the time being, I hope that you will try to grasp their general meaning. What we're doing now is very important.

In classical mechanics there is a very famous equation called **Newton's equation of motion.**

$$F = m\ddot{q}$$

Using this equation,

you can pinpoint where an object is, and when it is there.

The ability to get this information is the very core of classical mechanics.

F is the force that works on an object.
m is the mass (weight) of an object.
$\ddot{q}$ is the acceleration.

In most cases, the force that acts on the object is easily found, and using that information in the formula above, you can figure out the acceleration.

Acceleration is how an object changes its speed with respect to time. If we know the acceleration of something, then we can find its velocity, or speed.

Velocity is how an object changes its location. If we know this, we can find out where a given object is and when.

We know the acceleration $\ddot{q}$! → We know the velocity $\dot{q}$! → We know the position q!

Think about what happens when you pedal a bicycle.

If you push the pedals with tremendous force, what is the acceleration going to be?

It's high! You're making the F in $F = m\ddot{q}$ greater, so the acceleration $\ddot{q}$ should be high, too. Right?

Exactly so. If the acceleration is high it means that the speed of the bicycle rapidly increases; that's exactly what will happen if you try it on a bicycle. See for yourself! Now, try pedaling with the same force as before, but this time you've got a sumo wrestler sitting on the back. What's the acceleration in this case?

The mass m in $F = m\ddot{q}$ is much, much bigger, so the acceleration $\ddot{q}$ goes way down.

Bingo! Just one more. What happens when you take your feet off the pedals and the force is 0?

If the F in $F = m\ddot{q}$ is 0, then naturally the acceleration $\ddot{q}$ is also 0, so the bicycle doesn't move. Right?

Right. That's one answer, but there's another. When your bicycle is already rolling at a certain speed, what happens then if you take your feet off the pedals?

It keeps rolling at the same speed!

Exactly. You see how nicely we can describe the case of the bicycle using Newton's equation of motion. No matter what the object, if we know the force applied to it, we can find the acceleration from $F = m\ddot{q}$.

Oh, I see.

All right, now let's solve the problem of harmonic oscillation! When an electron is oscillating simply, we can find the m in $F = m\ddot{q}$ (the mass of the electron) from experiments. But what about force in the case of harmonic oscillation?

Let's see what happens when we pull on the spring! When we pull down on the spring, a force acting in the direction opposite to the direction of pulling tries to bring the spring back up. The more we pull, the greater that force becomes. The stiffer the spring, the greater that force is. Expressing this as an equation, we get

$$F = -kq$$

q is the position of the spring (or the position of the electron) measured from its position at rest. k is a constant that expresses the stiffness of the spring; the larger k is, the stiffer the spring. The minus sign means that the direction of the spring's force works opposite to the force pulling.

Now that we've found the force, let's substitute it in Newton's equation of motion $F = m\ddot{q}$.

$$-kq = m\ddot{q}$$

If we alter the equation slightly, it will be easier to use.

$$\boxed{\ddot{q} + \frac{k}{m}q = 0}$$

This is the equation of motion for harmonic oscillation. Next we will work out the equation to find the position q of the electron. This will tell us where the electron is and when it gets there.

Listen, wasn't it the number of electron transitions that we were trying to find?

Right. But that's the same thing as finding the position of the electron. According to Maxwell's electromagnetics, light waves are emitted in accordance with the movement of electrons. When the electrons make big oscillations, the light waves are big. When the oscillations are small, the waves are small. We're talking about amplitude, of course.

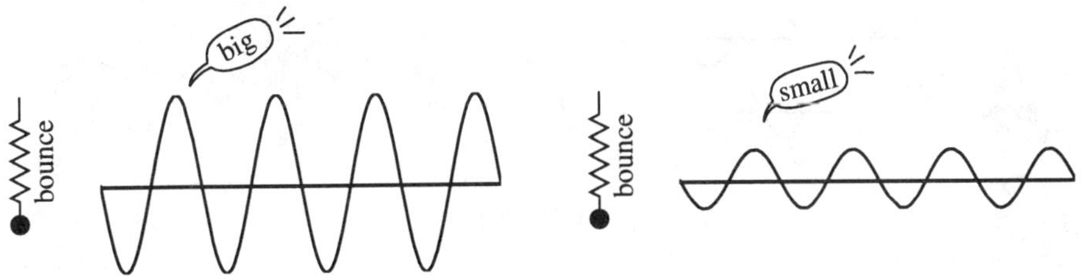

When the oscillations of the electron are rapid and narrowly-spaced, the light waves become narrow. When they oscillate slowly, the waves are widely-spaced. Here we're talking about frequency.

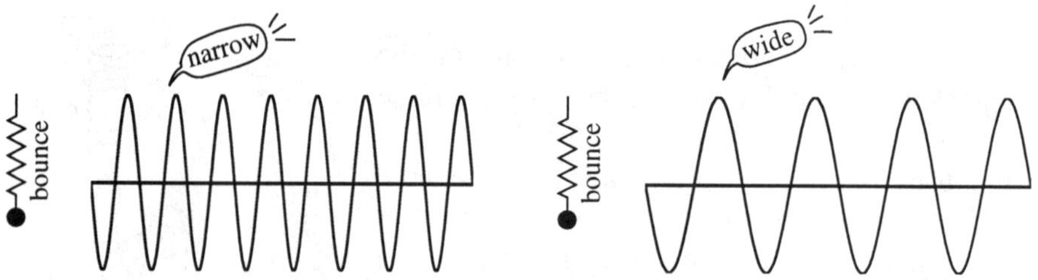

Therefore, if we know the position of the electron, then we also know about the light wave.

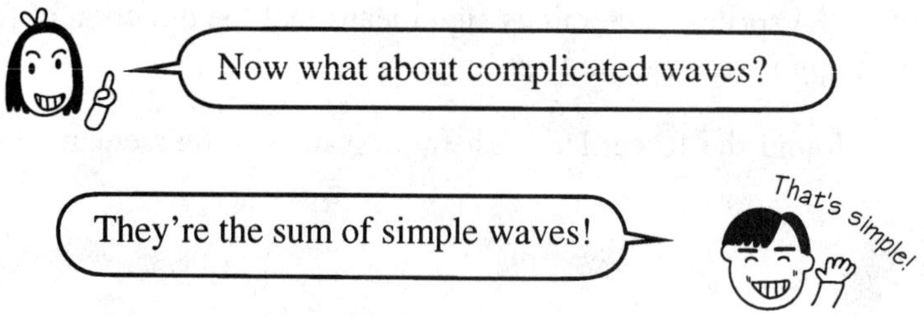

Yes! As we said before, we can express this using Fourier series.

So finding the position of the electron by solving the equation for motion,

ultimately means

finding the amplitude $Q(n, \tau)$ and the frequency $\nu(n, \tau)$ for each individual light wave. Now, when n is big, the square $|Q(n, \tau)|^2$ of the amplitude of the light wave is the number of electron transitions.

OK! Let's try the calculations! First, we determine the symbols for expressing simple waves.

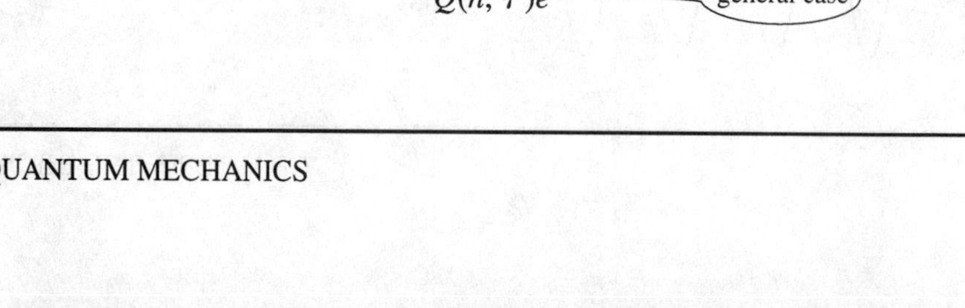

These equations look hard at first glance, but some of them are familiar.

here (amplitude) ↓ here (frequency) ↓

$$
\begin{array}{l}
\boxed{Q(n,1)}\, e^{i2\pi \boxed{\nu(n,1)}\, t} \\
\boxed{Q(n,2)}\, e^{i2\pi \boxed{\nu(n,2)}\, t} \\
\boxed{Q(n,3)}\, e^{i2\pi \boxed{\nu(n,3)}\, t} \\
\quad \vdots \\
\boxed{Q(n,\tau)}\, e^{i2\pi \boxed{\nu(n,\tau)}\, t}
\end{array}
$$

amplitude   frequency

$e^{i2\pi\Box t}$
Now this is a wave!

The remaining $e^{i2\pi\Box t}$ describes a simple wave.

A complicated wave is the sum of simple waves:

$$
\begin{aligned}
q = \cdots &+ Q(n,1)e^{i2\pi\nu(n,1)t} \\
&+ Q(n,2)e^{i2\pi\nu(n,2)t} \\
&+ Q(n,3)e^{i2\pi\nu(n,3)t} \quad \cdots
\end{aligned}
$$

complicated wave → q; simple waves → each term

It's a nuisance like this, so we write it with a Σ(summation).

The Equation For Complicated Light Waves

$$q = \sum_{\tau=-\infty}^{\infty} Q(n,\tau)e^{i2\pi\nu(n,\tau)t}$$

Imagine getting this equation in your repertoire and being able to reel it off whenever you wanted!

Finally, we enter the equation for complicated waves which describes the position of an electron

$$q = \sum_{\tau} Q(n,\tau)e^{i2\pi\nu(n,\tau)t}$$

into the equation of motion for harmonic oscillation

$$\ddot{q} + \frac{k}{m}q = 0$$

and start crunching away at the calculations!

There is something called $\ddot{q}$ in this equation. This is the second derivative of q with respect to time. First, let's see what happens to $\ddot{q}$.

For the derivative of e with respect to time, the exponents come down just as they are and stay that way.

So $e^{\triangle\square\bigcirc\diamond t}$ becomes $\triangle\square\bigcirc\diamond\, e^{\triangle\square\bigcirc\diamond t}$!

$$q=\sum_{\tau} Q(n,\tau)e^{i2\pi\nu(n,\tau)t}$$

first derivative with respect to time $\cdots$ $\dot{q}=\sum_{\tau} \underline{i2\pi\nu(n,\tau)}\,Q(n,\tau)e^{i2\pi\nu(n,\tau)t}$

second derivative with respect to time $\cdots$ $\ddot{q}=\sum_{\tau} \underline{\{i2\pi\nu(n,\tau)\}^2}\,Q(n,\tau)e^{i2\pi\nu(n,\tau)t}$

$$=\sum_{\tau} -4\pi^2\nu(n,\tau)^2Q(n,\tau)e^{i2\pi\nu(n,\tau)t}$$

Into the equation for the motion of harmonic oscillation,

$$\underline{\ddot{q}}+\frac{k}{m}\underline{q}=0$$

we insert $\ddot{q}$ and q:

$$\sum_{\tau} -4\pi^2\nu(n,\tau)^2Q(n,\tau)e^{i2\pi\nu(n,\tau)t}+\underline{\frac{k}{m}}\sum_{\tau} Q(n,\tau)e^{i2\pi\nu(n,\tau)t}=0.$$

Here, $\frac{k}{m}=(2\pi\nu)^2=4\pi^2\nu^2.$

m is the mass of the electron, and k is the spring constant. Both are fixed quantities already known from experiments. So, whether we use the expression

$$4\pi^2\nu^2=\frac{k}{m}$$

or express it in terms of ν as

$$\nu=\frac{1}{2\pi}\sqrt{\frac{k}{m}}$$

it ends up being the same thing.

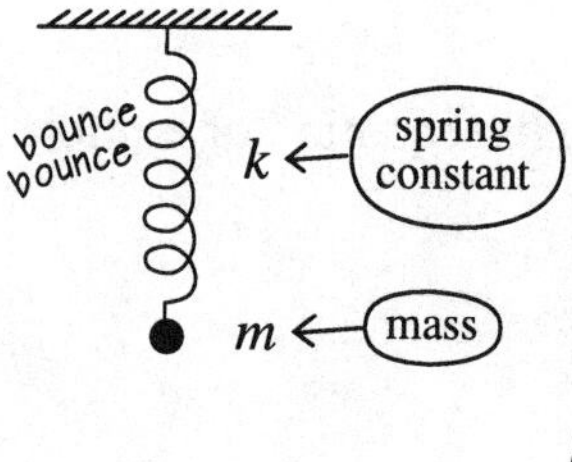

$$\underline{\sum_{\tau}} \underline{-4\pi^2}\,\nu(n,\tau)^2\underline{Q(n,\tau)e^{i2\pi\nu(n,\tau)t}}+\underline{4\pi^2}\,\nu^2\underline{\sum_{\tau}}\underline{Q(n,\tau)e^{i2\pi\nu(n,\tau)t}}=0$$

We've got a lot of identical terms, so let's clean this formula up!

$$\sum_{\tau} 4\pi^2\left\{\nu^2 - \nu(n, \tau)^2\right\}Q(n, \tau)e^{i2\pi\nu(n, \tau)t} = 0$$

Let's see what happens when this equation holds true, that is, when it equals 0.

In comparison to the equation for the sum of simple waves

$$q = \sum_{\tau} Q(n, \tau)e^{i2\pi\nu(n, \tau)t}$$

we get the amplitude:

$$4\pi^2\left\{\nu^2 - \nu(n, \tau)^2\right\}Q(n, \tau)\,.$$

Now we have an equation that is the sum of simple waves with this new amplitudes. What do we need for simple waves to add up to a complicated wave with a value of 0?

Well, I don't know.

Suppose we take, say, apples, tangerines and strawberries and try to make some juice with no flavor?

Don't use any of them!

That's right. The case of waves is the same; if you don't use anything, the value will be 0.

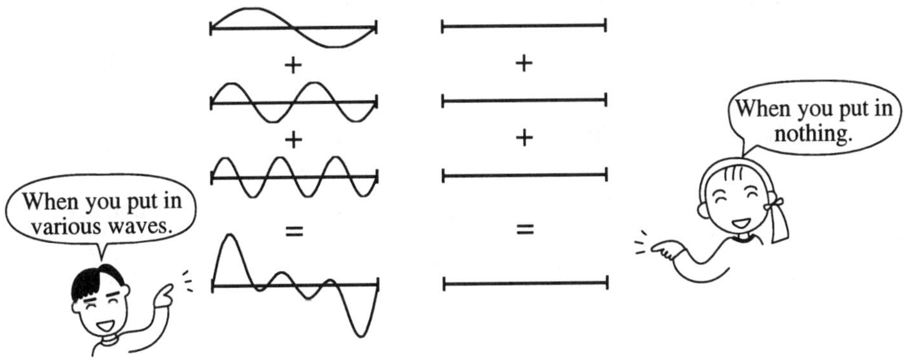

In the same way, as long as the respective amplitudes of simple waves

$$4\pi^2\left\{\nu^2 - \nu(n, \tau)^2\right\}Q(n, \tau)$$

end up as 0 for τ between $-\infty$ and ∞, the equation

$$\sum_{\tau} 4\pi^2\left\{\nu^2 - \nu(n, \tau)^2\right\}Q(n, \tau)e^{i2\pi\nu(n, \tau)t} = 0$$

holds true.

$$\underline{4\pi^2}\ \underline{\left\{\nu^2 - \nu(n, \tau)^2\right\}}\ \underline{Q(n, \tau)} = 0$$

$\hookrightarrow \neq 0$

The $4\pi^2$ in this equation absolutely cannot become 0, so either $\{\nu^2 - \nu(n, \tau)^2\}$ or $Q(n, \tau)$ must be 0.

So now let's first consider when $\{\nu^2 - \nu(n, \tau)^2\}$ equals 0!

The constant ν is determined by m and k. By comparison $\nu(n, \tau)$ is "The frequency of a simple wave that rotates in orbit n and has τ cycles per rotation."

So, its value can vary indefinitely depending on τ. That means for now we should stick to the case when $\tau = 1$, that is,

$$\nu(n, 1)^2 = \nu^2.$$

Apart from the fact that the frequency $\nu(n, \tau)$ is an integer multiple, nothing else is decided. Let's make some decisions now.

Now when τ is 1, the frequency $\nu(n, 1)$ becomes

$$\nu(n, 1) = \nu$$

so in this case the amplitude $Q(n, 1)$ has a value other than 0.

Since we decided that $\{\nu^2 - \nu(n, \tau)^2\}$ was 0 when $\tau = 1$, it will naturally *not* be 0 for the cases $\tau = 2, 3, 4$, and so on. Therefore, when $\tau = 2, 3, 4. . .$, the amplitude $Q(n, \tau)$ must always be 0.

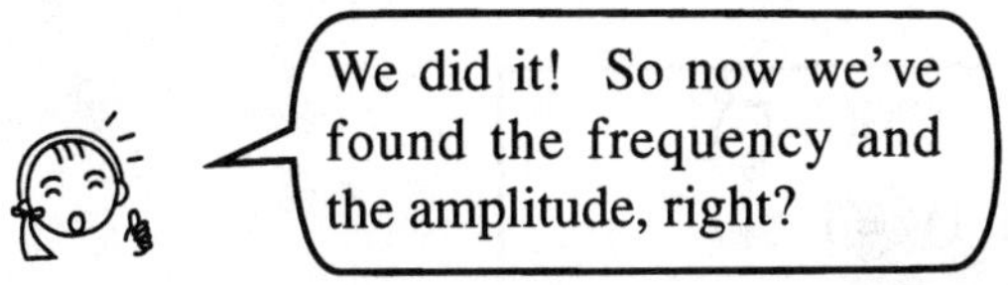

Before, we decided that $\nu(n, 1)^2 = \nu^2$. Clearly this will be true for $\nu(n, 1) = \nu$, but it also holds true for the case

$$-\nu(n, 1) = -\nu.$$

When this is squared, the result is the same $\nu(n, 1)^2 = \nu^2$ as above. Therefore, we must think about what

$$-\nu(n, 1)$$

might be.

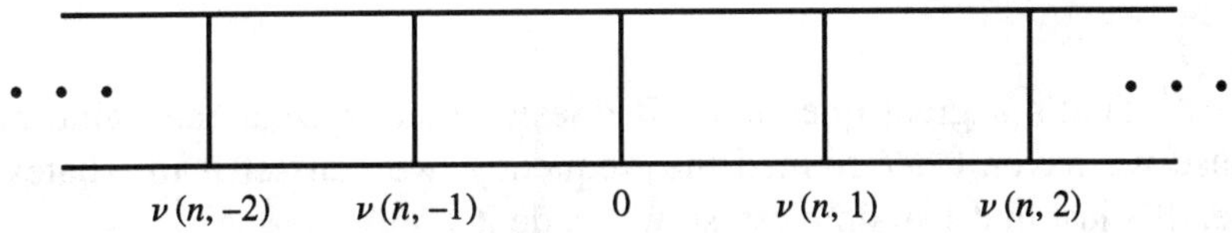

As we see from the chart, in classical mechanics the frequency $\nu(n, \tau)$ has values of integer multiples. Therefore,

> $\nu(n, \underline{2})$ is $\nu(n, 1)$ multiplied by $\underline{2}$,
> $\nu(n, \underline{3})$ is $\nu(n, 1)$ multiplied by $\underline{3}$, and so on.

It is the same when τ is negative, so

> $\nu(n, \underline{-1})$ is $\nu(n, 1)$ multiplied by $\underline{-1}$,
> $\nu(n, \underline{-2})$ is $\nu(n, 1)$ multiplied by $\underline{-2}$, and so on.

Therefore, $-\nu(n, 1)$ and $\nu(n, -1)$ are equivalent.

$$-\nu(n, 1) = \nu(n, -1).$$

Expressed generally,

$$-\nu(n, \tau) = \nu(n, -\tau).$$

We now know that when τ is 1 and also when it is −1, the amplitude $Q(n, \tau)$ has a value other than 0, and that for other values of τ, $Q(n, \tau)$ is 0.

SUMMARY

$\nu(n, 1) = \nu$
$\nu(n, -1) = -\nu$
$Q(n, 1) \neq 0$
$Q(n, -1) \neq 0$
$Q(n, \tau) = 0 \quad (\tau \neq \pm 1)$

I don't understand!!

What!? What don't you understand?

Just now we arbitrarily decided that when $\tau = 1$ then the equation $\{\nu^2 - \nu(n, \tau)^2\} = 0$ holds true. In that case, I guess we could just as well have set τ equal to 2 or 3 or anything else.

That's a great question! It doesn't matter what the value of τ is. Because we haven't determined the frequency, we can set it to whatever we please. It's just that 1 is simplest, so we made it 1.

Let $\{\nu^2 - \nu(n, \tau)^2\} = 0$ hold for $\tau = \pm 1$.

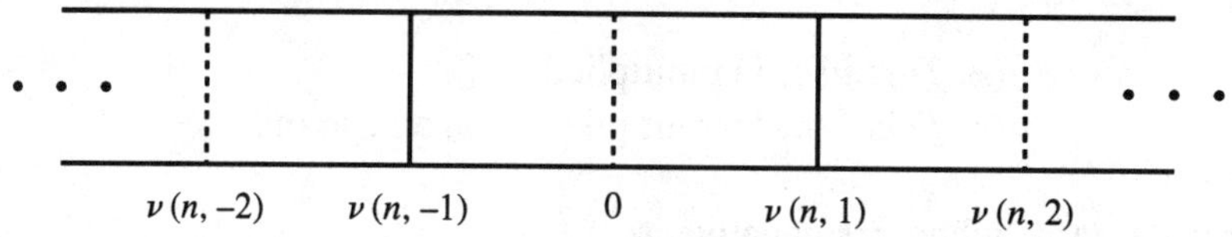

Then, when $\tau = 0, \pm 2, \pm 3$, as indicated by the dotted lines, the amplitudes $Q(n, \tau)$ all become 0.

Now let the equation $\{\nu^2 - \nu(n, \tau)^2\} = 0$ hold for $\tau = \pm 2$.

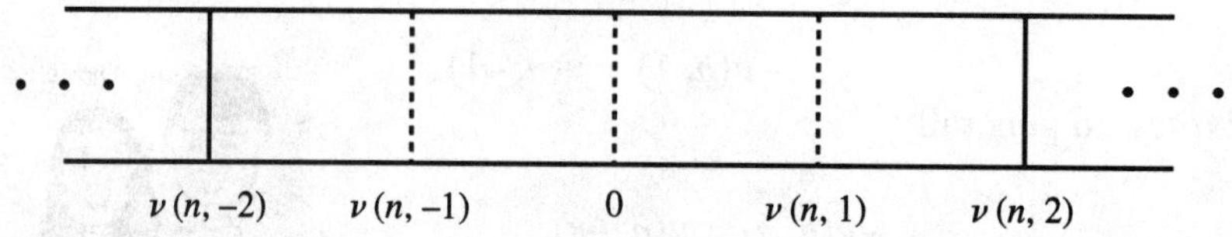

Doing so, the amplitudes for $\tau = 0, \pm 1, \pm 3 \ldots$ all become 0. Ultimately only two waves remain, and all other waves end up being 0. It's the same whether the two remaining waves are $\tau = \pm 1$ or $\tau = \pm 2$. The point is there's a "pair" of something.

Sure, I understand.

In that event, let's put the amplitude and the frequency that we found into the equation!

$$q = \sum_{\tau} Q(n, \tau) e^{i2\pi\nu(n, \tau)t}$$

We get:

$$q = Q(n, 1)e^{i2\pi\nu t} + Q(n, -1)e^{-i2\pi\nu t}$$

Point

This is the equation that describes the position of an electron at a given time!

Does this mean we've found the answer?

Yes. That's right.

Just now we found out that the amplitude $Q(n, \tau)$ can have a value, or be 0. But isn't it true that in fact we don't know "how much" its value is?

But that's all right.

For instance, if we pull a spring way down, it rebounds that much back, and if we pull a little, it rebounds just a little. So it's OK no matter what the value of the amplitude is.

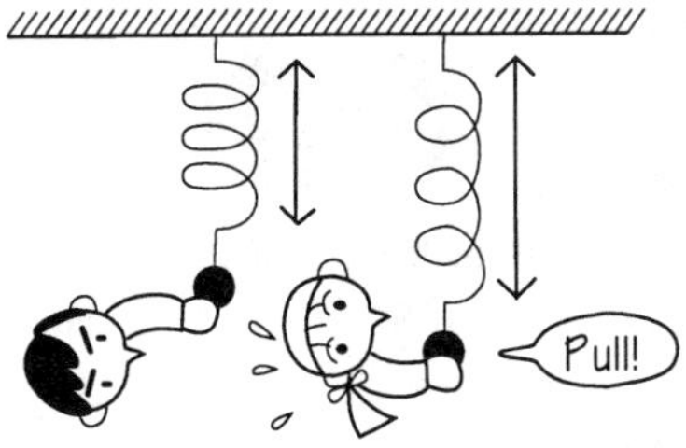

In the case of the hydrogen atom, when n is large, the amplitude of the light waves is large, and when n is small, the amplitude of the light waves is small.

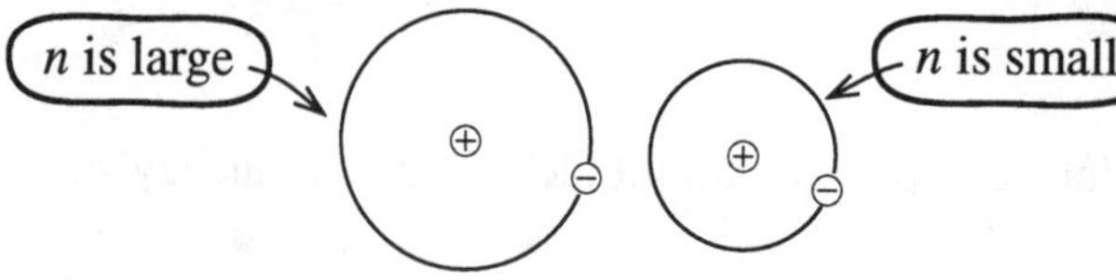

It is not necessary to actually find the value for amplitude. When we considered the correspondence principle, we placed classical mechanics in correspondence with Bohr's theory using n.

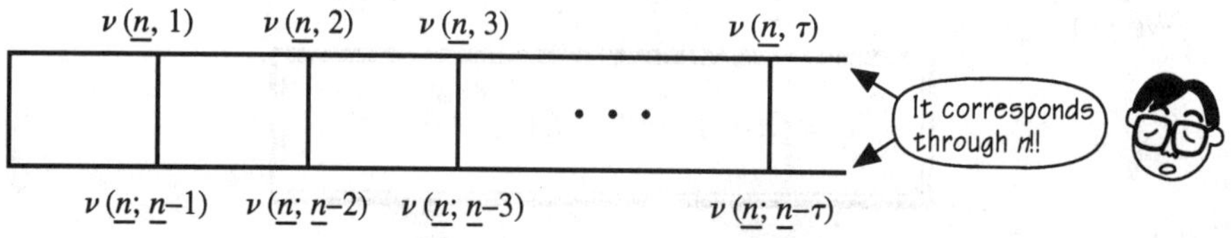

It seems, then, that classical mechanics is designed to determine the value of the amplitude for any given n. In other words, it expresses the amplitude as a function of n.

EXPRESSING AMPLITUDE AS A FUNCTION OF n

To do this, we use Bohr's quantum condition.

Bohr's Quantum Condition

$$\oint p\, dq = nh$$

This equation states that the orbits of an electron have values that are multiples of the integer h.

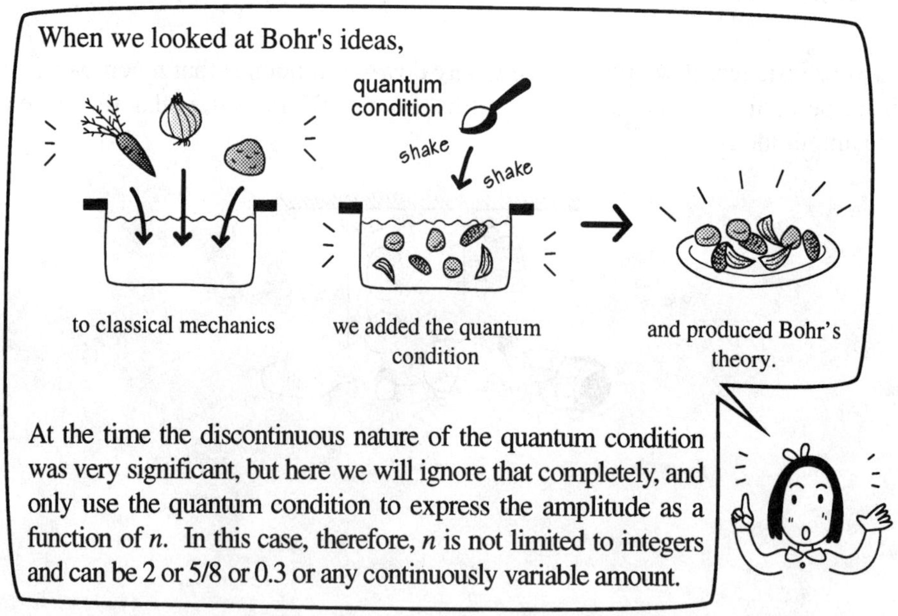

First, we modify the form of Bohr's equation.

$$\oint p\,dq = nh$$

- $\oint$ is a symbol for integration over one cycle and becomes $\int_0^{\frac{1}{\nu}}$.
- p is the momentum, and can be described as $p = m\dot{q}$.
- dq can be rewritten as $dq = \frac{dq}{dt}dt = \dot{q}dt$.

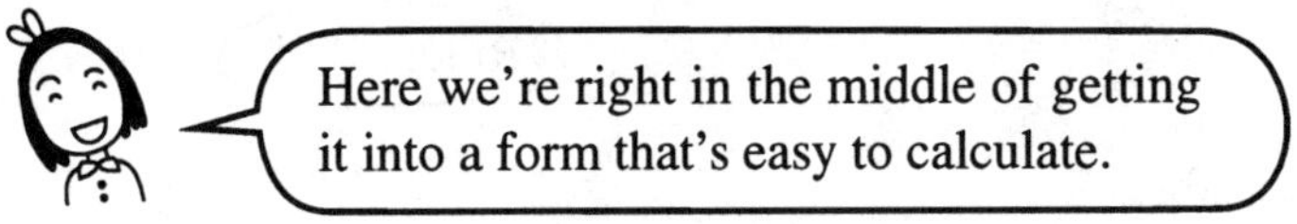

Applying these, Bohr's quantum condition formula changes.

$$\int_0^{\frac{1}{\nu}} m \cdot \underline{\dot{q} \cdot \dot{q}}\, dt = nh$$

$$\downarrow$$

$$(\dot{q})^2$$

For the q in this equation, we insert

$$q = Q(n, 1)e^{i2\pi\nu t} + Q(n, -1)e^{-i2\pi\nu t}$$

which we found by solving Newton's equation for motion.

First, the first derivative of q with respect to time.

$$\dot{q} = i2\pi\nu Q(n, 1)e^{i2\pi\nu t} - i2\pi\nu Q(n, -1)e^{-i2\pi\nu t}$$

We insert this in Bohr's equation.

$$\int_0^{\frac{1}{\nu}} m \cdot \underline{\left\{i2\pi\nu Q(n, 1)e^{i2\pi\nu t} - i2\pi\nu Q(n, -1)e^{-i2\pi\nu t}\right\}^2}\, dt = nh$$

The part inside the brackets is in the form of a square, so we can break it up using the formula $(A - B)^2 = A^2 + B^2 - 2AB$.

$$\int_0^{\frac{1}{\nu}} m \cdot \Big[\left\{i2\pi\nu Q(n, 1)e^{i2\pi\nu t}\right\}^2 + \left\{i2\pi\nu Q(n, -1)e^{-i2\pi\nu t}\right\}^2$$

$$- 2\left\{i2\pi\nu Q(n, 1)\underline{e^{i2\pi\nu t}}\right\}\left\{i2\pi\nu Q(n, -1)\underline{e^{-i2\pi\nu t}}\right\}\Big] dt = nh$$

For the multiplication of $e^{i2\pi\nu t}$ and $e^{-i2\pi\nu t}$ we use exponents according to the rule $e^a \times e^b = e^{a+b}$ and $i^2 = -1$:

$$\int_0^{\frac{1}{\nu}} m\Bigg[\left\{\underline{-4\pi^2\nu^2} Q(n,1)^2 e^{i4\pi\nu t}\right\} + \left\{\underline{-4\pi^2\nu^2} Q(n,-1)^2 e^{-i4\pi\nu t}\right\}$$

$$-2\left\{\underline{(-4)\pi^2\nu^2} Q(n,1)Q(n,-1)\,\underline{e^0}\right\}\Bigg]dt = nh$$

Rule: $e^0 = 1$

We factor out $-4\pi^2\nu^2$.

$$\int_0^{\frac{1}{\nu}} \underline{-4\pi^2\nu^2 m}\Big\{Q(n,1)^2 e^{i4\pi\nu t} + Q(n,-1)^2 e^{-i4\pi\nu t}$$

$$-2Q(n,1)Q(n,-1)\Big\}dt = nh$$

We take $-4\pi^2\nu^2 m$ out of the mdt, as it is unrelated to the integration.

$$-4\pi^2\nu^2 m\int_0^{\frac{1}{\nu}}\left\{\underline{Q(n,1)^2 e^{i4\pi\nu t}} + \underline{Q(n,-1)^2 e^{-i4\pi\nu t}} - \underline{2Q(n,1)Q(n,-1)}\right\}dt = nh$$

We split the integration.

$$-4\pi^2\nu^2 m\Bigg\{Q(n,1)^2\int_0^{\frac{1}{\nu}} \underline{e^{i4\pi\nu t}}\,dt + Q(n,-1)^2\int_0^{\frac{1}{\nu}} \underline{e^{-i4\pi\nu t}}\,dt$$

$$-2Q(n,1)Q(n,-1)\int_0^{\frac{1}{\nu}} \underline{1}\,dt\Bigg\} = nh$$

$e^{i4\pi\nu t}$ and $e^{-i4\pi\nu t}$ each represent a simple wave.

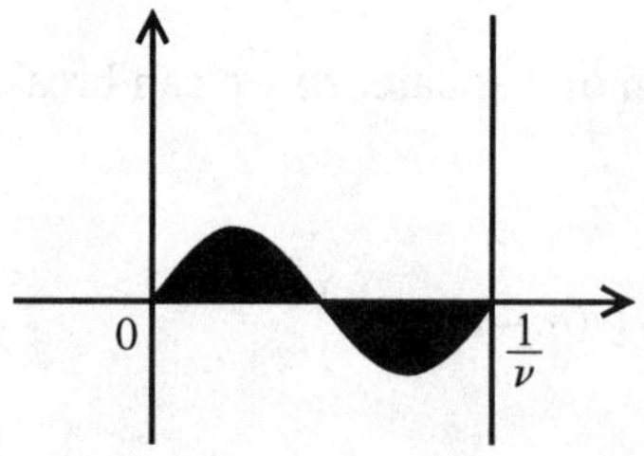

If we integrate a simple wave over one cycle the area is 0.

If we integrate for 1 from 0 to $\frac{1}{\nu}$

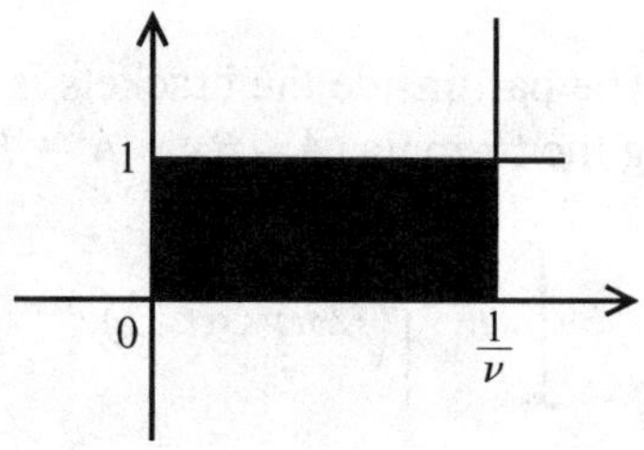

the area is $\frac{1}{\nu}$!

$$-4\pi^2\nu^{\cancel{2}}m\left\{0+0-2Q(n,1)Q(n,-1)\frac{1}{\cancel{\nu}}\right\} = nh$$

We remove the brackets.

$$8\pi^2\nu mQ(n,1)Q(n,-1) = nh$$

We divide both sides by $8\pi^2\nu m$.

$$Q(n,1)Q(n,-1) = \frac{h}{8\pi^2 m\nu}n$$

Oops! There's another tedious thing to take care of here.

You must be getting pretty fed up with calculations about now. I'm losing steam too. But I was thinking about the time when TCL's Heisenberg group was in training. The Heisenberg team had three brand-new first year students —Yuko, Pero, Ricky— a third year student (myself), senior students Hyon, Ban, Manatsu, and some others.

We started by letting people who knew a little about TCL's methods do the talking. Since I understood what we had done in previous years a little better than the first year students, I did a lot of talking at first. But even after doing the calculations once, twice, three times. . . they still didn't understand. Just as I was getting bored and sick of it all, wondering, "Will we ever get anywhere?" Hyon suddenly muttered something about music.

"Like Mr. D (a man at Hippo) said, you can't show someone how to sing exactly like the songs on the Hippo tapes. They have to do it themselves. Then anyone can learn how to sing." He remembered how much he admired Mr. D for his determination to do the same song over and over again, until he got it. That made me think. How happy I would be if someday Yuko or Pero could speak the language of mathematical formulae, because I had spoken it with them. I stopped caring how many times I had to explain or calculate. So, it helps to think of it as a song to learn. Sooner or later, you'll come to understand it.

Let's get back to our discussion.

$$\underline{Q(n,1)Q(n,-1)} = \frac{nh}{8\pi^2 m\nu}$$

↑

We were working on this part.

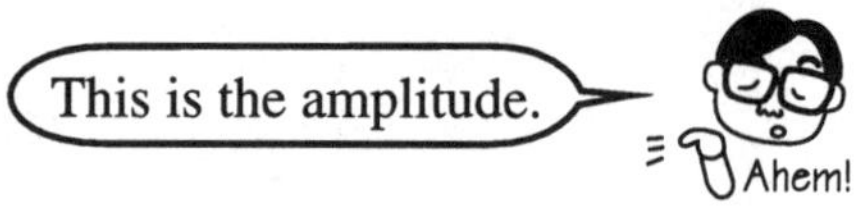

Let's look closely at this amplitude part!

real number → q ; complex number → $Q(n, \tau)\, e^{i2\pi\nu(n,\tau)t}$

$$\underline{q} = \sum_{\tau} \underline{Q(n,\tau)\, e^{i2\pi\nu(n,\tau)t}}$$

In this equation, q represents the position, it is a "real number" that can actually be observed. The amplitude $Q(n, \tau)$ is a "complex number" that cannot be observed. A complex number is a real number plus an imaginary number. Imaginary numbers exist only in the world of mathematics. They are used to make our calculations more manageable.

Given that amplitude is a complex number, let's see what the nature of the amplitude is.

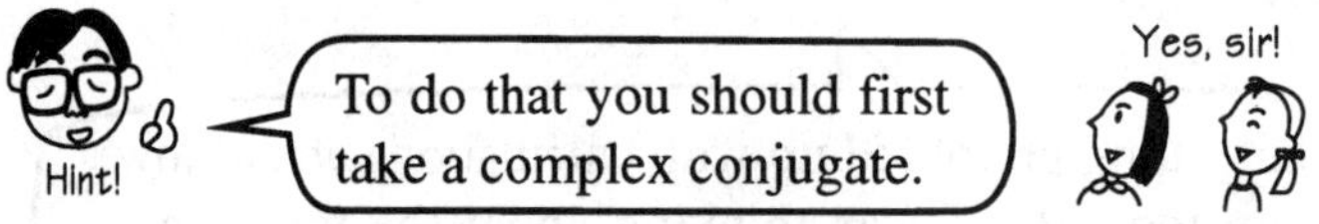

You get a **complex conjugate** when you change the symbol in front of an imaginary number. That symbol is written as * (star). Real numbers contain no imaginary numbers, so even if we take a complex conjugate, the original number does not change.

Quiz Corner

OK, which are real numbers and which are not!

1) How about $2^* = 2$?

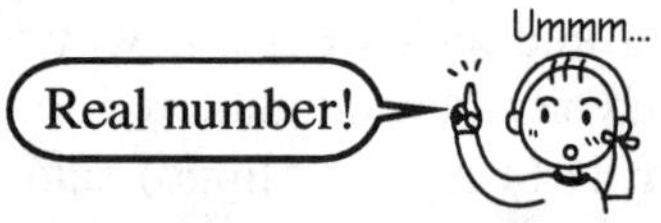

2) How about $5\,i^* = -5\,i$?

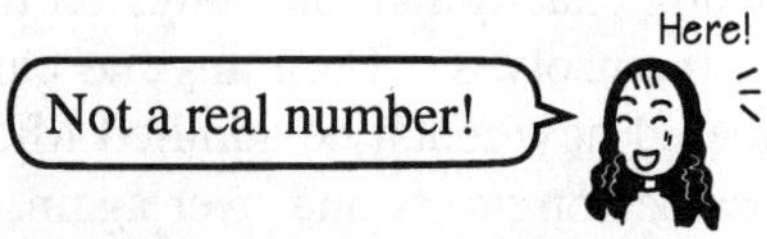

3) How about $(1 + 3i)^* = 1 - 3i$?

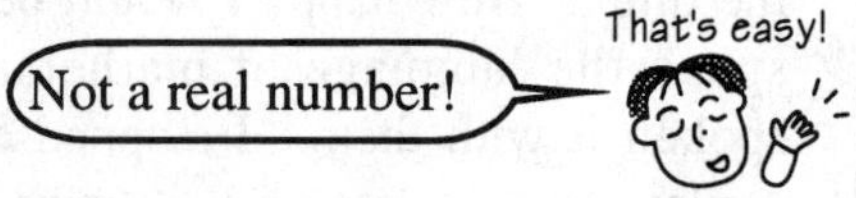

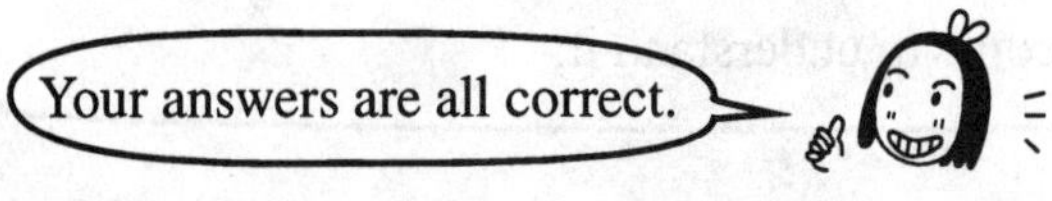

Now q is a real number, so we should get $q^* = q$. If this is the case, let's see what the nature of the amplitude is!

It'll be easier to understand if we write out Σ.

$$
\begin{aligned}
q = \cdots & Q(n,-1)e^{i2\pi\nu(n,-1)t} \\
&+ Q(n,0)e^{i2\pi\nu(n,0)t} \\
&+ Q(n,1)e^{i2\pi\nu(n,1)t} \cdots
\end{aligned}
$$

Now we take the complex conjugate.

$$
\begin{aligned}
q^* = \cdots & Q(n,-1)^* e^{-i2\pi\nu(n,-1)t} \\
&+ Q(n,0)^* e^{-i2\pi\nu(n,0)t} \\
&+ Q(n,1)^* e^{-i2\pi\nu(n,1)t} \cdots
\end{aligned}
$$

Since $-\nu(n,\tau) = \nu(n,-\tau)$,

$$
\begin{aligned}
q^* = \cdots & Q(n,-1)^* e^{i2\pi\nu(n,1)t} \\
&+ Q(n,0)^* e^{i2\pi\nu(n,0)t} \\
&+ Q(n,1)^* e^{i2\pi\nu(n,-1)t} \cdots
\end{aligned}
$$

We change the order.

$$
\begin{aligned}
q^* = \cdots & Q(n,1)^* e^{i2\pi\nu(n,-1)t} \\
&+ Q(n,0)^* e^{i2\pi\nu(n,0)t} \\
&+ Q(n,-1)^* e^{i2\pi\nu(n,1)t} \cdots
\end{aligned}
$$

In order to compare q and q^*, we should match up the frequencies of the simple waves.

$$
\begin{aligned}
q^* = \cdots & Q(n,1)^* e^{i2\pi\nu(n,-1)t} \\
&+ Q(n,0)^* e^{i2\pi\nu(n,0)t} \\
&+ Q(n,-1)^* e^{i2\pi\nu(n,1)t} \cdots
\end{aligned}
\qquad
\begin{aligned}
q = \cdots & Q(n,-1)e^{i2\pi\nu(n,-1)t} \\
&+ Q(n,0)e^{i2\pi\nu(n,0)t} \\
&+ Q(n,1)e^{i2\pi\nu(n,1)t} \cdots
\end{aligned}
$$

Because each of these has to be equivalent, the parts for the amplitude must be like this:

$$
\begin{aligned}
Q(n,1)^* &= Q(n,-1) \\
Q(n,0)^* &= Q(n,0) \\
Q(n,-1)^* &= Q(n,1)
\end{aligned}
$$

As a general expression, we have:

$$Q(n, \tau)^* = Q(n, -\tau).$$

Let's go back to the beginning! From the above, we now know that

$$Q(n, 1)Q(n, -1) = Q(n, 1)Q(n, 1)^*$$

so

$$Q(n, 1)Q(n, -1) = \frac{h}{8\pi^2 m\nu} n$$

becomes

$$Q(n, 1)Q(n, 1)^* = \frac{h}{8\pi^2 m\nu} n.$$

Now it happens that a given complex number multiplied by its complex conjugate is the square of its absolute value.

(complex number) · (complex number)* = |complex number|²

Therefore,

$$Q(n, 1)Q(n, 1)^* = \frac{h}{8\pi^2 m\nu} n$$

becomes

Point

$$\left|Q(n, 1)\right|^2 = \frac{h}{8\pi^2 m\nu} n.$$

This is what we get when we express the amplitude $Q(n, \tau)$ of harmonic oscillation as a function of n!

3. 3 BUILDING QUANTUM THEORY

RADICAL BREAKTHROUGH

OK everybody. You must be tired; thanks for your patience! From here on it's quantum mechanics! The time has come for Heisenberg to take center stage.

Heisenberg was one of the young people who, originally in association with Bohr, had been moving toward a theory of quantum mechanics. He had labored day after day, trying to find the spectral intensity of light. One day, unable to cope with a bad case of hay fever, he received two weeks leave from Professor Born, and went to Helgoland to recuperate.

Heisenberg was trying to find a method which could determine the spectral intensity, i.e., "$h\nu$, the number of transitions multiplied by the energy of a single light particle" even when n was small.

♦REGARDING THE CORRESPONDENCE WITH CLASSICAL MECHANICS

So far, when n was large, we were able to find the spectral intensity using classical mechanics.

The theory of classical mechanics made the mistake of treating light as waves. Even so, physics could use that theory to find the intensity of spectra when n was large. What that means is that the broadening of classical mechanics like so:

Newton's Equation of Motion + Bohr's Quantum Condition	
$\ddot{q} + \frac{k}{m} q = 0$	$\oint p\, dq = nh$

was correct.

The Classical Method

We take the equation that expresses the position of the electron in complicated waves,

$$q = \sum_{\tau} Q(n, \tau) e^{i2\pi\nu(n,\tau)t}$$

insert it in the equation of motion for harmonic oscillation,

$$\ddot{q} + \frac{k}{m} q = 0$$

and solve. In order to express the amplitude as a function of n, we place it in Bohr's formula for the quantum condition

$$\oint p\, dq = nh$$

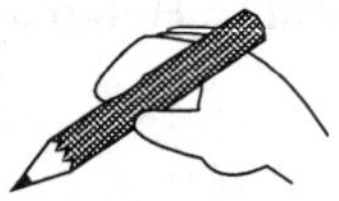

and solve.

We have found the spectral intensity.

Now we can rewrite the part of classical mechanics that says "light is composed of waves" to say "light is composed of particles that have energy $h\nu$."

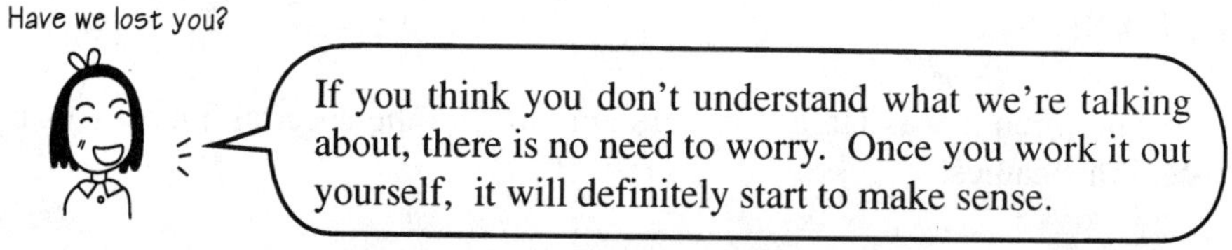

Let's start by considering the frequency of light. It was necessary to think of light as being emitted by electrons, not as they spun around, but as they underwent transition from one orbit to another.

At this point, "the frequency $\nu(n, \tau)$ of light emitted by a simple wave at τ cycles when an electron is in orbit n" must be rewritten in quantum mechanics as "the frequency $\nu(n; n-\tau)$ of the light emitted when there is a transition from orbit n to orbit $n-\tau$."

classical mechanics	rewrite →	quantum mechanics
$\nu(n, \tau)$		$\nu(n; n-\tau)$

Next, let's consider the amplitude of light!

In classical mechanics, the spectral intensity of a light wave was the square of the amplitude $Q(n, \tau)$. However, Einstein's discoveries indicated that the spectral intensity was really "$h\nu$, the number of transitions multiplied by the energy of a single light particle."

So let's take $\sqrt{\text{number of transitions} \times h\nu}$ and write it as $Q(n; n-\tau)$ and put this in place of the amplitude $Q(n, \tau)$ of classical mechanics. We have absolutely no idea what the "the root of the number of transitions multiplied by $h\nu$" actually is, but it is certain that it has a correspondence to $Q(n, \tau)$, "the root of the spectral intensity."

classical mechanics	rewrite →	quantum mechanics
$Q(n, \tau)$		$Q(n; n-\tau)$

Now, in classical mechanics a simple light wave of τ cycles (the Fourier component) was described as

$$\underline{Q(n, \tau)e^{i2\pi\nu(n, \tau)t}}$$

$Q(n, \tau)$ is equivalent to $Q(n; n-\tau)$ in quantum mechanics, and
$\nu(n, \tau)$ is equivalent to $\nu(n; n-\tau)$ in quantum mechanics.

So in quantum mechanics this simple wave becomes

$$\underline{Q(n; n-\tau)e^{i2\pi\nu(n; n-\tau)t}}$$

From now on we will call this the "transitional component."

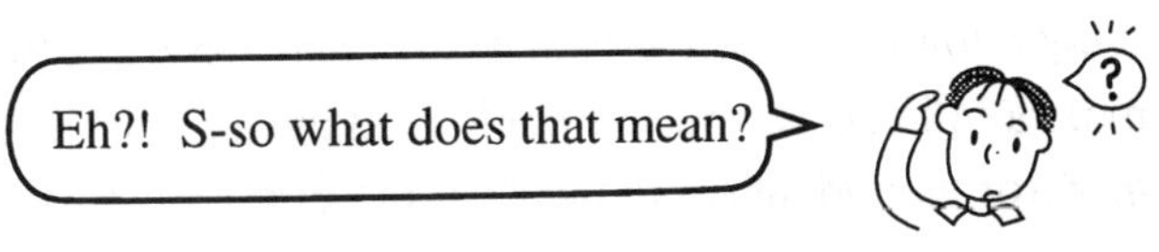

It doesn't make much sense, does it. But this is what happens when we follow Einstein's and Bohr's theories and replace "waves" with "quanta."

Again, in classical mechanics . . .

What about a complicated wave?

It's the summation of simple waves!

We see that Fourier's theory is valid here, so we can proceed to a summation of the above simple waves:

$$q = \sum_{\tau} Q(n, \tau)e^{i2\pi\nu(n, \tau)t} .$$

Similarly, in quantum mechanics this is

$$q = \sum_{\tau} Q(n; n - \tau)e^{i2\pi\nu(n; n-\tau)t} .$$

Say, w-what could that possibly mean?

It sure is hard.

In the case of classical mechanics, q for complicated light waves described how the electron changed position with time. That was because it was thought that the electron gave off light as it rotated.

Yes, but you know a quantum doesn't give off light as it rotates, it gives off light as it undergoes transition from one orbit to another.

Right. When an electron undergoes transition, we don't know what path it takes!! What that means is that the q of the quantum, which is the summation of the transition components, does not "describe" the position of the electrons.

My gosh—so q doesn't describe the position of the electron, right?

Coming this far with classical mechanics, we could insert

$$q = \sum_{\tau} Q(n, \tau)e^{i2\pi\nu(n, \tau)t}$$

into Newton's equation of motion $F = m\ddot{q}$. Now if we used Bohr's quantum condition formula a little at the end, we could find the amplitude $Q(n, \tau)$ and the frequency $\nu(n, \tau)$ for individual simple waves (the Fourier component).

OK, in the case of quantum mechanics, also, we take

$$q = \sum_{\tau} Q(n; n-\tau) e^{i2\pi\nu(n; n-\tau)t}$$

and put it in Newton's equation of motion $F = m\ddot{q}$. . . .

Hey! Hey! Wait a second!!

What?

The q in $F = m\ddot{q}$ expressed position, didn't it? That's why we were able to insert the q of classical mechanics. But what happens in the case of a quantum?

Then q is not "position"!

The change over time of the position q is expressed as $\dot{q}$ (first derivative with respect to time), and represents velocity; the change in velocity over time is expressed as $\ddot{q}$ (second derivative with respect to time), and represents acceleration. Further, acceleration times mass is force. If it all went like that, it would be easy.

But in the case of quanta, since we don't know what the position q is, we also don't know its change over time $\dot{q}$. Still less do we know $\ddot{q}$, the change in $\dot{q}$ over time. Even if we multiply such a thing by its mass, it's not likely to be equal to the force F.

I suppose we can't use Newton's equation of motion, $F = m\ddot{q}$ when we're dealing with quantum mechanics.

Yes, that's strange.

After all, putting a q that doesn't express position into $F = m\ddot{q}$ goes against common sense, doesn't it?

We're in a fix.

You know, in the end it's no good. Building something like a quantum mechanics seems impossible.

That's right. Starting with Bohr, many people struggled with it, and it still didn't work. It can't be solved that easily.

Maybe we should give up. . .

But Heisenberg was tough.

He was able to . . .

Force a Radical Breakthrough!!??

That's right. It may seem strange, but the equation

$$q = \sum_{\tau} Q(n; n-\tau) e^{i2\pi\nu(n; n-\tau)t}$$

turns out to be the same thing as the equation

$$q = \sum_{\tau} Q(n, \tau) e^{i2\pi\nu(n, \tau)t}$$

of classical mechanics when n is large. The reason is that when n is large, $Q(n; n-\tau)$ and $\nu(n; n-\tau)$ have the same values as $Q(n, \tau)$ and $\nu(n, \tau)$.

Because light is composed of quanta, q does not actually describe the "position" of a thing, even when n is large. In spite of this, $F = m\ddot{q}$ gave a correct answer. Maybe it will also work when n is small.

We can't tell without trying!

That is how Heisenberg boldly put q into $F = m\ddot{q}$ and continued his calculations.

I was thinking. If Heisenberg had not gotten sick and had not gone to Helgoland and forced his "great radical breakthrough," would Bohr have been able to complete his quantum theory? I wavered, sometimes thinking, "Hey it's Bohr; he could have done it!" and sometimes, "Bohr—no way!" I concluded that it would have been too much for Bohr after all. Bohr was older than Heisenberg, and he knew that much more physics. For that very reason he probably would have demurred at trying to force such a radical breakthrough—putting something that wasn't a "position" into an equation describing position. Heisenberg could do it because he was young and "naive." I love Heisenberg for daring to ignore conventional knowledge!

SOLVING HARMONIC OSCILLATION USING QUANTUM MECHANICS

Let's get going on our calculations!

Just as before when we used classical mechanics, we will proceed here by solving the equation of motion for harmonic oscillation.

The equation of motion for harmonic oscillation went like this:

$$\ddot{q} + \frac{k}{m} q = 0.$$

We insert $q = \sum_{\tau} Q(n; n-\tau) e^{i2\pi\nu(n;n-\tau)t}$ into this equation.

First, we calculate $\ddot{q}$.

Let's try taking the derivatives piece by piece, just like we did with classical mechanics!

first derivative with respect to time $\cdots \dot{q} = \sum_{\tau} i2\pi\nu(n; n-\tau) Q(n; n-\tau) e^{i2\pi\nu(n; n-\tau)t}$

second derivative with respect to time $\cdots \ddot{q} = \sum_{\tau} (i2\pi)^2 \nu(n; n-\tau)^2 Q(n; n-\tau) e^{i2\pi\nu(n; n-\tau)t}$

$$= \sum_{\tau} -4\pi^2 \nu(n; n-\tau)^2 Q(n; n-\tau) e^{i2\pi\nu(n; n-\tau)t}$$

We then insert $\ddot{q}$ and q in the equation of motion for harmonic oscillation.

$$\ddot{q} + \frac{k}{m} q = 0$$

$$\sum_{\tau} -4\pi^2 \nu(n; n-\tau)^2 Q(n; n-\tau) e^{i2\pi\nu(n; n-\tau)t} + \frac{k}{m} \sum_{\tau} Q(n; n-\tau) e^{i2\pi\nu(n; n-\tau)t} = 0$$

Here we let $\frac{k}{m} = (2\pi\nu)^2 = 4\pi^2\nu^2$.

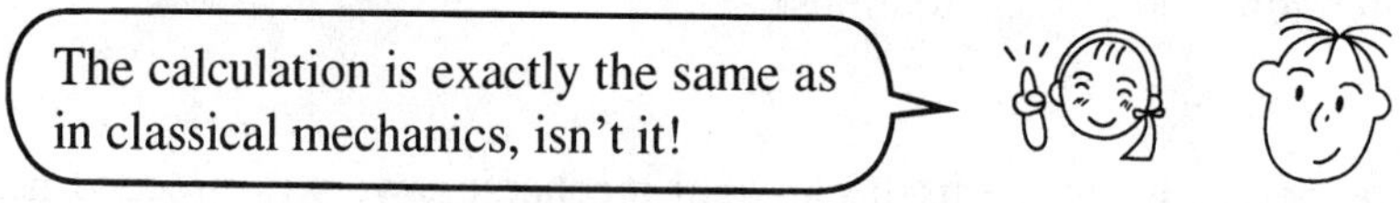

$$\sum_{\tau} -4\pi^2 \nu(n; n-\tau)^2 Q(n; n-\tau) e^{i2\pi\nu(n; n-\tau)t} + 4\pi^2\nu^2 \sum_{\tau} Q(n; n-\tau) e^{i2\pi\nu(n; n-\tau)t} = 0$$

There are a lot of redundancies, so let's clean up the equation!

$$\sum_{\tau} 4\pi^2 \left\{ \nu^2 - \nu(n; n-\tau)^2 \right\} Q(n; n-\tau) e^{i2\pi\nu(n; n-\tau)t} = 0$$

Now consider the requirements for this equation to hold true for 0.

In order for this equation to hold true for classical mechanics (as the summation of simple waves with new amplitudes), the new amplitudes for each respective simple wave have to equal 0.

In quantum mechanics, light is not considered to be a wave. But superficially, at least, the equation has the same form as the equation above, for the summation of simple waves. Thus for this equation to hold true, the new amplitude of each new "wave" must be 0.

$$\underline{4\pi^2}\ \underline{\left\{\nu^2 - \nu(n; n-\tau)^2\right\}}\ \underline{Q(n; n-\tau)} = 0$$

$$\hookrightarrow \neq 0$$

Because $4\pi^2$ can never be 0, either $\{\nu^2 - \nu(n; n-\tau)^2\}$ or $Q(n; n-\tau)$ must be equal to 0.

Just as we did with classical mechanics, we decide that $\{\nu^2 - \nu(n; n-\tau)^2\}$ is 0 when τ is 1.

$$\nu^2 - \nu(n; n-1)^2 = 0$$

From this we know that

$$\nu(n; n-1) = \nu$$

and so we know in turn that here the amplitude $Q(n; n-1)$ has a value other than 0. Similarly, when $\tau = 2, 3, 4\cdots$, then $\{\nu^2 - \nu(n; n-\tau)^2\}$ doesn't become 0, so in that case $Q(n; n-\tau)$ must be 0.

With this we've found half the answer. But just as with classical mechanics, the equation also holds for one more case: when $-\nu(n; n-1) = -\nu$. Therefore, we must consider what will happen to the equation

$$-\nu(n; n-1)\,.$$

If we use the same approach as in classical mechanics, the equation becomes $\nu(n; n+1)$.

Frequencies in classical mechanics had the property of being integer multiples, right?

But in quantum mechanics, as a glance at the spectra will show, the frequencies are not integer multiples. So it would be wrong to use the same approach as in classical mechanics.

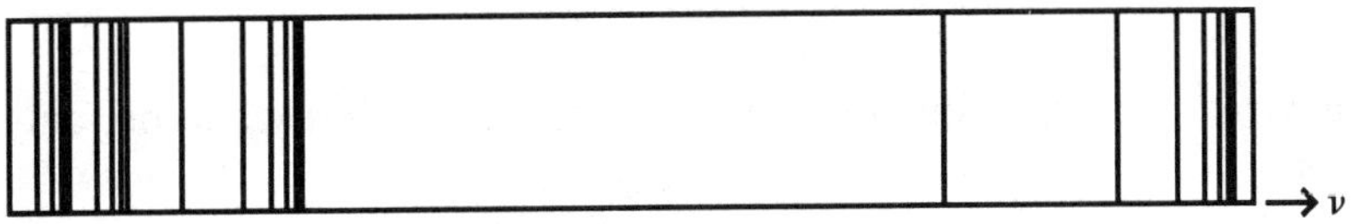

So in quantum mechanics, what should we do with the minus signs on the frequencies?

There is an equation that gives the correct frequencies for quantum mechanics. This is Rydberg's equation

$$\nu = \frac{Rc}{m^2} - \frac{Rc}{n^2}\,.$$

Maybe this will tell us something.

That's a good idea! Let's take a look.

Rydberg's equation, according to Bohr, gives the frequency when there is a transition from orbit n to orbit m. If we express this with the symbols we are currently using, then when there is a transition from n to $n - \tau$, the frequency $\nu(n; n - \tau)$ is

$$\nu(n; n - \tau) = \frac{Rc}{(n - \tau)^2} - \frac{Rc}{n^2}$$

Let's see what happens to $-\nu(n; n - \tau)$ in this equation!

$$-\nu(n; n - \tau) = -\left\{\frac{Rc}{(n - \tau)^2} - \frac{Rc}{n^2}\right\} = \frac{Rc}{n^2} - \frac{Rc}{(n - \tau)^2}$$

Compared to Rydberg's original equation, we have $\nu(n - \tau; n)$, that is, the frequency when there is a transition from $n - \tau$ to n. In the case of quantum mechanics, a minus sign on the frequency means that a reverse transition is occurring.

$$-\nu(n; n - \tau) = \nu(n - \tau; n)$$

Therefore, with $-\nu(n; n - 1)$, we get

$$-\nu(n; n - 1) = \nu(n - 1; n)$$

I see! Have you noticed what we're doing? We are exploiting its correspondence with classical theory to work out the theory of quantum mechanics, but we are not just imitating it. We just suppress the parts that don't fit in quantum mechanics.

At any rate, we have found the answer. For harmonic oscillation, only the two cases

amplitude $Q(n; n - 1)$ for a transition from n to $n - 1$
amplitude $Q(n - 1; n)$ for a transition from $n - 1$ to n

have a value. We have found that for all other cases the amplitude must be 0.

In addition,

the frequency $\nu(n; n-1)$ for a transition from n to $n-1$ is ν
the frequency $\nu(n-1; n)$ for a transition from $n-1$ to n is $-\nu$

There is a special condition that applies only in the case of harmonic oscillation. The frequency of harmonic oscillation $\nu(n; n-1) = \nu$ behaves like this:

$$\left.\begin{array}{l}\nu(5;4)\\ \nu(4;3)\\ \nu(3;2)\end{array}\right\} = \nu$$

Thus, when there is a transition one orbit inward, regardless of what n is, the frequency is always ν. Similarly, for $\nu(n-1; n) = -\nu$,

$$\left.\begin{array}{l}\nu(4;5)\\ \nu(3;4)\\ \nu(2;3)\end{array}\right\} = -\nu$$

When there is a transition one orbit outward, regardless of what n is, the frequency is always $-\nu$.

So whether we write $(n-1; n)$ or $(n; n+1)$, it amounts to the same thing.

SUMMARY

$Q(n; n-1) \neq 0$

$Q(n; n+1) \neq 0$

$Q(n; n-\tau) = 0 \quad (\tau \neq \pm 1)$

$\nu(n; n-1) = \nu$

$\nu(n; n+1) = -\nu$

EXPRESSING AMPLITUDE $Q\ (n; n - \tau)$ AS A FUNCTION OF n IN QUANTUM MECHANICS

As in the case of classical mechanics, we solved Newton's equation of motion to find when the amplitude $Q(n; n - \tau)$ has a value other than 0. Now we use Bohr's quantum condition $\oint p\, dq = nh$ and express the amplitude as a function of n. If we can do this, we will be able to find concrete values for the frequencies of any and all transitions.

Bohr's Quantum Condition Corner

Say, why are you bringing up the quantum condition now?

What's wrong with that?

We don't need it if we're trying to build a theory of quantum mechanics, right?

Well, in Bohr's case,

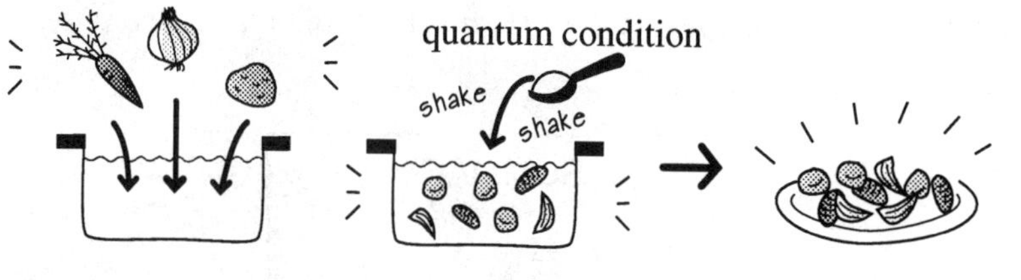

to classical mechanics — we add the quantum condition — and produce quantum mechanics!

the quantum condition was something that you added later.

The only reason we said that the n in the quantum condition $\oint p\, dq = nh$ was an integer in the first place was because that could explain the experimental results. There wasn't any other good reason.

Hmm

But Heisenberg isn't simply taking a theory and adding the concept of "jumping" to it after the fact. He is trying to build quantum mechanics by studying the components of classical mechanics, one by one.

Yeah. Heisenberg is trying to rewrite the parts of classical mechanics that say "light is composed of waves" to say "light is composed of quanta."

In that case, we shouldn't need to add any quantum condition after the fact, right?

What? We don't really understand.

All right, let's explain it in a bit more detail! First of all, in classical mechanics τ expresses the number of times a complicated wave undulates during one cycle. It follows that τ can only be an integer.

Now the τ in quantum mechanics was taken directly from the τ in classical mechanics, so it remained an integer.

Next, in the case of quantum mechanics, n takes the form $n - \tau$.

As an example, let's assume that n is 5. Because τ is an integer, the next orbit is $5 - 1 = 4$, and the next after that is $5 - 2 = 3$. In this manner, n is always an integer.

Understand?

No!

???

In other words, in quantum mechanics, if we say that τ is an integer, then it naturally follows that n is an integer. We know this even without resorting to the quantum condition ($n = 0, 1, 2, 3, \cdots$)

In that case, if we don't need the quantum condition any more, why is it appearing again?

Remember earlier we said that classical mechanics and quantum mechanics correspond through "n".

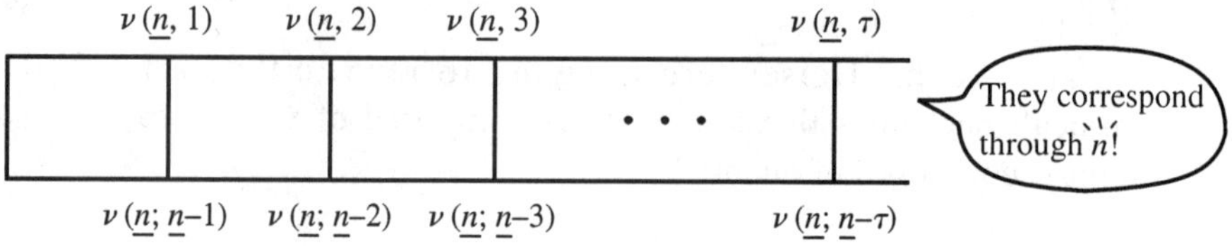

If we want to develop quantum mechanics theory by rewriting classical mechanics, it is necessary to specify the value of n, whether we're talking about frequency or amplitude. For example, in classical mechanics when n is 3 and τ is 2, then the amplitude is $Q(3, 2)$. In quantum mechanics this becomes $Q(3; 3 - 2)$.

n is not an arbitrary number; it is determined according to the series $n = 1, 2, 3 \cdots$ and has a definite meaning. That's why we have to use this formula.

Somehow I feel like I understand.

In fact, Heisenberg rewrote the quantum condition in the following manner to make it suitable for its new use:

$$\sum_{\tau} P(n; n-\tau)Q(n-\tau\,; n) - \sum_{\tau} Q(n; n+\tau)P(n+\tau\,; n) = \frac{h}{2\pi i}$$

What? All of a sudden I don't understand anything!

That's all right. This calculation is too much trouble. When we put the q of quantum mechanics into Bohr's equation, it's also a bit of a bother, and so we won't use it. But please remember that this equation is actually necessary!

OK. Got it.

All right, now let's do the calculations!

Just as in classical mechanics, we use a modified form of Bohr's quantum condition.

$$\int_0^{\frac{1}{\nu}} m \cdot (\dot{q})^2 \, dt = nh$$

In quantum mechanics, q took this form:

$$q = \sum_{\tau} Q(n; n-\tau) e^{i2\pi\nu(n; n-\tau)t} .$$

We next insert the amplitude and frequency that we found for simple waves.

$$q = Q(n; n-1)e^{i2\pi\nu t} + Q(n; n+1)e^{-i2\pi\nu t}$$

Remember, this doesn't represent the position of the electron, as in classical theory!

The first derivative with respect to time:

$$\dot{q} = i2\pi\nu Q(n; n-1)e^{i2\pi\nu t} - i2\pi\nu Q(n; n+1)e^{-i2\pi\nu t} .$$

We place this into our earlier equation $\int_0^{\frac{1}{\nu}} m \cdot (\dot{q})^2 \, dt = nh.$

$$\int_0^{\frac{1}{\nu}} m \underline{\left\{ i2\pi\nu Q(n; n-1)e^{i2\pi\nu t} - i2\pi\nu Q(n; n+1)e^{-i2\pi\nu t} \right\}^2} dt = nh$$

Because the figure in the brackets is a square, we use the formula $(A-B)^2 = A^2 + B^2 - 2AB$ to break it down.

$$\int_0^{\frac{1}{\nu}} m \left\{ \underline{-4\pi^2\nu^2} Q(n; n-1)^2 e^{i4\pi\nu t} + \underline{\left(-4\pi^2\nu^2\right)} Q(n; n+1)^2 e^{-i4\pi\nu t} \right.$$

$$\left. + 2\underline{\left(-4\pi^2\nu^2\right)} Q(n; n-1) Q(n; n+1) e^0 \right\} dt = nh$$

We factor out $-4\pi^2\nu^2$.

$$\int_0^{\frac{1}{\nu}} \underline{-4\pi^2 m\nu^2} \Big\{ Q(n;\, n-1)^2 e^{i4\pi\nu t} + Q(n;\, n+1)^2 e^{-i4\pi\nu t} - 2Q(n;\, n-1)Q(n;\, n+1) \Big\} dt = nh$$

We put $-4\pi^2 m\nu^2$ outside the integration.

$$-4\pi^2 m\nu^2 \int_0^{\frac{1}{\nu}} \Big\{ \underline{Q(n;\, n-1)^2 e^{i4\pi\nu t}} + \underline{Q(n;\, n+1)^2 e^{-i4\pi\nu t}} \underline{- 2Q(n;\, n-1)Q(n;\, n+1)} \Big\} dt = nh$$

Then we do the integration.

$$-4\pi^2 m\nu^2 \Big\{ Q(n;\, n-1)^2 \int_0^{\frac{1}{\nu}} \underline{e^{i4\pi\nu t}}\, dt + Q(n;\, n+1)^2 \int_0^{\frac{1}{\nu}} \underline{e^{-i4\pi\nu t}}\, dt - 2Q(n;\, n-1)Q(n;\, n+1) \int_0^{\frac{1}{\nu}} \underline{1}\, dt \Big\} = nh$$

$e^{i4\pi\nu t}$ and $e^{-i4\pi\nu t}$ each represent a simple wave. If we integrate this, the area is 0.

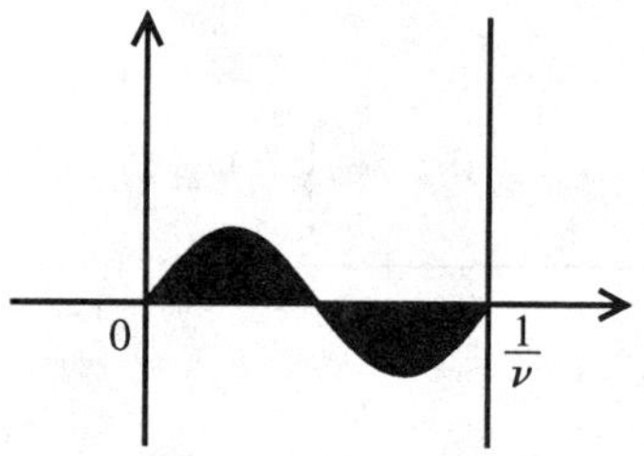

If we integrate for 1 from 0 to $\frac{1}{\nu}$ the area is $\frac{1}{\nu}$.

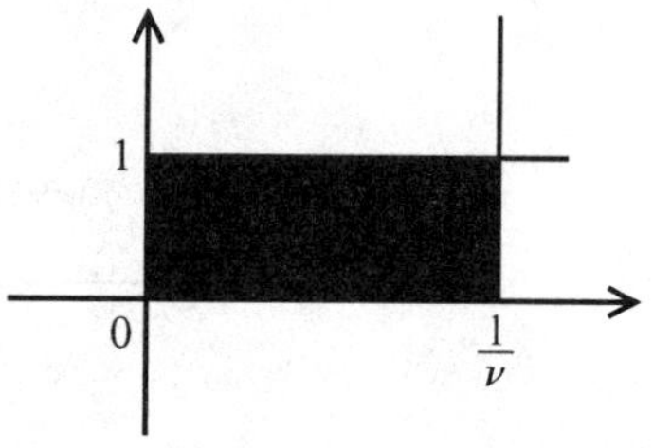

$$-4\pi^2 m\nu^2 \Big\{ 0 + 0 - 2Q(n;\, n-1)Q(n;\, n+1)\frac{1}{\nu} \Big\} = nh$$

We remove the brackets.

$$8\pi^2 m\nu\, Q(n;\, n-1)Q(n;\, n+1) = nh$$

We divide both sides by $8\pi^2 m\nu$.

$$\underline{Q(n;\, n-1)Q(n;\, n+1)} = \frac{h}{8\pi^2 m\nu}\, n$$

Now if we write $Q(n;\, n-1)\; Q(n;\, n+1)$ in its generalized form, we get $Q(n;\, n-1)\; Q(n-1;\, n)$, but we have to think about what this means.

In classical mechanics, from the property $\{Q(n,\, \tau)^* = Q(n,\, -\tau)\}$ of the amplitude, $Q(n,\, \tau)\; Q(n,\, -\tau)$ became $|Q(n,\, \tau)|^2$. In quantum mechanics, can we also just say that $Q(n;\, n+\tau) = Q(n;\, n-\tau)^*$?

For the frequency, the $\nu(n,\, -\tau) = -\nu(n,\, \tau)$ of classical mechanics has to be thought of as the reverse transition $\nu(n-\tau;\, n) = -\nu(n;\, n-\tau)$ in quantum mechanics. Following this, we now take the property of amplitude in classical mechanics $\{Q(n,\, 1)^* = Q(n,\, -1)\}$ and rewrite it for quantum mechanics as a reverse transition.

$$Q(n;\, n-\tau)^* = Q(n-\tau;\, n)$$

We then get $Q(n;\, n+1) = Q(n-1;\, n) = Q(n;\, n-1)^*$, and then

$$Q(n;\, n-1)Q(n;\, n+1) = \left| Q(n;\, n-1) \right|^2.$$

Finally, we get

$$\boxed{\left| Q(n;\, n-1) \right|^2 = \frac{h}{8\pi^2 m\nu}\, n.}$$

Now, when we compare this to the experimental values. . .Wow! A perfect match!!

Wait a second!

The amplitude of harmonic oscillation found with classical mechanics	The amplitude of harmonic oscillation found with quantum mechanics
$\left\| Q(n, \tau) \right\|^2 = \frac{h}{8\pi^2 m\nu} n$	$\left\| Q(n; n-\tau) \right\|^2 = \frac{h}{8\pi^2 m\nu} n$

Why are classical mechanics and quantum mechanics the same? Nothing's changed. At this rate I don't see how we've gotten anywhere with quantum mechanics!

For those of you who feel this way:

Actually, we ended up with this result because using simple waves was too simplistic. For those who are still unsatisfied, you should tackle a problem that's a bit more complicated, such as that of an anharmonic oscillator. In fact, it was by solving the problem of an anharmonic oscillator that Heisenberg discovered quantum mechanics.

In the case of an anharmonic oscillator, the force that acts on the electron is described as

$$\underline{F = -kq - \lambda q^2}.$$

Compared to the force $F = -kq$ in harmonic oscillation, there is an extra term $-\lambda q^2$, which expresses a more complicated oscillation.

If we place $F = -kq - \lambda q^2$ in Newton's equation of motion, we produce the equation of motion for an anharmonic oscillator:

$$m\ddot{q} + kq + \lambda q^2 = 0.$$

If we can solve this, we should be OK.

As in the case of harmonic oscillation, all we need to do is insert

$$\underline{q = \sum_{\tau} Q(n; n-\tau) e^{i2\pi\nu(n; n-\tau)t}}$$

in the equation and complete the calculation. But there is a q^2 (a square) that was not present in the case of harmonic oscillation. We must think about how to calculate this in quantum mechanics.

At this point, let's consider how to perform multiplication in quantum mechanics.

MULTIPLICATION IN QUANTUM MECHANICS

First, what happens to multiplication in classical mechanics?

For now, let's assume that x and y both take the form of an aggregate of simple waves.

$$x = \sum_{\tau} X(n, \tau) e^{i2\pi\nu(n, \tau)t}$$
$$y = \sum_{\tau} Y(n, \tau) e^{i2\pi\nu(n, \tau)t}$$

If we multiply x and y. . .

$$xy = \sum_{\tau} X(n, \tau) e^{i2\pi\nu(n, \tau)t} \cdot \sum_{\tau} Y(n, \tau) e^{i2\pi\nu(n, \tau)t}$$

Because Σ expresses a sum, we can proceed in the same way as below:

$$\underline{(a_1 + a_2) \cdot (b_1 + b_2)} = a_1(b_1 + b_2) + a_2(b_1 + b_2)$$
$$= \underline{a_1 b_1 + a_1 b_2 + a_2 b_1 + a_2 b_2}$$

(multiplication of sums) (addition of products)

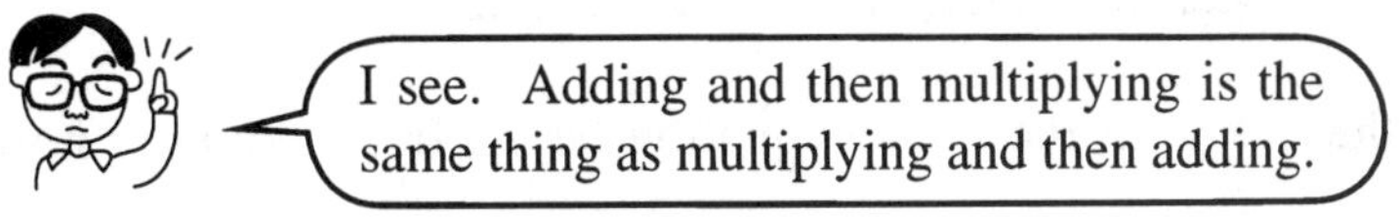

$$xy = \sum_{\tau}\sum_{\tau'} X(n, \tau) e^{i2\pi\nu(n, \tau)t} \cdot Y(n, \tau') e^{i2\pi\nu(n, \tau')t}$$

To multiply the e's we add the exponents, like here:

$$xy = \sum_{\tau}\sum_{\tau'} X(n, \tau) Y(n, \tau') e^{i2\pi\nu(n, \tau)t + i2\pi\nu(n, \tau')t}$$
$$= \sum_{\tau}\sum_{\tau'} X(n, \tau) Y(n, \tau') e^{i2\pi\left\{\underline{\nu(n, \tau) + \nu(n, \tau')}\right\}t}$$

Now let's see what happens to the exponent of e, that is $\nu(n, \tau) + \nu(n, \tau')$. In classical mechanics, the frequency of light is an integer multiple.

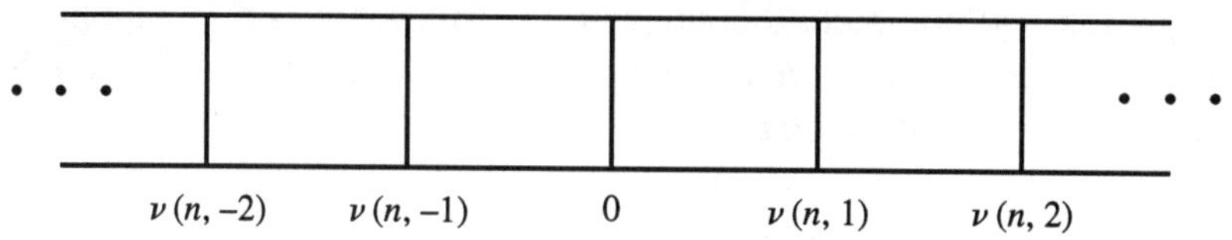

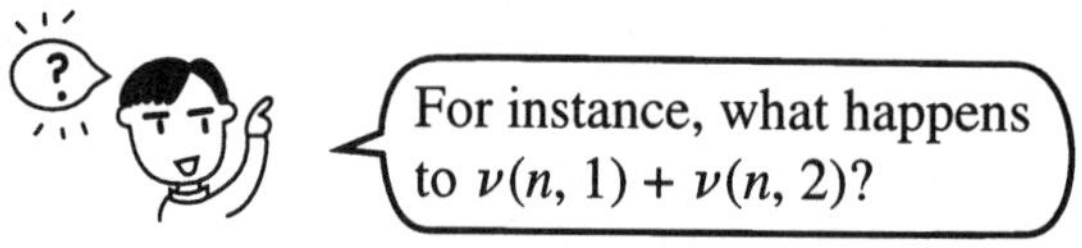

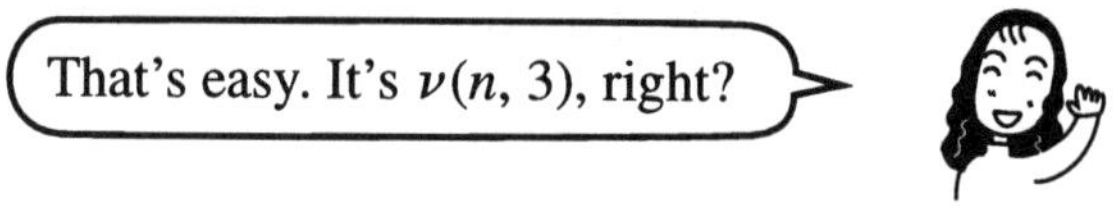

Right. All we do is add 1 + 2. To generalize, we add $\tau + \tau'$.

$$\nu(n, \tau) + \nu(n, \tau') = \nu(n, \tau + \tau')$$

Now xy becomes

$$xy = \sum_{\tau} \sum_{\tau'} X(n, \tau) Y(n, \tau') e^{i2\pi\nu(n, \tau + \tau')t}$$

Now let's refine it a little.

Both τ and τ' in $\nu(n, \tau + \tau')$ include all of the integers between $-\infty$ and ∞. It is natural, therefore, that sometimes $\tau + \tau'$ has the same value as τ.

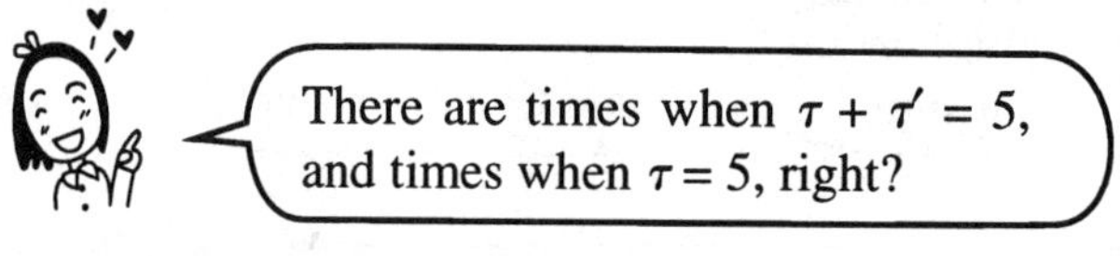

We now let the $\tau + \tau'$ in the above equation be τ. In so doing, τ now becomes $\tau - \tau'$.

The Rule for Multiplication in Classical Mechanics

$$xy = \sum_{\tau} \sum_{\tau'} X(n, \tau - \tau') \, Y(n, \tau') e^{i2\pi\nu(n, \tau)t}$$

Actually, there is a very basic reason for these refinements. If we look at our original x and y

$$x = \sum_{\tau} X(n, \tau) e^{i2\pi \underline{\nu(n, \tau)t}}$$

$$y = \sum_{\tau} Y(n, \tau) e^{i2\pi \underline{\nu(n, \tau)t}}$$

Lo and behold, the frequencies are the same for both x, y and xy.

> **Here's The Point!**
>
> In classical mechanics, you do not get different frequencies even if you multiply!

Let's keep this in mind as we think about the rule for multiplication in quantum mechanics!

$$x = \sum_{\tau} X(n; n-\tau) e^{i2\pi\nu(n; n-\tau)t}$$
$$y = \sum_{\tau} Y(n; n-\tau) e^{i2\pi\nu(n; n-\tau)t}$$

Let's multiply these.

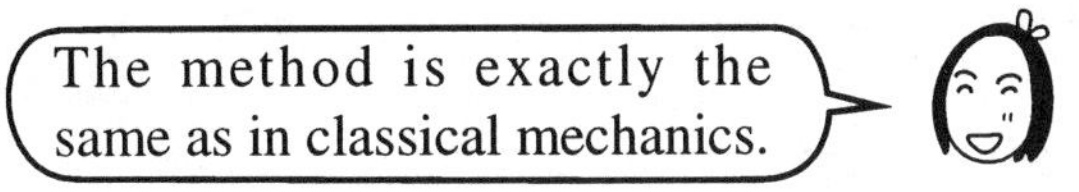

$$\begin{aligned} xy &= \sum_{\tau} X(n; n-\tau) e^{i2\pi\nu(n; n-\tau)t} \cdot \sum_{\tau'} Y(n; n-\tau') e^{i2\pi\nu(n; n-\tau')t} \\ &= \sum_{\tau}\sum_{\tau'} X(n; n-\tau) e^{i2\pi\nu(n; n-\tau)t} \cdot Y(n; n-\tau') e^{i2\pi\nu(n; n-\tau')t} \\ &= \sum_{\tau}\sum_{\tau'} X(n; n-\tau) Y(n; n-\tau') e^{i2\pi \underline{\left\{\nu(n; n-\tau) + \nu(n; n-\tau')\right\} t}} \end{aligned}$$

Now let's consider what happens to the exponent of e, $\nu(n; n-\tau) + \nu(n; n-\tau')$.

As we have said many times, frequencies in quantum mechanics are not integer multiples. Simply adding them, as we would in classical mechanics

$$\nu(n; n-\tau) + \nu(n; n-\tau') = \nu(n; n-\tau-\tau')$$

does not work. If we proceed via classical mechanics methods, the frequencies of the variables that have been multiplied will end up being different from the frequencies before multiplication.

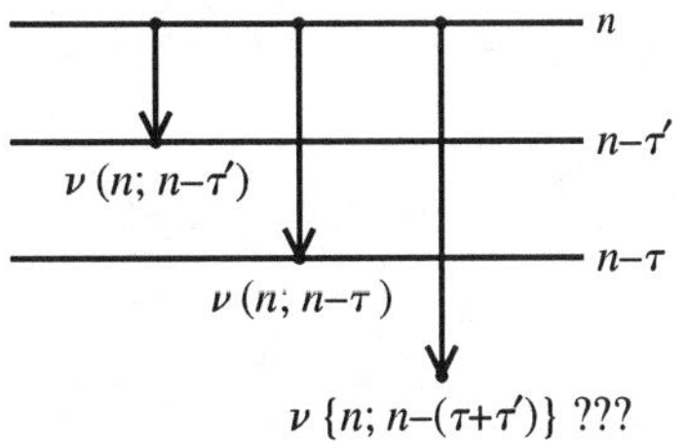

In classical mechanics, the frequencies remain the same even when we multiply. This will become very important as we continue our calculations. In quantum mechanics we want to be able to perform basically the same calculations as in classical mechanics, so we need to establish a rule for multiplication that does not yield different frequencies after multiplication.

$$xy = \sum_{\tau} \sum_{\tau'} X(\ ?\ )Y(\ ?\ )e^{i2\pi\nu(n;\, n-\tau)t}$$

If we use the following rule for adding frequencies in quantum mechanics, we can avoid getting frequencies that are different from the original ones.

$$\underline{\nu(n; n-\tau') + \nu(n-\tau'; n-\tau) = \nu(n; n-\tau)}$$

This is easy to understand if we look at the chart.

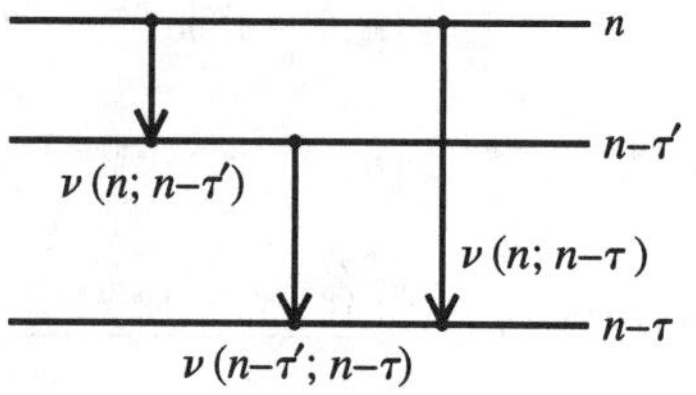

If we take this and make a rule for xy, the product of x and y, we get:

The Rule for Multiplication in Quantum Mechanics

$$xy = \sum_{\tau} \sum_{\tau'} X(n; n-\tau')Y(n-\tau'; n-\tau)e^{i2\pi\nu(n;\, n-\tau)t}$$

With this rule, we can solve the equation of motion for an anharmonic oscillator.

Pauli, Wolfgang [1900-1958]

This matched the experimental results very well. And, using this method, Wolfgang Pauli unraveled the structure of the hydrogen atom. This too perfectly matched the experimental results.

CONSERVATION OF ENERGY

But wait!! It's too early for celebration!! In *Physics and Beyond*, Heisenberg says:

> Then I noticed that there was no guarantee that the new mathematical scheme could be put into operation without contradictions.

When Heisenberg first calculated spectral amplitudes and frequencies and found that they corresponded with experimental results, he was overjoyed. But when he looked at the problem more objectively, he was concerned.

In spite of the fact that the q of the sum of the transition components no longer represented the electron's position, Heisenberg "forced" it into the equation $F = m\ddot{q}$. He was indeed able to obtain results that matched the experiments. But was it really valid to do this?

But Heisenberg didn't force the q in out of recklessness.

Right. He was able to do it because he was faithful to the concept of correspondence with classical mechanics.

In that case, perhaps we could show that quantum mechanics corresponds to classical mechanics in a consistent way, even in areas other than $F = m\ddot{q}$ . . .

Say, that's right. Maybe it was just a coincidence that $F = m\ddot{q}$ matched up.

If we're talking about classical mechanics, what else is there besides $F = m\ddot{q}$?

Isn't energy really the most important thing? The law of the conservation of energy is valid in all circumstances.

Oh, I see.

Besides, Planck, Einstein and Bohr entered the world of quanta through this thing called energy, didn't they?

$$E = nh\nu \quad (n = 0, 1, 2, 3 \cdots)$$

$$E = h\nu$$

$$\nu = \frac{W_n - W_m}{h}$$

So even if q no longer represents the position of the electron, all we have to do is show that this energy properly corresponds to classical mechanics.

That's right.

That is, it must be consistent with the law of the conservation of energy and also satisfy Bohr's frequency relation.

Good. Let's try and confirm that.

Hawking, Stephen William
[b. 1942]

According to Stephen Hawking, the law of the conservation of energy is "a physical law that can be neither created nor destroyed."

Let's think about energy. There are two kinds of energy, kinetic energy and potential energy; and the sum of both kinds, i.e., total energy, always has the same fixed value.

kinetic energy	+	potential energy	=	constant
$\frac{1}{2}m(\dot{q})^2$	+	$V(q)$	=	W

This is called the law of the conservation of energy. It has never been proven wrong.

For example, when you drop a ball from the top of a building:

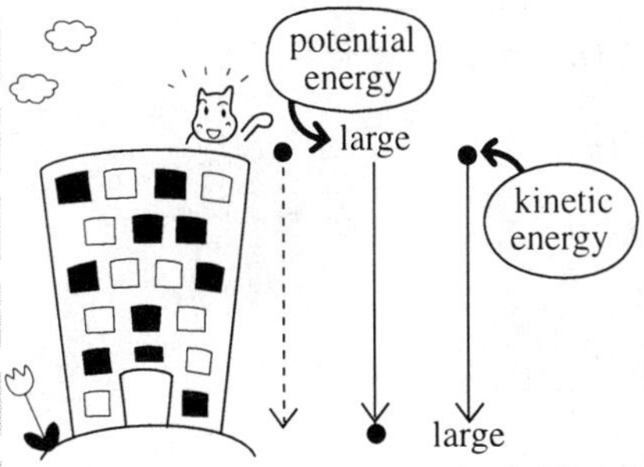

The potential energy starts out large, and keeps decreasing as the ball falls. In contrast, the kinetic energy is 0 at first, and it keeps increasing as the ball falls. The sum of the two at any given point in the fall is always the same as at any other point.

Let's look at Heisenberg's quantum mechanics theory and see if it is consistent with the law of the conservation of energy.

This is the equation for energy.

$$W = \frac{1}{2} m(\dot{q})^2 + V(q)$$

With harmonic oscillation, the potential energy $V(q)$ is $\frac{1}{2} kq^2$, so the total energy of harmonic oscillation is

$$W = \frac{1}{2} m \underline{(\dot{q})^2} + \frac{1}{2} k \underline{q^2}$$

First, let's see what happens to q^2 and $(\dot{q})^2$.

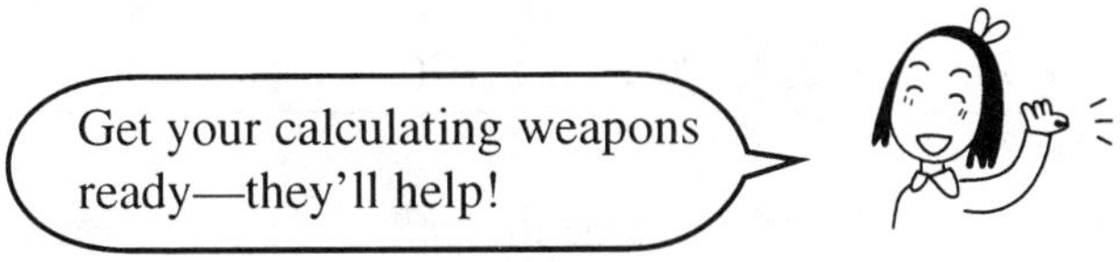

$$q = \sum_{\tau} Q(n; n-\tau) e^{i2\pi\nu(n; n-\tau)t}$$

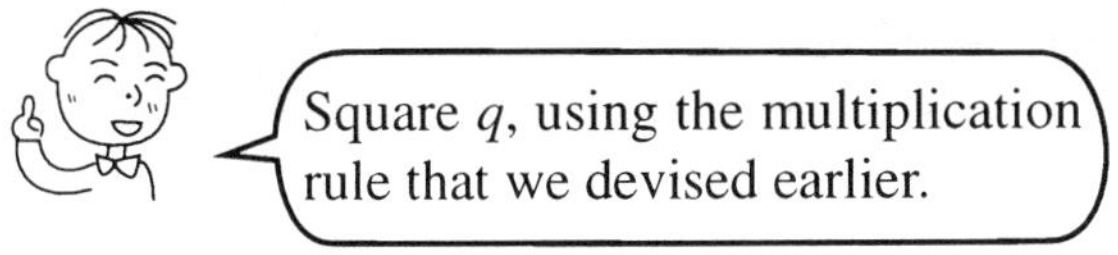

square

$$q^2 = \sum_{\tau} \sum_{\tau'} Q(n; n-\tau') Q(n-\tau'; n-\tau) e^{i2\pi\nu(n; n-\tau)t}$$

first derivative with respect to time

$$\frac{dq}{dt} = \dot{q} = \sum_{\tau} \underline{i2\pi\nu(n; n-\tau)}\, Q(n; n-\tau) e^{i2\pi\nu(n; n-\tau)t}$$

square of the first derivative with respect to time

$$\left(\frac{dq}{dt}\right)^2 = (\dot{q})^2 = \sum_{\tau}\sum_{\tau'} (i2\pi)^2 \nu(n; n-\tau')\nu(n-\tau'; n-\tau)$$
$$Q(n; n-\tau')\,Q(n-\tau'; n-\tau)e^{i2\pi\nu(n;\,n-\tau)t}$$

$$= \sum_{\tau}\sum_{\tau'} -4\pi^2\nu(n; n-\tau')\nu(n-\tau'; n-\tau)$$
$$Q(n; n-\tau')\,Q(n-\tau'; n-\tau)e^{i2\pi\nu(n;\,n-\tau)t}$$

Next, change the form of k slightly.

Because $\frac{k}{m} = (2\pi\nu)^2 = 4\pi^2\nu^2$, we arrive at $k = 4\pi^2 m\nu^2$.

Get those weapons out, put them into the equation for energy, and let's attack the calculations!

$$W = \frac{1}{2}m\sum_{\tau}\sum_{\tau'} -4\pi^2\nu(n; n-\tau')\nu(n-\tau'; n-\tau)$$
$$Q(n; n-\tau')\,Q(n-\tau'; n-\tau)e^{i2\pi\nu(n;\,n-\tau)t}$$
$$+\frac{1}{2}(4\pi^2 m\nu^2)\sum_{\tau}\sum_{\tau'} Q(n; n-\tau')\,Q(n-\tau'; n-\tau)e^{i2\pi\nu(n;\,n-\tau)t}$$

We clean up the equation like this:

$$W = \underline{2\pi^2 m \sum_{\tau}\sum_{\tau'}} -\nu(n; n-\tau')\nu(n-\tau'; n-\tau)$$
$$\underline{Q(n; n-\tau')Q(n-\tau'; n-\tau)e^{i2\pi\nu(n;\,n-\tau)t}}$$
$$+\ \underline{2\pi^2 m\,\nu^2 \sum_{\tau}\sum_{\tau'}}\ \underline{Q(n; n-\tau')Q(n-\tau'; n-\tau)e^{i2\pi\nu(n;\,n-\tau)t}}$$

There sure are a lot of the same things.

Oh! We've had this pattern before!!
I think it was when we solved Newton's equation of motion.

Let's make the equation look a little better!

$$W = 2\pi^2 m\sum_{\tau}\sum_{\tau'}\left\{\nu^2 - \nu(n; n-\tau')\nu(n-\tau'; n-\tau)\right\}$$
$$Q(n; n-\tau')Q(n-\tau'; n-\tau)e^{i2\pi\nu(n;\,n-\tau)t}$$

When we found the amplitude and frequency of harmonic oscillation, without regard to n, we knew that:

When there is one transition inward, the frequency is ν.
When there is one transition outward, the frequency is $-\nu$.

Moreover, the amplitude $Q(n; n-\tau)$ only had a value in these two cases; we learned that at other times it was always 0.

$$\begin{aligned}
&\nu(n; n-1) = \nu \\
&\nu(n; n+1) = -\nu \\
&Q(n; n-1) \neq 0 \\
&Q(n; n+1) \neq 0 \\
&Q(n; n-\tau) = 0 \quad (\tau \neq \pm 1)
\end{aligned}$$

Therefore, it is clear that in the above equation for W, both $Q(n; n-\tau')$ and $Q(n-\tau'; n-\tau)$ are always 0, except when there is only one transition.

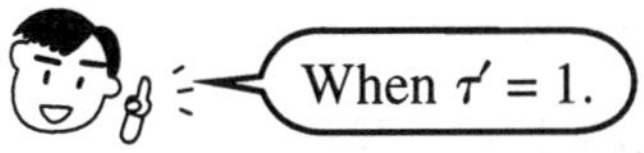

$$\begin{aligned}
&Q(n; n-1)Q(n-1; n-2) \quad (\tau = 2) \\
&Q(n; n-1)Q(n-1; n-0) \quad (\tau = 0)
\end{aligned}$$

$$\begin{aligned}
&Q(n; n+1)Q(n+1; n+2) \quad (\tau = -2) \\
&Q(n; n+1)Q(n+1; n-0) \quad (\tau = 0)
\end{aligned}$$

What do you know! The amplitudes $Q(n; n-\tau')$ and $Q(n-\tau'; n-\tau)$ never have values other than 0 except in the above four cases! The frequencies for these cases are as follows:

$$\begin{aligned}
\nu(n; n-1)\nu(n-1; n-2) &= \text{inside} \cdot \text{inside} &&= \nu \cdot \nu &&= \nu^2 \\
\nu(n; n-1)\nu(n-1; n-0) &= \text{inside} \cdot \text{outside} &&= \nu \cdot (-\nu) &&= -\nu^2 \\
\nu(n; n+1)\nu(n+1; n+2) &= \text{outside} \cdot \text{outside} &&= (-\nu) \cdot (-\nu) &&= \nu^2 \\
\nu(n; n+1)\nu(n+1; n-0) &= \text{outside} \cdot \text{inside} &&= (-\nu) \cdot \nu &&= -\nu^2
\end{aligned}$$

We insert them in the previous equation for energy.

$\tau' = 1, \tau = 2$

$$W = 2\pi^2 m\underbrace{\left(\nu^2 - \nu^2\right)}_{=0}Q(n; n-1)Q(n-1; n-2)e^{i2\pi\nu(n; n-2)t} \quad (= 0)$$

$\tau' = 1, \tau = 0$

$$+ 2\pi^2 m\underbrace{\left\{\nu^2 - (-\nu^2)\right\}}_{=2\nu^2}Q(n; n-1)Q(n-1; n)e^{i2\pi\nu(n; n)t}$$

$\tau' = -1, \tau = -2$

$$+ 2\pi^2 m\underbrace{\left(\nu^2 - \nu^2\right)}_{=0}Q(n; n+1)Q(n+1; n+2)e^{i2\pi\nu(n; n+2)t} \quad (= 0)$$

$\tau' = -1, \tau = 0$

$$+ 2\pi^2 m\underbrace{\left\{\nu^2 - (-\nu^2)\right\}}_{=2\nu^2}Q(n; n+1)Q(n+1; n)e^{i2\pi\nu(n; n)t}$$

The first term and the third term fall out.

$$W = 4\pi^2 m\nu^2 Q(n; n-1)Q(n-1; n)e^{i2\pi \underline{\nu(n; n)t}}$$
$$+ 4\pi^2 m\nu^2 Q(n; n+1)Q(n+1; n)e^{i2\pi \underline{\nu(n; n)t}}$$

$\nu(n; n)$ refers to the frequency when there is a transition from n to n, but since transition from n to n is actually no transition at all, it turns out that $\nu(n; n) = 0$.

Therefore, $e^{i2\pi\nu(n; n)t} = e^{i2\pi 0t} = 1$.

$$W = 4\pi^2 m\nu^2\left\{Q(n; n-1)\underline{Q(n-1; n)} + \underline{Q(n; n+1)}\,Q(n+1; n)\right\}$$

We take the complex conjugates

$$Q(n-1; n) = Q^*(n; n-1)$$
$$Q(n; n+1) = Q^*(n+1; n)$$

and work them in:

$$W = 4\pi^2 m\nu^2\left\{\underline{Q(n; n-1)Q^*(n; n-1)} + \underline{Q^*(n+1; n)Q(n+1; n)}\right\}$$

Next, we get

$$Q(n;n-1)Q^*(n;n-1) = \left|Q(n;n-1)\right|^2$$
$$Q^*(n+1;n)Q(n+1;n) = \left|Q(n+1;n)\right|^2$$

so that

$$\boxed{W = 4\pi^2 m\nu^2\left\{\left|Q(n;n-1)\right|^2 + \left|Q(n+1;n)\right|^2\right\}.}$$

Done! This is the energy of harmonic oscillation!

This equation doesn't contain t (time)! What's going on?

The energy of harmonic oscillation doesn't change over time! So it follows that the law of the conservation of energy holds, doesn't it!

Now take our equation for the intensity of light

$$\left|Q(n;n-1)\right|^2 = \frac{h}{8\pi^2 m\nu}n$$

and put that in:

$$W = 4\pi^2 m\nu^2\left\{\left|Q(n;n-1)\right|^2 + \left|Q(n+1;n)\right|^2\right\}$$
$$\uparrow \qquad\qquad \uparrow$$
$$\frac{h}{8\pi^2 m\nu}n \qquad \frac{h}{8\pi^2 m\nu}(n+1)$$

$$= 4\pi^2 m\nu^2\left\{\frac{h}{8\pi^2 m\nu}n + \frac{h}{8\pi^2 m\nu}(n+1)\right\}$$

$$= 4\pi^2 m\nu^2\left(\frac{h}{8\pi^2 m\nu}n + \frac{h}{8\pi^2 m\nu}n + \frac{h}{8\pi^2 m\nu}\right)$$

We take $\frac{h}{8\pi^2 m\nu}$ out of the brackets.

$$= 4\pi^2 m\nu^2 \frac{h}{8\pi^2 m\nu}(n + n + 1)$$

$$= \frac{1}{2} h\nu(2n + 1)$$

$$= h\nu\left(n + \frac{1}{2}\right)$$

$$\boxed{W = \left(n + \frac{1}{2}\right)h\nu}$$

The only difference between this and Planck's value for energy $E = nh\nu$ is $\frac{1}{2}h\nu$.

But we confirmed that Heisenberg's value had better explanatory value!

Finally, let's make sure that this satisfies Bohr's frequency relation $\nu = \frac{W_n - W_m}{h}$.

Bohr's frequency relation matched the experimental results perfectly. So if there's an inconsistency between Heisenberg and Bohr, we've got a big problem.

We'll try putting the equation for energy that we just found into Bohr's equation for frequency relation.

$$\nu(n; n-1) = \frac{W_{(n)} - W_{(n-1)}}{h}$$

$$= \frac{\left(n + \frac{1}{2}\right)h\nu - \left(n - 1 + \frac{1}{2}\right)h\nu}{h}$$

$$= \frac{nh\nu + \frac{1}{2}h\nu - nh\nu + h\nu - \frac{1}{2}h\nu}{h}$$

$$= \underline{\nu}$$

In harmonic oscillation, when there is one energy transition inward, the frequency is ν!

That means the energy calculated by Heisenberg's method satisfied all of the necessary conditions for energy.

But with this "energy," q no longer expresses the position of the electron, so this isn't "energy" in the usual sense. We have no idea what q is anymore, and so we don't have any idea what this "energy" is either. Nevertheless, the equation satisfies the conservation law as well as Bohr's frequency relation. So that means. . .

Yes, yes, ye—es!
We'll give it a new name—we'll call it "energy for quantum mechanics!"

Good! It satisfies all the conditions so far for energy, so who cares if it doesn't make sense!

Yes, yes, let's do that!

In *Physics and Beyond*, Heisenberg wrote of the time he constructed quantum mechanics in Helgoland.

> At first, I was deeply alarmed. I had the feeling that, through the surface of atomic phenomena, I was looking at a strangely beautiful interior, and felt almost giddy at the thought that I now had to probe this wealth of mathematical structures nature had so generously spread out before me. I was far too excited to sleep, and so, as a new day dawned, I made for the southern tip of the island, where I had been longing to climb a rock jutting out into the sea. I now did so without too much trouble, and waited for the sun to rise.

Physics and Beyond

3. 4 THE COMPLETION OF MATRIX MECHANICS

THE MATRIX

Pauli, Wolfgang
[1900-1958]

Heisenberg's hay fever cleared up, and he returned from Helgoland. He wrote up the great discovery he had made there, and presented the report to his close friends Wolfgang Pauli and Professor Born. He left once more, this time to go mountain climbing. Good for the health!

When Pauli and Born read the report, they thought,

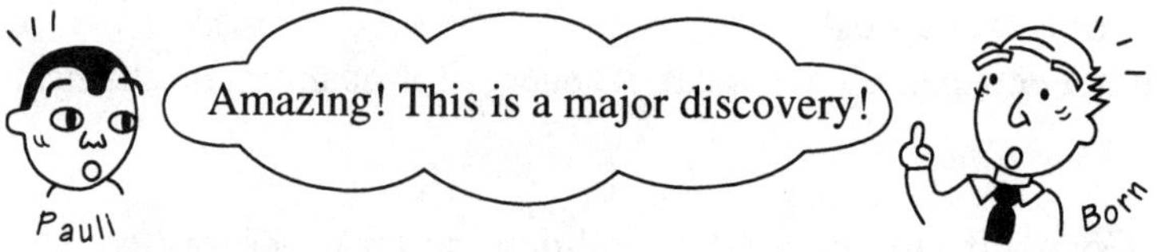

But they didn't know how to deal with Heisenberg's calculations. They were far too messy and complicated. Then, looking again at the equations, Born noticed that Heisenberg's method of calculation resembled something that he had run into only once before, in a university lecture twenty years earlier.

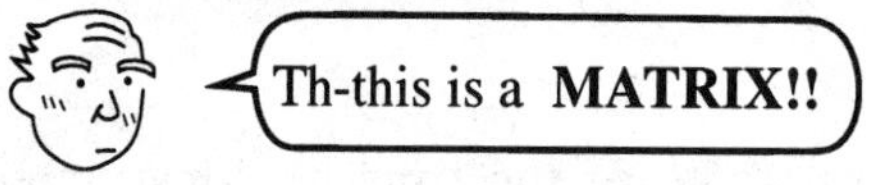

Born realized that Heisenberg's calculations were matrices.

Hey, what's a matrix?

It's an array of numbers laid out in a specific order.

Really—how?

$$A = \begin{pmatrix} A_{11} & A_{12} & A_{13} & \cdots \\ A_{21} & A_{22} & A_{23} & \cdots \\ A_{31} & A_{32} & A_{33} & \cdots \\ \vdots & \vdots & \vdots & \end{pmatrix}$$

The horizontal lines are called rows, and the vertical lines are called columns. The individual numbers or units in the matrix are called elements. The elements of a matrix may be written in general form as

$$A_{nn'}$$

Heisenberg had developed a "sum of transition components" to correspond with classical mechanics.

$$q = \sum_{\tau} \underbrace{Q(n; n-\tau)e^{i2\pi\nu(n;\, n-\tau)t}}_{\text{transition component}}$$

In classical mechanics, what does the sum of simple waves

$$q = \sum_{\tau} Q(n, \tau)e^{i2\pi\nu(n,\, \tau)t}$$

indicate?

Uh. . .Position!

Base hit! Now what about the sum of transition components?

Mmm. . .what was it? I don't know.

That's right—we had no clue what it was.

Transitions of electrons from one energy level to another cannot be summed up like waves. It might be clearer if instead we thought of each individual transition component as

$$Q(n; n-\tau)e^{i2\pi\nu(n;\, n-\tau)t}$$

where q is a "collection" of transition components. We can certainly express that using a matrix!

In order to make this easier to express as a matrix, let's change the symbols a bit and replace what we've been writing as $n - \tau$ with n'! If we do that, we can write the transition component as

$$Q_{nn'}e^{i2\pi\nu_{nn'}t}$$

Short and easy!

If we say that the nn' elements of the matrix q are $q_{nn'}$, then the matrix q may be written thus:

$$q = \begin{pmatrix} q_{11} & q_{12} & q_{13} & \cdots \\ q_{21} & q_{22} & q_{23} & \cdots \\ q_{31} & q_{32} & q_{33} & \cdots \\ \vdots & \vdots & \vdots & \end{pmatrix}$$

Of course!

From now on, let's call matrix q the "position" in quantum mechanics.

What!? But in quantum mechanics q doesn't express position any more!

Yes, but remember that here, q does not refer to the "position" as defined in classical mechanics. We can call it "position" in the sense that it has a correspondence to the classical mechanics definition.

In quantum mechanics, because the position q is a matrix, the q in

is also a matrix. So naturally F is a matrix, and all of the other physical quantities are matrices, as well.

So they all become collections of numbers!

This is because all the physical quantities contain q.

Physical Quantities

$\underline{q}$ (position) $\underline{\dot{q}}$ (velocity) $\underline{\ddot{q}}$ (acceleration)

$p = m\,\underline{\dot{q}}$ (momentum) $F = m\,\underline{\ddot{q}}$ (force)

$M = \dfrac{m(\,\underline{\dot{q}}\,)^2}{r}$ (angular momentum)

$E = \frac{1}{2}m(\,\underline{\dot{q}}\,)^2 + V(\,\underline{q}\,)$ (energy)

Here's The Point!
The language of quantum mechanics may be expressed entirely through matrices!

When we say matrix, however, it's not as if any matrix will do. It must meet certain conditions.

In quantum mechanics, amplitude had the property

$$\underline{Q(n; n-\tau)^* = Q(n-\tau; n)} \,.$$

If we represent this as a matrix, we get

$$Q_{nn'}{}^* = Q_{n'n} \,.$$

Now let's see what properties matrix q has!
The elements $q_{nn'}$ of q were

$$q_{nn'} = Q_{nn'} e^{i2\pi \nu_{nn'} t}$$

Let's take the complex conjugate (adding a star).

$$q_{nn'}^{\,*} = Q_{nn'}^{\,*} e^{-i2\pi \nu_{nn'} t}$$

Because $Q_{nn'}^{\,*} = Q_{n'n}$, $-\nu_{nn'} = \nu_{n'n}$ (expressed in terms of the symbols we have been using, $-\nu(n; n-\tau) = \nu(n-\tau; n)$). Therefore

$$\begin{aligned} q_{nn'}^{\,*} &= Q_{n'n} e^{i2\pi \nu_{n'n} t} \\ &= q_{n'n} \end{aligned}$$

That is,

$$q_{nn'}^{\,*} = q_{n'n}$$

Written in matrix form, it looks like this:

$$\begin{pmatrix} q_{11} & q_{12} & q_{13} & \cdots \\ q_{21} & q_{22} & q_{23} & \cdots \\ q_{31} & q_{32} & q_{33} & \cdots \\ \vdots & \vdots & \vdots & \end{pmatrix} = \begin{pmatrix} q_{11}^{\,*} & q_{21}^{\,*} & q_{31}^{\,*} & \cdots \\ q_{12}^{\,*} & q_{22}^{\,*} & q_{32}^{\,*} & \cdots \\ q_{13}^{\,*} & q_{23}^{\,*} & q_{33}^{\,*} & \cdots \\ \vdots & \vdots & \vdots & \end{pmatrix}$$

The rows and columns of this matrix have been inverted diagonally and its complex conjugate taken, yet it is equivalent to the original matrix. A matrix of this type is called an "Hermitian matrix". This type of matrix was studied by the mathematician Charles Hermite. If we use the language of the Hermitian matrix,

Hermite, Charles
[1822-1901]

RULES FOR CALCULATION

We now know that in quantum mechanics, physical quantities are expressed as matrices. But when Born first saw Heisenberg's calculations and thought, "This is a matrix!" it was because he assumed that the rules Heisenberg had used in his calculations were similar to the rules for calculating matrices.

What are the rules for calculation?

They tell you how to perform operations, like addition or multiplication.

Let's see how Heisenberg's rules for calculation compare with the rules for calculating matrices.

OK, **ADDITION** first!

When we solved the equation of motion for harmonic oscillation,

$$\ddot{q} + \frac{k}{m} q = 0$$

we performed addition transition component by transition component.

In adding matrices, we can add elements in this way:

$$\begin{pmatrix} A_{11} & A_{12} & \cdots \\ A_{21} & A_{22} & \cdots \\ \vdots & \vdots & \end{pmatrix} + \begin{pmatrix} B_{11} & B_{12} & \cdots \\ B_{21} & B_{22} & \cdots \\ \vdots & \vdots & \end{pmatrix} = \begin{pmatrix} A_{11}+B_{11} & A_{12}+B_{12} & \cdots \\ A_{21}+B_{21} & A_{22}+B_{22} & \cdots \\ \vdots & \vdots & \end{pmatrix}$$

That is, we perform addition element by element.

Heisenberg's addition and the addition for matrices are exactly the same!

OK, on to **DERIVATIVES WITH RESPECT TO TIME!**

There are a whole pile of derivatives with respect to time in Heisenberg's work!

Do $\dot{}$ (dot) or $\ddot{}$ (double dot) have something to do with derivatives with respect to time?

Right. They were calculated like this:

$$q = \sum_{\tau} Q(n; n-\tau) e^{i2\pi\nu(n; n-\tau)t}$$

first derivative with respect to time · · ·

$$\dot{q} = \sum_{\tau} \underline{i2\pi\nu(n; n-\tau)}\, Q(n; n-\tau) e^{i2\pi\nu(n; n-\tau)t}$$

Calculations were done for each transition, just as in classical mechanics.

Now, the derivative of the matrix with respect to time is

$$\frac{d}{dt}\begin{pmatrix} q_{11} & q_{12} & \cdots \\ q_{21} & q_{22} & \cdots \\ \vdots & \vdots & \end{pmatrix} = \begin{pmatrix} \dot{q}_{11} & \dot{q}_{12} & \cdots \\ \dot{q}_{21} & \dot{q}_{22} & \cdots \\ \vdots & \vdots & \end{pmatrix}$$

$$= \begin{pmatrix} \underline{i2\pi\nu_{11}} Q_{11} e^{i2\pi\nu_{11}t} & \underline{i2\pi\nu_{12}} Q_{12} e^{i2\pi\nu_{12}t} \cdots \\ \underline{i2\pi\nu_{21}} Q_{21} e^{i2\pi\nu_{21}t} & \underline{i2\pi\nu_{22}} Q_{22} e^{i2\pi\nu_{22}t} \cdots \\ \vdots & \vdots \end{pmatrix}$$

Here too we take derivatives on the elements one by one.

MULTIPLICATION is next!

Now this is a problem. Heisenberg decided upon a particular form for his rule for multiplication.

$$\boxed{xy = \sum_{\tau}\sum_{\tau'} X(n; n-\tau')Y(n-\tau'; n-\tau) e^{i2\pi\nu(n; n-\tau)t}}$$

If we look at its terms one at a time, we have

$$\sum_{\tau'} X(n; n-\tau')Y(n-\tau'; n-\tau)e^{i2\pi\nu(n; n-\tau)t} \ .$$

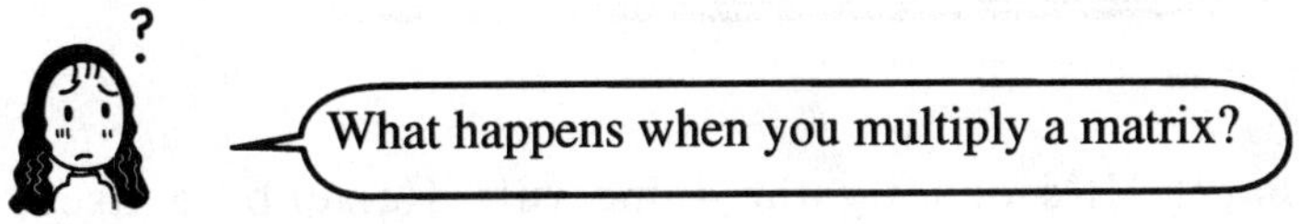

Multiplication of a matrix is done this way:

$$\begin{pmatrix} A & B \\ C & D \end{pmatrix} \times \begin{pmatrix} a & b \\ c & d \end{pmatrix} = \begin{pmatrix} Aa+Bc & Ab+Bd \\ Ca+Dc & Cb+Dd \end{pmatrix}$$

Then, using the following format:

$$x = \begin{pmatrix} x_{11} & x_{12} & \cdot\cdot \\ x_{21} & x_{22} & \cdot\cdot \\ \vdots & \vdots & \end{pmatrix} \qquad y = \begin{pmatrix} y_{11} & y_{12} & \cdot\cdot \\ y_{21} & y_{22} & \cdot\cdot \\ \vdots & \vdots & \end{pmatrix}$$

the general form is written

$$xy = \begin{pmatrix} x_{\underline{1}\underline{1}}y_{\underline{1}\underline{1}} + x_{\underline{1}\underline{2}}y_{\underline{2}\underline{1}} \cdot\cdot & x_{\underline{1}\underline{1}}y_{\underline{1}\underline{2}} + x_{\underline{1}\underline{2}}y_{\underline{2}\underline{2}} \cdot\cdot \\ x_{\underline{2}\underline{1}}y_{\underline{1}\underline{1}} + x_{\underline{2}\underline{2}}y_{\underline{2}\underline{1}} \cdot\cdot & x_{\underline{2}\underline{1}}y_{\underline{1}\underline{2}} + x_{\underline{2}\underline{2}}y_{\underline{2}\underline{2}} \cdot\cdot \\ \vdots & \vdots \end{pmatrix}$$

$$= \begin{pmatrix} \sum_n x_{\underline{1n}}y_{\underline{n1}} & \sum_n x_{\underline{1n}}y_{\underline{n2}} \cdot\cdot \\ \sum_n x_{\underline{2n}}y_{\underline{n1}} & \sum_n x_{\underline{2n}}y_{\underline{n2}} \cdot\cdot \end{pmatrix}.$$

Matrix element $(xy)_{nn'}$ is then

$$(xy)_{nn'} = \sum_{n''} x_{nn''}y_{n''n'} \ .$$

When x, y are

$$x_{nn'} = X_{nn'}e^{i2\pi\nu_{nn'}t}$$

$$y_{nn'} = Y_{nn'}e^{i2\pi\nu_{nn'}t}$$

the matrix x, y is

$$(xy)_{nn'} = \sum_{n''} X_{nn''}e^{i2\pi\nu_{nn''}t} \cdot Y_{n''n'}e^{i2\pi\nu_{n''n'}t}$$

$$= \sum_{n''} X_{nn''} \cdot Y_{n''n'}e^{\underline{i2\pi\left(\nu_{nn''}+\nu_{n''n'}\right)t}} \ .$$

If we use the property $\nu_{nn''} + \nu_{n''n'} = \nu_{nn'}$ of frequencies,

$$(xy)_{nn'} = \sum_{n''} X_{nn''} \cdot Y_{n''n'} e^{i2\pi \nu_{nn'} t}$$

W-what?! It's exactly the same rule Heisenberg used for multiplication!

If we replace n with n, $n - \tau'$ with n'', and $n - \tau$ with n', it's exactly the same as Heisenberg's multiplication!

Heisenberg's calculation rules for addition, derivation and multiplication were exactly the same as the calculation rules for matrices. Unmodified, Heisenberg's calculations were complicated. He understood them perfectly well, but it was hard for others to do so.

But if they are rearranged as a matrix, then anyone can understand them!

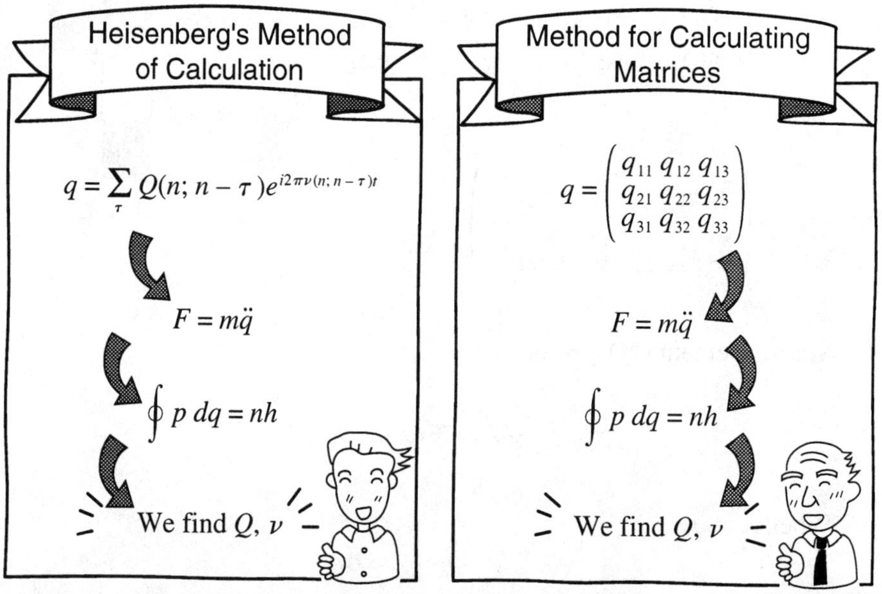

Actually, when I developed the theory of quantum mechanics on Helgoland, I didn't know a thing about matrices.

But if you're going to push the frontiers of physics forward, you have to discover or invent whatever mathematics you need.

Hey, it's Yama-chan (assistant to Heisenberg for eleven years, currently senior fellow at TCL, Professor Kazuo Yamazaki)!

Point! The important thing is, just do it, whatever it takes!

A CANONICAL COMMUTATIVE RELATION

When I used matrices to arrange Heisenberg's calculations, I realized that his calculations were even more significant.

All right, I see I've got to lay it out for you. Look, when matrix calculations are used,

Bohr's quantum condition
$\oint p\, dq = nh$

and

Newton's equation of motion
$F = m\ddot{q}$

may be rewritten. This gives us three advantages.

Huh? What?

If you rewrite these two equations, then

1. you can prove that the law of the conservation of energy applies in all circumstances.
2. you can prove that Bohr's frequency relation always holds true.
3. the problem becomes one of eigenvalues, which we'll explain later.

Uhh, I'm totally lost!

That's all right. You'll understand eventually. For now, just remember that there are these three advantages.

As I wrote in *Physics and Beyond*, my group and I worked for many months. It nearly did us in.

All right, let's knuckle down and see what we've got here.

"· · · the extremely intensive work · · · kept us breathless for a few months." Even Heisenberg said, in *Physics and Beyond*, that the months and months of work nearly did him in. But there aren't many things as marvelous as Heisenberg's discovery in Helgoland! It might make you dizzy, but you'll feel the majesty of mathematics. Go for it! You can do it!

When Bohr's quantum condition is rewritten in the form of quantum mechanics, we get the following:

$$\oint p\,dq = nh$$

$$\downarrow$$

$$\sum_{\tau} P(n;\, n-\tau)Q(n-\tau\,;\, n) - \sum_{\tau} Q(n;\, n+\tau)P(n+\tau\,;\, n) = \frac{h}{2\pi i}$$

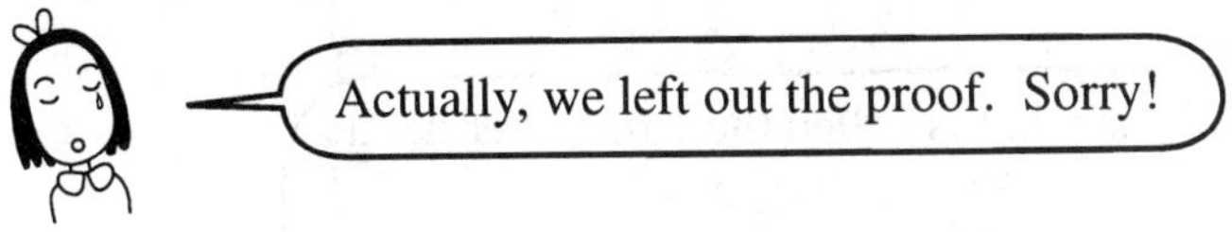

When it is written with matrix symbols, we get this:

$$\sum_{n''} P_{nn''}Q_{n''n} - \sum_{n''} Q_{nn''}P_{n''n} = \frac{h}{2\pi i}$$

If we consider the rule for multiplication of matrices

$$\boxed{(xy)_{nn'} = \sum_{n''} x_{nn''}y_{n''n'}}$$

we see that in the last equation, PQ, QP are multiplied by the nn elements (the diagonal elements). Applying this, we rewrite the equation:

$$(PQ)_{nn} - (QP)_{nn} = \frac{h}{2\pi i}$$

In addition, we let all the elements except for the nn elements be 0.

$$(PQ)_{nn'} - (QP)_{nn'} = \begin{cases} \dfrac{h}{2\pi i} & (n = n') \\ 0 & (n \neq n') \end{cases}$$

A matrix such as this, where only the diagonal elements have values other than 0 and the rest are all 0, is called a **diagonal element matrix**. It may also be written this way

$$\begin{pmatrix} \frac{h}{2\pi i} & 0 & 0 & \cdots \\ 0 & \frac{h}{2\pi i} & 0 & \cdots \\ 0 & 0 & \frac{h}{2\pi i} & \cdots \\ \vdots & \vdots & \vdots & \end{pmatrix} = \frac{h}{2\pi i}\begin{pmatrix} 1 & 0 & 0 & \cdots \\ 0 & 1 & 0 & \cdots \\ 0 & 0 & 1 & \cdots \\ \vdots & \vdots & \vdots & \end{pmatrix} = \frac{h}{2\pi i}\,1$$

A matrix where the diagonal elements are 1 and the rest are all 0 is called an **identity matrix** and is written as **1.**

$$\text{matrix} \cdots PQ - QP = \frac{h}{2\pi i}\,1$$

$$\text{matrix elements} \cdots (PQ)_{nn'} - (QP)_{nn'} = \frac{h}{2\pi i}\,\delta_{nn'}$$

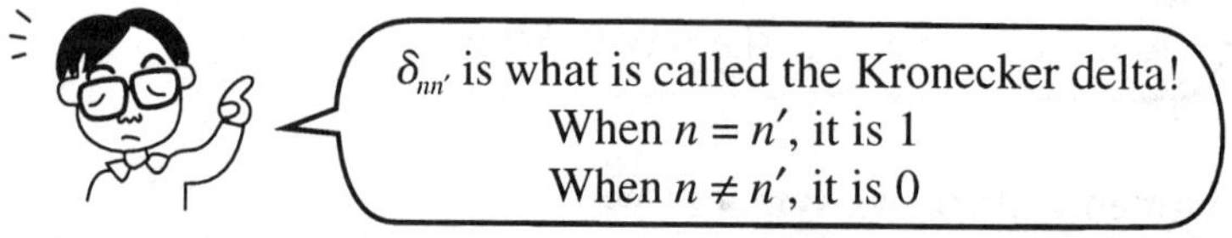

$$q_{nn'} = Q_{nn'}\,e^{i2\pi\nu_{nn'}t}$$

The upper-case P, Q were amplitudes; assuming that P, Q are related in the ways we have studied so far, what relationships do we find for lower-case p, q, which express energy transitions?

$$(pq - qp)_{nn'} = \sum_{n''} p_{nn''}q_{n''n'} - \sum_{n''} q_{nn''}p_{n''n'}$$

We change it into the form for transition components.

$$= \sum_{n''} P_{nn''}e^{i2\pi\nu_{nn''}t}Q_{n''n'}e^{i2\pi\nu_{n''n'}t} - \sum_{n''} Q_{nn''}e^{i2\pi\nu_{nn''}t}P_{n''n'}e^{i2\pi\nu_{n''n'}t}$$

We adjust the equation.

$$= \sum_{n''} P_{nn''}Q_{n''n'}e^{i2\pi\nu_{nn'}t} - \sum_{n''} Q_{nn''}P_{n''n'}e^{i2\pi\nu_{nn'}t}$$

We factor out $e^{i2\pi\nu_{nn'}t}$.

$$= \left\{\sum_{n''} P_{nn''}Q_{n''n'} - \sum_{n''} Q_{nn''}P_{n''n'}\right\}e^{i2\pi\nu_{nn'}t}$$

We rewrite it in the form of matrix elements.

$$= (PQ - QP)_{nn'}\cdot e^{i2\pi\nu_{nn'}t}$$

In the end, we get

$$= \frac{h}{2\pi i}\,\delta_{nn'}\cdot e^{i2\pi\nu_{nn'}t}$$

Here when $n = n'$, $e^{i2\pi\nu_{nn'}t} = e^0 = 1$,. When $n \neq n'$, $\delta_{nn'}$ becomes 0.

SUMMARY

$$pq - qp = \frac{h}{2\pi i} 1$$

$$(pq - qp)_{nn'} = \frac{h}{2\pi i} \delta_{nn'}$$

$$\delta_{nn'} = \begin{cases} n = n' \cdots 1 \\ n \neq n' \cdots 0 \end{cases}$$

In this way, when we express Bohr's quantum condition as a matrix, a new meaning appears.

What kind of meaning?

In matrix multiplication, if we change the order, the solution changes.

In the case of

$$A = \begin{pmatrix} 1 & 2 \\ 3 & 4 \end{pmatrix} \quad B = \begin{pmatrix} 5 & 6 \\ 7 & 8 \end{pmatrix}$$

for example,

$$A \times B = \begin{pmatrix} 1 & 2 \\ 3 & 4 \end{pmatrix}\begin{pmatrix} 5 & 6 \\ 7 & 8 \end{pmatrix} = \begin{pmatrix} 5+14 & 6+16 \\ 15+28 & 18+32 \end{pmatrix} = \begin{pmatrix} 19 & 22 \\ 43 & 50 \end{pmatrix}$$

$$B \times A = \begin{pmatrix} 5 & 6 \\ 7 & 8 \end{pmatrix}\begin{pmatrix} 1 & 2 \\ 3 & 4 \end{pmatrix} = \begin{pmatrix} 5+18 & 10+24 \\ 7+24 & 14+32 \end{pmatrix} = \begin{pmatrix} 23 & 34 \\ 31 & 46 \end{pmatrix}$$

In this way, $\boldsymbol{AB \neq BA}$.

I know!

Using ordinary numbers, we can say that $AB = BA$.

$5 \times 3 = 3 \times 5$

Right. In the case of matrices, the commutative law for multiplication is not valid!

But if that's so, our calculations are going to run into trouble.

If you turn the order of a matrix upside down, what will happen? Unless you know this, there are a number of calculations you can't do. What you need to provide is

$$pq - qp = \frac{h}{2\pi i} 1$$

which is what we have been working with here.

When we change the order in which we multiply the p and q of the matrix, the difference between them is determined to be $\frac{h}{2\pi i}$.

This is called the

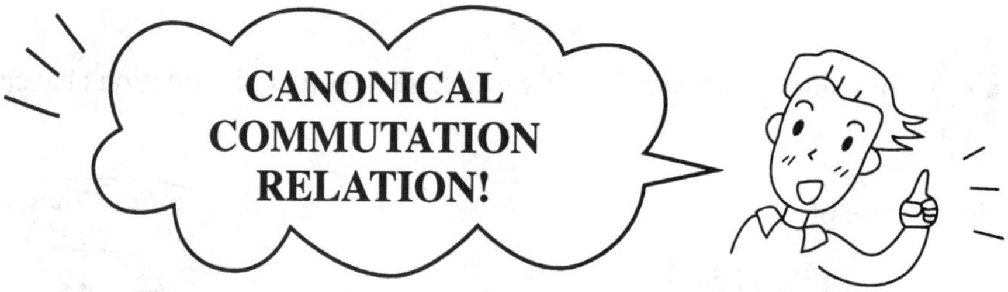

It is an important rule for calculation in matrix mechanics.

The basis of the equation for the canonical commutative relation is Bohr's quantum condition,

$$\oint p \, dq = nh .$$

Because quantum mechanics was developed from

classical mechanics + quantum condition,

in a way the quantum condition was superfluous. But by now it has become a rule for calculation, and matrix math can't do without it!

quantum mechanics quantum condition

HEISENBERG'S EQUATION OF MOTION

Thus, calculations in quantum mechanics are no longer done by the commutative law $AB = BA$, and the canonical commutative relation

$$pq - qp = \frac{h}{2\pi i} 1$$

is applied as the commutative rule for multiplication.

When the canonical commutative relation is used, however, Newton's equation of motion

$$F = m\ddot{q}$$

is reincarnated as a more powerful equation. In fact, the canonical commutative relation plays the role of a derivative.

The canonical commutative relation is a derivative?

Yep. Let's try an actual calculation! For example, consider the function of matrix p, q

$$f(p, q) = 2p + 3q^2 + pq$$

If we take a partial derivative of $f(p, q)$ with respect to q, we get

$$\boxed{\frac{\partial f(p, q)}{\partial q} = 6q + p}$$

In the case of the partial derivation of $f(p, q)$ with respect to q, the remaining p is calculated as if it were a normal number. This is how partial derivatives work.

Yes, I see.

Let's do some calculating.

$$pf(p, q) - f(p, q)p$$

p, q is a matrix, so you can't change the order of multiplication.

$$f(p, q) = 2p + 3q^2 + pq$$

$$pf(p, q) - f(p, q)p = p(2p + 3q^2 + pq) - (2p + 3q^2 + pq)p$$

We remove the brackets.

$$= 2p^2 + 3pq^2 + p^2q - 2p^2 - 3q^2p - pqp$$

We factor out 3

$$= 3\{pq^2 - q^2p\} + p\,\underline{(pq - qp)}$$

Now we use the canonical commutative relation $pq - qp = \frac{h}{2\pi i}1$.

$$= 3(pq^2 - q^2p) + \frac{h}{2\pi i}p$$

$$= 3\{\underline{(pq)}q - q^2p\} + \frac{h}{2\pi i}p$$

From the canonical commutative relationship $pq - qp = \frac{h}{2\pi i}1$, we get $pq = qp + \frac{h}{2\pi i}1$.

$$= 3\left\{\underline{\left(qp + \frac{h}{2\pi i}\right)}q - q^2p\right\} + \frac{h}{2\pi i}p$$

We remove the brackets.

$$= 3\left(qpq + \frac{h}{2\pi i}q - q^2p\right) + \frac{h}{2\pi i}p$$

We factor out q.

$$= 3\left\{\frac{h}{2\pi i}q + q\,\underline{(pq - qp)}\right\} + \frac{h}{2\pi i}p$$

We bring in the canonical commutative relation once again.

$$= 3\left(\frac{h}{2\pi i}q + \frac{h}{2\pi i}q\right) + \frac{h}{2\pi i}p$$

$$= 3\frac{h}{2\pi i}2q + \frac{h}{2\pi i}p$$

We factor out $\frac{h}{2\pi i}$.

$$\boxed{pf - fp = \frac{h}{2\pi i}(6q + p)}$$

Now then, let's compare the derivative of this same function $f(p, q)$ with our results when we calculated using the canonical commutative relationship!

derivative	canonical commutative relation
$\frac{\partial f(p,q)}{\partial q} = 6q + p$	$pf - fp = \frac{h}{2\pi i}(6q + p)$

Super! Aside from the $\frac{h}{2\pi i}$ it's exactly the same!

Right. When we put it together we can write it like this!

$$\frac{\partial f(p,q)}{\partial q} = \frac{2\pi i}{h}(pf - fp)$$

That makes sense.

In the same way, if we take a derivative of $f(p, q)$ for p, we get

$$\frac{\partial f(p,q)}{\partial p} = -\frac{2\pi i}{h}(qf - fq)$$

Wow! $pf - fp$ and $qf - fq$ played the roles of derivatives, didn't they!

Born took one look and thought, "That's it!" It was

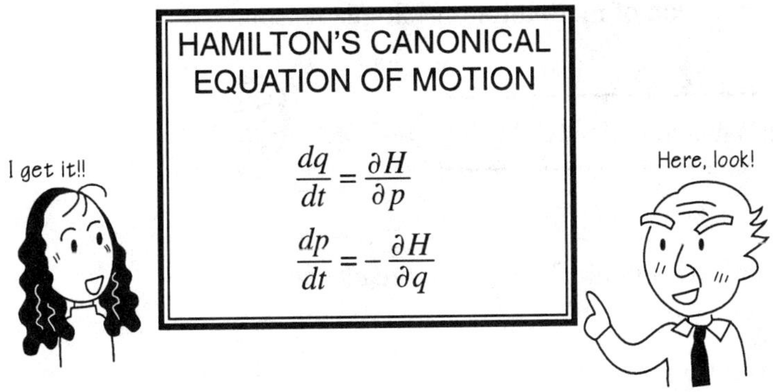

This is Newton's equation of motion $F = m\ddot{q}$ expressed in the form of derivatives of p, q. H is called the "Hamiltonian" and it expresses energy in the form of a function of p, q.

$$H(p, q) = \frac{1}{2m} p^2 + V(q)$$

In the case of harmonic oscillation, the potential energy $V(q)$ is

$$V(q) = \frac{k}{2} q^2 .$$

Therefore, the Hamiltonian for harmonic oscillation is

$$H(p, q) = \frac{1}{2m} p^2 + \frac{k}{2} q^2 .$$

Let's try putting this in Hamilton's canonical equation of motion!

$$\frac{dq}{dt} = \frac{\partial H}{\partial p} = \frac{\partial}{\partial p}\left\{\frac{1}{2m} p^2 + \frac{k}{2} q^2\right\} = \frac{p}{m} = \underline{v}$$

Here $\frac{dq}{dt} = \dot{q}$, and describes velocity v, exactly as we would expect. If we perform the same calculation for $\frac{dp}{dt}$, we get

$$\frac{dp}{dt} = -\frac{\partial H}{\partial q} = -\frac{\partial}{\partial q}\left\{\frac{1}{2m} p^2 + \frac{k}{2} q^2\right\} = -kq = \underline{F} \ .$$

Because $dp/dt = m\,(dv/dt) = m\ddot{q}$, this is equivalent to $F = m\ddot{q}$.

Hamilton, Sir William Rowan
[1805-1865]

Newton's equation of motion and Hamilton's canonical equation of motion are essentially the same. Sir William Hamilton deliberately fashioned a separate canonical equation of motion for one simple reason.

It's mathematically elegant!

What? I think $F = m\ddot{q}$ is more elegant. . .

I'm talking about a kind of elegance that is deeper than visual beauty. But let's not go into such things here.

For solving problems it doesn't particularly matter whether it is elegant or not. Newton's equation was simpler, and almost everyone liked it better. Hamilton's canonical equation of motion hardly ever saw the light of day.

However. . . if we take Hamilton's canonical equation of motion

$$\boxed{\begin{aligned} \frac{dq}{dt} &= \frac{\partial H}{\partial p} \\ \frac{dp}{dt} &= -\frac{\partial H}{\partial q} \end{aligned}}$$

and compare it carefully to the familiar

$$\frac{\partial f(p,q)}{\partial q} = \frac{2\pi i}{h}(pf - fp)$$

$$\frac{\partial f(p,q)}{\partial p} = -\frac{2\pi i}{h}(qf - fq)$$

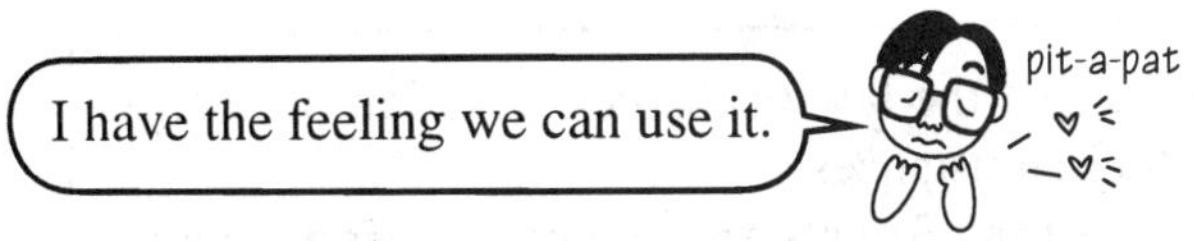

If f is a function of p and q, it can be anything. Because H is a function of p and q, we can replace f with H in the above equation.

$$\frac{\partial H}{\partial q} = \frac{2\pi i}{h}(pH - Hp)$$

$$\frac{\partial H}{\partial p} = -\frac{2\pi i}{h}(qH - Hq)$$

We combine this with Hamilton's canonical equation of motion.

$$\frac{dp}{dt} = -\frac{2\pi i}{h}(pH - Hp)$$

$$\frac{dq}{dt} = -\frac{2\pi i}{h}(qH - Hq)$$

Now it looks really nice! Moreover, if we think of this as function g of p and q and put them together into one function, we have:

$$\frac{dg}{dt} = -\frac{2\pi i}{h}(gH - Hg)$$

This is called

HEISENBERG'S EQUATION OF MOTION.

By using the canonical commutative relation, it is possible to rewrite Newton's equation of motion in this form.

Why do you think we've spent all this time rewriting Newton's equation of motion?

Because, as we said before, there are three advantages.

1. you can prove that the law of the conservation of energy applies in all circumstances.
2. you can prove that Bohr's frequency relation always holds true.
3. the problem becomes one of eigenvalues.

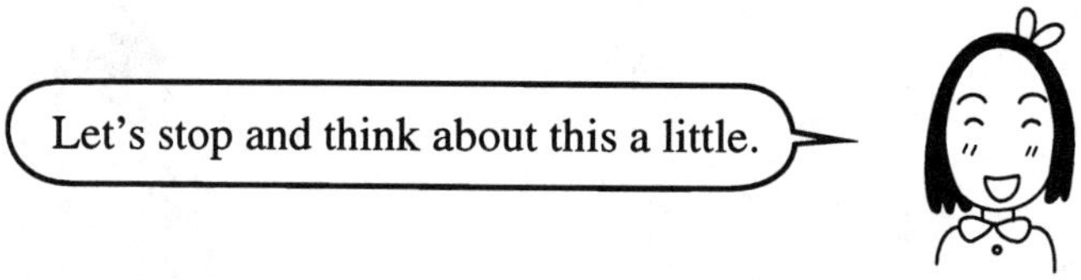

FIRST, CONCERNING POINTS 1 AND 2

Heisenberg was able to solve the problem by "forcing" something that was not the position of an electron into Newton's equation of motion. Nevertheless, he was able to verify that energy is conserved, and to fulfill Bohr's frequency relation.

The energy that was calculated by introducing something that was not position was entirely different from energy as it had been previously conceived. But it was consistent with the law of energy conservation and with Bohr's frequency relation. The term "energy" was therefore acceptable, and other terms in the language of classical mechanics could be retained and used in quantum mechanics.

In sum, Heisenberg's equation of motion

> 1) shows that energy is conserved.
> 2) is consistent with Bohr's frequency relation.

Although it was found that Heisenberg's equation worked for harmonic oscillation (or, for Heisenberg, an anharmonic oscillator), no one knew whether it would hold in all other cases. If Heisenberg's theory were to have any meaning, it had to be valid in every case.

1. The Conservation of energy!

In Heisenberg's equation of motion

$$\frac{dg}{dt} = -\frac{2\pi i}{h}(gH - Hg)$$

as long as g is a function of p and q, it can be anything.

However, the Hamiltonian H of the matrix describing energy is

$$H(p, q) = \frac{1}{2m}p^2 + V(q)\ .$$

It is apparent that this is a function of p and q.

If we take the g in Heisenberg's equation of motion to be H, we get

$$\frac{dH}{dt} = -\frac{2\pi i}{h}\,(\underline{HH - HH})\,.$$

It goes without saying that $HH - HH = 0$, so

$$\frac{dH}{dt} = 0\,.$$

The meaning of this equation is that the change of energy over time dH/dt is 0. And, if energy does not increase or decrease over time, then **ENERGY IS CONSERVED.**

How easy it was to prove finally that energy is conserved (i.e., it does not change over time) not only in the case of harmonic oscillation, but in any and all cases!

I feel like I've been tricked!
Am I the only one who feels this way?

We have proved that energy does not change over time, and now we know something else, too. Energy H is a matrix, in the same way that p or q are.

Physical quantities in quantum mechanics are all matrices!

When we define H for all elements, we write:

$$\boxed{H_{nn'} = \bar{H}_{nn'} e^{i2\pi \nu_{nn'} t}}$$

($\bar{H}_{nn'}$ is amplitude)

Because $H_{nn'}$ is a function of time, obviously it varies over time. But there is only one situation when it doesn't change over time.

When $n = n'$?

Exactly! When $n = n'$, the frequency ν_{nn} indicates the frequency when there is transition from n to n, that is to say when there is no transition, and therefore equals 0.

Thus, we obtain:

$$H_{nn} = \bar{H}_{nn} e^{i2\pi \underline{\nu_{nn}} t} = \bar{H}_{nn} e^{i2\pi 0 t} = \bar{H}_{nn} e^{0} = \bar{H}_{nn} \, .$$

If matrix H does not change over time, then only H_{nn}, the elements of the form $n = n'$ which do not change over time (that is, only the diagonal elements), can have values other than 0; all other elements in H must be 0.

$$\begin{pmatrix} H_{11} & 0 & 0 & \cdots \\ 0 & H_{22} & 0 & \cdots \\ 0 & 0 & H_{33} & \cdots \\ \vdots & \vdots & \vdots & \end{pmatrix}$$

If we denote the values of the diagonal elements of matrix H by W_1, W_2, $W_3 \ldots$, matrix H then becomes:

$$\begin{pmatrix} W_1 & 0 & 0 & \cdots \\ 0 & W_2 & 0 & \cdots \\ 0 & 0 & W_3 & \cdots \\ \vdots & \vdots & \vdots & \end{pmatrix}$$

MATRIX *H* FOR ENERGY BECOMES A DIAGONAL MATRIX!!

If we express the elements of matrix H using the Kronecker delta $\delta_{nn'}$ we get:

$$H_{nn'} = W_n \delta_{nn'}$$

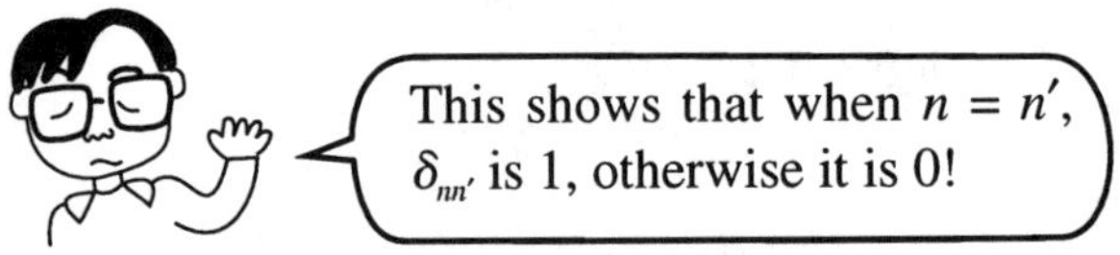

2. Bohr's frequency relation

Let's look again at Heisenberg's equation of motion!

$$\frac{dg}{dt} = -\frac{2\pi i}{h}(gH - Hg)$$

Now, all we do is use this equation to prove that Bohr's frequency relation holds. . .

OK, Pero, give it a try!

The g in Heisenberg's equation of motion is, of course, a matrix, and its elements are

$$g_{nn'} = G_{nn'} e^{i2\pi \nu_{nn'} t} .$$

Now let's look at each side of Heisenberg's equation of motion and see what their respective elements are!

Taking the left side, dg/dt, first, the elements are:

$$\left(\frac{dg}{dt}\right)_{nn'} = i2\pi \nu_{nn'} G_{nn'} e^{i2\pi \nu_{nn'} t} .$$

But, $G_{nn'} e^{i2\pi \nu_{nn'} t} = g_{nn'}$, so it follows that the

$$\text{left side} = i2\pi \nu_{nn'} g_{nn'} .$$

That takes care of the **left side!**

Now let's go to the right side. We obtain

$$\left\{-\frac{2\pi i}{h}(gH - Hg)\right\}_{nn'} = -\frac{2\pi i}{h}\left(\sum_{n''} g_{nn''} H_{n''n'} - \sum_{n''} H_{nn''} g_{n''n'}\right).$$

But we know that energy H is a diagonal matrix with the form

$$H_{nn'} = W_n \delta_{nn'} .$$

We insert this into the above equation, and obtain

$$H_{n''n'} = W_{n''} \delta_{n''n'}$$

$$H_{nn''} = W_n \delta_{nn''} .$$

It follows that

$$= -\frac{2\pi i}{h}\left(\sum_{n''} g_{nn''} W_{n''} \delta_{n''n'} - \sum_{n''} W_n \delta_{nn''} g_{n''n'}\right).$$

The Kronecker delta $\delta_{n''n'}$ is 1 only if $n'' = n'$; otherwise it is 0. In the same way, $\delta_{nn''}$ is 1 only if $n = n''$; otherwise it is 0. Therefore, $\sum_{n''}$ disappears.

$$= -\frac{2\pi i}{h}\left(g_{nn'}W_{n'} - W_n g_{nn'}\right)$$

We factor out $g_{nn'}$.

$$= -\frac{2\pi i}{h}\left(W_{n'} - W_n\right)g_{nn'}$$

If we put the minus sign inside the brackets, the order inside the brackets is reversed.

$$= \frac{2\pi i}{h}\left(W_n - W_{n'}\right)g_{nn'}$$

Last of all, let's put the h inside the brackets.

$$\text{right side} = 2\pi i\left(\frac{W_n - W_{n'}}{h}\right)g_{nn'}$$

The **right side** is finished!

So far we have worked out the left and right sides of Heisenberg's equation of motion.

$$\frac{dg}{dt} = -\frac{2\pi i}{h}(gH - Hg)$$

left side	right side
$i2\pi\, \nu_{nn'} g_{nn'}$	$2\pi i \dfrac{W_n - W_{n'}}{h} g_{nn'}$

We now connect the left half and the right half with an equal sign, and obtain:

$$\cancel{i2\pi}\, \nu_{nn'}\cancel{g_{nn'}} = \cancel{2\pi i}\frac{W_n - W_{n'}}{h}\cancel{g_{nn'}}$$

$$\boxed{\nu_{nn'} = \frac{W_n - W_{n'}}{h}}$$

With this we have proven that Bohr's frequency relation always holds!

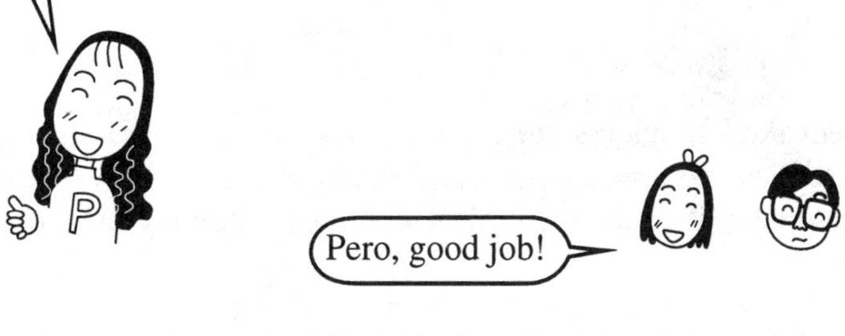

SUMMARY

Using Heisenberg's equation of motion

$$\frac{dg}{dt} = -\frac{2\pi i}{h}(gH - Hg)$$

we have neatly proven that

1) energy is always conserved and
2) Bohr's frequency relation always holds true.

EIGENVALUE PROBLEMS

OK, now let's move on to the major advantage of Heisenberg's equation of motion, which is that **THE PROBLEM BECOMES ONE OF EIGENVALUES!**

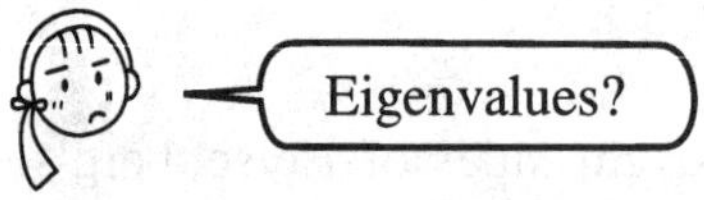

Since it's an unfamiliar term, we'll interview someone who knows matrix mathematics well and can explain.

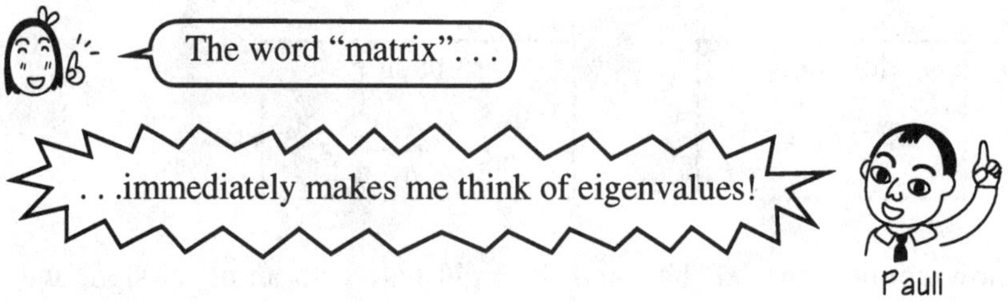

Just as "baseball" makes us think of "hot dogs,"

IF WE TALK ABOUT **"MATRICES,"**
WE HAVE TO DISCUSS **"EIGENVALUES".**

We are trying to find the frequencies and amplitudes of spectra. In order to find them, all we need to do is solve Heisenberg's equation of motion. However, Born discovered a method for finding Q and ν directly, without solving the equation of motion. This is the famous "eigenvalue problem."

Eigenvalues problems are an important part of matrix mathematics. They come into play in various contexts. Because solutions have been studied for so long, material written on this subject would fill a bulging manual.

Just think how easy it would be if there were a manual!

Now, how can we find the amplitude and frequency of a spectrum using eigenvalues? Let's try it!

First Step: Lower-case *p*, *q* and upper-case *P*, *Q*

We gather the spectral amplitudes $P_{nn'}$, $Q_{nn'}$ and write them as a matrix.

$$P = \begin{pmatrix} P_{11} & P_{12} & P_{13} & \cdots \\ P_{21} & P_{22} & P_{23} & \cdots \\ P_{31} & P_{32} & P_{33} & \cdots \\ \vdots & \vdots & \vdots & \end{pmatrix} \qquad Q = \begin{pmatrix} Q_{11} & Q_{12} & Q_{13} & \cdots \\ Q_{21} & Q_{22} & Q_{23} & \cdots \\ Q_{31} & Q_{32} & Q_{33} & \cdots \\ \vdots & \vdots & \vdots & \end{pmatrix}$$

In so doing, finding the amplitude $P_{nn'}$, $Q_{nn'}$ becomes the same thing as finding the matrix P, Q.

Do we gain anything by going to the trouble of gathering the amplitudes $P_{nn'}$, $Q_{nn'}$ and write them as a matrix?

Sure we do.

In fact, matrix P, Q has the following interesting property:

$$f(p, q)_{nn'} = f(P, Q)_{nn'}\, e^{i2\pi\nu_{nn'}t}$$

To obtain the lower-case function, simply multiply the upper-case function by $e^{i2\pi\nu_{nn'}t}$.

First, in the case of $f(p, q) = p$ and $f(p, q) = q$, we obtain

$$p_{nn'} = P_{nn'}\, e^{i2\pi\nu_{nn'}t}$$
$$q_{nn'} = Q_{nn'}\, e^{i2\pi\nu_{nn'}t}$$

This is great: they simply become the elements of matrix p, q.

Next, we consider **addition.**

$$
\begin{aligned}
(p+q)_{nn'} &= P_{nn'}e^{i2\pi\nu_{nn'}t} + Q_{nn'}e^{i2\pi\nu_{nn'}t} \\
&= \left(P_{nn'} + Q_{nn'}\right)e^{i2\pi\nu_{nn'}t}
\end{aligned}
$$

Yup! The lower-case function becomes the upper-case function multiplied by $e^{i2\pi\nu_{nn'}t}$.

Finally, we tackle **multiplication.**

$$
\begin{aligned}
(pq)_{nn'} &= \sum_{n''} p_{nn''}q_{n''n'} \\
&= \sum_{n''} P_{nn''}e^{i2\pi\nu_{nn''}t}Q_{n''n'}e^{i2\pi\nu_{n''n'}t} \\
&= \sum_{n''} P_{nn''}Q_{n''n'}e^{i2\pi\left(\nu_{nn''}+\nu_{n''n'}\right)t} \\
&\qquad\qquad\qquad\qquad\quad \uparrow \\
&\qquad\qquad\qquad\qquad\quad \nu_{nn'} \\
&= \sum_{n''} P_{nn''}Q_{n''n'}e^{i2\pi\nu_{nn'}t} \\
(pq)_{nn'} &= (PQ)_{nn'}e^{i2\pi\nu_{nn'}t}
\end{aligned}
$$

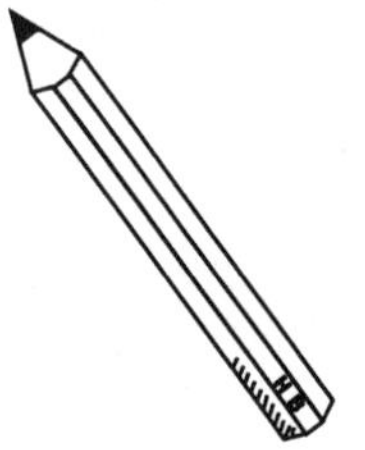

Here too the lower-case function is the upper-case function multiplied by $e^{i2\pi\nu_{nn'}t}$!

So that means that for both addition and multiplication, the lower-case function is the upper-case function multiplied by $e^{i2\pi\nu_{nn'}t}$!

Almost all functions are combinations of additions and multiplications. So whether you are adding p,q or are multiplying them, the rule that the lower-case function is the upper-case function multiplied by $e^{i2\pi\nu_{nn'}t}$! will apply for all functions $f(p, q)$ of p and q.

I see.

It really gets interesting now.

Let's go on to the canonical commutative relation for lower-case p, q.

$$
\boxed{(pq - qp)_{nn'} = \frac{h}{2\pi i}}
$$

Because the $(pq - qp)_{nn'}$ on the left is a lower-case function, it equals the upper-case function multiplied by $e^{i2\pi\nu_{nn'}t}$.

$$(pq - qp)_{nn'} = (PQ - QP)_{nn'}\, e^{i2\pi\nu_{nn'}t}$$

Here, we use the canonical commutative relation $(pq - qp)_{nn'} = \dfrac{h}{2\pi i}$.

$$(PQ - QP)_{nn'}\, e^{i2\pi\nu_{nn'}t} = \frac{h}{2\pi i}\,\delta_{nn'} = \begin{cases} \dfrac{h}{2\pi i} & (n = n') \\ 0 & (n \neq n') \end{cases}$$

This equation means that

When $n = n'$, $e^{i2\pi\nu_{nn'}t} = 1$, and so $(PQ - QP)_{nn'} = \dfrac{h}{2\pi i}$, and

when $n \neq n'$, $e^{i2\pi\nu_{nn'}t} \neq 0$, and so $(PQ - QP)_{nn'} = 0$.

SUMMARY

$$(PQ - QP)_{nn'} = \frac{h}{2\pi i}\,\delta_{nn'}$$

When the canonical commutative relation holds for lower-case p, q, the canonical commutative relation also holds for upper-case P, Q.

Let's consider one last thing—the Hamiltonian $H(p, q)$! Since the lower-case function is the upper-case function multiplied by $e^{i2\pi\nu_{nn'}t}$, we get

$$H(p, q)_{nn'} = H(P, Q)_{nn'}\, e^{i2\pi\nu_{nn'}t}$$

Here the lower-case Hamiltonian $H(p, q)$ is a diagonal matrix.

If $\quad H(p, q)_{nn'} = W_n \delta_{nn'}$

then $\quad H(P, Q)_{nn'}\, e^{i2\pi\nu_{nn'}t} = W_n \delta_{nn'}$

The situation is the same as for the canonical commutative relation.

SUMMARY

$$H(P, Q)_{nn'} = W_n \delta_{nn'}$$

If the Hamiltonian is a diagonal matrix for lower-case p, q, it will also be a diagonal matrix for upper-case P, Q.

It's interesting that the same things hold true for both lower and upper-cases, isn't it?

Yes, but doesn't it seem then like we could do something with it? We've been concentrating on lower-case p, q so far, and yet. . .

We could switch our focus to upper-case!

Bingo! The upper-case P, Q are amplitudes $P_{nn'}$, $Q_{nn'}$ arranged in a matrix, so it'll be easier if we treat them as upper-case from the start.

Can we do that?

Sure we can! We have already proven that

1. upper-case P, Q fulfills the canonical commutative relation, and
2. when the Hamiltonian $H(P, Q)$ is a diagonal matrix,

then lower-case p, q fulfills both the canonical commutative relation and Heisenberg's equation for motion.

Now what did that mean again?

Well, until now we have found the amplitude and frequency by looking for a lower-case p, q which fulfills the canonical commutative relation and Heisenberg's equation of motion.

But now we don't have to do that anymore?

Right. From now on we can look for an upper-case P, Q that will fulfill the two previous conditions, and find the amplitude and frequency directly.

OK, let's get to the proof.

Right on!

First, consider upper-case P, Q

$$P = \begin{pmatrix} P_{11} & P_{12} & P_{13} & \cdots \\ P_{21} & P_{22} & P_{23} & \cdots \\ P_{31} & P_{32} & P_{33} & \cdots \\ \vdots & \vdots & \vdots & \end{pmatrix} \quad Q = \begin{pmatrix} Q_{11} & Q_{12} & Q_{13} & \cdots \\ Q_{21} & Q_{22} & Q_{23} & \cdots \\ Q_{31} & Q_{32} & Q_{33} & \cdots \\ \vdots & \vdots & \vdots & \end{pmatrix}$$

Now let its Hamiltonian H

$$H(P, Q) = \frac{1}{2m} P^2 + V(Q)$$

fulfill the canonical commutative relation,

$$PQ - QP = \frac{h}{2\pi i} 1$$

and form a diagonal matrix.

$$H(P, Q)_{nn'} = W_n \delta_{nn'}$$

Let's take as amplitude the elements of upper-case P, Q , and take as frequency the $\nu_{nn'}$ that we derived, using Bohr's frequency relation

$$\boxed{\nu_{nn'} = \frac{W_n - W_{n'}}{h}}$$

from the Hamiltonian $H\,(P, Q)$ diagonal elements W_1, W_2, W_3. . .

Now, let's consider transition components possessing this amplitude and frequency

$$p_{nn'} = P_{nn'} e^{i2\pi \nu_{nn'} t}$$

$$q_{nn'} = Q_{nn'} e^{i2\pi \nu_{nn'} t}$$

as well as the lower-case matrix with elements $p_{nn'}$, $q_{nn'}$.

We do not know whether p, q fulfills the canonical commutative relation. This can be proven in the same way as when we derived the canonical commutative relation from Bohr's quantum condition, so we will skip it here.

The only thing left is to find out if it satisfies Heisenberg's equation of motion.

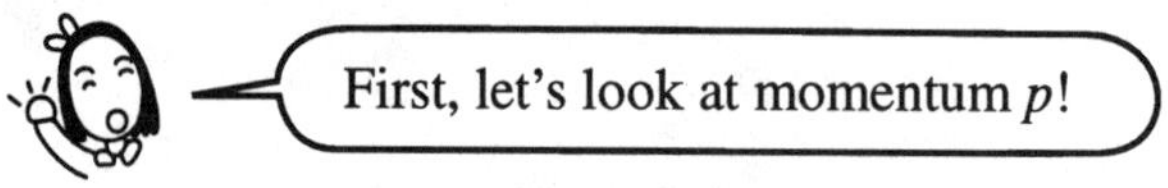

With regard to momentum p, Heisenberg's equation of motion is as follows:

$$\frac{dp}{dt} = -\frac{2\pi i}{h}(pH - Hp).$$

Then let's see what happens to the elements on both sides of the equation!

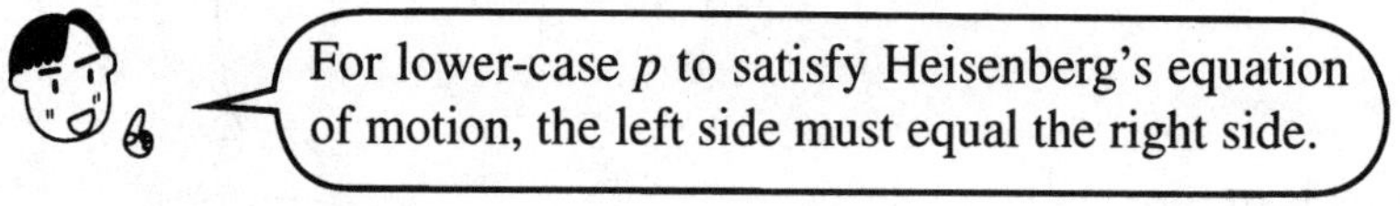

The left side is

$$\left(\frac{dp}{dt}\right)_{nn'} = i2\pi \nu_{nn'} P_{nn'} e^{i2\pi \nu_{nn'} t}.$$

Because $P_{nn'} e^{i2\pi \nu_{nn'} t} = p_{nn'}$, we have

$$\boxed{\text{left side} = i2\pi \nu_{nn'} p_{nn'}.}$$

Next, the right side is

$$-\left(\frac{2\pi i}{h}\right)\left\{pH(p, q) - H(p, q)p\right\}.$$

However, since $H(p, q)$ is a lower-case function—indeed, since the entire left side is a lower-case function—we can use our old trick "lower-case = upper-case multiplied by $e^{i2\pi\nu_{nn'}t}$."

$$\left[-\frac{2\pi i}{h}\left\{pH(p, q) - H(p, q)p\right\}\right]_{nn'}$$

$$= \left[-\frac{2\pi i}{h}\left\{PH(P, Q) - H(P, Q)P\right\}\right]_{nn'} e^{i2\pi \nu_{nn'} t}$$

We do multiplication using elements.

$$= -\frac{2\pi i}{h}\left\{\sum_{n''} P_{nn''} H(P,Q)_{n''n'} - \sum_{n''} H(P,Q)_{nn''} P_{n''n'}\right\} e^{i2\pi \nu_{nn'} t}$$

Because the upper-case Hamiltonian $H\,(P,\,Q)$ is a diagonal matrix, we get

$$H(P,Q)_{nn''} = W_n \delta_{nn''}$$

$$H(P,Q)_{n''n'} = W_{n''} \delta_{n''n'} \,.$$

From this, we arrive at the following:

$$= -\frac{2\pi i}{h}\left\{\sum_{n''} P_{nn''} W_{n''} \delta_{n''n'} - \sum_{n''} W_n \delta_{nn''} P_{n''n'}\right\} e^{i2\pi \nu_{nn'} t} \,.$$

Here, $W_{n''}\delta_{n''n'}$ equals 0, except for elements where $n'' = n'$. Because $W_{n''}\delta_{n''n}$ equals 0, except for elements where $n'' = n$, $\sum_{n''}$ drops out.

$$= -\frac{2\pi i}{h}(P_{nn'} W_{n'} - W_n P_{nn'}) e^{i2\pi \nu_{nn'} t}$$

We place the minus sign inside the brackets.

$$= \frac{2\pi i}{h}(W_n P_{nn'} - W_{n'} P_{nn'}) e^{i2\pi \nu_{nn'} t}$$

We place h inside the brackets and factor out $p_{nn'}$.

$$= 2\pi i\left(\frac{W_n - W_{n'}}{h}\right) P_{nn'} e^{i2\pi \nu_{nn'} t}$$

$$\hookrightarrow = p_{nn'}$$

We finally have:

$$\boxed{\text{right side} = 2\pi i \nu_{nn'} p_{nn'} \,.}$$

Now, compare the right and left sides of Heisenberg's equation of motion. . .

left side	right side
$i2\pi\nu_{nn'}p_{nn'}$	$2\pi i\nu_{nn'}p_{nn'}$

THEY'RE EXACTLY THE SAME!!!!

We can treat the case of q in exactly the same manner.

Our calculations have proven that lower-case $p_{nn'}$, which was derived from upper-case P, Q, satisfies Heisenberg's equation of motion!

SUMMARY

If an upper-case P, Q can be found that fulfills the canonical commutative relation and whose Hamiltonian forms a diagonal matrix, it is then possible to find the amplitude and frequency of a spectrum.

Next step: Unitary transformation

Thus, if an upper-case P, Q can be found

1. that fulfills the canonical commutative relation, and
2. whose Hamiltonian forms a diagonal matrix,

then the spectral amplitude and frequency may be found.

Well then, how do we go about finding a P, Q that fulfills these conditions?

There's a trick to it.

First we propose a matrix P°, Q°.

P°, Q° can be anything, as long as it satisfies the canonical commutative relationship

$$P^{\circ}Q^{\circ} - Q^{\circ}P^{\circ} = \frac{h}{2\pi i}1.$$

It doesn't matter where we find it.

If that is so, then it should be easy to find.

This means that we've reduced the number of conditions by one. However, P°, Q° was stuck in arbitrarily, and so normally its Hamiltonian

$$H(P^{\circ}, Q^{\circ})$$

will not form a diagonal matrix.

You're right. But what should we do?

Actually, there is a technique for making P°, Q° into a diagonal matrix. The technique is called

UNITARY TRANSFORMATION!

Well, let's see what kind of beast this unitary transformation is!

A unitary transformation is possible when a matrix is placed within a unitary matrix U.

$$U^{\dagger}AU$$

A unitary matrix looks like this:

$$U^{\dagger}U = UU^{\dagger} = 1 \quad \text{(identity matrix)}$$

The † sign is called a "dagger." It tells you to switch the positions of rows and columns and then take the complex conjugate.

$$\begin{pmatrix} A & B \\ C & D \end{pmatrix}^{\dagger} = \begin{pmatrix} A^* & C^* \\ B^* & D^* \end{pmatrix}$$

H (P°, Q°) is not a diagonal matrix. But fortunately, we can perform a unitary transformation, so that $U^{\dagger}$ $H(P^{\circ}, Q^{\circ})$ U becomes a diagonal matrix.

$$U^{\dagger}H(P^{\circ}, Q^{\circ})U = \begin{pmatrix} W_1 & 0 & 0 & \cdot\cdot \\ 0 & W_2 & 0 & \cdot\cdot \\ 0 & 0 & W_3 & \cdot\cdot \\ \vdots & \vdots & \vdots & \end{pmatrix}$$

But remember, we were trying to find the upper-case P, Q.

In fact, there is a way to find it. That's the great thing about unitary transformation!

Take harmonic oscillation as an example. With harmonic oscillation, the Hamiltonian $H\,(P^{\circ}, Q^{\circ})$ of P°, Q° is the following:

$$\begin{aligned} H(P^{\circ}, Q^{\circ}) &= \frac{1}{2m}(P^{\circ})^2 + \frac{k}{2}(Q^{\circ})^2 \\ &= \frac{1}{2m}P^{\circ}P^{\circ} + \frac{k}{2}Q^{\circ}Q^{\circ}. \end{aligned}$$

We sandwich (P°, Q°) inside the unitary matrix $U^{\dagger}$, U and turn it into a diagonal matrix.

$$U^{\dagger}H(P^{\circ}, Q^{\circ})U = \begin{pmatrix} W_1 & 0 & 0 & \cdot\cdot \\ 0 & W_2 & 0 & \cdot\cdot \\ 0 & 0 & W_3 & \cdot\cdot \\ \vdots & \vdots & \vdots & \end{pmatrix}$$

Now insert the Hamiltonian for harmonic oscillation and work it out. First, we remove the brackets.

$$U^{\dagger}\left(\frac{1}{2m}P^{\circ}P^{\circ} + \frac{k}{2}Q^{\circ}Q^{\circ}\right)U = \frac{1}{2m}U^{\dagger}P^{\circ}P^{\circ}U + \frac{k}{2}U^{\dagger}Q^{\circ}Q^{\circ}U$$

Here is where the unitary matrix can show off its special character. We insert $U^{\dagger}U$ between P° and P° and between Q° and Q°.

$$= \frac{1}{2m}U^{\dagger}P^{\circ}UU^{\dagger}P^{\circ}U + \frac{k}{2}U^{\dagger}Q^{\circ}UU^{\dagger}Q^{\circ}U$$

$U^{\dagger}U$ is 1, so it has no effect on the equation.

Now for something new. We let

$$P = U^{\dagger}P^{\circ}U$$
$$Q = U^{\dagger}Q^{\circ}U.$$

If we do this, lo and behold, we get

$$= \frac{1}{2m}P^2 + \frac{k}{2}Q^2 .$$

Since this was placed in a unitary matrix and is therefore now a diagonal matrix, we can write this:

$$\frac{1}{2m}P^2 + \frac{k}{2}Q^2 = \begin{pmatrix} W_1 & 0 & 0 & \cdots \\ 0 & W_2 & 0 & \cdots \\ 0 & 0 & W_3 & \cdots \\ \vdots & \vdots & \vdots & \end{pmatrix}$$

That is to say, P°, Q°, which was chosen arbitrarily, is placed in the unitary matrix $U^{\dagger}$, U, which gives us

$$\boxed{\begin{aligned} P &= U^{\dagger}P^{\circ}U \\ Q &= U^{\dagger}Q^{\circ}U \end{aligned}}$$

This is the upper-case P, Q that we wanted to find—the spectral amplitude.

Does that mean that all we have to find now is a unitary matrix U that will turn H (P°, Q°) into a diagonal matrix when we do the unitary transformation?

That's right. And the method for finding U hinges on the use of eigenvalues.

Since $U^{\dagger}H$ (P°, Q°) U will be a diagonal matrix, we get this:

$$U^{\dagger}H(P^{\circ}, Q^{\circ})U = \begin{pmatrix} W_1 & 0 & 0 & \cdots \\ 0 & W_2 & 0 & \cdots \\ 0 & 0 & W_3 & \cdots \\ \vdots & \vdots & \vdots & \end{pmatrix}$$

If we multiply both sides by U, beginning with the left side, we get $U^{\dagger}U = 1$.

Therefore,

$$H(P^{\circ}, Q^{\circ})U = U\begin{pmatrix} W_1 & 0 & 0 & \cdot\cdot \\ 0 & W_2 & 0 & \cdot\cdot \\ 0 & 0 & W_3 & \cdot\cdot \\ \vdots & \vdots & \vdots & \end{pmatrix}$$

$$= \begin{pmatrix} U_{11} & U_{12} & U_{13} & \cdot\cdot \\ U_{21} & U_{22} & U_{23} & \cdot\cdot \\ U_{31} & U_{32} & U_{33} & \cdot\cdot \\ \vdots & \vdots & \vdots & \end{pmatrix}\begin{pmatrix} W_1 & 0 & 0 & \cdot\cdot \\ 0 & W_2 & 0 & \cdot\cdot \\ 0 & 0 & W_3 & \cdot\cdot \\ \vdots & \vdots & \vdots & \end{pmatrix}$$

$$= \begin{pmatrix} U_{11}W_1 & U_{12}W_2 & U_{13}W_3 & \cdot\cdot \\ U_{21}W_1 & U_{22}W_2 & U_{23}W_3 & \cdot\cdot \\ U_{31}W_1 & U_{32}W_2 & U_{33}W_3 & \cdot\cdot \\ \vdots & \vdots & \vdots & \end{pmatrix}$$

If you look at the right side, you see that the first column contains only W_1; the second column, only W_2, and the third column, only W_3. Therefore, those groupings remain intact even if you move the individual columns around. Now, let the unitary matrix with the disordered columns be ξ (xi).

$$\xi = \begin{pmatrix} \xi_1 \\ \xi_2 \\ \xi_3 \\ \vdots \end{pmatrix}$$

Point

$$H(P^{\circ}, Q^{\circ})\xi - W\xi = 0$$

Eigenvalues are the key to solving this equation!

And when we solve the eigenvalue problem here, we can find upper-case P, Q and, therefore, find the spectral amplitude and frequency.

3. 5 A CONVERSATION WITH EINSTEIN

So you see that Heisenberg's discovery was formulated into a system of matrix mathematics. His theory had huge reverberations in the world of physics and mathematics, and beyond. He had discovered a method for finding spectral intensity, something that had seemed impossible until then.

Soon he was invited to speak on his matrix mechanics theory at a physics conference at the University of Berlin. At the time, the University of Berlin was considered a bastion of physics. Planck and Einstein were both working there. Whenever a physics conference was held, they and other prominent members of the academic community attended.

Having this opportunity to get to know some world-class physicists, Heisenberg was eager and determined. He prepared with great care so that his discovery would be properly understood. He rehearsed his presentation countless times with his close friend Pauli.

On the day of the conference, Heisenberg's lecture went exactly as planned. And just as he had hoped, Einstein expressed interest in his topic.

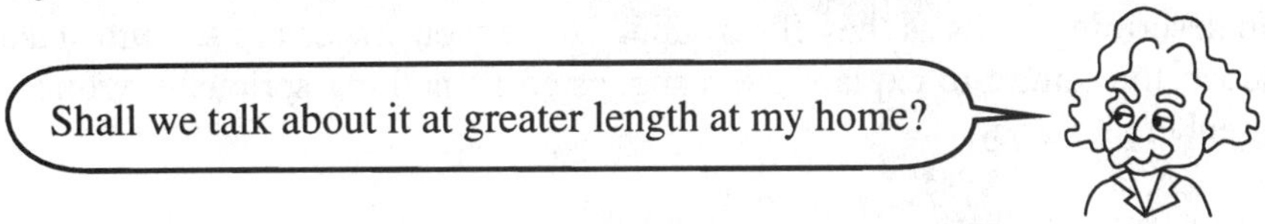

This was the renowned Einstein speaking to him! Heisenberg's knees were shaking. Before he could say yes or no, Einstein started in.

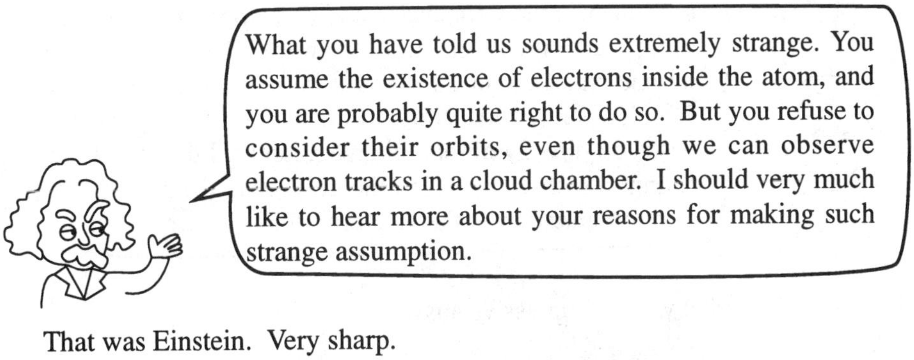

Physics and Beyond

That was Einstein. Very sharp.

Heisenberg developed his quantum mechanics theory from the perspective of a correspondence with classical mechanics. He worked within the main framework of classical mechanics. But where classical mechanics considered light to be composed of waves, he followed Einstein and said that light is composed of quanta. In so doing, he successfully explained the spectrum, the only available clue in the quest to unravel the mystery of the atom.

But along the way Heisenberg had done something unthinkable. Despite the fact that the sum of transitions

$$q = \sum_{\tau} Q(n; n-\tau) e^{i2\pi\nu(n;\, n-\tau)t}$$

could no longer be used to describe the position—or in Einstein's words, the orbit—of the electron, he had forcibly maneuvered it into Newton's equation of motion $F = m\ddot{q}$. Finally, q was taken to be a collection of numbers called a matrix.

This "radical breakthrough" was not simply a devil-may-care error. Although q no longer described the orbit of the electron and ended up becoming a matrix, Heisenberg's "energy" was in full accord with the law of energy conservation and Bohr's frequency relation. Yet that did not change the fact that Heisenberg had built a theory on a base other than the orbit of the electron.

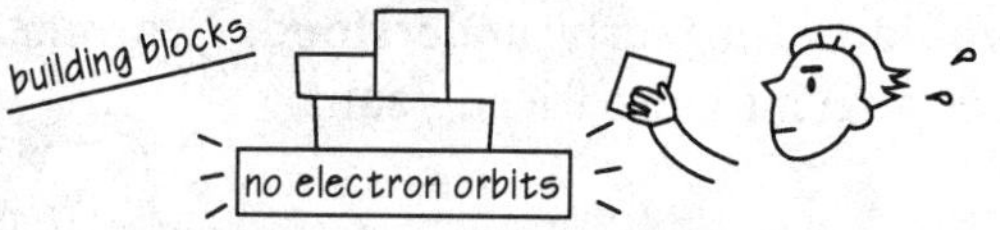

The cloud chamber experiment clearly demonstrates that the orbits of electrons exist and that electrons describe a certain path as they move from a given location to another. Inside the cloud chamber, electrons can be clearly seen describing paths as they fly around. Since their traces are so unmistakably evident, the failure to explain them suggested something seriously wrong with Heisenberg's theory.

But Heisenberg had given ample thought to this point, too. It was almost inevitable that this question would come up. Heisenberg met Einstein's challenge with his response already prepared.

Physics and Beyond

We cannot observe electron orbits inside the atom. But the radiation which an atom emits during discharges enables us to deduce the frequencies and corresponding amplitudes of its electrons. After all, even in the older physics wave numbers and amplitudes could be considered substitutes for electron orbits. Now, since a good theory must be based on directly observable magnitudes, I thought it more fitting to restrict myself to these, treating them, as it were, as representatives of the electron orbits.

Yes indeed, that was an impressive answer.

Electrons are regarded as "invisible." Although we can see their tracks as vapor in a cloud chamber, we certainly cannot see the electrons themselves. From its spectrum, however, we can find the frequency and amplitude of the light emitted by the electrons. Of course, electrons were considered invisible in classical mechanics also, but it was assumed that if the frequency $\nu(n, \tau)$ and amplitude $Q(n, \tau)$ of an electron's light were known, then its orbit could also be identified.

$$q = \sum_{\tau} \underline{Q(n, \tau)}\, e^{i2\pi \underline{\nu(n, \tau)t}}$$

But when classical mechanics is rewritten "correctly" for quanta, we obtain

$$q = \sum_{\tau} \underline{Q(n; n-\tau)}\, e^{i2\pi \underline{\nu(n; n-\tau)t}}$$

and the orbits have disappeared. This tells us that thinking in terms of "orbits" was a mistake right from the start. Instead of thinking of orbits as things that exist even though we can't see them, wouldn't it be better to regard things we can't see as not existing?

That is the way Heisenberg thought.

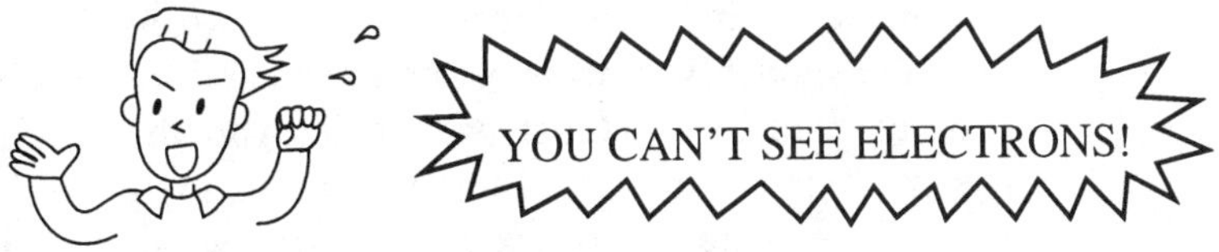

But Einstein didn't accept that.

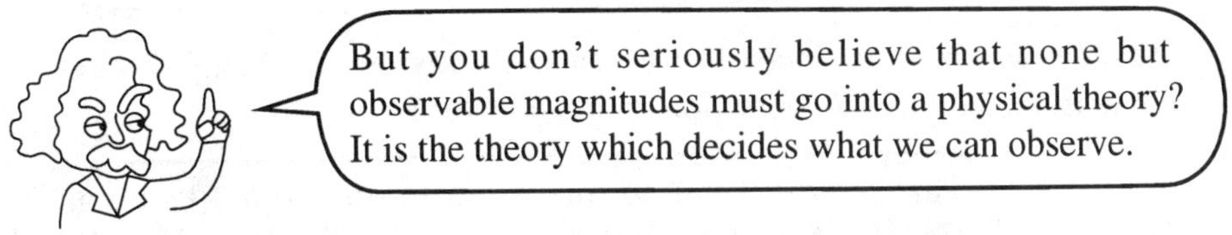

It is too simplistic to say that just because you can't see it, it's not there.

Let's say you hear a thumping sound in the next room, for example. As long as you know that the room belongs to a child, and that he or she likes kicking a ball around, you can deduce from the sound that there is a child playing with a ball in the next room, even without looking in the room. It is the same with the inside of an atom. Even if you can't see electrons, from the light that electrons give off, you can deduce that something is happening. That is physics: people trying to explain physical phenomena. That is why it is a huge mistake to find satisfaction, as Heisenberg did, in explaining the light emitted by electrons without asking how and why they are moving.

Einstein haltingly reasoned this way with Heisenberg.

But Heisenberg would not be beaten. No matter what Einstein might say, he would try to refute it. All things considered, however, Heisenberg was at a disadvantage.

WHAT IS HAPPENING INSIDE THE ATOM?

Heisenberg had no answer to Einstein's question.

Finally Einstein asked:

Physics and Beyond

> How can you really have so much faith in your theory when so many crucial problems remain completely unsolved?

Heisenberg could not respond right away. But after a while, he said:

Physics and Beyond

> I believe, just like you, that the simplicity of natural laws has an objective character, that it is not just the result of thought economy. If nature leads us to mathematical forms of great simplicity and beauty - by forms I am referring to coherent systems of hypotheses, axioms, etc. - to forms that no one has previously encountered, we cannot help thinking that they are 'true,' that they reveal a genuine feature of nature.
>
> You must have felt this, too: the almost frightening simplicity and wholeness of the relationships which nature suddenly spreads out before us and for which none of us was in the least prepared. And this feeling is something completely different from the joy we feel when we have done a set task particularly well. That is one reason why I hope that the problems we have been discussing will be solved in one way or another.

Einstein was not convinced by Heisenberg's answer. Although he did not accept it, he ended their conversation with these words:

Physics and Beyond

> That is why I am so interested in your remarks about simplicity. Still, I should never claim that I really understood what is meant by the simplicity of natural laws.

From this conversation with Einstein, Heisenberg realized that quantum mechanics was still very much a work in progress.

CHAPTER 4

Luis Victor de Broglie
and
Erwin Schrödinger

WAVE MECHANICS

As long as electrons were thought of as particles, physicists could explain their behavior very well. But with Heisenberg's statement, "Let's do away with orbits," it became impossible to imagine how they behaved.

Then de Broglie, drawn to physics by Einstein's work, presented the daring theory that electrons also have the characteristics of waves. At the same time, experiments were performed showing that electrons were in fact waves.

When Schrödinger learned of these developments, he worked out a series of equations based on the image of electrons as waves.

4. 1 OUR ADVENTURE SO FAR

We're almost halfway through our adventure. As a reminder of what we've done so far, let's quickly go over the first half.

Long ago, light was thought to be waves. Why? Because the wave theory of light nicely accounted for certain important experiments.

These experiments concerned interference and diffraction. Briefly, the height of a wave is its amplitude, and the energy of a wave may be expressed as $|\text{amplitude}|^2$. Since waves can attain any height, the amplitude, and therefore the energy, should be able to assume any value.

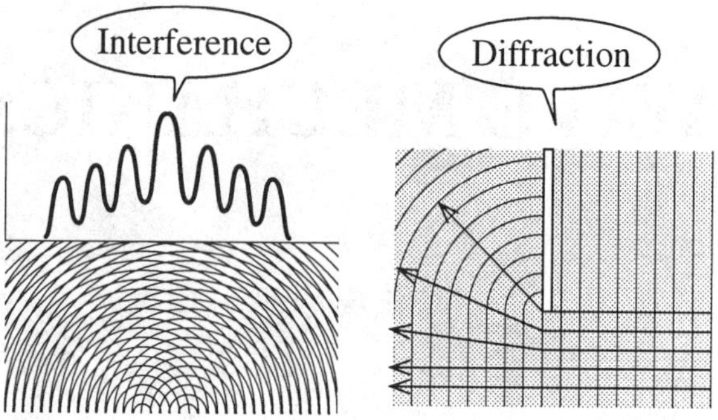

But!!!

Seeing the results of the blackbody radiation experiment, Planck stated,

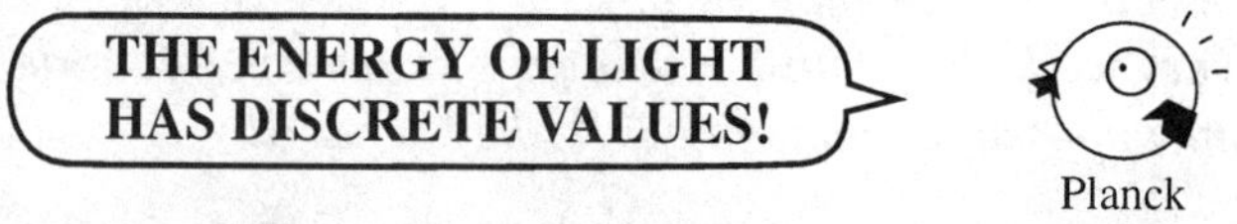

In the language of numerical expressions, this may be expressed as

$$E = nh\nu \ \ (n = 0, 1, 2, 3 \cdots)$$

The energy of a wave should be able to have any value along a continuum of values, but the energy of light is discontinuous. It's odd, isn't it?

Planck thought his own discovery was so strange that he tried not to talk about it.

But without realizing it, Planck had opened the door to the adventure of quantum mechanics.

Then Einstein made his appearance.

Planck had discovered that the energy of light increases in discrete intervals. This was odd if light was thought of as waves, but Einstein suggested that the experimental results would make sense if

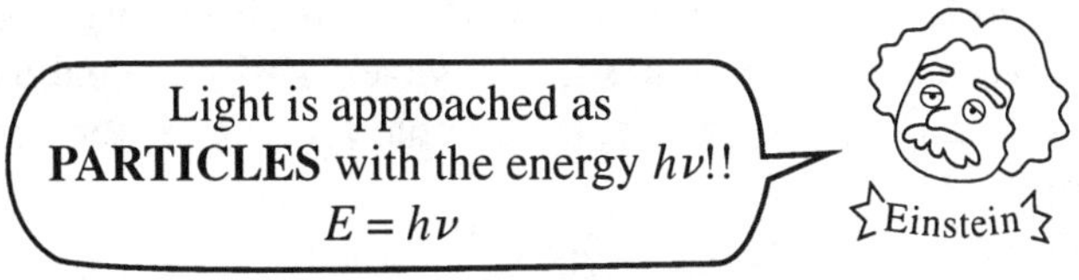

Let's imagine a small box with a hole inside a larger box in which there is a vacuum, as in the drawings below. If light were particles, the number of light particles inside the little box ought to increase and decrease one at a time, as illustrated below.

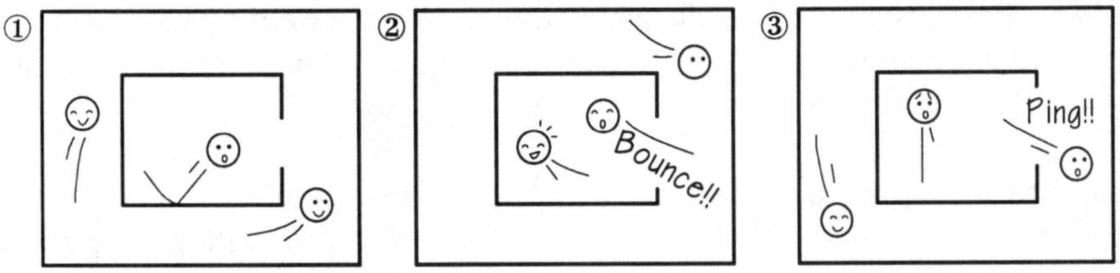

There was only one light particle in the little box, but then there were two, and then one again.

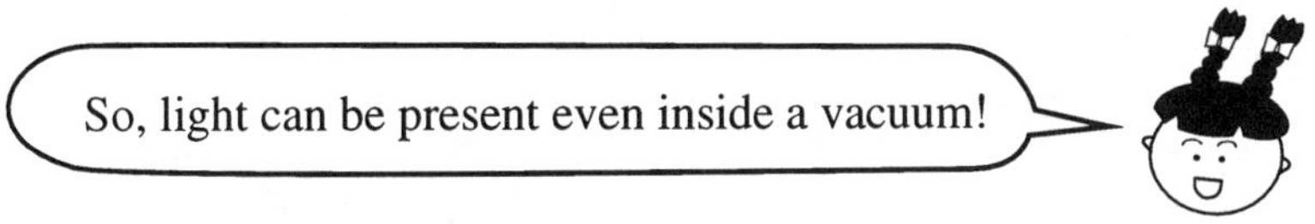

Next, since the energy of a single particle is $h\nu$, it follows that the energy of light changes in discrete intervals.

The energy inside the little box goes

①  $\times 1 = h\nu \longrightarrow$ ②  $\times 2 = 2h\nu \longrightarrow$ ③  $\times 1 = h\nu$

thus changing by one unit of $h\nu$ at a time!

This was Einstein's photon hypothesis.

In addition, thinking of light as a particle made it possible to explain the results of certain experiments that the wave theory of light could not account for.

Those results were the photoelectric effect and the Compton effect.

The experiment showing the photoelectric effect was easily explained by taking the energy of a single light particle to be $h\nu$.

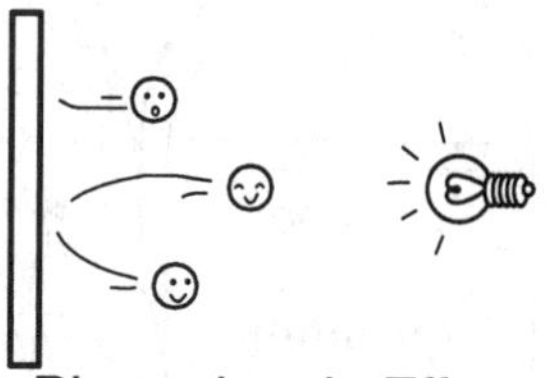

Photoelectric Effect

Furthermore, according to the Compton effect, the momentum of a light particle was found to be

$$p = \frac{h}{\lambda} \ .$$

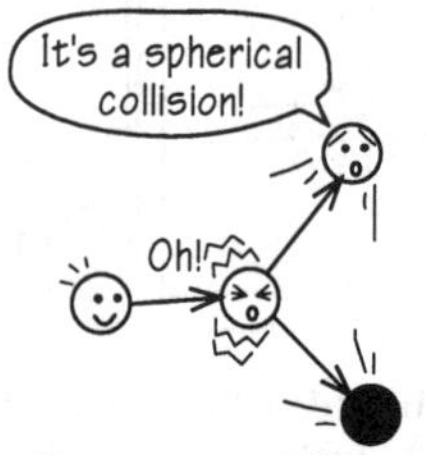

Compton Effect

But experiments on interference and diffraction, which could only be explained by the wave theory of light, were by no means abandoned. At times light behaves like a particle, at other times like a wave. This odd dual nature of light was to become a challenging and yet unsolvable problem as the adventure of quantum mechanics progressed.

At this point, the focus of our story moves from light to the star of quantum mechanics, **Mr. ELECTRON.** In terms of what was known at the time, the behavior of electrons seemed bizarre, and the question of how electrons moved inside the atom was a big problem for physicists. Because electrons were not visible, the only clue to their behavior was the spectrum of the light they emitted. Physicists tried to understand how electrons moved by explaining the order of the spectrum they emitted. But since this could not be explained using existing theories, the physicists were in a bind.

Bohr then made his appearance. He drew on Planck's, "the energy of light takes on discrete values," and Einstein's "light is a particle with energy $h\nu$" to construct a hypothesis that neatly explained the spectra emitted by atoms.

1. Electrons only rotate along stepped orbits. They do not emit light while rotating.
2. Electrons emit light when they undergo sudden transitions (instant relocation) from orbit to orbit.
3. The order of the stepped orbits is determined by

$$\oint p \, dq = nh \qquad (n = 1, 2, 3, \cdots)$$

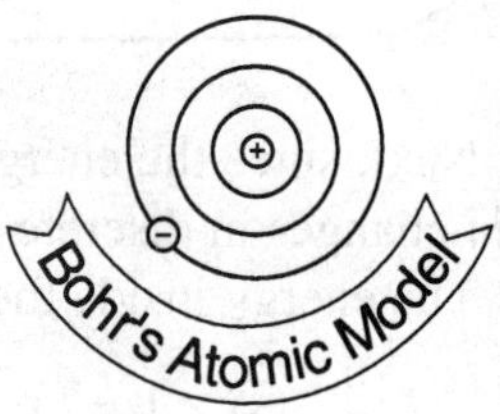

According to prevailing theory, Bohr's hypothesis would have been unthinkable. It only became possible if it was based on the idea that **THE ATOM IS STABLE.**

Bohr

Using this model of the atom, Bohr was able to find frequency ν of the spectra of light. But the question of how and why this hypothesis worked could not be answered.

Why is the n in $\oint p\,dq = nh$ an integer?

When, where, and how does transition occur?

Why doesn't the electron give off light when it rotates?

Now, it is the young, handsome and clever Heisenberg who makes his dashing entry! Heisenberg stated that the problem was in assuming that there were orbits.

JUST GET RID OF THE IDEA OF ORBITS!

Heisenberg

If we don't think about orbits, then we don't need to think about how transition occurs or why electrons don't emit light when they rotate. This is what led Heisenberg to construct matrix mechanics, by which he could find the frequency ν and intensity $|Q|^2$ of the spectra of light. Then Heisenberg said,

If we can explain the frequency and the intensity of the spectra of light emitted by the atom, we don't need to explain the orbits of electrons!!

But if we dismiss the orbits, we won't be able to determine the position of an electron at any given time. We've been reading *What is Quantum Mechanics? A Physics Adventure* to find out how electrons move inside an atom, and now we're told that there is no way to envision the state of an electron inside an atom.

Einstein became angry when he heard Heisenberg's statement.

Physics is about creating mental images of how things move. If you can't envision something, it isn't physics!

Where will this adventure take us? We're not supposed to envision the behavior of electrons. Really! So much for our review. It's time to charge ahead into the last half of our adventure.

4. 2 ELECTRONS ARE WAVES

MR. NONCHALANT DE BROGLIE ON THE SET!

de Broglie, Louis Victor [1892-1987]

Setting us on our way after half-time is **LOUIS VICTOR DE BROGLIE.**

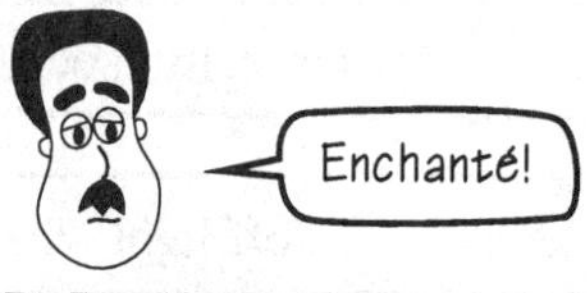

De Broglie

Luis de Broglie was a very easy-going sort of fellow. Unlike most of the other physicists we have met, de Broglie did not start out in physics.

The de Broglie Story

Many years ago, two brothers named Louis and Maurice lived in a large castle in France. Their parents were aristocrats and they were very wealthy. Because of this, they were able to live extremely comfortably without having to work. The brothers were raised with few constraints, and were able to spend their time as they liked. The elder brother, Maurice, wondered how things moved, and pursued research in physics; Louis was interested in how the people of the past lived, and he studied history.

One day, Maurice attended a gathering (the Solvay Conference) where physicists exchanged information about their research. When he returned, he told his brother Louis about the people at the conference and the things they had talked about. At the conference, the physicists devoted their discussions to the question of light, which at the time was a popular topic. Louis found the subject very stimulating, and he became deeply interested in physics. Louis began to acquire the language physicists used to explain the movements of things, and also to acquire the language of equations by reading and learning a little from his older brother every day.

At the time, the star in the world of physics was **EINSTEIN.**

De Broglie became a fan of Einstein, and read his papers avidly. What was especially interesting to de Broglie was Einstein's photon hypothesis:

$$E = h\nu \quad \text{and} \quad p = h\frac{1}{\lambda}$$

E describes the energy of a light particle, ν is the frequency of a light wave, p stands for the momentum of a light particle, and λ the length of a light wave. Normally, a particle and a wave would never be paired with an equal (=) sign.

Use your imagination!

First try picturing a wave in your head.

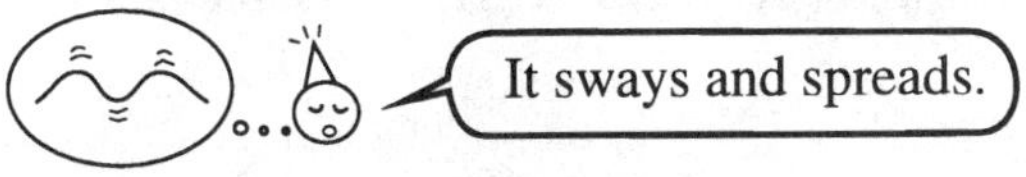

Next, imagine a particle.

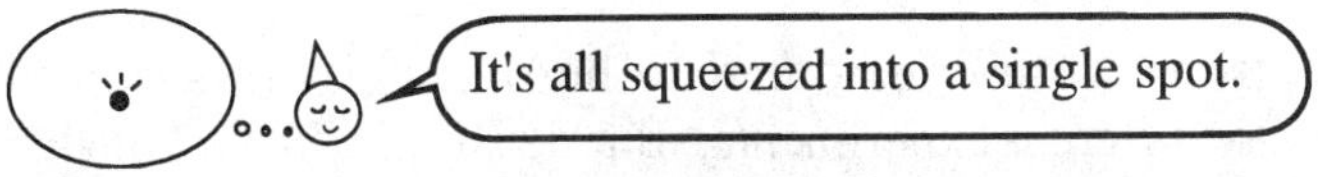

Now, to picture something that is both a particle and a wave.

There can't be something that sways and spreads and is squeezed into a single spot at the same time. Waves and particles are completely different.

Regardless of the fact that waves and particles are different, Einstein said that light could also be described as a particle even though physicists were used to thinking of it as a wave.

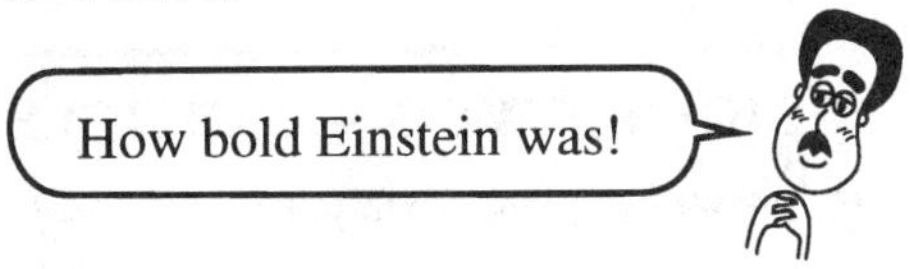

That was what de Broglie loved about Einstein.

But around that time, World War I began and de Broglie had to go to war. When he returned from the battlefield, the age of Einstein was over. The new hero was. . . **Niels Bohr.**

De Broglie was a bit disappointed, but as he began to understand Bohr's research, he became aware that it included a very thorny problem, which was. . .

> No one could explain the discrete values of the orbits of the electrons in an atom!

According to Bohr, the angular momentum of electrons was

$$M = \frac{h}{2\pi} n \qquad (n = 1, 2, 3, \cdots)$$

It was thus limited to integral multiples. Bohr, together with Sommerfeld, expressed this in the form

$$\oint p\, dq = nh \qquad (n = 1, 2, 3, \cdots)$$

Using this, the spectra of light emitted by the atom could be described beautifully, but nobody could answer **WHY THEY WERE INTEGRAL MULTIPLES.**

DE BROGLIE'S INTUITION

At the time, electrons were considered to be particles; this had been confirmed by many different experiments. But de Broglie had a hunch.

Before Einstein, the notion that light was a wave had been confirmed experimentally. But Einstein was daring enough to declare that electrons were particles, and experiments showed that to be true, too.

IF DE BROGLIE WAS RIGHT, an **ELECTRON,** which everyone assumed was a particle, **MIGHT ALSO BE A WAVE!**

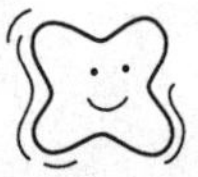

EINSTEIN	**LIGHT :**	**WAVE → PARTICLE**
DE BROGLIE	**ELECTRON :**	**PARTICLE → WAVE**

This idea was as bold as Einstein's.

In addition, up until that time, integral multiples appeared in physics only in phenomena related to waves.

A complicated wave is the sum of simple waves whose **FREQUENCIES ARE INTEGRAL MULTIPLES.**

De Broglie thought that Einstein's photon hypothesis would also hold for electrons.

$$E = h\nu \quad \text{and} \quad p = h\frac{1}{\lambda}$$

That means that the energy of an electron is E and the momentum p, while at the same time the electron is a wave with frequency ν and wavelength λ.

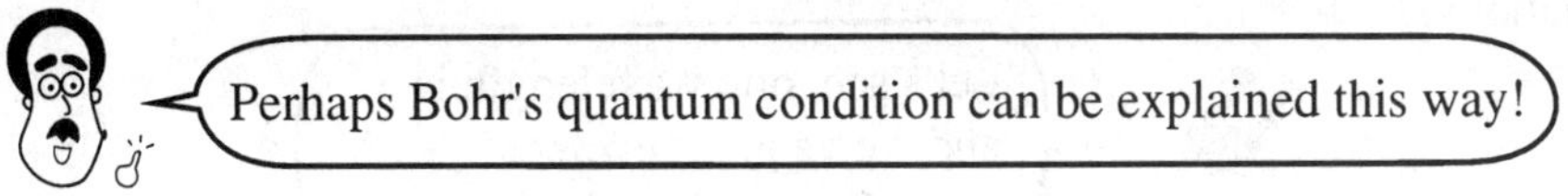

Let's try it.

THE ROAD TO DE BROGLIE'S NOBEL PRIZE

Let's consider the most simple atom — hydrogen — just as Bohr did. If an electron in a hydrogen atom is a wave. . .

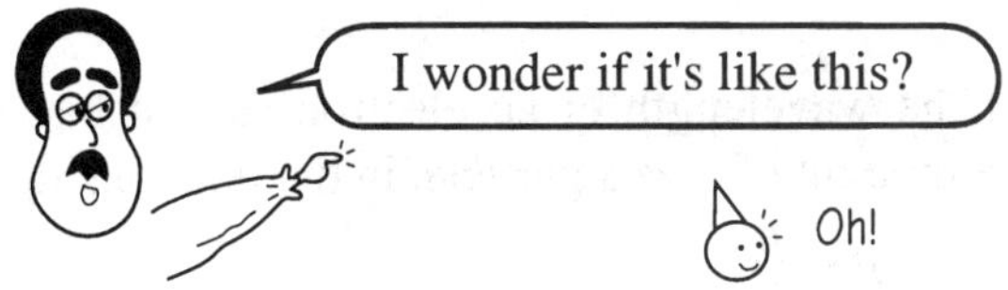

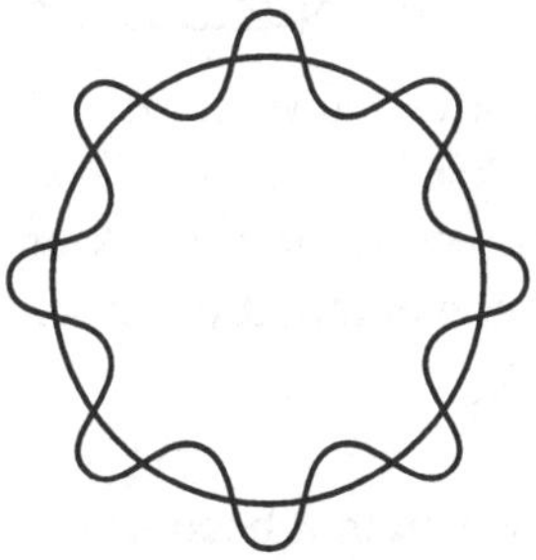

Thus, the number of times that a wave undulates must always **BE AN INTEGRAL VALUE.**

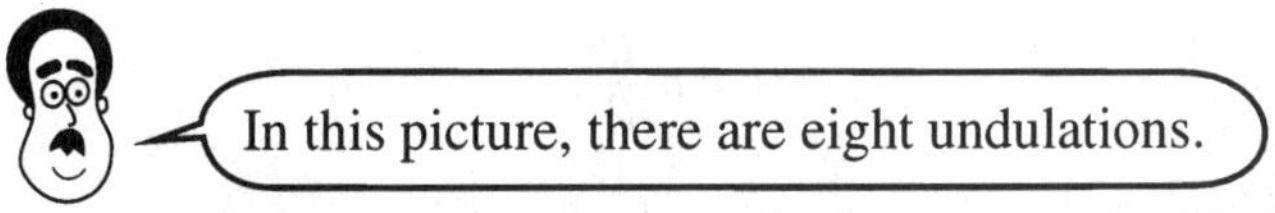

If the number of undulations of the wave were not an integer. . .

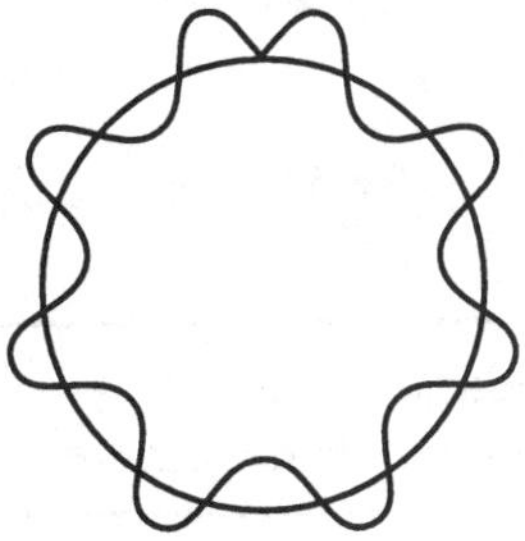

The wave would end up being "chopped off"; it would be weakened and be unable to maintain a constant, stable state.

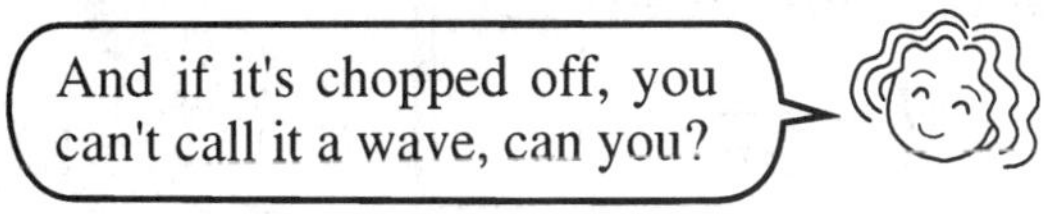

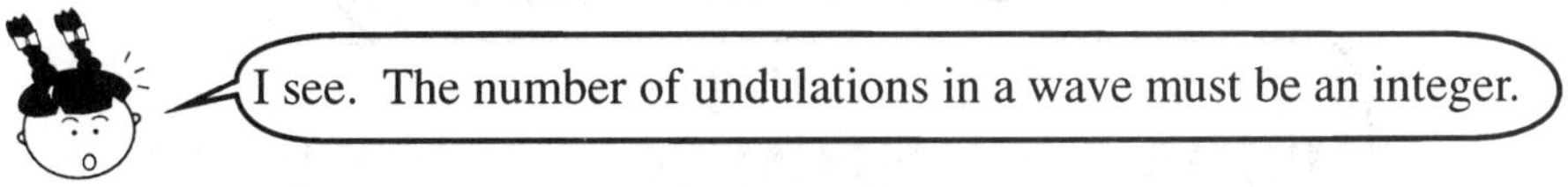

Now, let's put that in the language of numerical expressions. If the radius is r, what is the circumference?

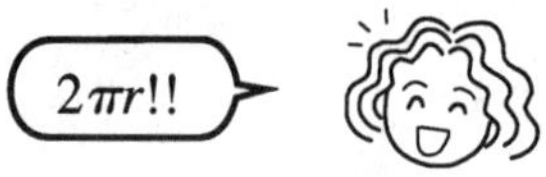

That's right! Next, what is the total length of a wave with wavelength (that is, the distance a wave covers in one undulation) λ and n cycles (number of undulations)?

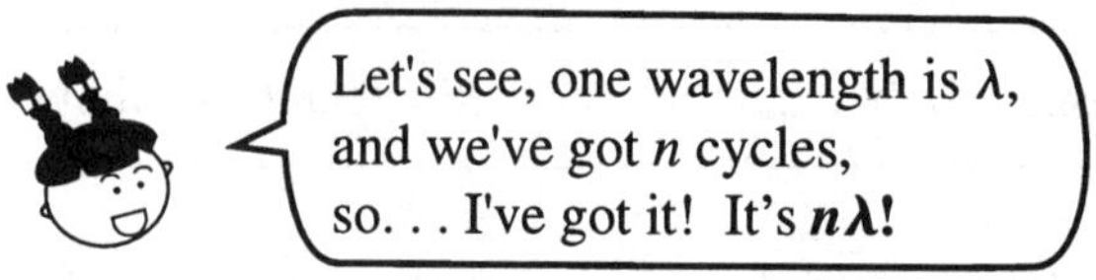

Right!! Furthermore, the circumference and the length of a wave with n cycles are equivalent, so. . .

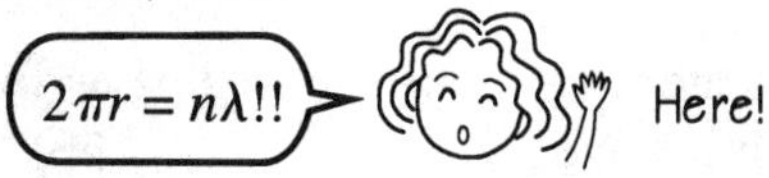

Great! You've got it!

But, we're now thinking of the wavelength of an electron as if it had the same momentum it did when we thought of it as a particle, in the relationship

$$p = \frac{h}{\lambda} .$$

So wavelength λ becomes

$$\lambda = \frac{h}{p} .$$

If we replace λ in $2\pi r = n\lambda$ with this, we get

$$2\pi r = n\frac{h}{p} .$$

Now, to get rid of the fraction, we multiply both sides by p and come up with

$$2\pi rp = nh .$$

Because $rp = M$, we have

$$2\pi M = nh .$$

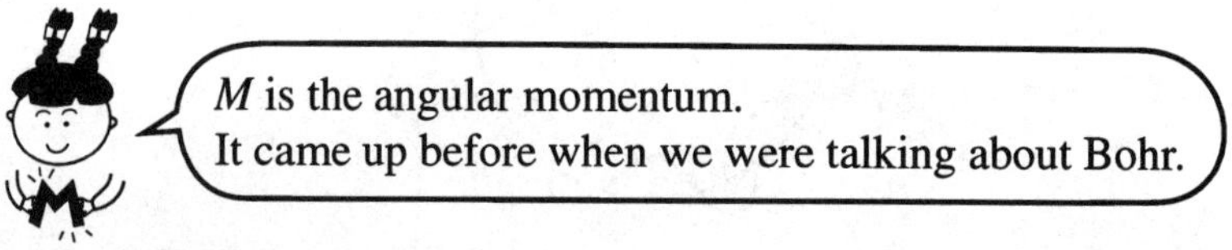

Dividing both sides by 2π, we get

Point

$$M = \frac{h}{2\pi} n .$$

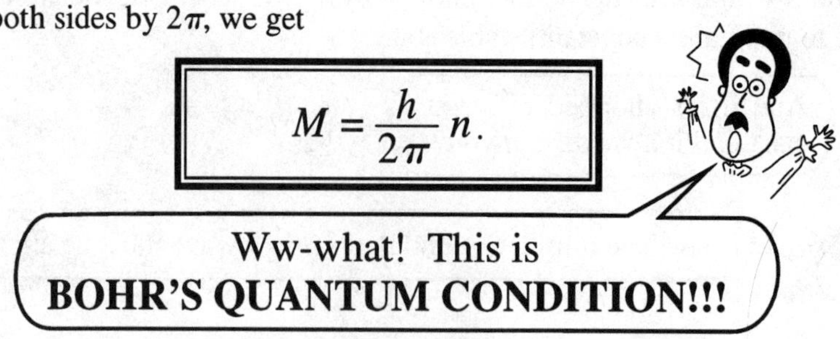

n was the number of cycles, or the number of times a wave undulates, so it will always be an integer ($n = 1, 2, 3...$).

No one could explain the angular momentum of an electron before, but now it could be shown that electrons have discrete integral values. If one thought of electrons as waves, **IT WAS NATURAL, A MATTER OF COURSE.**

Great! Mr. de Broglie, you did it!

De Broglie published a paper describing his discovery.

FINDING AN EXPERIMENT

You know, Mr. de Broglie, no matter how brilliant your theory is, we can't say it's true until there is an experiment to prove it, can we? Have you got that covered?

Experiment? One has been found, you know. In fact, after I published my paper saying that electrons are waves, Clinton Davisson and L. H. Germer noticed that in their experiments electrons behaved like waves.

Davisson, Clinton Joseph [1881-1958]

Germer, Lester Halbert [1896-1971]

The word "noticed" bothers me. Just what do you mean by that?

That is, until they noticed that behavior, they didn't understand the results of their experiments.

What are you trying to say?

Well, you see, until I said that electrons are waves, physicists believed that electrons were particles because this was indicated by experimental results. For that reason, all the phenomena caused by electrons that had been discovered so far were thought to reflect only the behavior of particles. There was, however, one experimental result that did not make sense with respect to the electron as a particle. That was Davisson and Germer's experiment.

While carrying out numerous experiments trying to discover something about the structure of the atom by investigating electrons, they obtained experimental results that did not make any sense.

They thought the experiment had probably been a failure. But after de Broglie published his paper stating that electrons are waves, a physicist named W. Elsasser asked,

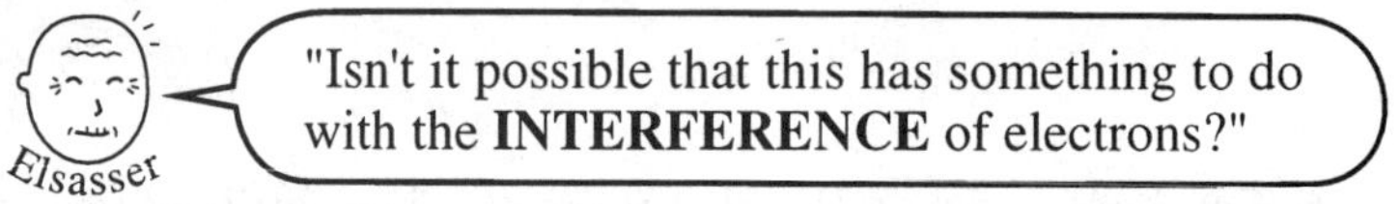

This caused Davisson and Germer to perform their experiment more thoroughly, and they discovered a surprisingly beautiful and orderly interference pattern. The results turned out to corroborate de Broglie's theory. They also indicated that without de Broglie's theory stating that electrons are waves, it would have been impossible to explain the experimental results.

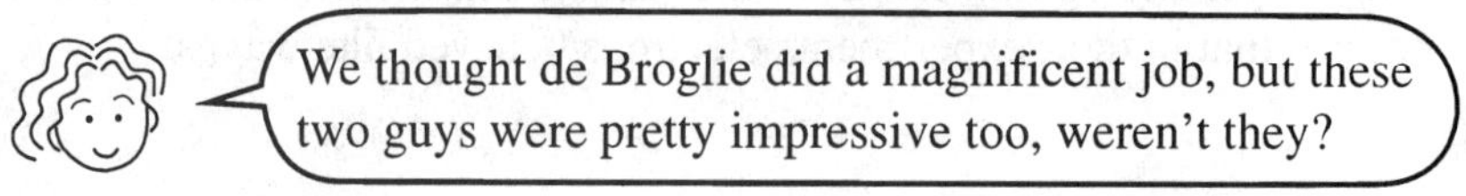

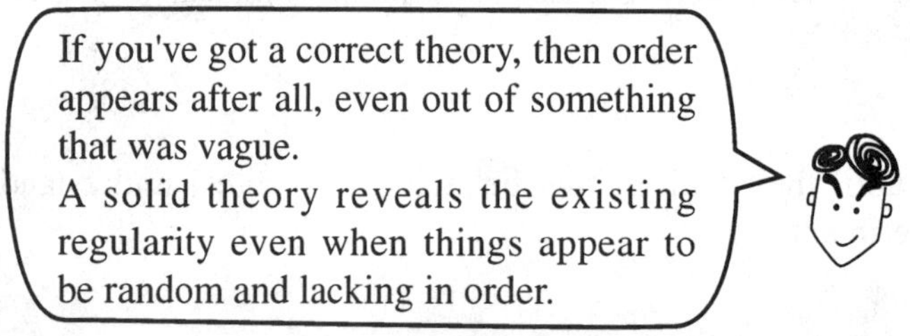

De Broglie dared to claim that **ELECTRONS ARE WAVES.** In doing so, he was able to derive Bohr's quantum condition with **SURPRISING EASE.** Moreover, it was **CONFIRMED EXPERIMENTALLY** that **ELECTRONS INTERFERE.** Having achieved so much, de Broglie was awarded the **NOBEL PRIZE!** With this, we end our tale of de Broglie.

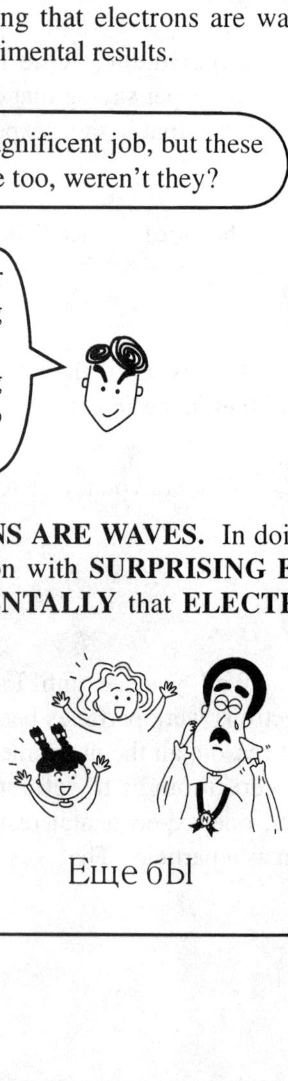

Coffee Break

How about a short rest?

THE STORY OF DE BROGLIE'S ELECTRON WAVE

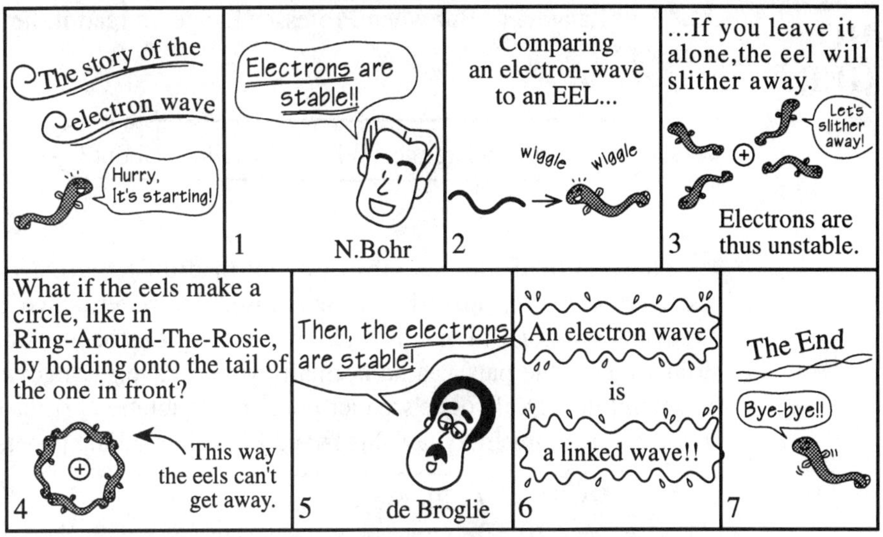

The number of eels that are linked together must be an integer, such as three or four. There can't be such a thing as a ring of 3.5 eels, right?

THE STRANGE BEHAVIOR OF PARTICLES AND WAVES

At Hippo Family Club activities. . .

Although many sounds from the Hippo story tapes may run through a member's head, in some cases, he may be able to vocalize only a few of them. If we think of the things running through his head as being a wave, what comes out of his mouth is like a particle, isn't it?

4. 3 LET'S MAKE WAVE MECHANICS

MR. GUNG-HO, SCHRÖDINGER

Langevin, Paul
[1872-1946]

De Broglie wrote his paper and showed it to his advisor, Professor Paul Langevin. But when Professor Langevin read it, he had no idea what it meant.

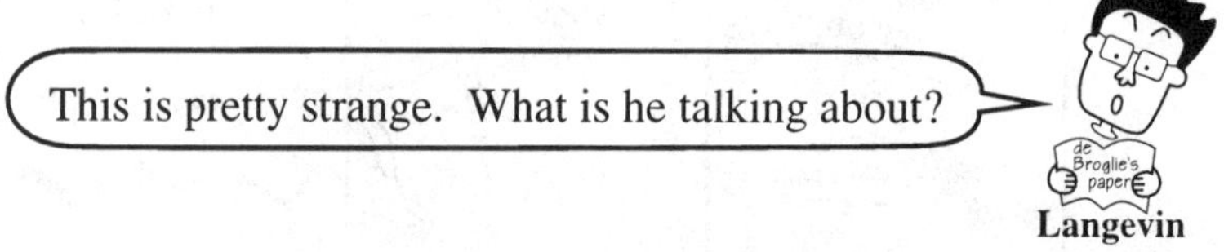

The practical and sensible Langevin didn't realize that de Broglie's discovery was both historic and immense. However, since de Broglie was a duke and his social rank was high even among aristocrats, Langevin could not simply ignore the paper as he normally would have. Langevin wondered what he should do. De Broglie's paper contained quotations from Einstein's theory, so Langevin arranged to have his friend Einstein read the paper.

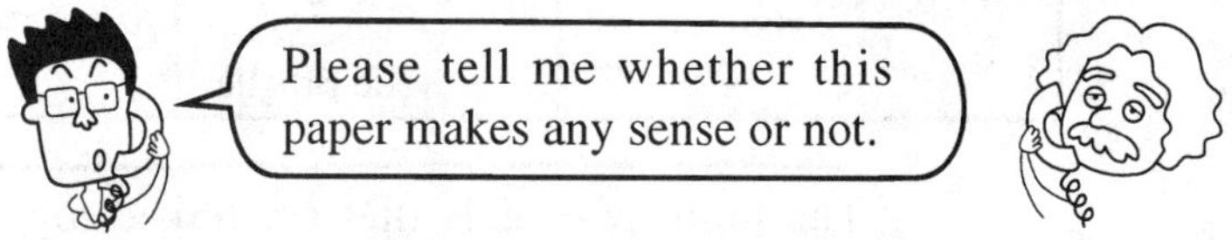

Even Einstein was not able to completely understand de Broglie's theory.

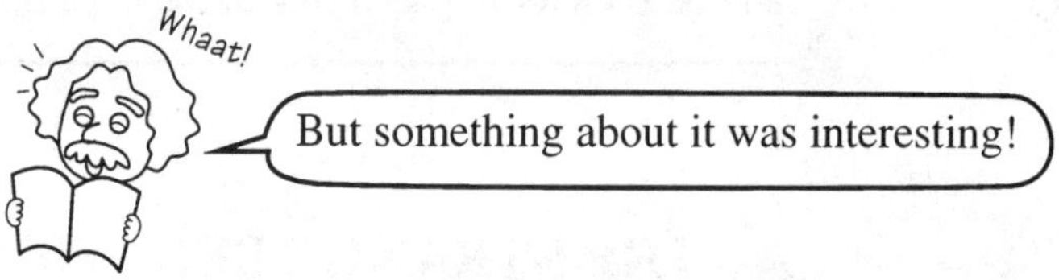

Schrödinger, Erwin
[1887-1961]

At this point, Einstein handed the paper over to an acquaintance of his, **ERWIN SCHRÖDINGER,** and told him to introduce it at the next seminar.

Schrödinger had a totally different personality from that of de Broglie. Whatever he did, he undertook it at a furious pace. Schrödinger started reading the paper with some reluctance, but soon realized that it might hold a great discovery.

De Broglie pointed out that electrons are waves. He also stated in his paper that it should be possible to set forth the laws that the electron waves followed. When electrons are particles, their behavior can be described by the laws of Newtonian mechanics. But since it had become evident that electrons are also waves, naturally they would also have to follow laws pertaining to waves.

De Broglie called these laws **WAVE MECHANICS** in contrast to Newtonian mechanics.

Schrödinger was excited by the idea of wave mechanics. The fact is that he had already been thinking along these lines for some time.

In order to explain the workings of the atom, Bohr had accepted that **the orbits of an electron are discrete.**

This was unthinkable according to the theories of the time.

Then Heisenberg, talking about the behavior of the electron within the atom, had declared,

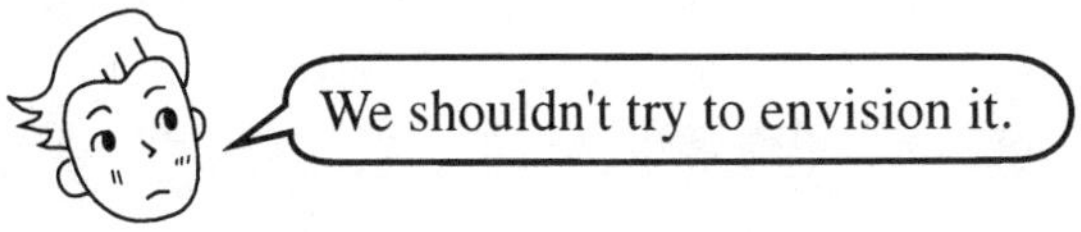

That statement would put an end to any such discussion.

Bohr and Heisenberg both started from the idea that electrons are particles. However, as de Broglie pointed out, if electrons are thought of as waves, then the seemingly impossible fact that the angular momentum of an electron having discrete integral multiple values as in Bohr's quantum condition could be explained. If de Broglie's wave mechanics could be demonstrated, it might be possible to take Heisenberg's statement, "Just get rid of the mental image," and prove it wrong. Schrödinger decided to tackle this problem.

LET'S ESTABLISH WAVE MECHANICS!

According to de Broglie's theory, an electron with energy E and a momentum p can also be described as was a wave with frequency ν and wave length λ.

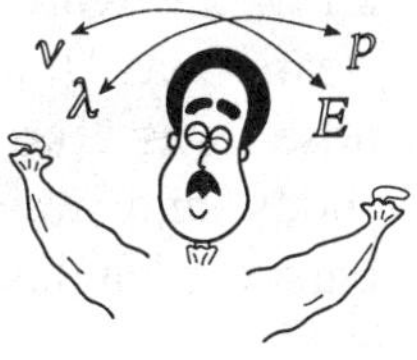

However, if you think of electrons as particles, you assume that energy E is conserved and does not change, whereas momentum p changes with respect to time. The law that describes the change in momentum is. . .

Newtonian Mechanics
$F = m\ddot{q}$

By solving this equation, we can determine exactly what values momentum p will assume under given conditions.

On the other hand, when electrons are thought of as particles, frequency ν corresponds to energy and does not change; but wavelength λ corresponds to the momentum, so naturally it changes. However, de Broglie's theory alone does not tell us **HOW WAVELENGTH λ CHANGES.**

But, we need to know this in order to develop wave theory.

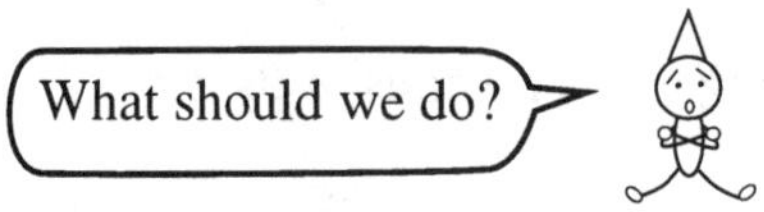

How should we go about finding a law that describes the change in wavelength λ?

AT TIMES LIKE THIS

When you learn various languages at Hippo, this sort of thing often happens:

One day, when I was in Mexico, I was discussing my schedule with my host family, saying, "Today I'm going here, tomorrow I'll be going there, and then..." I was going on like this in Spanish, but I didn't know how to say "the day after tomorrow (pasado de mañana)." So I said "mañana y mañana (tomorrow's tomorrow)" and they understood me.

Something similar happened to me when I was doing a homestay with a family in Korea. It was during the summer, so it was very hot. I wanted to tell my Korean friend that I was sweating a lot, but I didn't know the Korean word for "sweat." I knew that the word for "tears" was "[nun mul] (eye water)" and that the word for "runny nose" was "[ko mul] (nose water)" so I made up a word using "body" and "water" and said "[mom mul] (body water)." My friend burst out laughing and said, "You mean '[tam] (sweat),' don't you!"

At the time, I only used one word, "[mul] (water)," to express "water," "sweat," "ocean," "river," or anything else related to "water."

Children do the same thing. When our child could only say a few words, he used a single word to describe many things. Whether it was an apple, a strawberry or a persimmon, he said "tomato."

I know why he did that! The logic behind it is, they're all red foods.

We often make do with the words we know at the time. Haven't you all had a similar experience?

That's right! When we don't know a word, the best thing is to make do with the words you do know.

Although there is no law for the change in wavelength λ in de Broglie's theory, there is a law that corresponds to wavelength, the law for the change in momentum. That's Newtonian mechanics!

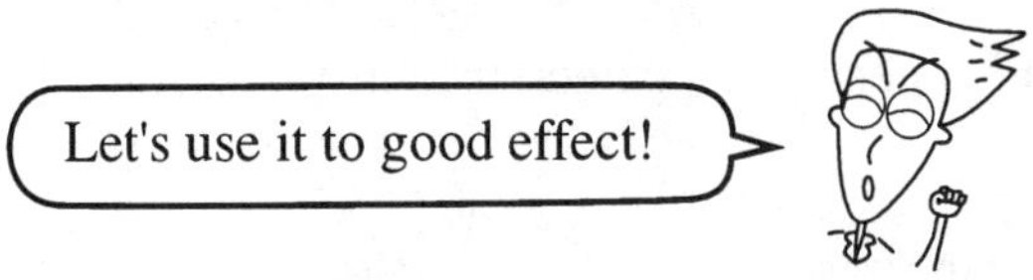

Schrödinger started working away.

Because he used frequency ν and wavelength λ to explain the notion of electrons as waves, we can say that those words are **THE LANGUAGE OF WAVES.**

In contrast, Newtonian mechanics, which we use when we think of electrons as particles, can be said to be **THE LANGUAGE OF PARTICLES.**

There was no law for changes in wavelength λ in the language of waves, so Schrödinger thought of trying to use the language of particles.

When integration is performed on both sides of Newton's equation for motion,

the law of the conservation of energy
$$E = \frac{p^2}{2m} + V$$

results. E is the energy, p is the momentum and V is the potential energy. We may rewrite the equation as:

$$E - V = \frac{p^2}{2m}$$

$$p^2 = 2m(E - V)$$

And finally,

$$p = \sqrt{2m(E - V)}$$

Let's think a bit about what this means. In this equation, if we increase the potential energy, what happens to momentum p?

Mass m and energy E are fixed, which means we are drawing from something that is fixed. . . so momentum p decreases!

That's it! So what happens when potential energy V is small?

Momentum p increases!

Right! This is what we get:

Potential energy V	big,	Momentum p	small
Potential energy V	small,	Momentum p	big

Let's do an experiment!!

We drop a ball from the top of a building. When the ball is first released, it falls at a slow speed. But as it falls further, its speed gradually increases.

The higher the building is, that is, the farther the ball is from the ground, the greater its potential energy V. Momentum p of the ball is

$$\underset{\text{(momentum)}}{p} = \underset{\text{(mass)}}{m} \cdot \underset{\text{(velocity)}}{v}$$

Therefore, the greater the speed is, the greater the momentum. In other words, when potential energy V of the ball is high, momentum p is small; when potential energy V is low, momentum p is large.

So, the equation we just looked at now, $p = \sqrt{2m(E - V)}$, describes the change in momentum, doesn't it?

Newtonian mechanics can explain anything related to the movement of particles.

Hey, doesn't this remind you of something?

Yes. There was an equation $p = \dfrac{h}{\lambda}$, wasn't there?

Since the equation $p = \sqrt{2m(E - V)}$ perfectly describes changes in momentum, if we use the same p in equation

$$p = \frac{h}{\lambda}$$

and then solve for λ, we can probably see how wavelength λ changes.

That's right. We can also write $E = h\nu$ in place of energy E!

Hey, that's great!! So we can translate the language of particles (Newtonian mechanics) entirely into the language of waves.

This means that Einstein's two equations

$$E = h\nu \quad \text{and} \quad p = \frac{h}{\lambda}$$

are the bridge that joins the language of waves to the language of particles.

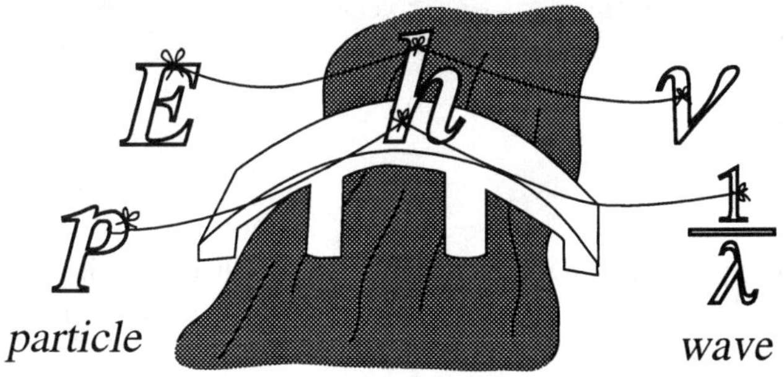

Right, Planck's constant h had that sort of significance, too.

Let's do the translation!

$$p = \sqrt{2m(E - V)}$$

We rewrite p and E above as

$$E = h\nu \quad \text{and} \quad p = \frac{h}{\lambda}$$

Placing them in the equation, we get

$$\frac{h}{\lambda} = \sqrt{2m(h\nu - V)}$$

Solving for λ, we get

$$\lambda = \frac{h}{\sqrt{2m(h\nu - V)}}$$

It's done! So now we know how wavelength λ changes!

But wait a second. Mass m and potential energy V of the particle are still with us..

You're right. We shouldn't have the language of particles mixed in with the language of waves, should we?

But is there such a thing as the mass of a wave?

Hmm...

AHH, LET'S JUST MAKE IT UP!

What!?

Taking from $E = h\nu$ and $p = \dfrac{h}{\lambda}$, we can just make it

$$m = h\mathfrak{M} \qquad V = h\mathfrak{V}$$

But what are $\mathfrak{M}$ and $\mathfrak{V}$?

Don't worry if you don't understand. For the time being, let's just say they correspond to mass and potential energy.

All right. I can understand that.

Taking Schrödinger's opinion into account, if we let $m = h\mathfrak{M}$ and $V = h\mathfrak{V}$, we get

$$\lambda = \frac{h}{\sqrt{2h\mathfrak{M}(h\nu - h\mathfrak{V})}}$$

Factoring h out of the term in the square root, we get

$$\lambda = \frac{h}{\sqrt{h^2 2\mathfrak{M}(\nu - \mathfrak{V})}}$$

$$\lambda = \frac{h}{h\sqrt{2\mathfrak{M}(\nu - \mathfrak{V})}}$$

Dividing by h/h, we come up with

$$\lambda = \frac{1}{\sqrt{2\mathfrak{M}(\nu - \mathfrak{V})}}$$

It was not simply a matter of determining changes in wavelength λ.

By translating Newtonian mechanics using Einstein's equations, we have derived a law describing changes in wavelength λ.

EQUATIONS FOR THE ELECTRON WAVE

That is how Schrödinger derived a law for changes in wavelength λ, but he realized that this is still not enough.

It was not simply a matter of determining changes in wavelength λ.

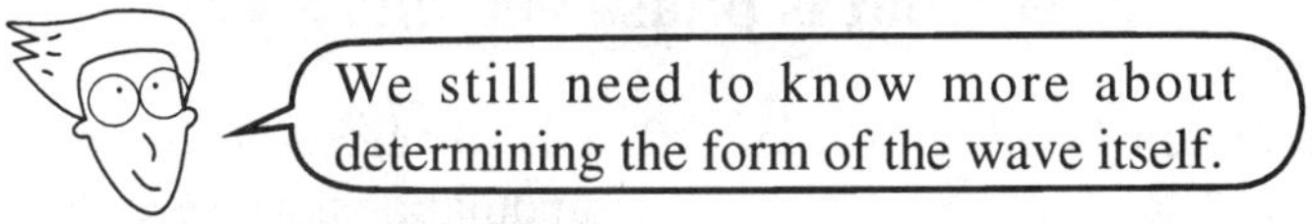

And this would involve creating a visual image.

Schrödinger was truly skilled when it came to the mathematics of waves. He knew an equation that could describe the form of any wave. Here is that equation:

$$\boxed{\nabla^2 \Psi + \left(\frac{2\pi\nu}{u}\right)^2 \Psi = 0}$$

It is known as **the equation of wave motion.**

Consider the meaning of the equation!

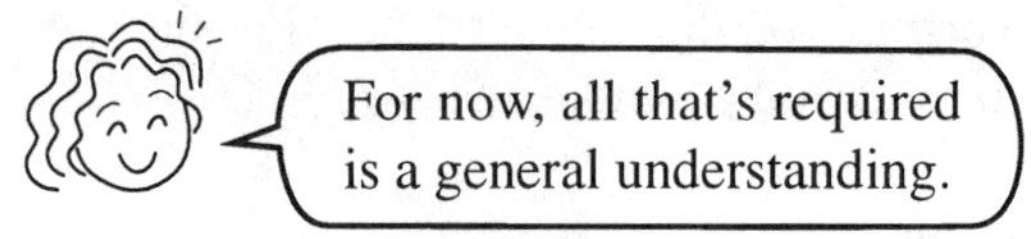

∇^2: This means to change the form by performing differentiation twice on Ψ with respect to position. This will determine the amount of spatial change at a given location.

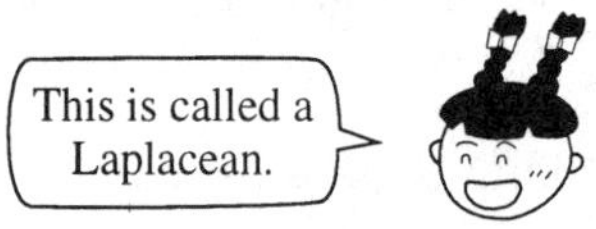

Ψ: This describes the form of the wave. It describes how high a wave is at a given time and location. If this is known, we can find what form the wave has at a given time. Naturally, this can also describe an electron wave.

π: Circumference ratio

ν: Frequency

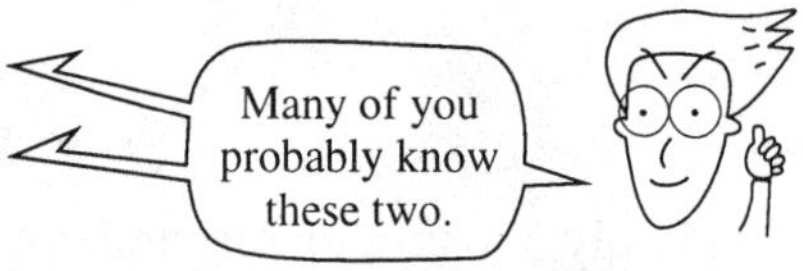

u: Wave speed (phase velocity)

By solving this equation and finding the wave motion function Ψ, you can find the form of the wave. But to do that, the phase velocity u must be known. What might the phase velocity of an electron wave be?

Just what is phase velocity?

1. A watermelon floating on top of a wave

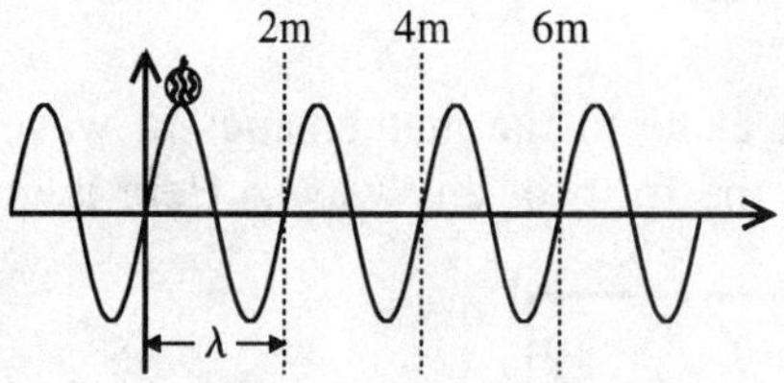

2. has advanced the distance of two undulations one second later.

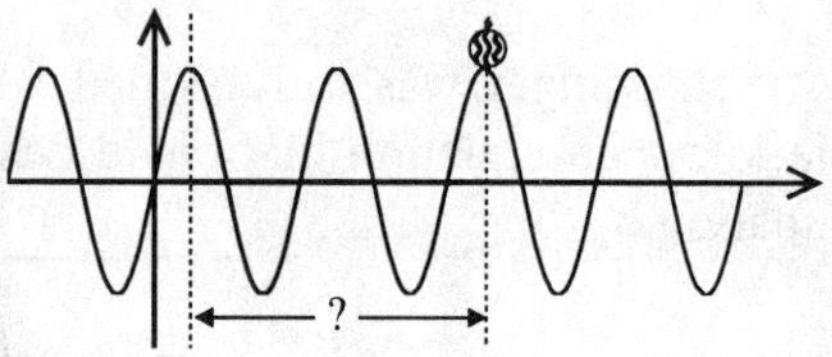

The length of one undulation of a wave (wavelength) is

$$\lambda = 2\text{ m}$$

The number of undulations per second (frequency) is

$$\nu = 2 \text{ cycles/sec}$$

Therefore, the distance a wave travels in one second is

$$2 \times 2 = 4 \text{ m/sec}$$

The distance a wave travels in one second is the speed at which it progresses. For phase velocity u, it will suffice to multiply wavelength λ by ν, the number of times the wave undulates in one second. If we write this as an equation, we get:

$$u = \lambda\nu$$

In the case of the electron wave, we know wavelength λ:

$$\lambda = \frac{1}{\sqrt{2\mathfrak{M}(\nu - \mathfrak{V})}}$$

Therefore, phase velocity $u = \lambda\nu$ is:

$$u = \frac{\nu}{\sqrt{2\mathfrak{M}(\nu - \mathfrak{V})}}$$

To obtain the equation that tells us the form of the electron wave, that is, the equation for electron waves, we can take the equation for wave motion

$$\nabla^2\Psi + \left(\frac{2\pi\nu}{u}\right)^2 \Psi = 0$$

and put in the just derived phase velocity u of the electron.

If you are doing this for the first time, get together with Schrödinger and try making an equation for the motion of electron waves!

MAKING OUR FIRST ELECTRON WAVE EQUATION

By combining various elements, we can come up with the equation for electron waves. We won't be doing any difficult calculations, so even first-timers will be able to enjoy doing the equations. Procedure is the most important thing when making equations. At this point you will need to learn the steps for constructing an equation. First you'll master the basics, such as gathering your tools and materials and making other preliminary arrangements.

Division, Multiplication, Addition, Subtraction

A $\nabla^2\Psi + \left(\frac{2\pi\nu}{u}\right)^2 \Psi = 0$

B $u = \frac{\nu}{\sqrt{2\mathfrak{M}(\nu - \mathfrak{V})}}$

A is an equation that can tell us the form of all sorts of waves. Placing the speed of the wave you want to solve for in the *u* part of the equation, you can find the form.

B is an equation that describes the speed at which an electron wave travels. This means that if you place equation *B* in the *u* portion of equation *A*, you will have an equation to find the form of an electron wave.

OK, now let's do it all at once. Have you got all your materials ready? All you have to do is combine *A* and *B* while looking at the instructions.

We place *B* into the *u* part of *A*

$$\nabla^2\Psi + \left(\frac{2\pi\nu}{\frac{\nu}{\sqrt{2\mathfrak{M}(\nu - \mathfrak{V})}}}\right)^2 \Psi = 0$$

$$\nabla^2\Psi + \left(2\pi\nu\,\frac{\sqrt{2\mathfrak{M}(\nu - \mathfrak{V})}}{\nu}\right)^2 \Psi = 0$$

$$\nabla^2\Psi + 4\pi^2 \cdot 2\mathfrak{M}(\nu - \mathfrak{V})\Psi = 0$$

Point

$$\boxed{\nabla^2\Psi + 8\pi^2\mathfrak{M}(\nu - \mathfrak{V})\Psi = 0}$$

THE EQUATION FOR ELECTRON WAVES IS DONE!

This equation is also called the de Broglie wave equation because it was de Broglie who first proposed that electrons are waves.

EQUATIONS FOR COMPLICATED ELECTRON WAVES

Schrödinger finally found an equation that described electron waves! He was able to express his thoughts in the language of equations!

However, this equation contains ν, which describes the frequency. Because ν can only have a certain values such as 21 or 100, wave Ψ derived from this equation is a wave that oscillates at a specific frequency. More precisely, it is a simple wave.

But the waves produced in nature aren't simple waves; they are complicated waves and are made up of a number of waves put together. It looks like we'll be able to say the same thing about electron waves, doesn't it?

In order to determine this, an equation that can derive Ψ for complicated waves is necessary.

Because complicated waves are the sum of simple waves, we can find Ψ for complicated waves by adding up the Ψs for simple waves from the equation that we have just made.

(complicated Ψ) = (simple Ψ①) + (simple Ψ②) + (simple Ψ③) + · · ·

To solve the equation, first we have to formulate an equation that will give us complicated waves in the form

(simple Ψ①) + (simple Ψ②) + (simple Ψ③) + · · ·

For that, we must put the equation in a form that does not include ν.

Because if it includes ν, it would be a simple wave.

Schrödinger had a lot of formulas jammed in his head, and he quickly recalled

$$\boxed{\frac{\partial^2 \Psi}{\partial t^2} = -(2\pi\nu)^2 \Psi}$$

This is an equation that is also used for simple waves. It is used for most harmonic oscillation, such as the movement of a spring.

Both are equations for simple waves, and both contain ν. Perhaps if we put these two equations together, the ν's would cancel each other out.

$$\nabla^2 \Psi + 8\pi^2 \mathfrak{M}(\nu - \mathfrak{V})\Psi = 0 \qquad \cdots ①$$

$$\frac{\partial^2 \Psi}{\partial t^2} = -(2\pi\nu)^2 \Psi \qquad \cdots ②$$

As it happens, this doesn't work.

Please pay particular attention to the ν in equation ②. For example, when $\nu = 5$, we obtain

$$\frac{\partial^2 \Psi}{\partial t^2} = -(2\pi \cdot 5)^2 \Psi = -100\pi^2 \Psi$$

Well, what if we try $\nu = -5$? We get

$$\frac{\partial^2 \Psi}{\partial t^2} = -(2\pi \cdot -5)^2 \Psi = -100\pi^2 \Psi$$

so whether it is 5 or –5, the result is exactly the same.

Now then, let's next look at equation ① when $\nu = 5$ and when $\nu = -5$.

When $\nu = 5$

$$\nabla^2 \Psi + 8\pi^2 \mathfrak{M}(5 - \mathfrak{V})\Psi = 0$$

$$\nabla^2 \Psi + 40\pi^2 \mathfrak{M}\Psi - 8\pi^2 \mathfrak{M}\mathfrak{V}\Psi = 0$$

When $\nu = -5$

$$\nabla^2 \Psi + 8\pi^2 \mathfrak{M}(-5 - \mathfrak{V})\Psi = 0$$

$$\nabla^2 \Psi - 40\pi^2 \mathfrak{M}\Psi - 8\pi^2 \mathfrak{M}\mathfrak{V}\Psi = 0$$

In equation ①, ν's sign changes from 5 to –5, and a different answer results.

So look, equation ① changes depending on whether ν is 5 or –5. Equation ② doesn't change, whether ν is 5 or –5. Equations ① and ② have entirely different characteristics with respect to ν, so do you think it is all right to think about them together?

We've done something wrong.
Let's give it another try!

Schrödinger continued calculating day after day, trying to form a new equation.

In equation ②, $2\pi\nu$ is a square, so whether ν is 5 or –5, the form of the equation is the same. To see why this is true, let's consider the meaning of the equation.

$$\frac{\partial^2 \Psi}{\partial t^2} = -(2\pi\nu)^2 \Psi$$

When a second order derivative of Ψ is taken with respect to t (time), Ψ appears again, and in this case ν is a square. . .

So, we find that if we look for an equation in a form such that ν is not a square after differentiation, but is to the power of one ($\nu \times \Psi$), we will be fine. In the previous equation, ν was squared when the second order derivative was taken with respect to time, so it seems likely that if we take a first order derivative with respect to time, the power of ν will be one.

This means that it will be an equation for harmonic oscillation, resulting in $\nu \times \Psi$ to the first power when a first order derivative of Ψ is taken with respect to time.

Well, what takes its original form when a first derivative is taken with respect to time?

Sine!

Cosine!

I thought that $e^{i\square t}$ would work, too. . .

Well, let's try it.

What's the first derivative of sin(t) with respect to t?

cos(t)!

What's the first derivative of the cos(t) with respect to t?

– sin(t)!

What happens if we take the first derivative of $e^{i\square t}$ with respect to t?

$$\frac{\partial}{\partial t} e^{i\square t} = i\square\, e^{i\square t}$$

When the first derivative is taken with respect to time, only $e^{i\square t}$ reverts to its original form. Thus, there seems to be no form for ψ other than $e^{i\square t}$.

When we look at the previous second derivation equation,

$$\frac{\partial^2 \Psi}{\partial t^2} = -(2\pi\nu)^2 \Psi$$

it seems that if we put $-2\pi\nu$ in place of $i\square$, then it will work out, doesn't it?

All right, let's now take a first derivative of $e^{-i2\pi\nu t}$ with respect to time and try to confirm it.

$$\frac{\partial}{\partial t} e^{-i2\pi\nu t} = -i2\pi\nu\, e^{-i2\pi\nu t}$$

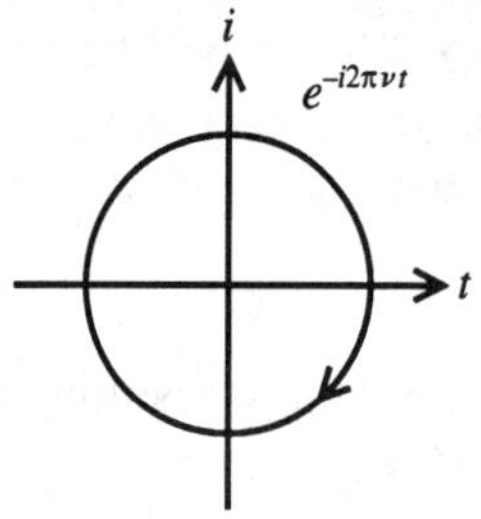

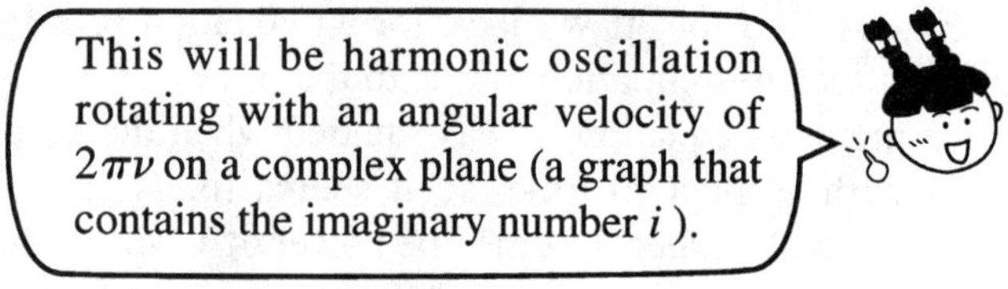

In that case, it does seem that the correct term for Ψ for time is

$$\boxed{e^{-i2\pi\nu t}}$$

after all.

At first, we used

$$\frac{\partial^2 \Psi}{\partial t^2} = -(2\pi\nu)^2 \Psi$$

and tried to make ν disappear, but it didn't work out. If we use

$$\frac{\partial \Psi}{\partial t} = -i2\pi\nu\Psi$$

instead, ν is no longer a square. In that case, if we join this to the equation for a simple electron wave, perhaps we can form an equation that will derive Ψ for a complicated electron wave in one shot. Let's try it.

$$\nabla^2 \Psi + 8\pi^2 \mathfrak{M}(\nu - \mathfrak{V})\Psi = 0 \quad \cdots ①$$

$$\frac{\partial \Psi}{\partial t} = -i2\pi\nu\Psi \quad \cdots ②$$

We remove the parentheses from the equation marked ① and deconstruct it.

$$\nabla^2 \Psi + 8\pi^2 \mathfrak{M}\nu\Psi - 8\pi^2 \mathfrak{M}\mathfrak{V}\Psi = 0$$

Now, let's try putting together the equation marked ① and the equation marked ② and find the elements common to both equations.

Here it is! $\nu\Psi$ is in both equations!

$$\nabla^2 \Psi + 8\pi^2 \mathfrak{M}\underline{\nu\Psi} - 8\pi^2 \mathfrak{M}\mathfrak{V}\Psi = 0 \qquad \frac{\partial \Psi}{\partial t} = -i2\pi\underline{\nu\Psi}$$

Okay, now let's manipulate $\nu\Psi$! We change the form of the equation marked ② to $\nu\Psi = \square$.

$$\nu\Psi = \frac{-1}{2\pi i}\frac{\partial \Psi}{\partial t}$$

$$\nu\Psi = \frac{i^2}{2\pi i}\frac{\partial \Psi}{\partial t}$$

$$\nu\Psi = \frac{i}{2\pi}\frac{\partial \Psi}{\partial t}$$

We insert this equation into the equation marked ①.

$$\nabla^2 \Psi + 8\pi^2 i \mathfrak{M} \cdot \frac{i}{2\pi} \frac{\partial \Psi}{\partial t} - 8\pi^2 \mathfrak{M}\mathfrak{B}\Psi = 0$$

$$\boxed{\nabla^2 \Psi + 4\pi i \mathfrak{M} \frac{\partial \Psi}{\partial t} - 8\pi^2 \mathfrak{M}\mathfrak{B}\Psi = 0}$$

Yes! We have managed to get rid of the ν. We've now got an equation that can derive the form of the electron wave in one pass.

THE FORM OF THE ELECTRON WAVE

But what form does Ψ have?

The electron exists in the three-dimensional space that we occupy. Thus the Ψ in the electron wave is a function that describes what is happening in three-dimensional space x, y, z at time t.

In addition, when we looked for an equation for complicated electron waves, we used

$$\frac{\partial \Psi}{\partial t} = -i2\pi\nu\Psi \ .$$

We thought that the term for time for Ψ could only be

$$e^{-i2\pi\nu t}.$$

But unless we can make up some function that describes the remaining term for space in Ψ, (spatial coordinates x, y, z), we cannot know the full identity of Ψ. So, let's assume that the function that expresses the spatial term of Ψ is $\Phi(x, y, z)$. By doing so, we can express Ψ as

$$\Psi(x, y, z, t) = \Phi(x, y, z)e^{-i2\pi\nu t} \ .$$

Now Ψ for a complicated electron wave may be expressed as

complicated Ψ = (simple Ψ①) + (simple Ψ②) + (simple Ψ③) + · · ·

So, Ψ may be expressed as

$$\Psi(x, y, z, t) = \Psi_1(x, y, z, t) + \Psi_2(x, y, z, t) + \Psi_3(x, y, z, t) + \cdots$$
$$= \Phi_1(x, y, z)e^{-i2\pi\nu_1 t} + \Phi_2(x, y, z)e^{-i2\pi\nu_2 t} + \Phi_3(x, y, z)e^{-i2\pi\nu_3 t} + \cdots$$
$$= \sum_n \Phi_n(x, y, z)\, e^{-i2\pi\nu_n t}$$

But look, we just talked about getting the form

$$\Psi(x, y, z, t) = \Phi(x, y, z)e^{-i2\pi\nu t}.$$

But the fact that the imaginary number i is in there means. . . it's a **COMPLEX NUMBER WAVE!?** What's that?

The imaginary number i is a number such that $i^2 = -1$, right? Somehow I can't imagine what it might be.

That's all right!

The strength of a wave may be expressed by the square of its amplitude. So, let's try squaring the magnitude of Ψ.

$$|\Psi|^2 = \Phi e^{-i2\pi\nu t} \times (\Phi e^{-i2\pi\nu t})^*$$
$$= \Phi e^{-i2\pi\nu t} \times \Phi^* e^{+i2\pi\nu t}$$
$$= \Phi \Phi^* e^{-i2\pi\nu t + i2\pi\nu t}$$
$$= \Phi \Phi^* e^0$$
$$= \Phi \Phi^*$$
$$= |\Phi|^2$$

$e^0 = 1$

When you want to determine the size of a complex number, just change the sign in front of the i and multiply. This is called **taking the complex conjugate.**

* is used when taking a complex conjugate.

Wow! The complex number has disappeared!

Schrödinger thought of this $|\Psi|^2 = |\Phi|^2$ as the "material density."

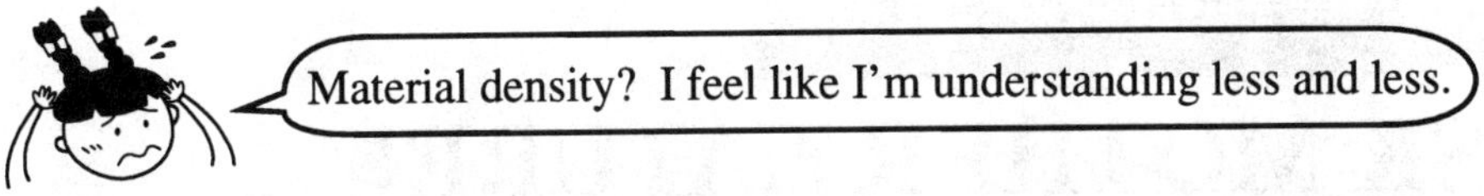

People think that inside the atom there are electron waves which are dense in some places and not dense in others. If you put a grain of a bouillon cube into the middle of a pot of water, the flavor of the soup will gradually even out, but in the beginning, it will be weak in some places and strong in others. Electron waves inside the atom are something like that.

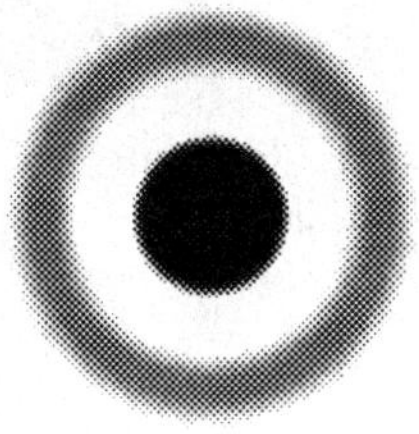

The dark areas indicate where the material density is high. Although Ψ is a complex number, $|\Psi|^2$, the material density is a real number, so there is no great problem.

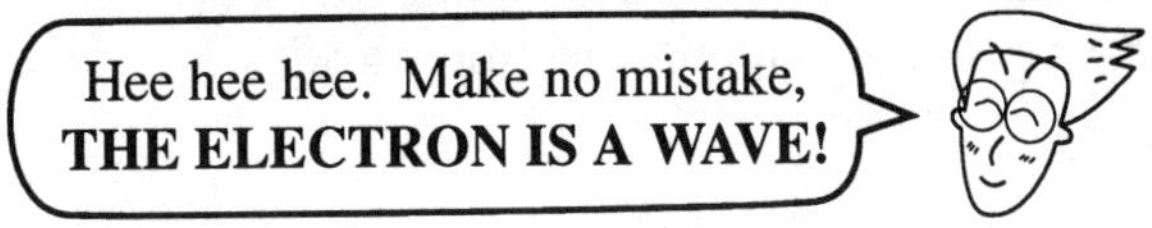

4. 4 LET'S ASK MOTHER NATURE!

$$\nabla^2\Psi + 8\pi^2\mathfrak{M}(\nu - \mathfrak{B})\Psi = 0$$

$$\nabla^2\Psi + 4\pi i\mathfrak{M}\frac{\partial\Psi}{\partial t} - 8\pi^2\mathfrak{M}\mathfrak{B}\Psi = 0$$

Hey, with these equations you can find out what's going on with the electron wave!

Schrödinger desperately wanted to confirm whether he could explain the electron with the equations he had formed. Following Heisenberg's theory he thought, "One should not draw a mental picture of the electron's form within an atom."

But that was unacceptable. Starting from a theory that assumes a clear image of electrons as waves, would it be possible to explain all phenomena caused by electrons, such as the energy levels of an atom or the light spectra emitted by atoms? Electrons exist not only inside atoms, but in all sorts of places. Schrödinger wanted to determine the form of electron waves under various conditions and whether his equations could explain natural phenomena. In the world of physics, no matter how elegant an equation may be, if it doesn't describe natural phenomena, it has no meaning. After all, physics explains what happens in nature.

With that, let's brace ourselves and proceed. The theme is, **LET'S GO ASK MOTHER NATURE!**

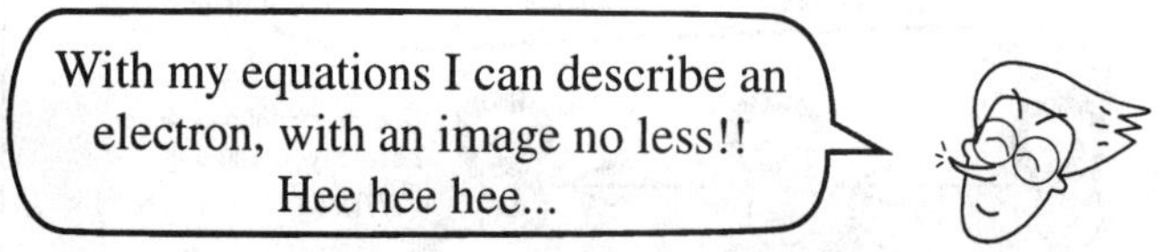

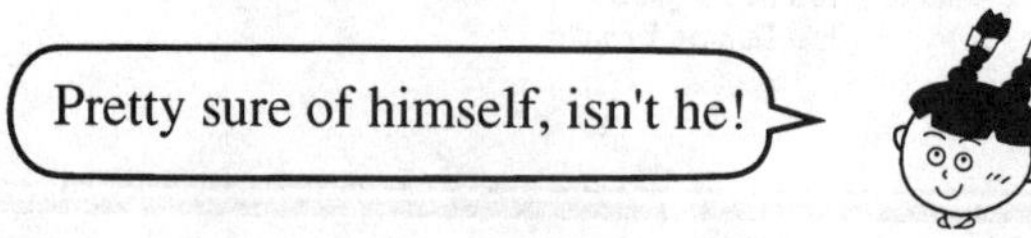

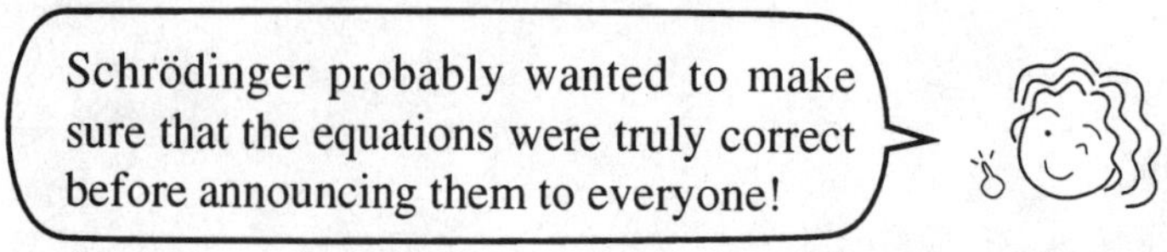

Very easy conditions .... **step 1**
Slightly complicated conditions .... **step 2**
Conditions close to those found in nature ..... **step 3**
Natural conditions .... **step 4**

Now let's follow these four steps and see if Schrödinger's equations really describe what happens in the physical world.

Why are we following these steps?

You can't do something difficult all at once!

By the way, I discovered that the characteristics of an electron and the characteristics of a father who attends the Hippo Family Club are exactly the same!

How can an electron and a father be the same?

Well, think of it this way. We are checking to see if Schrödinger's equations really describe the behavior of electrons under different conditions. It seems to me that the changes in the behavior of the electrons that occur as conditions vary are just like the process of change that we see in a typical father as he becomes more and more involved in Hippo Family Club activities.

But everyone who joins the Hippo Family Club is the same, right? Why does it have to be a father?

We have a clear image of "fathers" so it's easy to talk about them. And besides, they're fun! Of course it could be anyone, but we actually do see a common pattern of change among many fathers as they participate in the Hippo Family Club.

Hmm

Generally speaking, it's like this.

	Step 1	Step 2	Step 3	Step 4
Father	At home	Hippo room	The "carpeted room"	China
Electron	Free space	Inside a box	Hooke field	Hydrogen atom

What's this? I don't get it!

Right, you probably don't get it just by looking, but the characteristics are similar. Don't worry. I'll go into more detail after we finish our discussion.

Now, first we'll look at the experience of a father and then apply it to electrons.

That will make it easier to understand the conditions that affect the behavior of electrons.

Then we will discuss what happens with the electrons themselves.

Okay, on to the tale of the electron and the father!

4. 4. 1 STEP 1: FREE SPACE

THE CASE OF THE FATHER

In my family there is my wife Kanoko, my daughter Sonoko, my son Yuta, and myself. Recently we joined the Hippo Family Club as a family.

Do you know what the Hippo Family Club is?

Well, ever since we started going there is always some tape playing when I get home at night, but I'm not sure why.

I'll explain. At "Hippo Family Club", we listen to the Hippo story tapes in English, Korean, Spanish and some other languages as well as in Japanese.

And, every Friday night my wife takes the kids and goes off somewhere.

> When you join the Hippo Family Club, you start attending meetings. We call our groups "families," but being there is more like being at an international amusement park where many different languages are being spoken at the same time. In our case, we get together every Friday at the home of a "fellow" named Mrs. Yako Nakashiro. What's a fellow? That's the person who looks after the "family."

But since I have to work, I have never been to a gathering at Mrs. Nakashiro's house. I don't really know what they do there.

> We sing and dance to the music and act out the Hippo stories in several languages. It's a lot of fun!

Sing and dance? I could never do that! For generations the people in my family have worked as teachers. If my ancestors found out that I was singing and dancing. . . Besides, I'm busy with work, and there's no way I can get home in time for the start of the "family" meetings. So I usually spend Friday night all by myself.

One day I had some free time. I stretched out on the carpet. Suddenly, the sounds of the Hippo tape began flowing through my head: "Ra-ko-shanpiao-pooshee-pyen." I remembered hearing my wife and children say, "Recitation Time!" and then begin repeating after the tape. Recitation seems to be something they do so they can successfully imitate the words on the tape. I thought I'd try it. Amazing! Although I had never listened carefully to the tape, I was repeating the phrases I had so often heard echoing throughout our house!! But my words were swallowed up by the walls, with no response. I felt lonely.

THE CASE OF THE ELECTRON

So what does this father have to do with an electron?

> They seem totally unrelated, but. . .

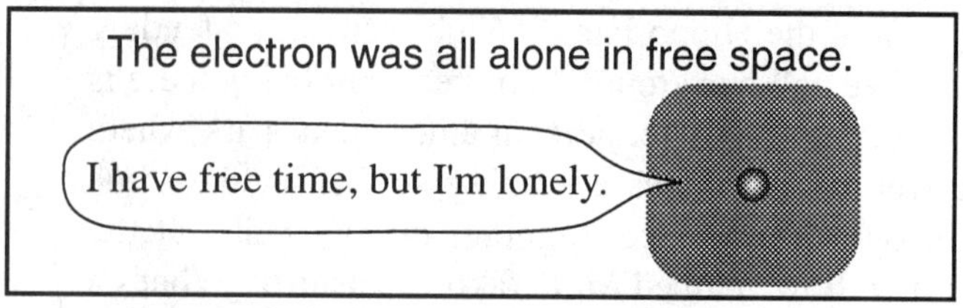

The state of being all alone and not being influenced by other forces is called free space.

When an electron is all alone, just like the father, no force is being applied to it; there is nothing restraining it.

I see. Step 1 is to get into that simple state.

What form does the electron wave have in free space? Let's use the equations developed by Schrödinger.

PREPARATORY STEP 1: SIMPLIFYING THE EQUATION FOR ELECTRON WAVES

I've hated mathematics since high school, especially derivatives. Then I entered TCL and took part in a project where we formulated equations. Not-so-clever me made many mistakes, but seeing the equations gradually come together through everyone's efforts was very satisfying.

At some point in the course of countless failures, I learned that, for people like me who have butterfingers when it comes to mathematics, there are butterfingered ways of doing equations. Rather than worrying about fine calculations, it's enough to pour your energy into understanding the basic idea behind the equation.

Please don't be afraid of making mistakes. Then see if you don't come to love equations, too.

multiplication, division, differentiation

A $\nabla^2\Psi + 8\pi^2\mathfrak{M}(\nu - \mathfrak{V})\Psi = 0$

B $\Psi(x, y, z, t) = \Phi(x, y, z)e^{-i2\pi\nu t}$

Having collected our tools and materials, let's think about the meaning of the equation.

First, study the equation. Then, when you calculate it, repeat the steps to yourself as though you were talking to a friend. That way you'll learn to like equations!

$$A \qquad \nabla^2\Psi + 8\pi^2\mathfrak{M}(\nu - \mathfrak{V})\Psi = 0$$

This equation describes the electron wave, doesn't it?

$$B \qquad \Psi(x, y, z, t) = \Phi(x, y, z)e^{-i2\pi\nu t}$$

When we set up our equation for complicated electron-waves, Ψ was a complex number wave. We found that it took this form when written in an equation.

Since Ψ takes a form similar to B, let's apply it to equation A.

First, we insert equation B into equation A.

$$\nabla^2\Phi\, e^{-i2\pi\nu t} + 8\pi^2\mathfrak{M}(\nu - \mathfrak{V})\Phi\, e^{-i2\pi\nu t} = 0$$

$e^{-i2\pi\nu t}$ is a function of t. It has no relationship to ∇^2, which will affect the values related to only x, y, z. Therefore, it is safe to divide both sides by $e^{-i2\pi\nu t}$.

$$\nabla^2\Phi + 8\pi^2\mathfrak{M}(\nu - \mathfrak{V})\Phi = 0$$

Modifying this slightly, we obtain

$$\nabla^2\Phi = -8\pi^2\mathfrak{M}(\nu - \mathfrak{V})\Phi$$

The equation for electron waves is a bit simpler now. Let's find Φ from this equation. Then, if we multiply the Φ that we get by $e^{-i2\pi\nu t}$, we can find Ψ.

Φ is a function of (x, y, z) , and describes the height of a wave at a given location.

You say that, but I still don't understand Φ. . .

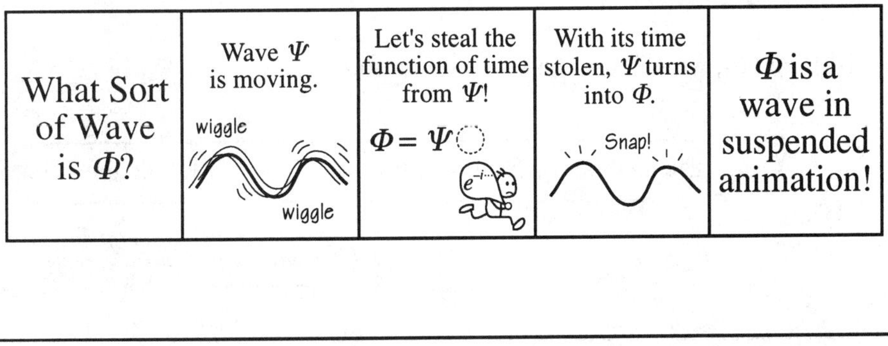

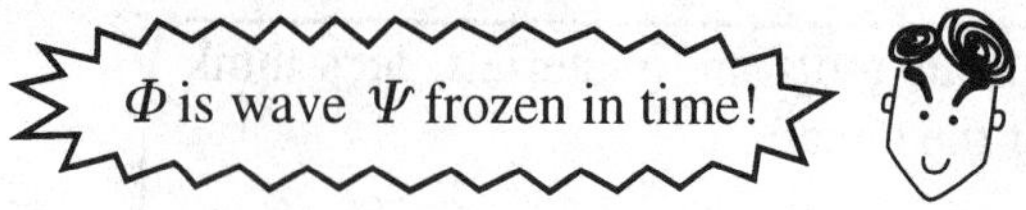

Now, let's prepare for Step 2 and the rest of the steps as well. From here on, we will not refer back to Preparatory Step 1.

PREPARATORY STEP 2: ADJUSTING $\mathfrak{V}$ TO THE CONDITION

As we explained earlier, in free space the electron is not acted upon by any other forces.

This means that it does not have any potential energy V.

$$V = 0$$

Then

$$V = h\mathfrak{V}$$

So,

$$\mathfrak{V} = \frac{V}{h}$$

$$\mathfrak{V} = \frac{0}{h}$$

$$= 0$$

The equation for the electron wave is then

$$\nabla^2\Phi = -8\pi^2\mathfrak{M}(\nu - \mathfrak{V})\Phi$$

$$\boxed{\nabla^2\Phi = -8\pi^2\mathfrak{M}\nu\Phi}$$

This is the equation for electron waves in free space.

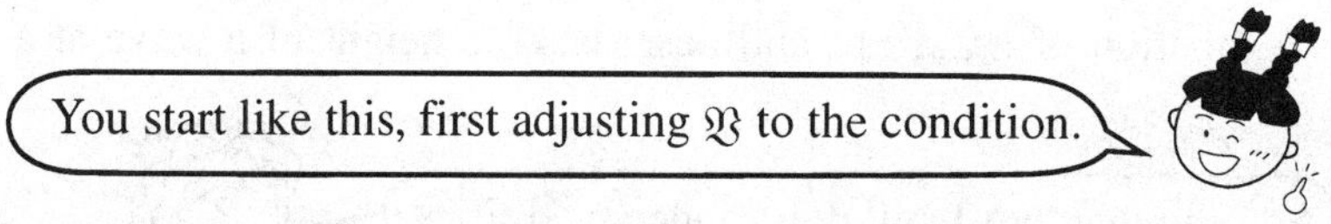

◆ ESTIMATING Φ

Now, at last, we will use this equation to find Φ.

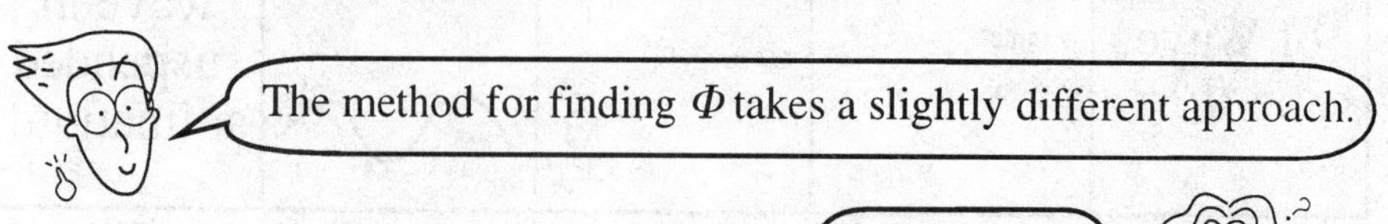

Well, we make an estimate that fits the form of the wave in this particular case, and then we put it into the equation for Φ. By doing this, we can find a Φ that can be used in the electron wave equation.

We're solving for the Φ produced by simple waves. Since there aren't many different kinds of waves, the mathematical expressions can be learned quickly.

Is that so?

First of all, $\Phi\,(x, y, z)$ is a wave that spreads out in three directions, x, y, z. In this case, we should take the waves in each direction and multiply them.

$$\Phi\,(x, y, z) = (\text{wave in direction } x) \times (\text{wave in direction } y) \times (\text{wave in direction } z)$$

A wave in free space may be described using $e^{ik_x x}$.

k_x is the wave number. It expresses how many times a wave oscillates in one meter.

Therefore, if we let the amplitude of a wave in direction x be A_{k_x}, we should have the form

$$A_{k_x} e^{ik_x x}$$

I'll bet sine or cosine would be okay, too.

In fact, the sine and cosine can be described with $e^{i\square}$.

It should be

$$A_{k_y} e^{ik_y y}\ ,\ A_{k_z} e^{ik_z z}$$

for both direction y and direction z, so when we multiply the directions for the three-dimensional wave $\Phi\,(x, y, z)$,, we use the following form

$$\Phi\,(x, y, z) = A_{k_x} e^{ik_x x} \cdot A_{k_y} e^{ik_y y} \cdot A_{k_z} e^{ik_z z}$$

If we collect the frequencies A_{k_x}, A_{k_y}, A_{k_z}, into one as $A_{k_x k_y k_z}$, then Φ is

$$\boxed{\Phi\,(x, y, z) = A_{k_x k_y k_z} e^{ik_x x} e^{ik_y y} e^{ik_z z}}$$

Now we have an estimate for Φ!

◆ LET'S INSERT THE ESTIMATED Φ INTO THE EQUATION FOR ELECTRON WAVES AND SEE WHAT HAPPENS!

Up to now we've pictured wave Φ of an electron in free space and assumed its behavior. Now we must determine whether this supposition accurately matches the equation for electron waves.

The equation for the electron wave

$$\nabla^2\Phi = -8\pi^2\mathfrak{M}\nu\Phi$$

means that when we take the second derivative of Φ, the original reappears as a multiple of the fixed quantity $-8\pi^2\mathfrak{M}\nu$.

Let's try to take the second derivative of Φ with respect to position that we just estimated.

Finally, it's time for the calculations. Procedure is very important when doing calculations. Once you get used to the procedure, it's easy. But if you forget something or get the order wrong, the calculation can become quite troublesome. That's when you can make mistakes. The procedure followed here can be used for electrons in a box or for electrons in a Hooke field, as described below. So, try to get the flow of the calculations clear in your mind. If you do, they will be a whole lot easier.

The symbol ∇^2 means

$$\nabla^2\Phi = \frac{\partial^2\Phi}{\partial x^2} + \frac{\partial^2\Phi}{\partial y^2} + \frac{\partial^2\Phi}{\partial z^2}$$

So, in this case, we will have

$$\begin{aligned}\nabla^2\Phi &= \frac{\partial^2}{\partial x^2} A_{k_xk_yk_z} e^{ik_xx}e^{ik_yy}e^{ik_zz} \\ &+ \frac{\partial^2}{\partial y^2} A_{k_xk_yk_z} e^{ik_xx}e^{ik_yy}e^{ik_zz} \\ &+ \frac{\partial^2}{\partial z^2} A_{k_xk_yk_z} e^{ik_xx}e^{ik_yy}e^{ik_zz}\end{aligned}$$

$A_{k_x k_y k_z}$ is a constant with no relationship to the derivative. Many derivative signs have appeared, so let's clean them up, one by one.

$$\text{the wave in direction } x: \quad \frac{\partial^2}{\partial x^2} e^{ik_x x} e^{ik_y y} e^{ik_z z}$$

$$\text{the wave in direction } y: \quad \frac{\partial^2}{\partial y^2} e^{ik_x x} e^{ik_y y} e^{ik_z z}$$

$$\text{the wave in direction } z: \quad \frac{\partial^2}{\partial z^2} e^{ik_x x} e^{ik_y y} e^{ik_z z}$$

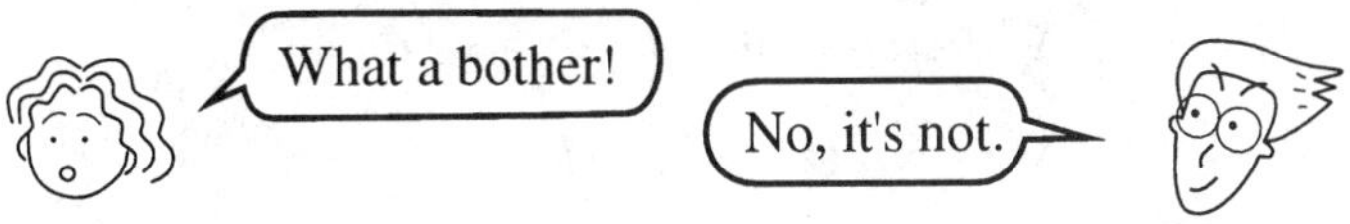

Look, all the forms are the same, aren't they? If you take the derivative of any one of them like x, you can put it in the spot for variable (x) in the other two equations.

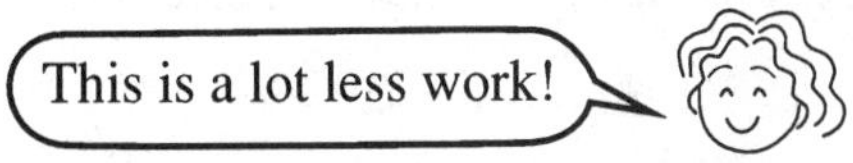

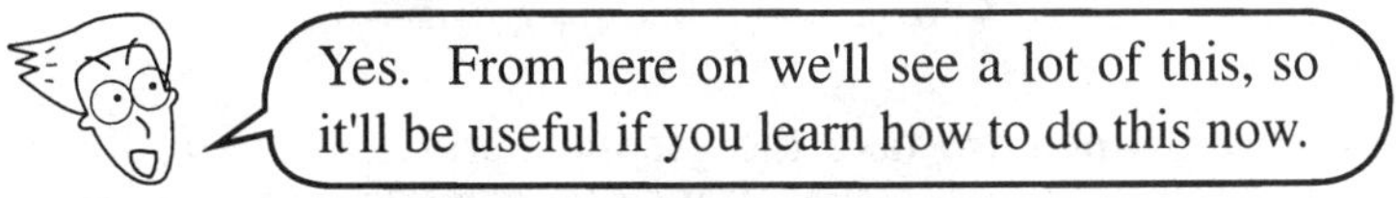

Let's take the derivative with respect to x only.

$$\frac{\partial^2 \Phi}{\partial x^2}$$

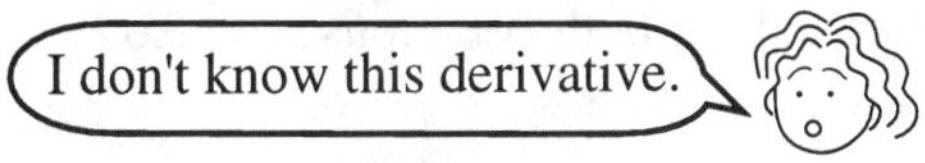

Here, what you do is take the second derivative of Φ with respect to x. In this case, there is no relationship to y or z, so you can just think of them as a number. That way, the coefficient in the superscript comes down twice.

$$\text{1st derivative}: \quad \frac{\partial \Phi}{\partial x} \rightarrow A_{k_x k_y k_z} e^{ik_x x} e^{ik_y y} e^{ik_z z}$$

$$\rightarrow ik_x A_{k_x k_y k_z} e^{ik_x x} e^{ik_y y} e^{ik_z z}$$

$$\text{2nd derivative}: \quad \frac{\partial^2 \Phi}{\partial x^2} \rightarrow ik_x A_{k_x k_y k_z} e^{ik_x x} e^{ik_y y} e^{ik_z z}$$

$$\rightarrow (ik_x)^2 A_{k_x k_y k_z} e^{ik_x x} e^{ik_y y} e^{ik_z z}$$

$$\rightarrow -k_x^2 A_{k_x k_y k_z} e^{ik_x x} e^{ik_y y} e^{ik_z z}$$

Because $i \times i = -1$

$$\frac{\partial^2 \Phi}{\partial x^2} = -k_x^2 A_{k_x k_y k_z} e^{ik_x x} e^{ik_y y} e^{ik_z z}$$

$$= -k_x^2 \Phi$$

That's because $\Phi = A_{k_x k_y k_z} e^{ik_x x} e^{ik_y y} e^{ik_z z}$.

Then, since y and z will have the same form,

$$\frac{\partial^2 \Phi}{\partial x^2} = -k_x^2 \Phi \ , \quad \frac{\partial^2 \Phi}{\partial y^2} = -k_y^2 \Phi \ , \quad \frac{\partial^2 \Phi}{\partial z^2} = -k_z^2 \Phi$$

we place these in the previous equation.

$$\nabla^2 \Phi = \frac{\partial^2 \Phi}{\partial x^2} + \frac{\partial^2 \Phi}{\partial y^2} + \frac{\partial^2 \Phi}{\partial z^2}$$

We then obtain

$$\nabla^2 \Phi = -k_x^{\ 2} \Phi - k_y^{\ 2} \Phi - k_z^{\ 2} \Phi$$

$$\nabla^2 \Phi = -(k_x^{\ 2} + k_y^{\ 2} + k_z^{\ 2}) \Phi$$

At last, we've completed the second derivative of Φ.

Now let's compare it to the equation for an electron in free space.

$$\nabla^2 \Phi = -8\pi^2 \mathfrak{M} \nu \Phi$$

$$\nabla^2 \Phi = -(k_x^{\ 2} + k_y^{\ 2} + k_z^{\ 2}) \Phi$$

In both cases, when we take the second derivative of Φ, the result is a constant multiplied by Φ. They have **EXACTLY THE SAME FORM.**

The left side of both equations is ∇^2, so

$$k_x^{\ 2} + k_y^{\ 2} + k_z^{\ 2} = 8\pi^2 \mathfrak{M} \nu$$

So the Φ for which we just gave an estimate is an electron wave in free space.

By rewriting the above equation, we get

$$\boxed{\nu = \frac{k_x^{\ 2} + k_y^{\ 2} + k_z^{\ 2}}{8\pi^2 \mathfrak{M}}}$$

Looking at it another way, we have also been able to find frequency ν for an electron wave.

What! We were finding Φ, but we ended up finding ν, too!

WE'VE FOUND Φ AND ν!

◆ FINDING Ψ

In free space, Φ is

$$\Phi(x, y, z) = A_{k_x k_y k_z} e^{ik_x x} e^{ik_y y} e^{ik_z z}$$
$$= A_{k_x k_y k_z} e^{i(k_x x + k_y y + k_z z)}$$

When multiplying two exponential numbers, you add their exponents!

But,

$$k_x^2 + k_y^2 + k_z^2 = 8\pi^2 \mathfrak{M} \nu$$

Ψ described how an electron wave moves.

Since

$$\Psi(x, y, z, t) = \Phi(x, y, z) e^{-i2\pi\nu t}$$

if we know Φ, we need only multiply by $e^{-i2\pi\nu t}$ in order to get Ψ.

After all, we've already found frequency ν.

$$\Psi(x, y, z, t) = A_{k_x k_y k_z} e^{i(k_x x + k_y y + k_z z)} e^{-i2\pi\nu t}$$

$$\Psi(x, y, z, t) = A_{k_x k_y k_z} e^{i(k_x x + k_y y + k_z z - i2\pi\nu t)}$$

$$\text{Provided that} \quad \nu = \frac{k_x^2 + k_y^2 + k_z^2}{8\pi^2 \mathfrak{M}}$$

Point

This means that we now know the **WHEN, WHERE AND HOW** of the behavior of **an electron wave Ψ in free space!**

描 像!
Visual image

But Mr. Schrödinger, even if we know what Ψ is, I don't quite understand when it's in equation language.

That's true. Okay, let's look at the wave it describes. I formed this equation because I wanted to know how an electron behaves inside an atom. My equation, unlike Heisenberg's, corresponds to a definite **VISUAL IMAGE.**

Let's actually look at an electron wave in free space.

First, let's look at the Ψ we just found.

$$\Psi(x, y, z, t) = A_{k_x k_y k_z} e^{i(k_x x + k_y y + k_z z - 2\pi\nu t)}$$

Ψ is a wave that spreads out in three dimensions, x, y and z. Right now we'll consider only the x dimension.

$$\Psi(x, t) = Ae^{i(k_x x - 2\pi\nu t)}$$

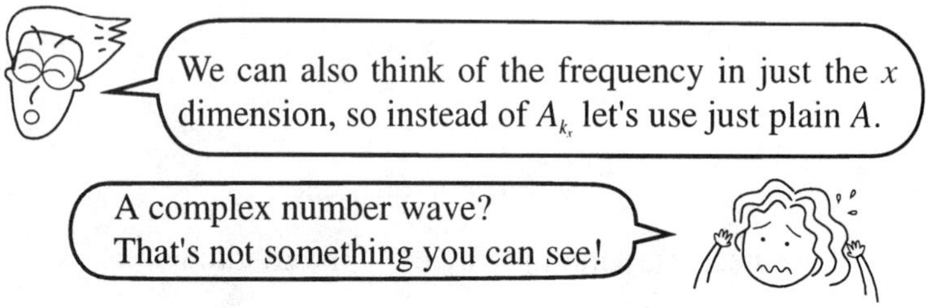

That's all right. Actually, we can apply

the Euler formula
$e^{i\theta} = \cos\theta + i \sin\theta$

In other words, $e^{i\theta}$ is the sum of a sine and a cosine.

To simplify things, let's take a sine wave.

$$\Psi(x, t) = A \sin(k_x x - 2\pi\nu t)$$

Because it's a simple wave, ν can assume only one value.

ν: Number of undulations per second
k_x: Number of radians traversed in a meter

Now, if $\nu = 1$ and $k_x = 2\pi$, the equation becomes

$$\Psi(x, t) = A \sin(2\pi x - 2\pi t)$$

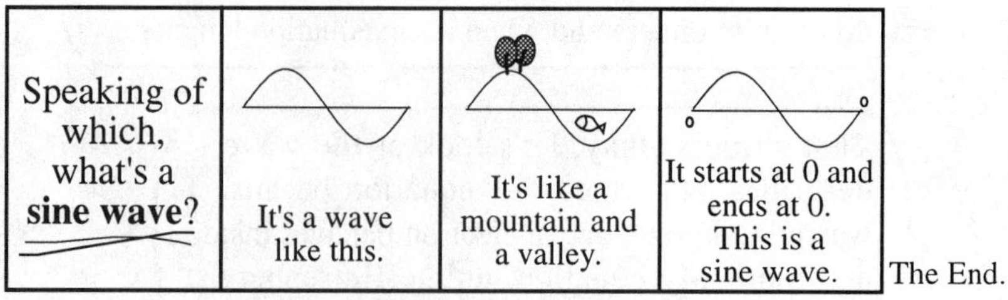

Next, let's see how this

$$\Psi(x, t) = A \sin(2\pi x - 2\pi t)$$

changes with time.

I was just about to explain that.

How It's Done!

1. Fix the time. At first, $t = 0$, so

$$\Psi(x, 0) = A \sin(2\pi x - 2\pi \cdot 0)$$
$$= A \sin 2\pi x$$

2. Next, we examine the form of the wave when $t = 0$. For that, we use

$$\Psi(x, 0) = A \sin 2\pi x$$

Then, all we have to do is change the value of x in the equation by increments of 0.25, so you get 0, 0.25, 0.5, 0.75. . . Then we find the height of the wave for each of these positions and join them by a line.

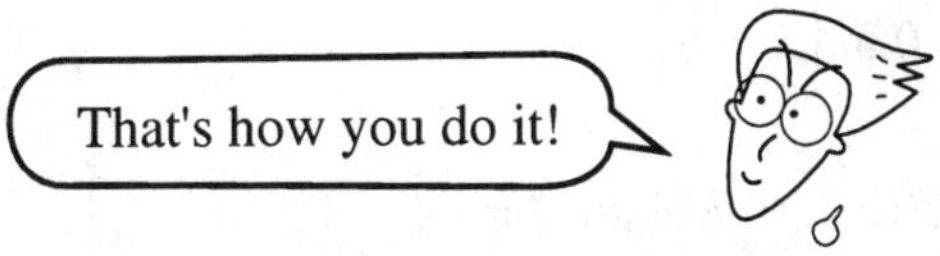

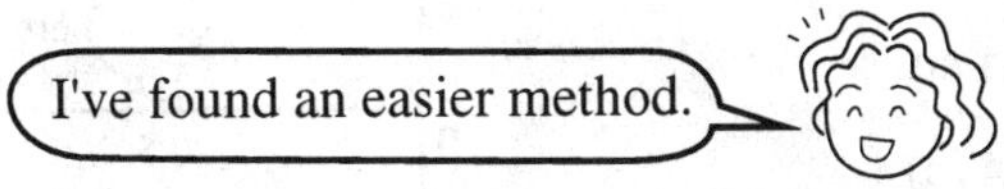

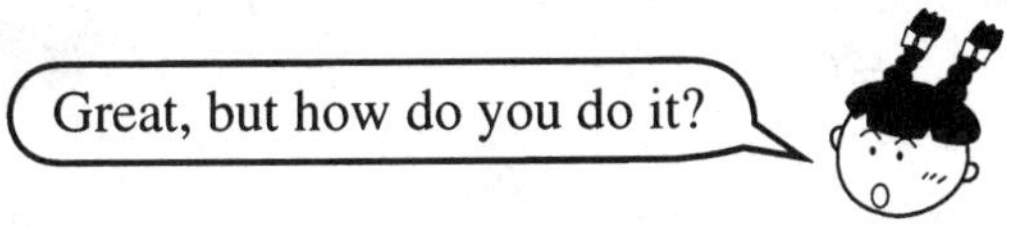

Sine wave

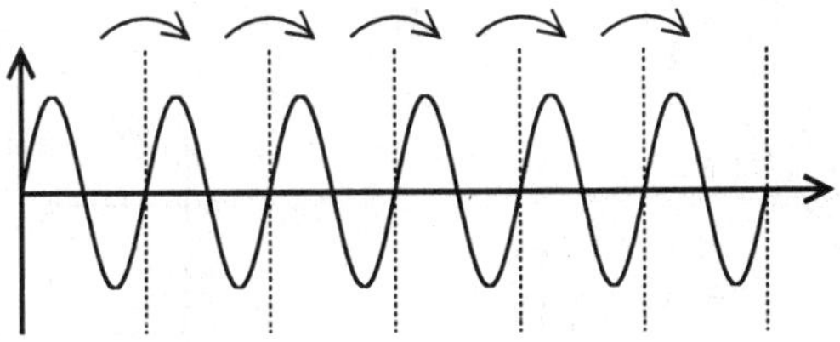

You make use of the cyclical property of a wave. A sine wave continuously repeats the same form, so if we examine only one undulation (one cycle), the rest will be the same.

1. **Let's start by placing $t = 0$ in this equation and see the form of the wave.**

$$\Psi(x, 0) = A \sin(2\pi x - 2\pi \cdot 0)$$
$$= A \sin 2\pi x$$

Let us insert 0, 0.25, 0.5, 0.75, and 1 as values for x.

Where $x = 0$

$$\Psi(0, 0) = A \sin 2\pi \cdot 0$$
$$= A \sin 0$$
$$= A \cdot 0$$
$$= 0$$

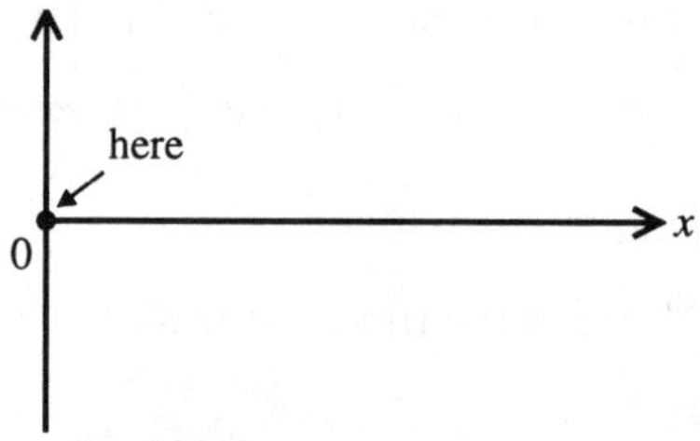

Where $x = 0.25$ $\left(x = \frac{1}{4}\right)$

$$\Psi(0.25, 0) = A \sin 2\pi \cdot \frac{1}{4}$$
$$= A \sin \left(\frac{1}{2}\right)\pi$$
$$= A \cdot 1$$
$$= A$$

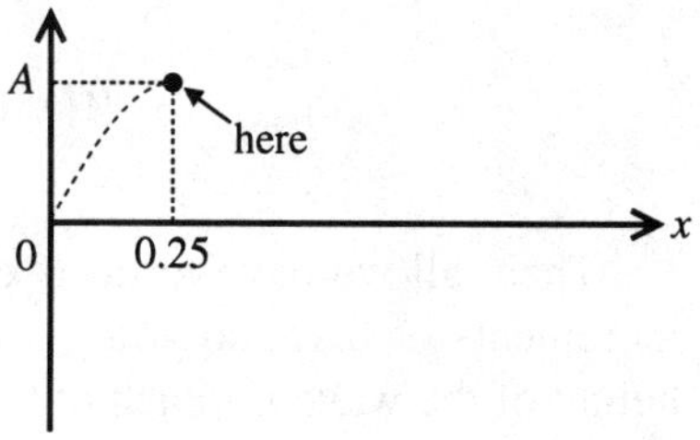

Where $x = 0.5$ $\left(x = \frac{1}{2}\right)$

$$\Psi(0.5, 0) = A \sin 2\pi \cdot \frac{1}{2}$$
$$= A \sin \pi$$
$$= A \cdot 0$$
$$= 0$$

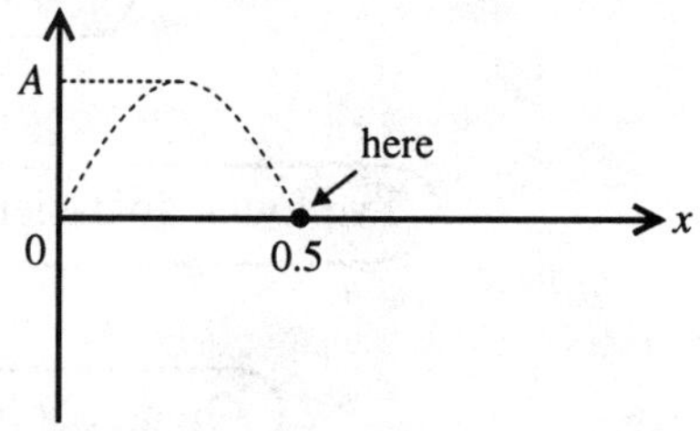

Where $x = 0.75$ $\left(x = \frac{3}{4}\right)$

$$\Psi(0.75, 0) = A \sin 2\pi \cdot \frac{3}{4}$$
$$= A \sin \left(\frac{3}{2}\right)\pi$$
$$= A \cdot -1$$
$$= -A$$

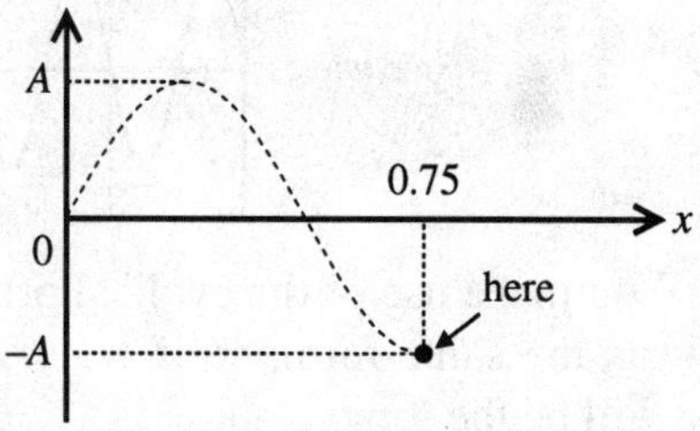

Where $x = 1$

$$\Psi(1, 0) = A \sin 2\pi \cdot 1$$
$$= A \sin 2\pi$$
$$= A \cdot 0$$
$$= 0$$

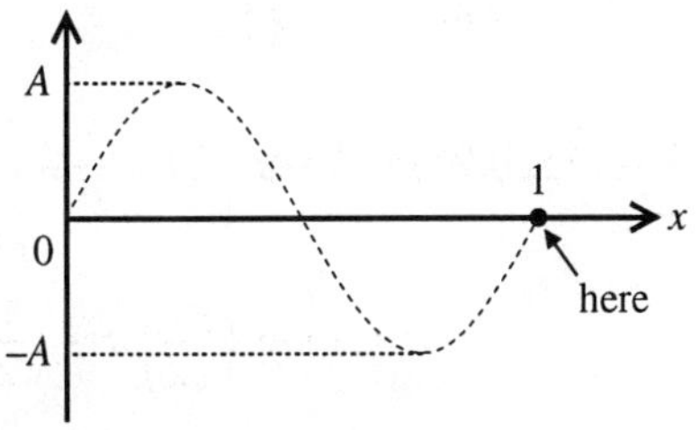

Okay, we'll put the height of the wave for each position when $t = 0$ into a table.

x	0	0.25	0.5	0.75	1
$\Psi(x, 0)$	0	A	0	$-A$	0

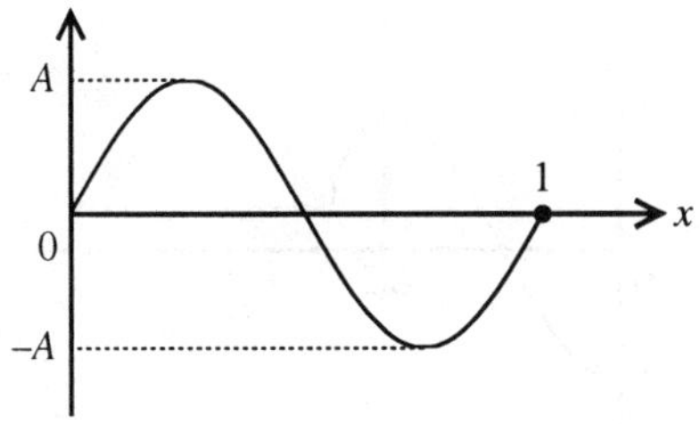

The more points you calculate in between, the more accurately the function is represented. So finally you get the sine wave.

This gives us one undulation. The rest are just repetitions of this, so A and $-A$ alternate between the zeros. Knowing this makes it a lot easier.

2. Next, let's insert $t = 0.25$ in the equation, and check the form of the wave when $t = 0.25$.

$$\Psi(x, 0.25) = A \sin\left(2\pi x - 2\pi \cdot \frac{1}{4}\right)$$
$$= A \sin\left\{2\pi x - \left(\frac{1}{2}\right)\pi\right\}$$

We insert 0, 0.25, 0.5, 0.75 and 1 as values for x.

Where $x = 0$

$$\Psi(0, 0.25) = A \sin\left\{2\pi \cdot - \left(\frac{1}{2}\right)\pi\right\}$$
$$= A \sin\left(-\frac{1}{2}\right)\pi$$
$$= A \cdot -1$$
$$= -A$$

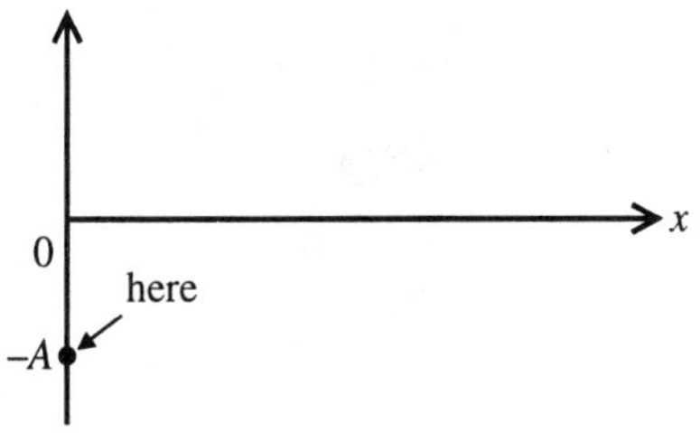

Where $x = 0.25$ $\left(x = \frac{1}{4}\right)$

$$\Psi(0.25, 0.25) = A \sin\left\{2\pi \cdot \frac{1}{4} - \left(\frac{1}{2}\right)\pi\right\}$$

$$= A \sin\left\{\left(\frac{1}{2}\right)\pi - \left(\frac{1}{2}\right)\pi\right\}$$

$$= A \sin 0$$

$$= A \cdot 0$$

$$= 0$$

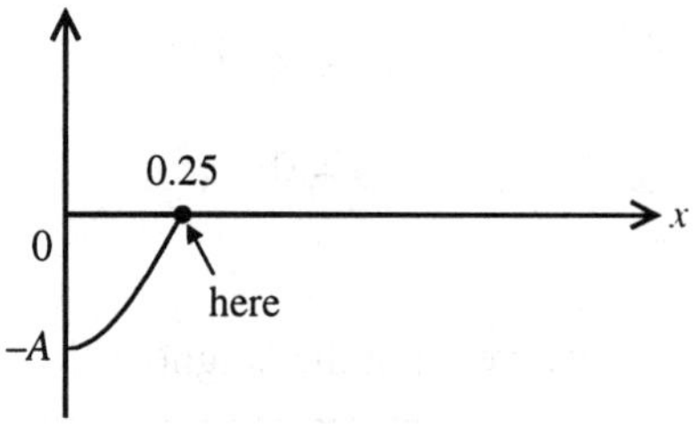

Where $x = 0.5$ $\left(x = \frac{1}{2}\right)$

$$\Psi(0.5, 0.25) = A \sin\left\{2\pi \cdot \frac{1}{2} - \left(\frac{1}{2}\right)\pi\right\}$$

$$= A \sin\left(\frac{1}{2}\right)\pi$$

$$= A \cdot 1$$

$$= A$$

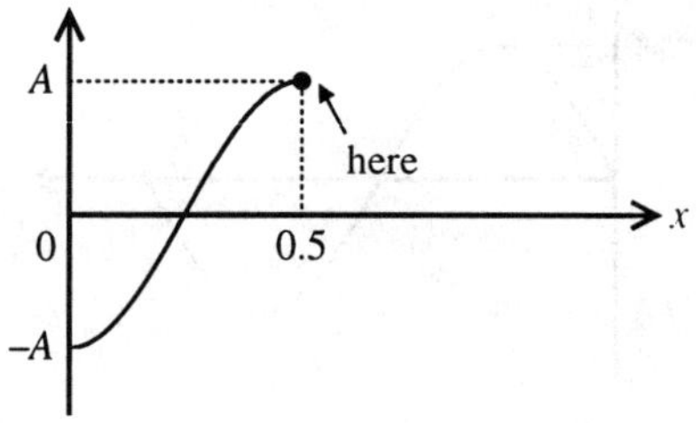

Where $x = 0.75$ $\left(x = \frac{3}{4}\right)$

$$\Psi(0.75, 0.25) = A \sin\left\{2\pi \cdot \frac{3}{4} - \left(\frac{1}{2}\right)\pi\right\}$$

$$= A \sin \pi$$

$$= A \cdot 0$$

$$= 0$$

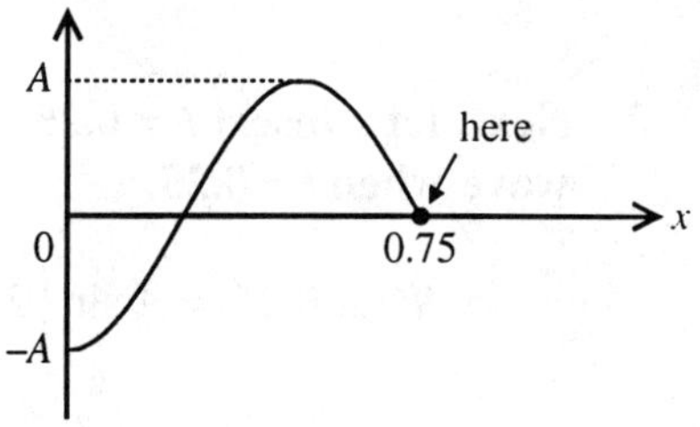

Where $x = 1$

$$\Psi(1, 0.25) = A \sin\left\{2\pi \cdot 1 - \left(\frac{1}{2}\right)\pi\right\}$$

$$= A \sin\left(\frac{2}{3}\right)\pi$$

$$= A \cdot -1$$

$$= -A$$

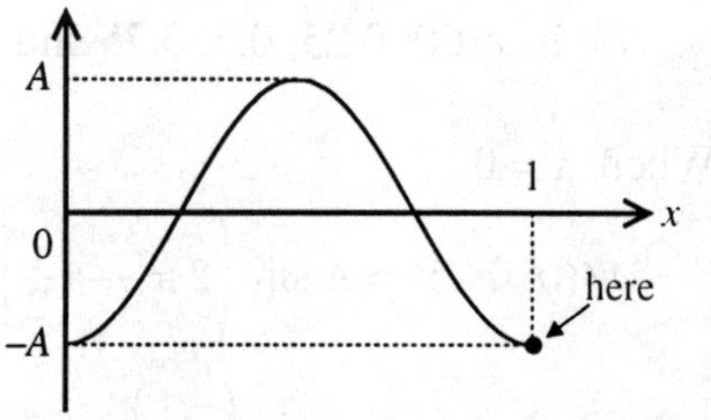

Let's combine this with what we found when $t = 0$ and make a single table.

t \ x	0	0.25	0.5	0.75	1
0	0	A	0	$-A$	0
0.25	$-A$	0	A	0	$-A$

Could this mean that they just slip down diagonally by one notch?

In the beginning, we said that the shape of a sine wave keeps repeating itself. So the numbers keep sliding down like this.

Over time, the position of the peaks and valleys of the wave changes. Okay, now let's look at the graph and see how Mr. Whale moves when he starts off floating at $x = 0.25$m.

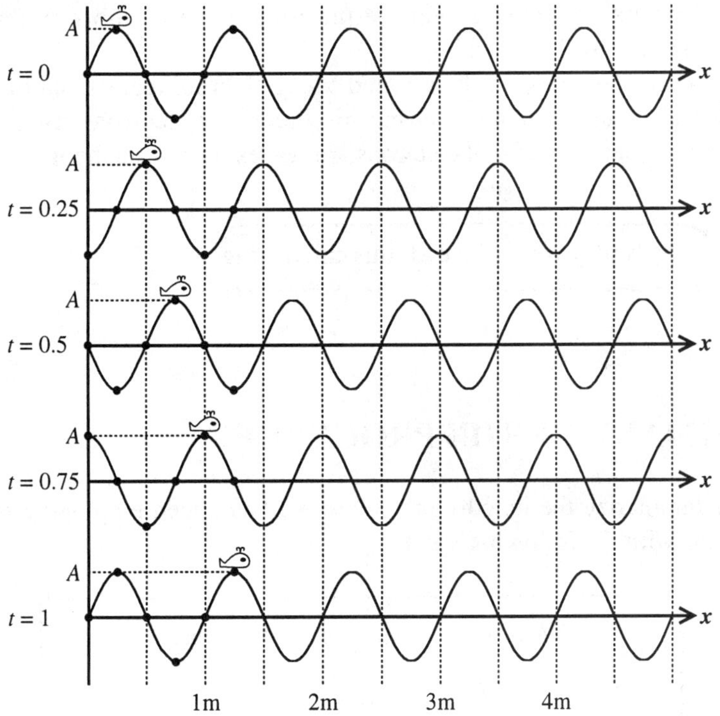

It seems that in free space, an electron wave progresses the same way.

This is called a **RUNNING WAVE.**

With the equations for electron waves

$$\nabla^2 \Phi + 8\pi^2 \mathfrak{M}(\nu - \mathfrak{V})\Phi = 0$$

$$\nabla^2 \Psi + 4\pi i \mathfrak{M} \frac{\partial \Psi}{\partial t} - 8\pi \mathfrak{M}\mathfrak{V}\Phi = 0$$

we've been able to form a **MENTAL PICTURE** of the wave!

◆ HOW TO FIND *E*

The energy can be easily found by placing the ν that we just obtained into the equation

$$E = h\nu$$

The energy of an electron in free space cannot be determined experimentally. In Steps 2 through 4, we will attempt to see whether the energy values found using Schrödinger's equations are still more complicated conditions in the physical world.

Only when the energy values found using Schrödinger's equations match experimental results can we say that his theory of electrons truly explains physical phenomenon, and that electrons are waves, just as he thought.

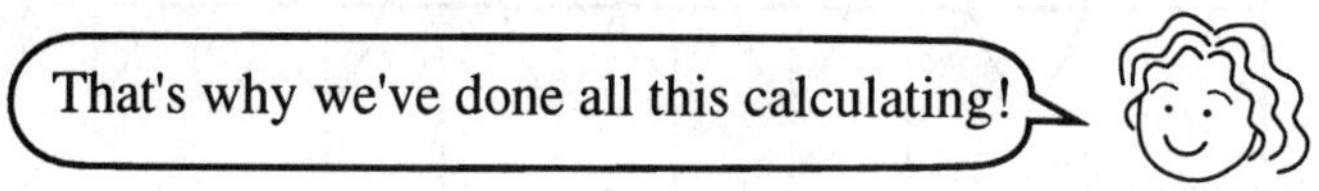

◆ SUMMARY OF THE PROCEDURE

Let's summarize the lengthy procedure we have been employing to do our calculations with the following steps:

Adjust $\mathfrak{V}$ to the given conditions.
↓
Make an estimate for Φ.
↓
Place the estimate in the equation for electron waves and confirm.
↓
Find Ψ
↓
Find E

Finally, let's consider the analogy between the father and the electron. How do they compare?

The Father

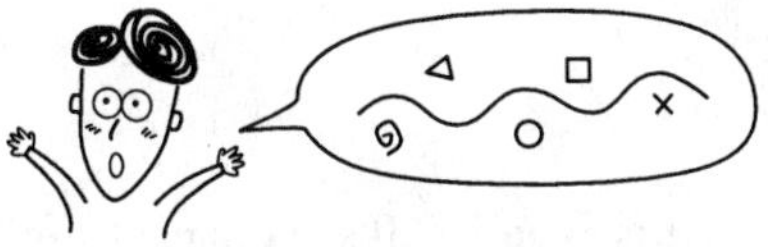

One day, a phrase from the Hippo Club tapes started running through Dad's head. He could recite it, but would anyone understand what he was saying?

The Electron

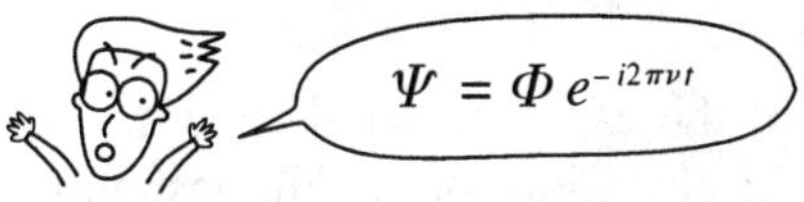

We were able to describe an electron in free space using the equation for electron waves. But there were no experimental results to compare this with. Was this really right?

We've completed our preparatory exercises for Step 1. Now, on to Step 2. The adventure of the father learning to speak a foreign language by participating in the Hippo Family Club activities and the adventure with the electron wave equation will both continue. There's more fun ahead, folks. . .

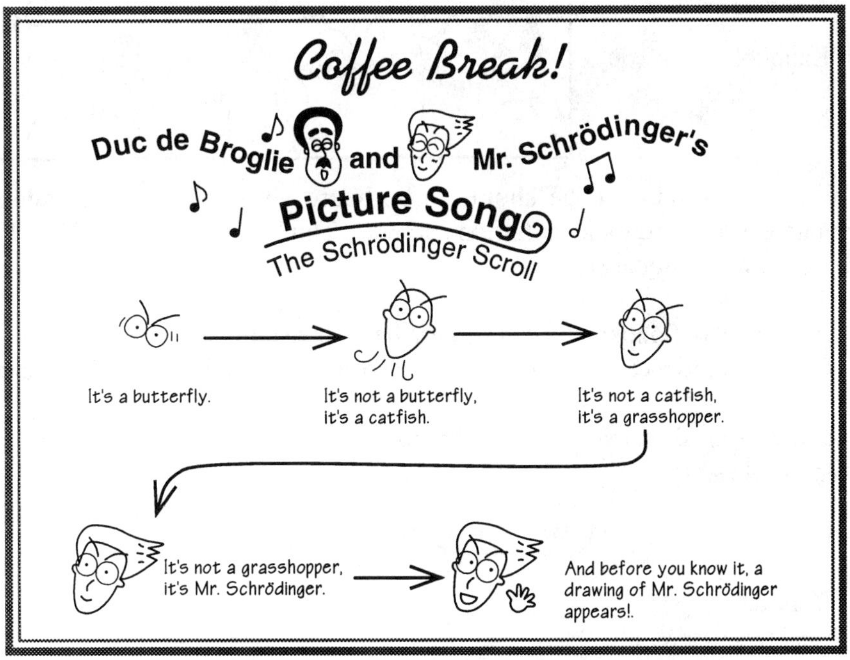

4. 4. 2 STEP 2: INSIDE THE BOX

THE CASE OF THE FATHER

Today is Friday. Dad is waiting outside in his car for Mom and the kids, who are still at a Hippo Club meeting.

"Boy, they're late."

He sneaks a glance at his watch. It's well past eight o'clock. They're not usually this late. What could they be doing?

"I'm not their chauffeur," Dad mutters ill-humoredly.

Tick, tick, tick goes his watch.

"I'll just have to go in and get them. . ."

He opens the door of the car. The wind is cold. With his collar turned up, Dad hurries toward the Hippo Club room. He hesitates slightly as the sound of the tape becomes louder.

"If I go in now, I'll end up having to dance around with them, won't I?"

Even so, he can't wait any longer. Resigning himself, Dad steps into the Hippo Club room. What is this? Everybody is in a circle excitedly talking about something or other. Yuta is there among the children crowded into the room. They have just left the tape running in the background.

"Uhh, excuse me. . ."

No one notices him.

"Kanoko!"

Without realizing it, he shouts to be heard above the din. Suddenly everyone is silent and looks at him in surprise. Thinking to himself, "Now I've done it," he hesitantly asks,

"Are Kanoko, Sonoko and Yuta Ogura here? I've come to get them."
"Oh, it's nice to meet you! So you're Sonoko and Yuta's father! Please come in!"

A middle-aged woman who appears to be the leader of the group stands up and approaches him.

"Uhh. . ."

Guided by the woman, Dad joins the circle. On the far side of the circle, Kanoko and Sonoko are smiling at him.

"My name is Yako Nakashiro. We hold our Hippo Club activities here every week. I'm very pleased you could join us today."

Dad takes a look around him. The group includes young mothers, babies, elementary school children and men of different ages.

"Well then, Mr. Ogura, please introduce yourself to the group."

There are welcoming shouts and applause from the group. Feeling rather embarrassed, Dad begins speaking in a halting manner.

"Well, uhh, I'm Gan Ogura. My wife and children enjoy coming here to these gatherings. I only came to pick them up tonight. I wasn't planning on participating or anything like that. . ."

Suddenly someone cries out, "Why don't you join us and give the Hippo Club activities a try? Just a few words in any language."

And then others begin shouting, "Go ahead, give it a whirl!"

With everyone looking at him so expectantly, Dad finds he just can't refuse.

"Well, let's see, I haven't really listened to the tapes very closely, so. . ."

Having made these excuses, Dad plunges in and lets loose with a torrent of words.

"Rah-koh-shianpiao-puushee-pyen. Zu-zuu shyeshye-ta-jah!"

"That's great! You sound just like the tape!!"

Dad is pleased to receive so much praise from everyone around him. He smiles to himself, thinking happily, "Well, everyone here listens to the tapes often so they ought to know. I guess I'm not so bad. At this rate I probably can learn to speak a foreign language."

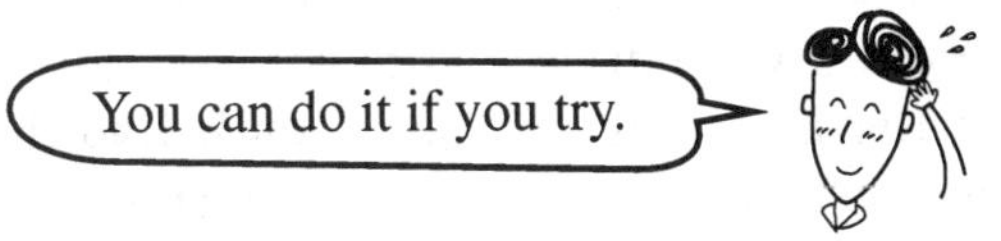

THE CASE OF THE ELECTRON

For Step 2, let's consider the state of the electron by comparing it to the father's situation at Hippo.

It is important to note that Dad is not at home but at someone else's house, in this case, Mrs. Nakashiro's house. Inside the Hippo Club room he is free to sing, dance and act freely, but that does not mean he can just go marching into the other rooms in the house. Dad is in a position where he has freedom, but is limited spatially.

Well then, what about an electron? An electron also has freedom, but is limited spatially. For example, the electron is free, with no forces acting upon it, but its boundaries are limited to

For Step 2, let's think of the electron as though it were in a box. What form does the electron wave have inside a box and will Schrödinger's equation be able to describe it?

Making mistakes along the way is part of the process of forming equations. In order to learn from your mistakes, when something goes wrong, be sure to always ask yourself, "Why didn't it work?" Equations are based on scientific formulations, and so coming up with an equation that works naturally requires a scientific approach.

After determining the characteristics of the equations for Ψ, Φ, E and for differentials, the best way to work with them is by considering them carefully and keeping their characteristics in mind. That's the key to formulating equations that work. Even if you fail once or twice, don't give up; keep going till you succeed no matter how long it takes. You'll find that as you keep making more equations, you'll become better and better at it.

The procedure was as follows:

Adjust $\mathfrak{V}$ to the given conditions.

↓

Make an estimate for Φ.

↓

Insert into the equation for electron waves and confirm.

↓

Find Ψ.

↓

Find E.

Right?

◆ PREPARATORY STEP: ADJUST $\mathfrak{V}$ TO THE GIVEN CONDITIONS

First, let's consider what happens to the $\mathfrak{V}$ in the equation for electron waves.

$$\nabla^2\Phi = -8\pi^2\mathfrak{M}(\nu - \mathfrak{V})\Phi$$

In this case, as in the case of free space, no force is acting on the electron, so

$$\mathfrak{V} = 0 \ .$$

Therefore, the equation for the electron wave inside a box is

$$\nabla^2\Phi = -8\pi^2\mathfrak{M}\nu\Phi \ .$$

◆ MAKING AN ESTIMATE FOR Φ

What kind of wave is inside the box?

What is the most obvious characteristic of a box?

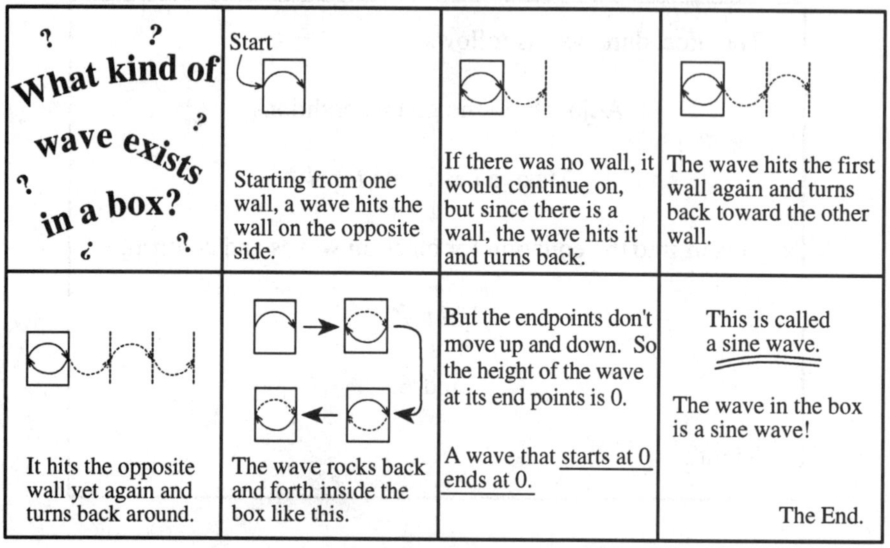

The wave inside the box hits the two walls at the same point each time. Its height is 0 at both ends, so it's a sine wave.

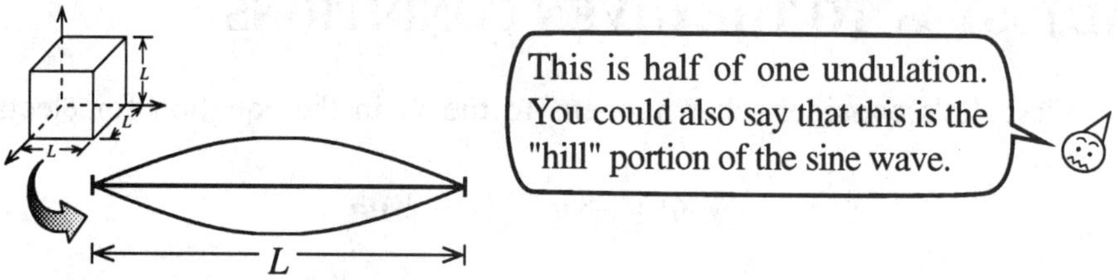

For the time being, think of the x dimension of the above wave. It has π radians for each L m (meter), and so the wave number k_x (the number of radians in 1 meter) is:

$$k_x = \frac{\pi}{L} \quad \text{rad / m} \cdot$$

One undulation is 2π radians, so one "hill" is π radians, right?

One could also imagine a case where there are 2π radians for L m. Then k_x is:

$$k_x = \frac{2\pi}{L} \quad \text{rad / m} \cdot$$

There could also be the case where there are 3π radians for L m. In this case, k_x is:

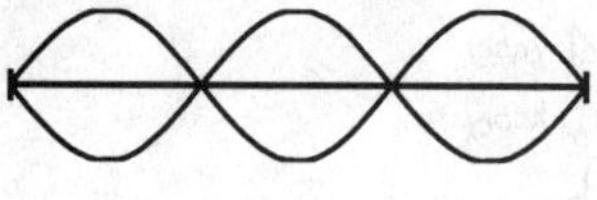

$$k_x = \frac{3\pi}{L} \quad \text{rad / m} \cdot$$

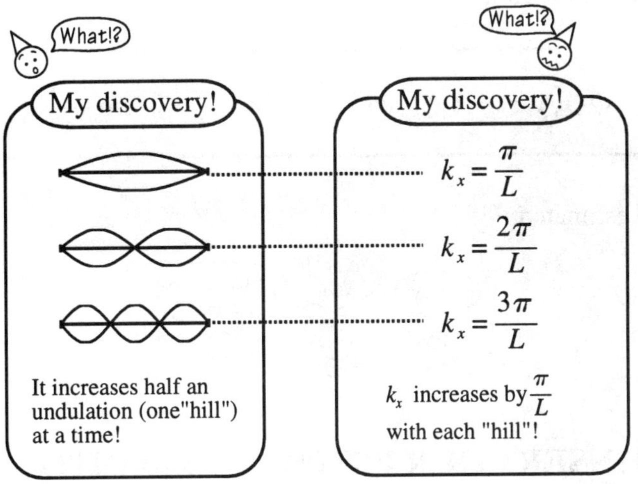

So, for the wave inside the box, k_x increases by discrete integral multiples of $\frac{\pi}{L}$. Expressed as an equation, this is written as:

$$k_x = \frac{n_x \pi}{L} \qquad (n = 1, 2, 3 \cdots)$$

Using what we have just found, let's estimate the value of Φ.

As in the case of free space, Φ has the three dimensions x, y and z. Since Φ is the product of multiplying the three dimensions, this is written as:

$$\Phi(x, y, z) = (x \text{ dimension wave}) \times (y \text{ dimension wave}) \times (z \text{ dimension wave})$$

Being a wave, each dimension will have an amplitude. Thus, the form of Φ will be:

$$\Phi = A_{n_x} \Box \cdot A_{n_y} \Box \cdot A_{n_z} \Box$$

The wave in the box is a sine wave with a height of 0 at both ends. In addition, the wave number k_x of that sine wave takes integral multiple values inside the box, such that $k_x = \frac{n_x \pi}{L}$. As seen below, this same form is also taken by the y and z dimensions:

$$k_y = \frac{n_y \pi}{L}, \qquad k_z = \frac{n_z \pi}{L}$$

Thus Φ takes the form

$$\Phi(x, y, z) = A_{n_x n_y n_z} \sin \frac{n_x \pi}{L} x \cdot \sin \frac{n_y \pi}{L} y \cdot \sin \frac{n_z \pi}{L} z$$

We have estimated Φ!!

◆ LET'S INSERT OUR ESTIMATED Φ INTO THE EQUATION FOR ELECTRON WAVES AND SEE WHAT HAPPENS!

Since we were able to estimate the value of Φ, let's now take the Φ,

$$\Phi(x, y, z) = A_{n_x n_y n_z} \sin \frac{n_x \pi}{L} x \cdot \sin \frac{n_y \pi}{L} y \cdot \sin \frac{n_z \pi}{L} z$$

and, as we did in the case of free space, insert it into the equation for electron waves in a box

$$\nabla^2 \Phi = -8\pi^2 \mathfrak{M} \nu \Phi$$

First, let's look at $\dfrac{\partial^2 \Phi}{\partial x^2}$ on the left side of the equation

$$\nabla^2 \Phi = \frac{\partial^2 \Phi}{\partial x^2} + \frac{\partial^2 \Phi}{\partial y^2} + \frac{\partial^2 \Phi}{\partial z^2}$$

The second derivative of sine with respect to x was

$$-\bigcirc^2 \sin \bigcirc x$$

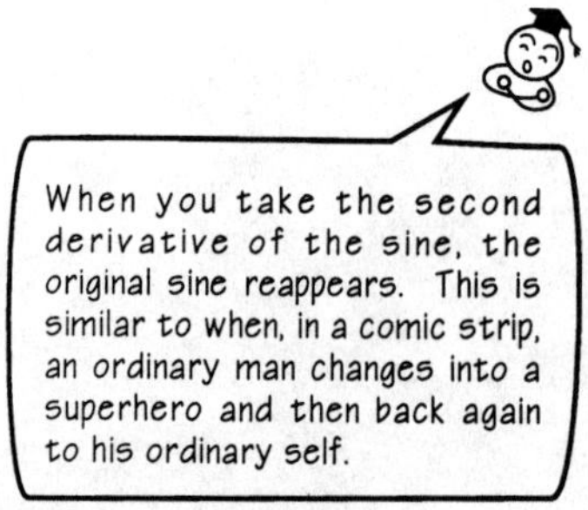

What goes in the $\bigcirc$ is $\dfrac{n_x \pi}{L}$, so

$$\frac{\partial^2 \Phi}{\partial x^2} = -\left(\frac{n_x \pi}{L}\right)^2 A_{n_x n_y n_z} \sin \frac{n_x \pi}{L} x \cdot \sin \frac{n_y \pi}{L} y \cdot \sin \frac{n_z \pi}{L} z$$

$$= -\left(\frac{n_x \pi}{L}\right)^2 \Phi$$

In the same way, both the y dimension and the z dimension are

$$\frac{\partial^2 \Phi}{\partial y^2} = -\left(\frac{n_y \pi}{L}\right)^2 \Phi, \quad \frac{\partial^2 \Phi}{\partial z^2} = -\left(\frac{n_z \pi}{L}\right)^2 \Phi$$

So, $\nabla^2 \Phi$ is

$$\nabla^2 \Phi = \frac{\partial^2 \Phi}{\partial x^2} + \frac{\partial^2 \Phi}{\partial y^2} + \frac{\partial^2 \Phi}{\partial z^2}$$

$$= -\left\{\left(\frac{n_x \pi}{L}\right)^2 + \left(\frac{n_y \pi}{L}\right)^2 + \left(\frac{n_z \pi}{L}\right)^2\right\}\Phi$$

With this, the second derivative of the estimated Φ is complete.

Let's compare it to the equation for the electron wave inside a box.

$$\nabla^2 \Phi = -8\pi^2 \mathfrak{M}\mathfrak{t} \nu \Phi$$

$$\nabla^2 \Phi = -\left\{\left(\frac{n_x \pi}{L}\right)^2 + \left(\frac{n_y \pi}{L}\right)^2 + \left(\frac{n_z \pi}{L}\right)^2\right\}\Phi$$

Because the left side of both equations is $\nabla^2 \Phi$, if

$$\left(\frac{n_x \pi}{L}\right)^2 + \left(\frac{n_y \pi}{L}\right)^2 + \left(\frac{n_z \pi}{L}\right)^2 = 8\pi^2 \mathfrak{M}\mathfrak{t} \nu$$

then the Φ we just estimated does indeed describe the electron wave inside a box!

Factoring out $\frac{\pi^2}{L^2}$, we get

$$\frac{\pi^2}{L^2}(n_x^2 + n_y^2 + n_z^2) = 8\pi^2 \mathfrak{M}\mathfrak{t} \nu$$

If we then divide both sides by $\frac{\pi^2}{L^2}$, we have

$$n_x^2 + n_y^2 + n_z^2 = 8\mathfrak{M}\mathfrak{t} L^2 \nu$$

Just like for free space, we can find frequency ν by looking for Φ.

Rewriting the equation in the form for $\nu = \square$, we get

$$\nu = \frac{1}{8\mathfrak{M}L^2}(n_x^2 + n_y^2 + n_z^2)$$

That's right. Now we've found ν.

Since the n_x, n_y, and n_z in the above equation describe the number of "hills" in the sine wave, the integral values 1, 2, 3. . . can be entered. Corresponding to this, frequency ν occurs at discrete intervals. Frequency ν, which occurs at discrete intervals when placed under specified conditions, such as inside a box, is called an

EIGENVALUE.

◆ FINDING Ψ

Now that we have found Φ and ν, let's find Ψ.

$$\Psi(x, y, z, t) = \Phi(x, y, z)e^{-i2\pi\nu t}$$

$$\Phi(x, y, z) = A_{n_x n_y n_z} \sin\frac{n_x \pi}{L}x \cdot \sin\frac{n_y \pi}{L}y \cdot \sin\frac{n_z \pi}{L}z$$

Therefore,

$$\Psi(x, y, z, t) = A_{n_x n_y n_z}\left(\sin\frac{n_x \pi}{L}x \cdot \sin\frac{n_y \pi}{L}y \cdot \sin\frac{n_z \pi}{L}z\right)e^{-i2\pi\nu t}$$

provided that $\nu = \frac{1}{8\mathfrak{M}L^2}(n_x^2 + n_y^2 + n_z^2)$

With this we know the **WHEN, WHERE AND HOW of an electron wave Ψ inside a box!**

◆ FINDING *E*

Okay, now let's find the energy of an electron inside a box.

The energy of an electron inside a box has been calculated by Bohr too, hasn't it?

If the energy values calculated by Bohr are the same as the value found using Schrödinger's theory that the electron is a wave, then it means that Schrödinger's theory applies to the natural world.

Right, although it's still only true with respect to an electron in a box.

So let's try to find the energy!

How exciting! It's such a thrill to think of what's going to happen next.

Energy was found using $\boldsymbol{E = h\nu}$

In the equation $E = h\nu$, ν will be the frequency of the electron in the box.

$$E = h\nu$$

$$= h \times \frac{1}{8\mathfrak{M}L^2}(n_x^2 + n_y^2 + n_z^2)$$

Since

$$m = h\mathfrak{M}, \qquad \mathfrak{M} = \frac{m}{h}$$

Therefore,

$$E = h \times \frac{1}{8\frac{m}{h}L^2}(n_x^{\,2} + n_y^{\,2} + n_z^{\,2})$$

$$= h \times \frac{h}{8mL^2}(n_x^{\,2} + n_y^{\,2} + n_z^{\,2})$$

$$\boxed{E = \frac{h^2}{8mL^2}(n_x^{\,2} + n_y^{\,2} + n_z^{\,2})}$$

WE'VE DONE IT!

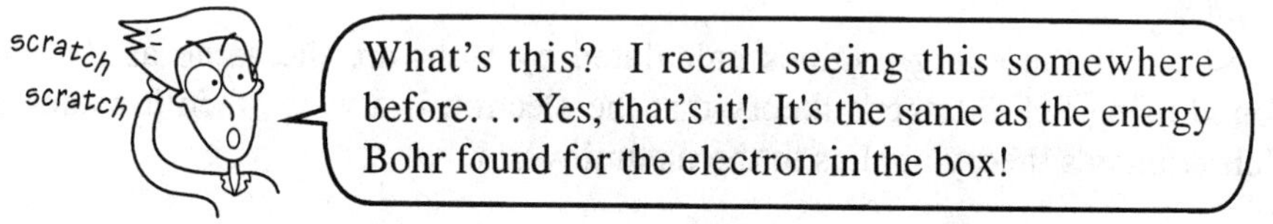

ELECTRON IN A BOX (PARTICLE THEORY)

Let's look at the energy that Bohr calculated for an electron in a box, assuming that electrons are particles!

First, the energy (E) of an electron is the sum of kinetic energy (K) and potential energy (V) and is expressed as:

$$E = K + V$$

There are no forces at work inside this box. To make an analogy, it is like placing a tiger inside a cage and leaving it undisturbed. In other words, the tiger can sit, sleep and move about freely within the confines of the cage.

In the same way, despite the limitations presented by the box, we can think of the electron within as being enclosed in a space in which freedom of movement is allowed.

In that case, $V = 0$, so

$$E = K$$

And since $K = \frac{1}{2}mv^2$, we have

$$E = \frac{1}{2}mv^2$$

The space inside the box has three dimensions (x, y, z) — up and down, right and left, and front and back. Thus,

$$E = \frac{1}{2}mv_x^2 + \frac{1}{2}mv_y^2 + \frac{1}{2}mv_z^2$$

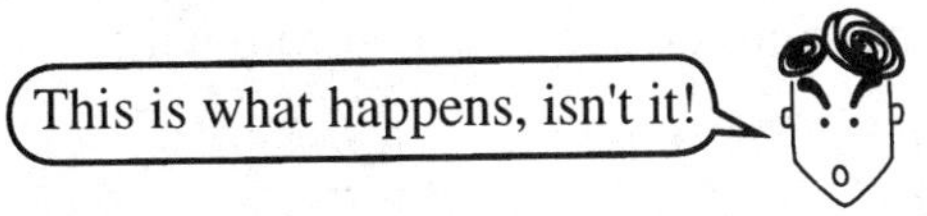

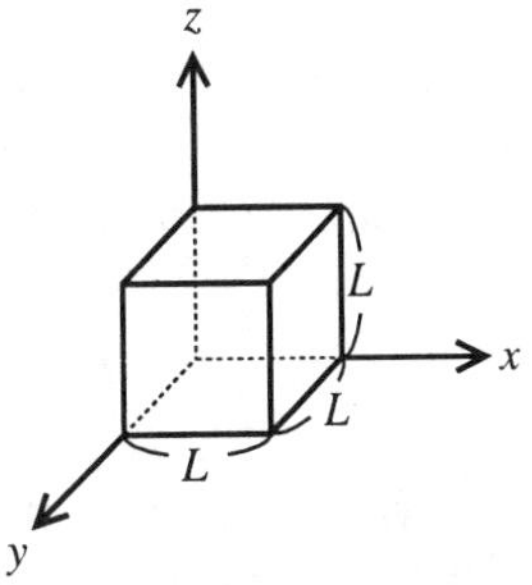

Now, let's see if you can solve this.

Using momentum p, try to make an equation where $E = \square$.

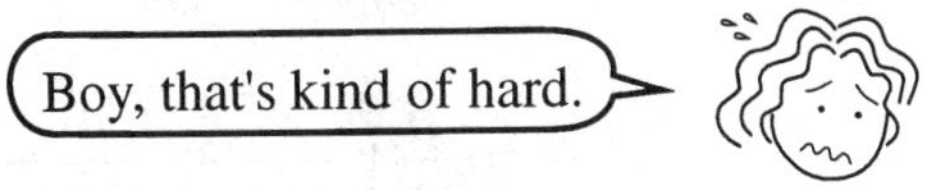

Hint! $p = mv$ (momentum = mass × velocity)

Answer: $E = \frac{p_x^2}{2m} + \frac{p_y^2}{2m} + \frac{p_z^2}{2m}$

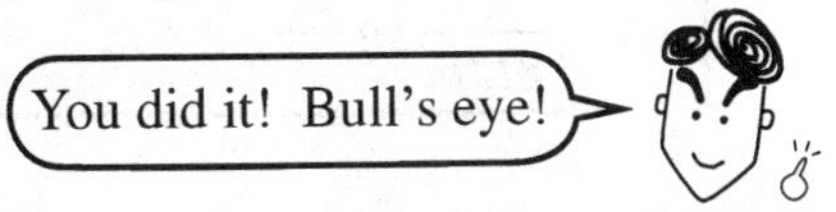

Let's leave this equation for the time being, and take the quantum condition that was used to explain electrons as particles. We'll rewrite it to suit the condition of the electron inside a box.

Quantum condition		Quantum condition for the inside of a box
↓		↓
$\oint p\,dq = nh \quad (n = 1, 2, 3 \cdots)$	➔	?

First, $\oint \square\, dq$ of the quantum condition means to take the integration for one cycle. One cycle inside the box is the distance an electron covers when going from the left side of the box to the right side, and then back again to the left side. This means that one cycle is equal to one round trip in a box from 0 to $2L$ where the length of the box is L m. Therefore, the quantum condition for the inside of a box will be

$$\int_0^{2L} p\,dq = nh \quad (n = 1, 2, 3 \cdots)$$

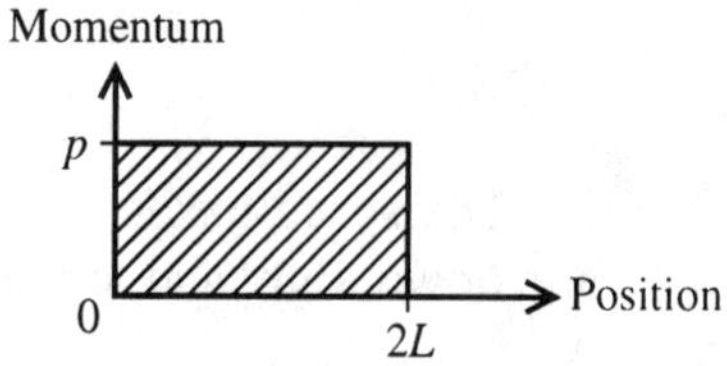

This is the area of the shaded section of the graph, $2L \cdot p$, isn't it?

$$2L \cdot p = nh$$

$$p = \frac{nh}{2L} \qquad (n = 1, 2, 3 \cdots)$$

Thinking in three dimensions (x, y, z): we come up with

$$p_x = \frac{n_x h}{2L}, \quad p_y = \frac{n_y h}{2L}, \quad p_z = \frac{n_z h}{2L}$$

When we substitute the respective p's in the previous equation for E, we have

$$E = \frac{\left(\frac{n_x h}{2L}\right)^2}{2m} + \frac{\left(\frac{n_y h}{2L}\right)^2}{2m} + \frac{\left(\frac{n_z h}{2L}\right)^2}{2m}$$

$$= \frac{1}{2m}\left(\frac{n_x^2 h^2}{4L^2} + \frac{n_y^2 h^2}{4L^2} + \frac{n_z^2 h^2}{4L^2}\right)$$

$$= \frac{1}{2m}\frac{h^2}{4L^2}(n_x^2 + n_y^2 + n_z^2)$$

$$\boxed{E = \frac{h^2}{8L^2 m}(n_x^2 + n_y^2 + n_z^2) \qquad (n = 1, 2, 3 \cdots)}$$

This is it. We've done it!

We did it! Bohr's energy for an electron in a box and Schrödinger's energy obtained from the theory that electrons are waves are now exactly the same!

Now this matches the slightly complicated conditions exactly, you know.

Right, so now we can say, **electrons are waves!**

Let's not get ahead of ourselves. We have to look at a few more things before we can say that with absolute certainty.

There's more fun to come!

Now, let's refer again to the electron-father analogy as we did in Step 1.

The Father

The Hippo Family Club members understood what Dad was saying when he spoke to them in a foreign language. Would a real native speaker of the foreign language understand him as well?

The Electron

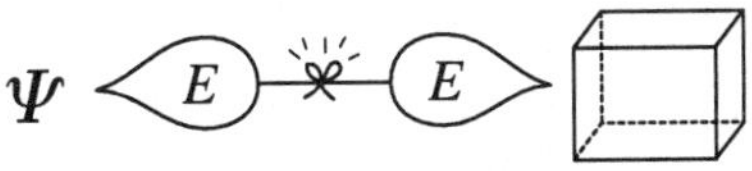

Even in slightly complicated conditions, the energy of the electron found using Schrödinger's equation matched previously determined results. But would this really describe the behavior of the electron in the natural world?

So far, both Dad and the equation for the electron wave have followed a pretty solid course. The possibility of describing nature becomes greater with every step. In Step 3, let's make this possibility a reality!

Do you understand? I didn't really understand why a wave inside a box is a sine wave, but in hoping to understand this, I eventually became able to make drawings of this concept. By making a sincere effort, you often become able to understand things you initially couldn't grasp.

4. 4. 3 STEP 3: HOOKE FIELDS

THE FATHER'S CASE

Come Sing and Dance Along!

The sounds from the Hippo tapes gradually become louder and louder as we approach a building in the Shoto district of Shibuya ward in Tokyo. The Hippo Club offices appear to be on the third and fourth floors. The Hippo College, called TCL, is on the second floor.

Dad doesn't use the elevator because he wants to get as much exercise as he can. We watch him climbing up the stairs of the building. Reaching the fourth floor, he pushes open the door and is dazzled by the bright blue and yellow walls he sees before him.

"Good evening! Please write your name on the sign-in sheet and then fill out a name tag," says the receptionist, smiling broadly at him.

"Wow, there sure are a lot of people here today," thinks Dad, glancing at the long list of names. Picking up a pen, Dad adds his own name to the list.

"Please write out your name tag. That way everyone around you will know your name."

"Oh, right. I forgot."

Using a black marker, Dad writes out "Ogura" in big letters and begins to feel slightly embarrassed. These name tags make him feel as if he's back in kindergarten. Entering the carpeted room, Dad is surprised to see that. . .

It's full of men!

But of course. This is the one day a month when the Starlight Workshop is held. At the Starlight Workshop, the Hippo Club members get together for a special program designed for men.

Although most of the people in the room are men, there are some women and children scattered about the group as well. Everyone is dancing joyfully to the music. A few are showing off some interesting dance steps that they have made up. What to do. . .

Overwhelmed by their excitement, Dad stands back against the wall of the room. Eventually though, he begins to notice that he might be calling more attention to himself by standing alone against the wall apart from everyone else. Glancing around, Dad sees that although a few of the fathers aren't quite with the swing of things, most people in the group are having a grand time dancing.

Dad hesitates, but then decides to give it a try. He realizes there is no need to feel self-conscious because his wife and children aren't around to watch him, and besides, dancing looks like so much fun.

Dad moves slowly towards the center of the room and copies the movements of the people around him. He finds that dancing comes quite naturally and easily. "Hey, I can dance, too!" he tells himself. Feeling suddenly happy, Dad moves in even closer to the center.

A little later the games and dancing end and everyone gets together. A language tape plays in the background. One of the men takes the microphone and begins to recite the words along with the tape.

With the tape-led activity in full swing, the fathers' conversations become quite interesting. They find themselves discussing topics such as how they got started at Hippo and what they like about it.

"So everyone was like me when they started out. I wonder if I too will become as good as the others are now," Dad wondered to himself.

At that point, the voice of the man conducting the meeting broke in.

"All right now, who wants to try reciting phrases from the Hippo story tapes by themselves? Any language is fine. It will be too late after the meeting is over, so step forward and don't be shy. Now is your chance!"

"Should I give it a try?" Dad raises his hand and volunteers.

"Okay, how about you over there."

Dad begins feeling a bit nervous with everyone's eyes on him, but there's no turning back.

"Pleased to meet you. My name is Ogura. I've only been to one other Hippo Club meeting so far."

Everyone is smiling and listening.

"At the first meeting, I repeated words off the tape and everyone praised me, which made me feel very good about myself. So today I will do it again. Okay, here goes. Rah-koh-shianpiao-puushee-pyen. Zu-zuu shyeshye-ta-jah!"

"Wow!!"

The other fathers in the group cheer in delight, and the man sitting in the very front stands up and happily shakes Dad's hand.

Well, what do you know, he's Chinese. And he understood me when I was speaking Chinese. Isn't that wonderful? It turns out I can actually communicate in another language.

At this rate. . .

Dad was convinced. From that point on, he was a believer.

THE CASE OF THE ELECTRON

Now then, let's continue. Having gone through "free space" and "inside the box," you know what we have to do next, don't you? Right! First, we need to draw a comparison between the electron and the father. For those of you who have forgotten, turn back for a quick review before we go on.

Dad was in the carpeted room at Hippo.

Since we're making an analogy between the inside of a box and the carpeted room, the idea of the carpeted room needs to be made more scientific.

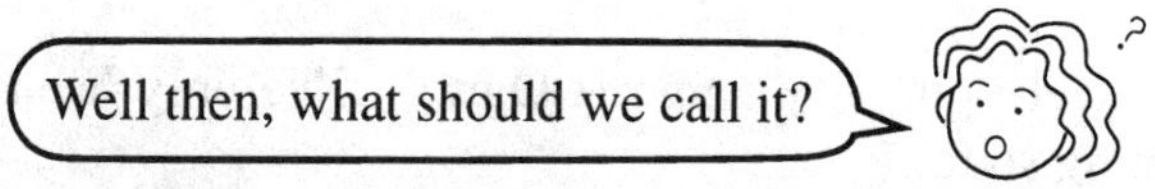

Well, let's first think about the characteristics of the carpeted room during the Starlight Workshop.

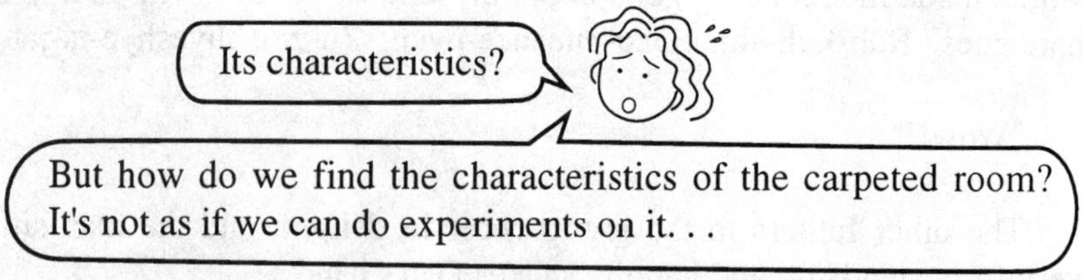

Well, let's start by thinking about what Dad did in the carpeted room.

What Dad did.

When Dad first entered the room, he stood next to a wall.

Thinking that what was going on around him was interesting, he moved toward the center of the room.

The next thing he knew, he was dancing around right in the middle of the room!

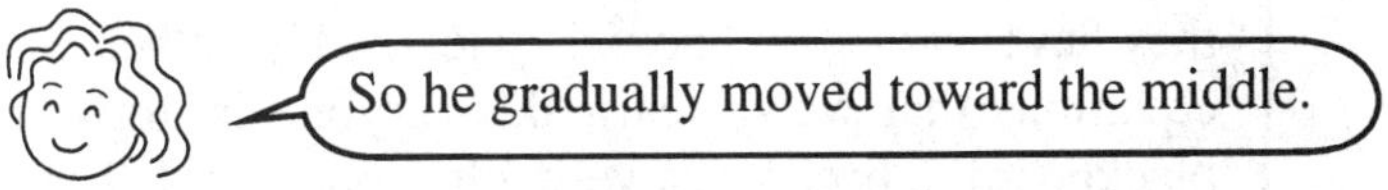

That's right. In physics, a Hooke field (Hooke field: See page 355) is a place where a force pulls toward the center.

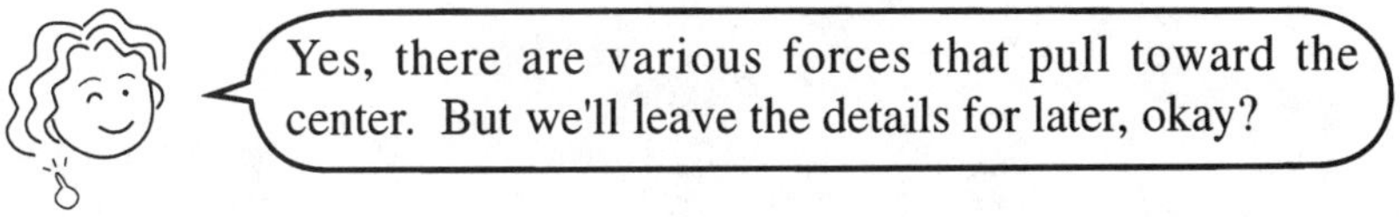

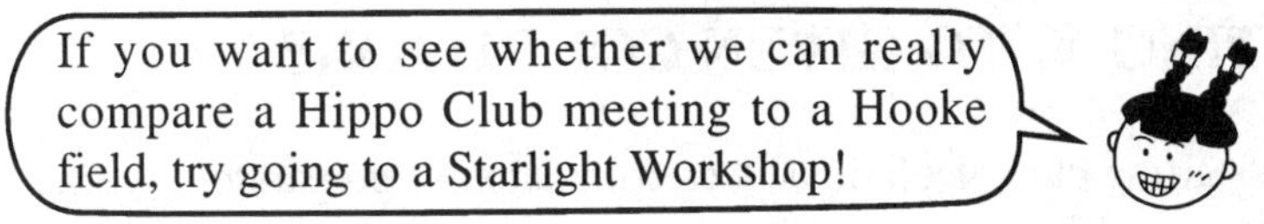

Let's use Schrödinger's equation for electron waves to find out what happens to an electron wave in a place where there is a force pulling toward the center.

If Schrödinger's equation is valid, we can say it describes nature. This is because an electron placed in a Hooke field is extremely close to its actual state in nature.

Maybe it's because calculators and personal computers are readily available these days, but many people, including physicists, seem to be avoiding doing calculations. But, if you randomly reduce the number of calculations, you'll lose sight of the meaning of the equations, and won't be able to experience the joy of working them out. This is especially true when you do physics. We want everyone who is worried they won't understand the equations to go back and read them over so that they, too, can experience the genuine pleasure of doing equations.

Let us proceed with our calculations for Hooke fields using the same method that we used for free space and for the inside of a box. An estimate is made for Φ, ν is derived and the energy is found. It takes some time to do this, but the rewards are great.

When we study quantum mechanics at TCL, the students who understand the equations tell the others what they have learned and how they learned it. When we write equations that we've learned, everyone is drawn to the blackboard; it becomes a veritable Hooke field. That's how interesting physics equations can be. I wish everyone could experience the joy of calculating and the sense of satisfaction it brings.

PREPARATORY STEP 1: ADJUSTING $\mathfrak{V}$ TO GIVEN CONDITIONS

Before starting our calculations, let's complete our preparatory work.

Hooke fields are so interesting that you are likely to lose sight of everything else when you get involved in them. Take care not to become so involved in your calculations that you forget why you are doing them; if you lose sight of your purpose, you will limit yourself to only understanding the mechanics of the calculations before you. Whenever you do something, always try to remember what you are actually trying to accomplish, and why you are making the calculation. Do this even when the train of thought is long.

In free space and inside a box, the force acting on the electron is 0, so $\mathfrak{V} = 0$. But that is not the case for Hooke fields. In a Hooke field, there is a force pulling toward the center.

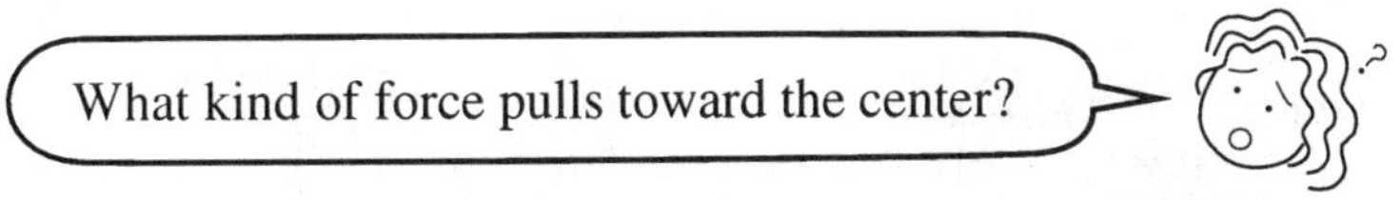

FAMILIAR HOOKE FIELDS

As an example of a Hooke field, imagine a big, deep pit into which about 10,000 people have fallen. What would you do if you were one of them?

Most people would react that way. But this pit is infinitely deep, and no one is able to get out. In that case, where in this pit do you think the greatest number of people are?

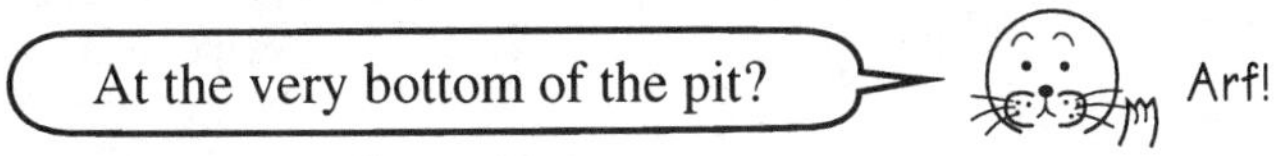

And where are the fewest number of people?

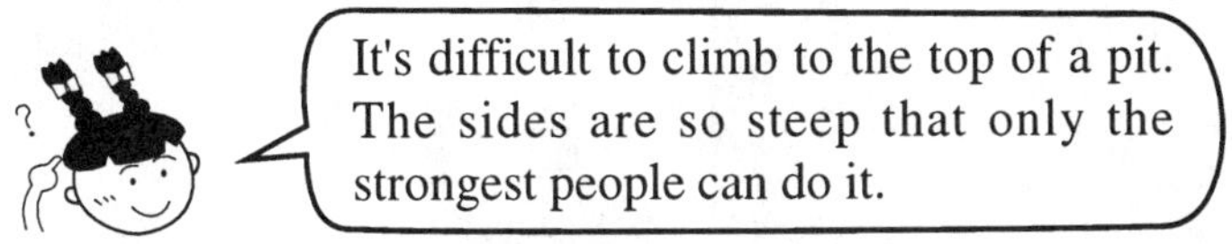

If we draw a diagram showing the distribution of the people in the pit, we get something like this.

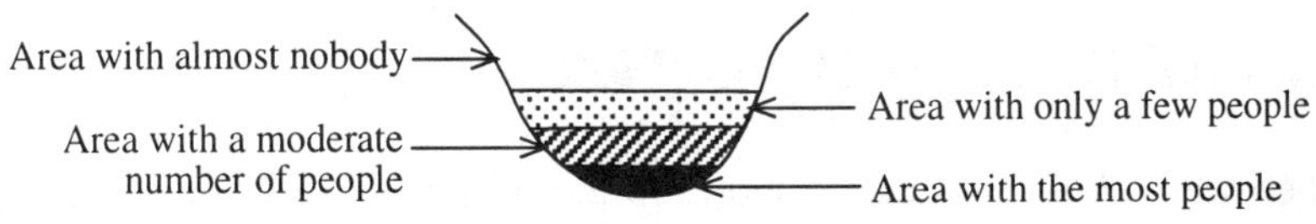

Next, let's take this diagram showing the distribution of people and consider it in three dimensions, viewing the pit from the bottom and showing the population density on a graph.

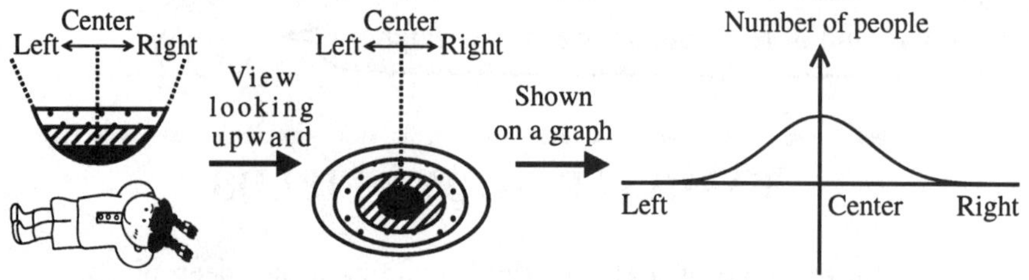

The density at the center is high; it decreases gradually as it moves toward the outer edges. When a force pulls things toward the center like this, it is said to follow Hooke's law. From here on, we will refer to a field which is ruled by Hooke's law as a Hooke field.

Consider the electron in a Hooke field. Because the electron wave is acted upon by a force pulling toward the center, a Hooke field may be thought of as something having a spring. If people were connected to this spring, the further out from the center they go, the stronger the force that pulls them back toward the center.

In this case, the force is

$$F = -kx$$

Backward pulling force (F) works in the direction opposite to the pull ($-$) Strength of the spring (k) × Distance from the point of stationary suspension (x)

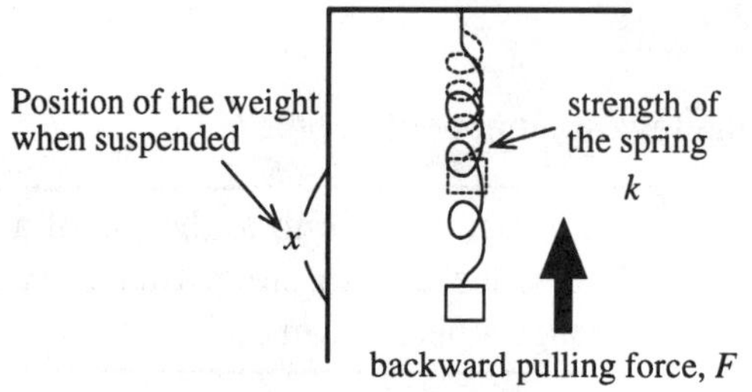

A force acts on the spring, trying to pull it in the opposite direction from which it is being pulled.

≪ Potential Energy in Hooke Fields ≫

When we pick something up and drop it, the impact varies according to the height from which it is dropped. This has to do with energy being stored in the form of potential energy. The higher an object is raised, the greater its potential energy.

Potential energy is determined by how far and with how much force something is being pulled.

Expressing potential energy V as an equation, we arrive at

$$V = -\int_0^x F\,dx$$

In the case of the spring, force $F = -kx$, so potential energy V is

$$\begin{aligned} V &= -\int_0^x F\,dx \\ &= -\int_0^x -kx\,dx \\ &= \int_0^x kx\,dx = \frac{1}{2}kx^2 \end{aligned}$$

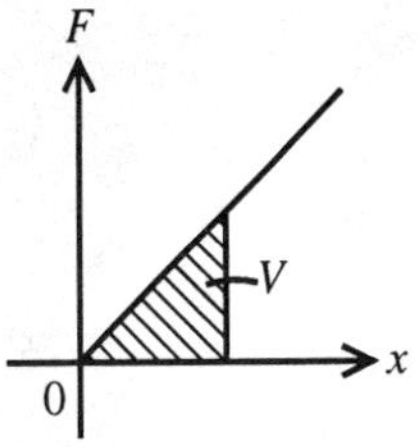

This tells us that potential energy V in a Hooke field is

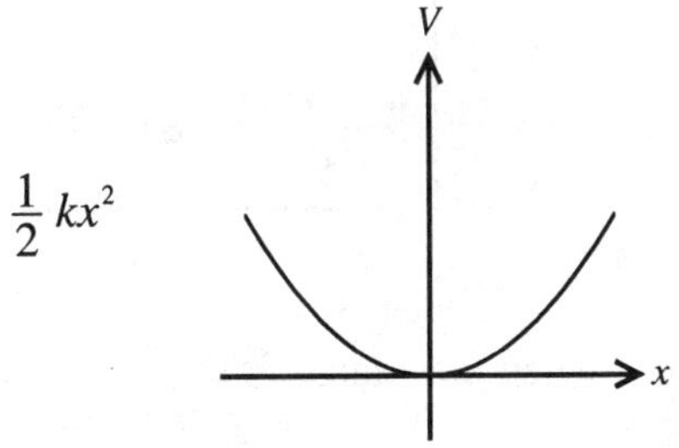

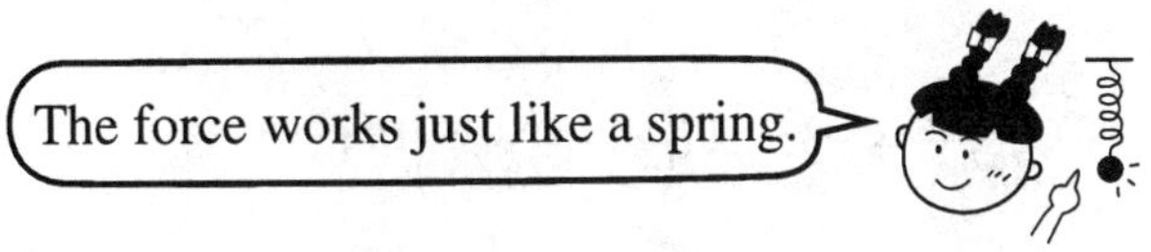

Now $\mathfrak{V}$ is

$$V = h\mathfrak{V}$$

$$\mathfrak{V} = \frac{V}{h}$$

Therefore, $\mathfrak{V}$ for a Hooke field is

$$\boxed{\mathfrak{V} = \frac{k}{2h}x^2}$$

PREPARATORY STEP 2:
PUTTING THE EQUATION IN ORDER

Φ is a wave that spreads out in three-dimensional space (x, y, z). In a Hooke field, however, the applied force is the same for all three dimensions, so in order to simplify the calculations let's consider only one dimension, x. In this case, the Laplacean

$$\nabla^2\Phi = \frac{\partial^2\Phi}{\partial x^2} + \frac{\partial^2\Phi}{\partial y^2} + \frac{\partial^2\Phi}{\partial z^2}$$ (For three dimensions)

becomes $$\frac{d^2\Phi}{dx^2}$$ (For x dimension only)

See, it's become a little simpler.

So, the equation for electron waves becomes

$$\nabla^2\Phi = -8\pi^2\mathfrak{M}(\nu - \mathfrak{V})\Phi$$

$$\frac{d^2\Phi(x)}{dx^2} = -8\pi^2\mathfrak{M}(\nu - \mathfrak{V})\Phi(x)$$

In addition, when we place $\mathfrak{V} = \frac{k}{2h}x^2$ for Hooke fields into the $\mathfrak{V}$ in this equation, we obtain:

$$\frac{d^2\Phi(x)}{dx^2} = -8\pi^2\mathfrak{M}\left(\nu - \frac{k}{2h}x^2\right)\Phi(x)$$

$$= \left(-8\pi^2\mathfrak{M}\nu + \frac{4\pi^2\mathfrak{M}k}{h}x^2\right)\Phi(x)$$

At this point, let's redefine things.

Redefinition 1

$$8\pi^2\mathfrak{M}\nu = \lambda$$

$$\frac{4\pi^2\mathfrak{M}k}{h} = \alpha^2$$

This λ doesn't refer to wavelength, you know.

Doing this, we get

$$\frac{d^2\Phi(x)}{dx^2} = (-\lambda + \alpha^2 x^2)\Phi(x)$$

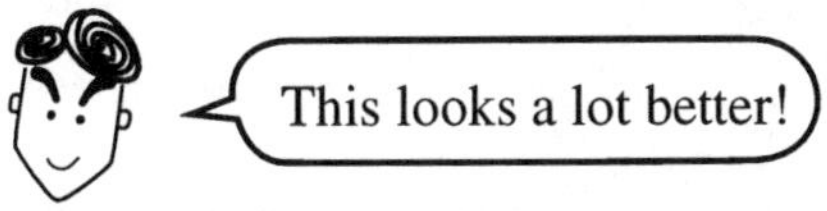

Let's simplify it even more.

Redefinition 2

$$\alpha x^2 = \xi^2$$

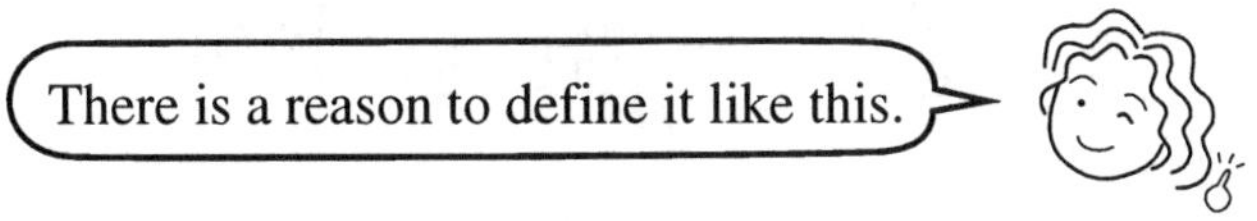

As $\alpha x^2 = \xi^2$, it can be further redefined as:

$$x^2 = \frac{\xi^2}{\alpha}$$

$$x = \frac{\xi}{\sqrt{\alpha}}$$

Let's now insert these.

$$\frac{d^2\Phi(x)}{dx^2} = (-\lambda + \alpha^2 x^2)\Phi(x)$$

$$\frac{d^2\Phi(\xi)}{d\left(\frac{\xi}{\sqrt{\alpha}}\right)^2} = (-\lambda + \alpha\xi^2)\Phi(\xi)$$

$$\alpha\frac{d^2\Phi(\xi)}{d\xi^2} = (-\lambda + \alpha\xi^2)\Phi(\xi)$$

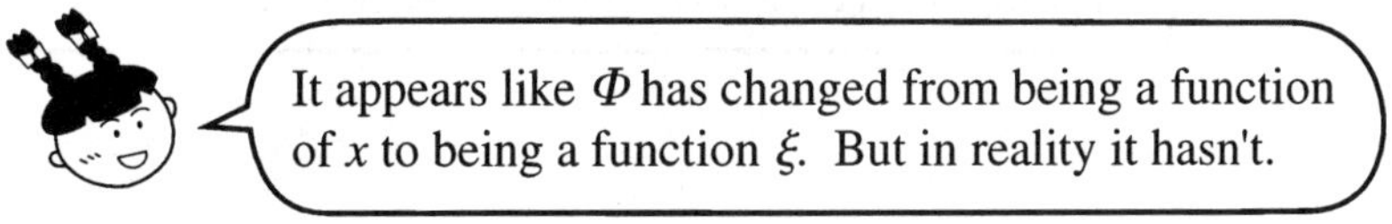

Now we divide this by α.

$$\frac{d^2\Phi(\xi)}{d\xi^2} = \left(-\frac{\lambda}{\alpha} + \xi^2\right)\Phi(\xi)$$

All right, let's do another redefinition.

Redefinition 3

$$\frac{\lambda}{\alpha} = a$$

We don't want fractions, so let's redefine this.

The result is that our first equation for the electron wave in Hooke fields,

$$\frac{d^2\Phi(x)}{dx^2} = -8\pi^2\mathfrak{M}\left(\nu - \frac{k}{2h}x^2\right)\Phi(x)$$

through the course of several redefinitions, has become this extremely simple equation

$$\frac{d^2\Phi(\xi)}{d\xi^2} = (-a + \xi^2)\Phi(\xi)$$

◆ ESTIMATING Φ

Now, let's estimate Φ. This time, the procedure for making the estimate is really long, so don't forget what you are trying to do.

In the case of Hooke fields, the farther away from the center, the more strongly the electron wave is drawn toward it. We can think of the center as being dense, with the outer edges becoming increasingly sparse. Thus, Φ takes the following form as shown in the graph below.

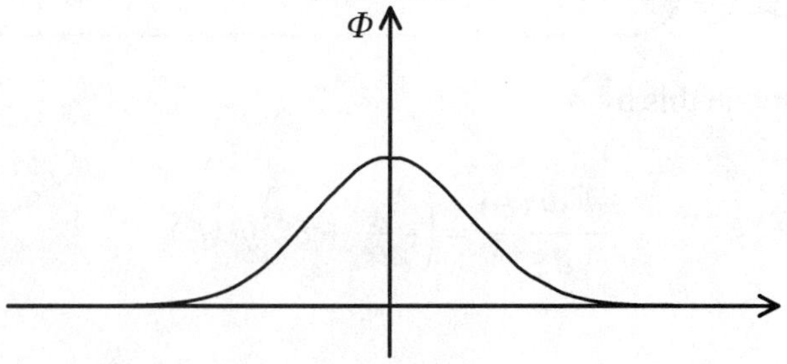

What kind of Φ would take such a form?

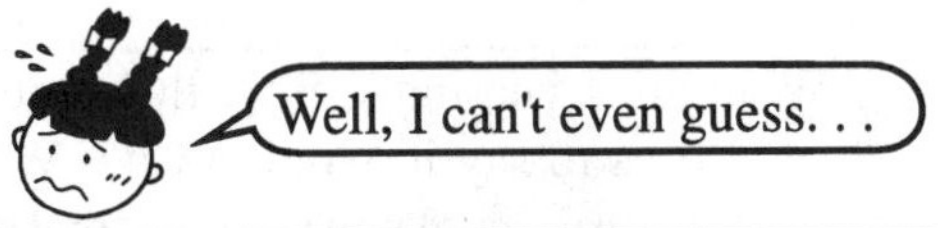

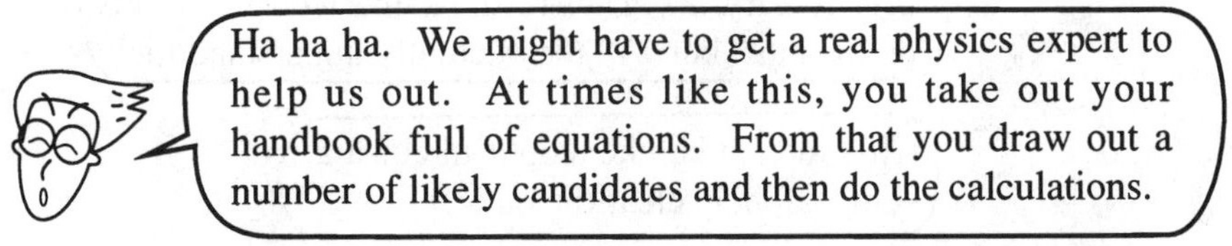

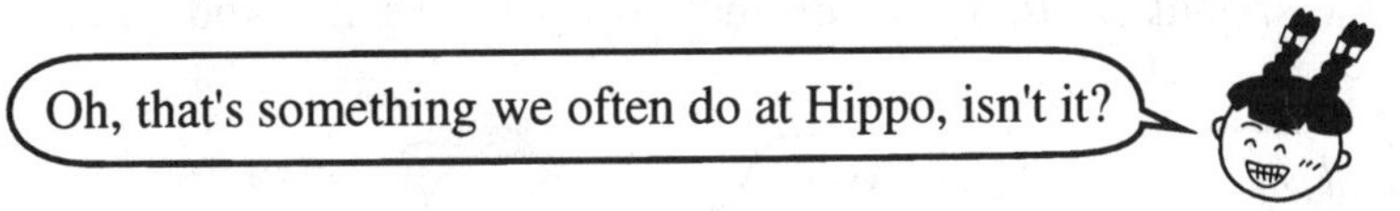

My Homestay in Korea

Hippo Family Club activities take place in many other countries besides Japan. The Club organizes a number of homestay programs to the United States, France, Germany, Mexico, Spain, Korea, China, Russia and other countries. After listening to the Hippo tapes many times over in Japan and reciting the phrases heard on the tape, many of us go overseas every year in the spring and summer. These homestays abroad give us the welcome opportunity to test out our skills in a completely natural setting.

We have an organization with which we do homestay exchanges in Korea, and when we go on a homestay there we stay with Korean families. Since they use the same tapes and engage in the same type of activities we do, we find there is a common language (the language of the tapes) between us.

Jirosa's Experience in Korea

When I first went to Korea, the only things I could say were simple greetings and words I'd heard on the Hippo tapes.

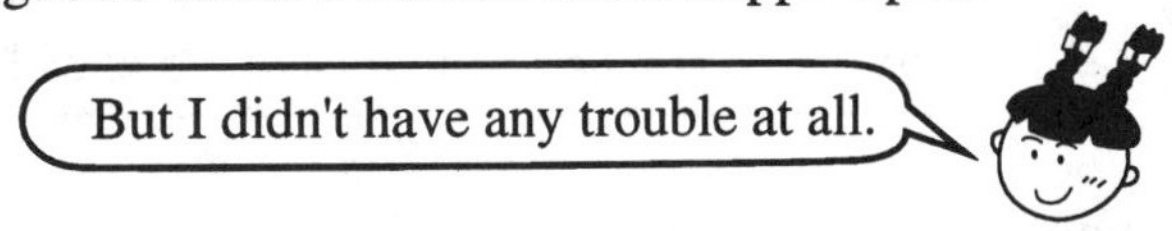

One day after we had finished eating dinner, some words from the Hippo tape began running through my head. "Cha! moudu hamke teopur-ul chi-uja." On the tape, this is what you say after a meal.

What am I hearing? Boy, this would be just the right time to say it, wouldn't it? Why don't I just give it a try. . . They're the same words that are on the tape, but will they actually understand me?

Cha! moudu hamke teopur-ul chi-uja.
[Let's all help clear the table!]

Although I didn't understand all of the words, I knew when this phrase should be used, so I decided to try saying it. And when I did. . .

Ahh — ken cha na yoh!
[Hey, no problem]

Rather than just praising me for my efforts, the members of my host family began a conversation with me that quickly became more and more animated.

A conversation began because the words I'd tried using happened to fit the situation perfectly. I figured out the meaning of "Ahh — ken cha na yoh!", and although making an educated guess can be risky, sometimes you come out a winner when you hit it right on the mark.

Schrödinger was also guided by intuition when he looked at the graph for Φ. With equations swimming around in his head, the answer came to him in a flash.

It's $\Phi(\xi) = e^{-\frac{\xi^2}{2}}$!!

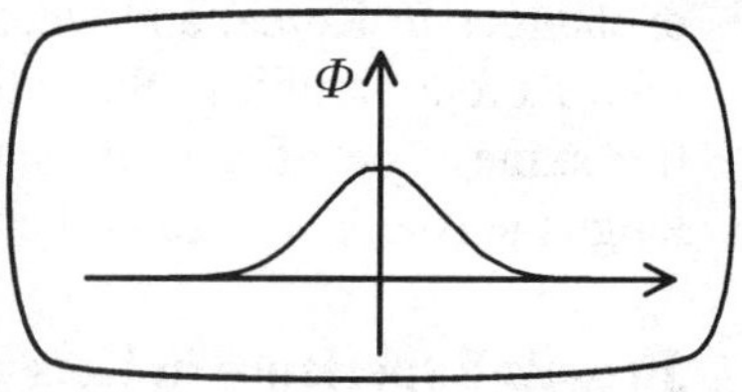

All at once, he had the answer. This function should result in the graph above.

For those of you who are interested, go ahead and confirm this.

Right now, let's confirm this by putting it in Schrödinger's equation for electron waves.

$$\frac{d^2\Phi(\xi)}{d\xi^2} = (-a + \xi^2)\Phi(\xi)$$

If we put $\Phi(\xi)$ in the form of the second derivative with respect to ξ, as in $(-a + \xi^2)\,\Phi(\xi)$, we'll be fine.

Marvelous! Let's try it.

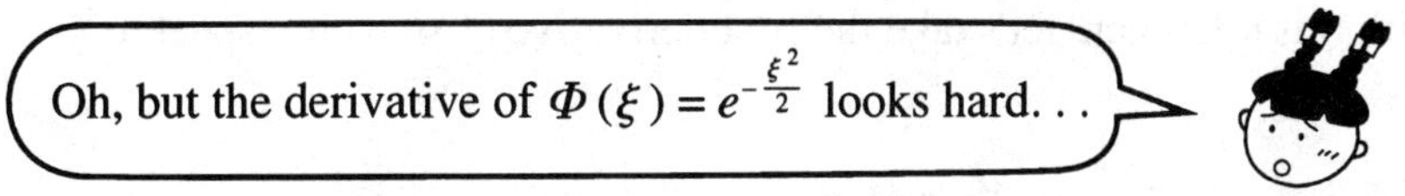

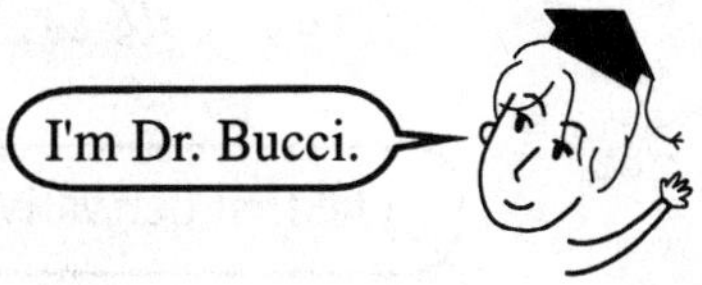

Dr. Bucci's Formula for the Derivative of Compound Functions

The function $\Phi(\xi) = e^{-\frac{\xi^2}{2}}$, by setting $-\frac{\xi^2}{2}$ equal to y, may be expressed as e^y. In this case, in order to take the derivative of $\Phi(\xi) = e^{-\frac{\xi^2}{2}}$, you can multiply the derivative of e^y with respect to y by the derivative of $-\frac{\xi^2}{2}$ with respect to ξ.

$$\frac{d}{d\xi} e^{-\frac{\xi^2}{2}} = \frac{d}{dy}(e^y) \cdot \frac{d}{d\xi}\left(-\frac{\xi^2}{2}\right)$$

$$= e^y \times \left(-\frac{1}{2}\right) \cdot 2\xi$$

$$= -\xi e^y$$

$$= -\xi e^{-\frac{\xi^2}{2}}$$

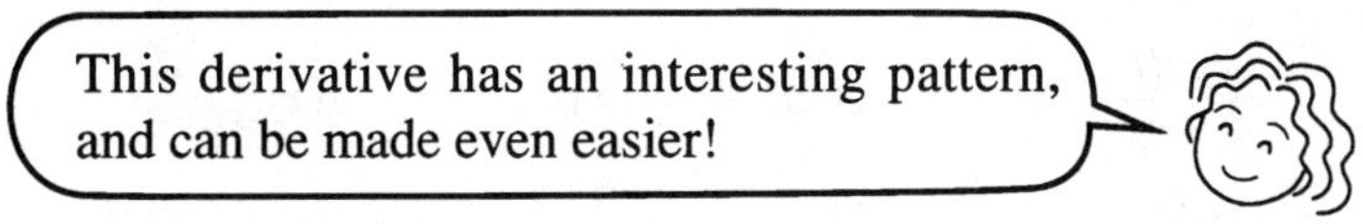

If you take the derivative of a compound function using the "snowman" method, it works out like this.

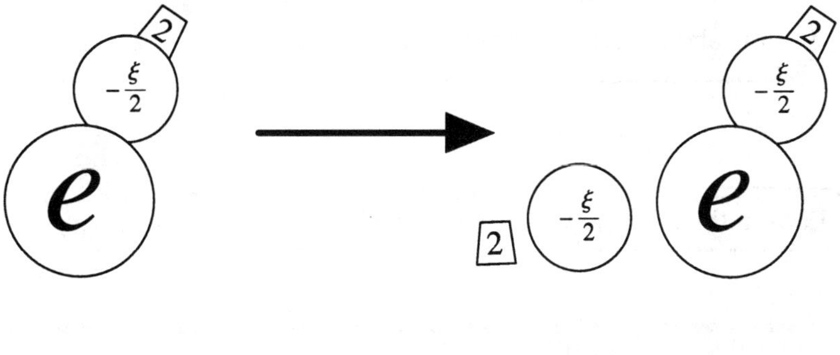

With this approach, let's take the first derivative of Φ with respect to ξ.

$$\frac{d\Phi}{d\xi} = \frac{d}{d\xi} e^{-\frac{\xi^2}{2}} = 2 \cdot \left(-\frac{\xi}{2}\right) \cdot e^{-\frac{\xi^2}{2}} = -\xi e^{-\frac{\xi^2}{2}}$$

The first derivative is done!!

Next, let's take on the second derivative!!

Taking the derivative of the first derivative again will result in the second derivative. There is another clever trick we can use for this, the generic derivative. Once again, let's ask Jirosa for her help with this.

Jirosa's Generic Derivative

For instance, when the derivative of an equation $\{f(x) \cdot g(x)\}$ is taken, the following form results:

$$\frac{d}{dx}\left\{f(x) \cdot g(x)\right\} = \frac{d}{dx} f(x) \cdot g(x) + f(x) \cdot \frac{d}{dx} g(x)$$

There's an easy way to remember that! Look closely and compare the right and left sides. A generic derivative of the type $\{f(x) \cdot g(x)\}$ will be:

$$\frac{d}{dx} f(x) \quad \times \quad g(x) \quad + \quad f(x) \quad \times \quad \frac{d}{dx} g(x)$$

Derivative   **A**s is   **A**s is   **D**erivative

Similar generic derivatives can always be calculated like this.

How about that! It's easier than you'd think.

Look at that! The key word to remember is DAAD!

Now then, using this strategy, let's take the first order derivative that we just found for Φ and take its derivative with respect to ξ.

$$\frac{d^2\Phi(\xi)}{d\xi^2} = \frac{d}{d\xi}\left(\frac{d\Phi}{d\xi}\right)$$

$$= \frac{d}{d\xi}\left(-\xi e^{-\frac{\xi^2}{2}}\right)$$

$$= \frac{d(-\xi)}{d\xi} e^{-\frac{\xi^2}{2}} + (-\xi)\underline{\frac{d}{d\xi} e^{-\frac{\xi^2}{2}}}$$

$\boxed{D}$ $\boxed{A}$ $\boxed{A}$ $\boxed{D}$

$$= -e^{-\frac{\xi^2}{2}} + (-\xi)\left(-\xi e^{-\frac{\xi^2}{2}}\right)$$

$$= \left(-1 + \xi^2\right) e^{-\frac{\xi^2}{2}}$$

Let's compare the forms of the estimated Φ with the Φ from the original equation for the electron wave.

Estimated $\Phi(\xi)$	$\frac{d^2\Phi(\xi)}{d\xi^2} = (-1 + \xi^2)\Phi(\xi)$
$\Phi(\xi)$ from the equation for electron waves	$\frac{d^2\Phi(\xi)}{d\xi^2} = (-a + \xi^2)\Phi(\xi)$

They are close, but the only time the estimated $\Phi(\xi)$ and the $\Phi(\xi)$ derived using the equation for electron waves will be exactly the same is when $a = 1$.

$$a = \frac{\lambda}{\alpha} = \frac{8\pi^2\mathfrak{M}\nu}{\sqrt{\frac{4\pi^2\mathfrak{M}k}{h}}}$$

$$\lambda = 8\pi^2\mathfrak{M}\nu$$

$$\alpha^2 = \frac{4\pi^2\mathfrak{M}k}{h}$$

As things stand, this will result in a special circumstance where the complicated numerator and denominator equal 1.

We would like to make it so that a doesn't correspond to just 1. Except for the a term, the forms are exactly the same. Isn't there some way we can use the estimate for $e^{-\frac{\xi^2}{2}}$ that we made in the beginning and come up with a solution?

Mmm. I don't see how. Maybe my repertoire of equations is too small. Mr. Schrödinger, please help us!!

What we do is apply a certain function to $e^{-\frac{\xi^2}{2}}$. For the time being, let us call that function $f(\xi)$. Look for a function $f(\xi)$ such that when the second derivative of $e^{-\frac{\xi^2}{2}} \cdot f(\xi)$ is taken, the result will be $(-a+\xi^2)e^{-\frac{\xi^2}{2}} \cdot f(\xi)$.

So that's how you can do it.

In that case, $\Phi(\xi)$ can be described as

$$\Phi(\xi) = e^{-\frac{\xi^2}{2}} \cdot f(\xi).$$

If we know $f(\xi)$, we could then solve for $\Phi(\xi)$

Let's insert $\Phi(\xi)$ in the equation for electron waves in Hooke fields,

$$\frac{d^2\Phi(\xi)}{d\xi^2} = (-a+\xi^2)\Phi(\xi) \;.$$

First, let's start with the second derivative of $\Phi(\xi)$ on the left side.

Here functions are being multiplied, so it's a generic derivative. That means we need to use DAAD.

$$\frac{d\Phi(\xi)}{d\xi} = \frac{d}{d\xi}\left\{e^{-\frac{\xi^2}{2}} \cdot f(\xi)\right\}$$

$$= \underset{\boxed{D}}{\frac{d}{d\xi}\left(e^{-\frac{\xi^2}{2}}\right)} \cdot \underset{\boxed{A}}{f(\xi)} + \underset{\boxed{A}}{e^{-\frac{\xi^2}{2}}} \cdot \underset{\boxed{D}}{\frac{d}{d\xi} f(\xi)}$$

$$= -\xi e^{-\frac{\xi^2}{2}} \cdot f(\xi) + e^{-\frac{\xi^2}{2}} \cdot \frac{d}{d\xi} f(\xi)$$

Next, let's find the second derivative by taking the derivative again.

$$\frac{d^2\Phi(\xi)}{d\xi^2} = \frac{d}{d\xi}\left\{-\xi e^{-\frac{\xi^2}{2}} \cdot f(\xi) + e^{-\frac{\xi^2}{2}} \cdot \frac{d}{d\xi} f(\xi)\right\}$$

$$= \frac{d}{d\xi}\left\{-\xi e^{-\frac{\xi^2}{2}} \cdot f(\xi)\right\} + \frac{d}{d\xi}\left\{e^{-\frac{\xi^2}{2}} \cdot \frac{d}{d\xi} f(\xi)\right\}$$

$$= \underline{\frac{d}{d\xi}\left(-\xi \cdot e^{-\frac{\xi^2}{2}}\right)} f(\xi) + \left(-\xi e^{-\frac{\xi^2}{2}}\right) \cdot \frac{d}{d\xi} f(\xi)$$

$$+ \frac{d}{d\xi}\left(e^{-\frac{\xi^2}{2}}\right) \cdot \frac{d}{d\xi} f(\xi) + e^{-\frac{\xi^2}{2}} \cdot \frac{d^2}{d\xi^2} f(\xi)$$

$$\frac{d^2\Phi(\xi)}{d\xi^2} = (-1 + \xi^2)e^{-\frac{\xi^2}{2}} \cdot f(\xi) - \xi \cdot e^{-\frac{\xi^2}{2}} \frac{d}{d\xi} f(\xi)$$

$$+ \left(-\xi e^{-\frac{\xi^2}{2}}\right) \frac{d}{d\xi} f(\xi) + e^{-\frac{\xi^2}{2}} \cdot \frac{d^2}{d\xi^2} f(\xi)$$

$$= \left\{(\xi^2 - 1)f(\xi) - 2\xi \cdot \frac{d}{d\xi} f(\xi) + \frac{d^2}{d\xi^2} f(\xi)\right\} e^{-\frac{\xi^2}{2}}$$

With this, we have succeeded in inserting our estimated $\Phi(\xi)$

$$\Phi(\xi) = e^{-\frac{\xi^2}{2}} \cdot f(\xi)$$

into the left side of the equation for electron waves in Hooke fields.

Now, let's work on the right side of the equation.

$$(-a + \xi^2)\Phi = (-a + \xi^2)e^{-\frac{\xi^2}{2}} \cdot f(\xi)$$

We have the right and left sides of the equation for electron waves, so naturally we can join them with an equal sign.

$$\left\{(\xi^2 - 1)f(\xi) - 2\xi \frac{d}{d\xi} f(\xi) + \frac{d^2}{d\xi^2} f(\xi)\right\} e^{-\frac{\xi^2}{2}}$$

$$= (-a + \xi^2) e^{-\frac{\xi^2}{2}} \cdot f(\xi)$$

$$(\xi^2 - 1)f(\xi) - 2\xi \frac{d}{d\xi} f(\xi) + \frac{d^2}{d\xi^2} f(\xi) = (-a + \xi^2) f(\xi)$$

$$-f(\xi) - 2\xi \frac{d}{d\xi} f(\xi) + \frac{d^2}{d\xi^2} f(\xi) = -af(\xi)$$

$$\boxed{\frac{d^2}{d\xi^2} f(\xi) = (1 - a) f(\xi) + 2\xi \frac{d}{d\xi} f(\xi)}$$

By inserting $\Phi(\xi) = e^{-\frac{\xi^2}{2}} \cdot f(\xi)$ in the equation for electron waves in Hooke fields, we are able to rewrite the equation as above.

The calculations were a lot of work, but the forms $f(\xi)$ as well as the derivative of $f(\xi)$ are in the actual result.

We still can't find $f(\xi)$ just with what we have now, can we?

Mmm. . .

Mr. Schrödinger, what else can we do? Help us, please.

In this case, we're forced to bring out the secret handbook within the handbook of equations we used earlier. This may be. . .

THE LAST RESORT.

There it is!

THE TAYLOR EXPANSION

What is the Taylor Expansion?

The Taylor expansion is a multipurpose formula that can be used to rewrite ordinary continuous functions.

The Taylor expansion takes the form

$$f(x) = C_0 + C_1 x + C_2 x^2 + C_3 x^3\ C_4 x^4 + \cdots = \sum_{n=0}^{\infty} C_n x^n$$

If the respective coefficients C_0, C_1, C_2. . . are known, then we can find the form for $f(x)$.

When physicists want to know the form of a certain function, they work it out as a Taylor expansion.

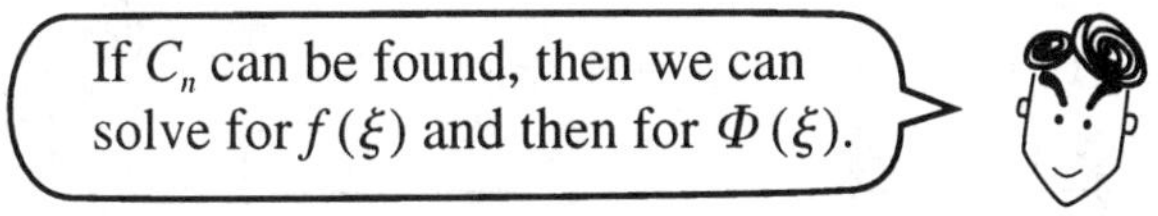

But is there a good reason to use the Taylor expansion?

Only as a last resort. And remember to be careful not to overuse it. It's true that even if we replace a function with a Taylor expansion, nothing really changes because it's only a replacement. The only difference is that now we are trying to find coefficient C_n instead of $f(\xi)$. But occasionally, there are unexpected breakthroughs.

Really? Well then, let's try it.

If we make $f(\xi)$ a Taylor expansion, we get

$$f(\xi) = C_0 + C_1 \xi + C_2 \xi^2 + C_3 \xi^3\ C_4 \xi^4 + \cdots = \sum_{n=0}^{\infty} C_n \xi^n$$

Next, the first derivative of $f(\xi)$ with respect to ξ, $\dfrac{df(\xi)}{d\xi}$ will be:

$$\frac{d}{d\xi} f(\xi) = 0 + C_1 + 2C_2\xi + 3C_3\xi^2 + 4C_4\xi^3 + \cdots$$

Multiplying by ξ, we get $\xi f(\xi)$. Then we have

$$\xi \frac{d}{d\xi} f(\xi) = 0 + C_1\xi + 2C_2\xi^2 + 3C_3\xi^3 + 4C_4\xi^4 + \cdots = \sum_{n=0}^{\infty} nC_n\xi^n$$

Next, taking the derivative of $\dfrac{d}{d\xi} f(\xi)$ with respect to ξ and solving for $\dfrac{d^2}{d\xi^2} f(\xi)$, we come up with

$$\frac{d^2}{d\xi^2} f(\xi) = 0 + 0 + 2 \cdot 1 \cdot C_2 + 3 \cdot 2 \cdot C_3\xi + 4 \cdot 3 \cdot C_4\xi^2 + \cdots$$

$$= 2 \cdot 1 \cdot C_2 + 3 \cdot 2 \cdot C_3\xi + 4 \cdot 3 \cdot C_4\xi^2 + \cdots$$

Let's let $n = 0$, $n = 1$, and $n = 2$ . . .

$$= (0 + 2)(0 + 1)C_{0+2}\xi^0 + (1 + 2)(1 + 1)C_{1+2}\xi^1 + (2 + 2)(2 + 1)C_{2+2}\xi^2 + \cdots$$

$$= \sum_{n=0}^{\infty} (n + 2)(n + 1)C_{n+2}\xi^n$$

Let's sum up what we have found.

$$f(\xi) = \sum_{n=0}^{\infty} C_n\xi^n$$

$$\xi \frac{d}{d\xi} f(\xi) = \sum_{n=0}^{\infty} nC_n\xi^n$$

$$\frac{d^2}{d\xi^2} f(\xi) = \sum_{n=0}^{\infty} (n + 2)(n + 1)C_{n+2}\xi^n$$

Next, let's take the rewritten equation for electron waves in Hooke fields

$$\frac{d^2}{d\xi^2} f(\xi) = (1-a)f(\xi) + 2\xi \frac{d}{d\xi} f(\xi)$$

and insert the $f(\xi)$, $\xi f(\xi)$, and $\frac{d^2}{d\xi^2} f(\xi)$ that were found by putting them into the form of a Taylor expansion.

$$\sum_{n=0}^{\infty} (n+2)(n+1)C_{n+2}\xi^n = (1-a)\sum_{n=0}^{\infty} C_n\xi^n + 2\sum_{n=0}^{\infty} nC_n\xi^n$$

Finding Σ and multiplying by ξ^n, we obtain

$$\sum_{n=0}^{\infty} \underline{\left\{(n+2)(n+1)C_{n+2} - (1-a+2n)C_n\right\}} \xi^n = 0$$

With this equation, when ξ to the power of 1, ξ to the power of 2, ξ to the power of 3, ξ to the power of 4, ξ to the power of 5, and so on are all added, the result is zero.

Do you know when an infinite sum like this will be 0?

Let me see. . .

The fact is this only happens when the coefficients of all of the terms in the equation are 0.

In other words,

$$(n+2)(n+1)C_{n+2} - (1-a+2n)C_n = 0$$

Only when

$$(n+2)(n+1)C_{n+2} = (1-a+2n)C_n$$

does the above equation hold true.

Changing this into a polynomial, we get

$$C_{n+2} = \frac{2n+1-a}{(n+2)(n+1)} C_n \qquad (n = 0, 1, 2, 3 \cdots)$$

Okay, take a good look at this relational equation. In this equation, if C_n is known, then C_{n+2} will be known; if C_{n+2} is known, then C_{n+4} will be known; if C_{n+4} is known, then. . .

That's certainly true.

So, once C_0 is determined, all the even-numbered coefficients, $C_2, C_4, C_6, C_8 \cdots$ will be known. In the same way, if C_1 is determined, then all the odd-numbered terms will be known.

That means that we've **FOUND THE COEFFICIENTS C_n** !!

When n is an even number: $C_0 \rightarrow C_2 \rightarrow C_4 \rightarrow C_6 \cdots$

When n is an odd number: $C_1 \rightarrow C_3 \rightarrow C_5 \rightarrow C_7 \cdots$

So, C_n is divided into two parts.

But Mr. Schrödinger, without more information, we don't know what values C_0 or C_1 will take.

Well, we'll just think up some suitable values.

What!!

Solving differential equations is like that. No need for concern.

So for now, we'll just do what Mr. Schrödinger suggested and say that

$$C_0 = 1, \qquad C_1 = 1$$

If we do that, we'll know C_n for both even and odd numbers.

Let's look at the values the coefficients take in the respective series for $C_0 = 1$ and $C_1 = 1$.

EVEN NUMBER

When n is an even number

when $n = 0$ $\quad C_2 = \frac{1-a}{2 \cdot 1} \cdot C_0 = \frac{1-a}{2\,!}$

when $n = 2$ $\quad C_4 = \frac{5-a}{4 \cdot 3} \cdot C_2 = \frac{(5-a)(1-a)}{4\,!}$

when $n = 4$ $\quad C_6 = \frac{9-a}{6 \cdot 5} \cdot C_4 = \frac{(9-a)(5-a)(1-a)}{6\,!}$

ODD NUMBER

When n is an odd number

when $n = 1$ $\quad C_3 = \frac{3-a}{3 \cdot 1} \cdot C_1 = \frac{3-a}{3\,!}$

when $n = 3$ $\quad C_5 = \frac{7-a}{5 \cdot 4} \cdot C_3 = \frac{(7-a)(3-a)}{5\,!}$

when $n = 5$ $\quad C_7 = \frac{11-a}{7 \cdot 6} \cdot C_5 = \frac{(11-a)(7-a)(3-a)}{7\,!}$

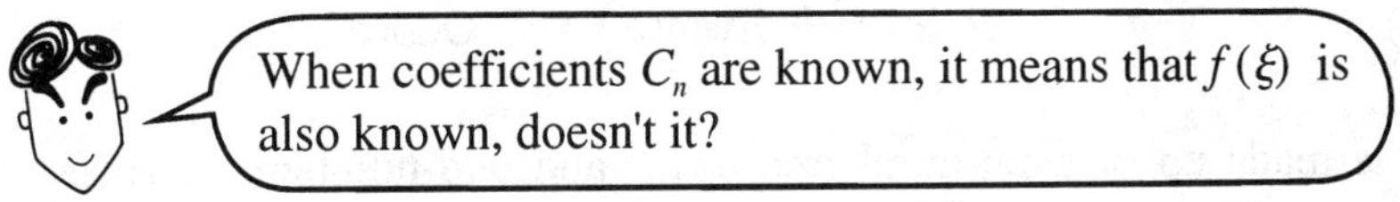

Since coefficients C_n of $f(\xi)$ are divided into even-numbered terms and odd-numbered terms, let's also divide $f(\xi)$ in the same way.

$$f\,\text{Even}(\xi) = C_0 + C_2\xi^2 + C_4\xi^4 + C_6\xi^6 + \cdots$$

$$= 1 + \frac{1-a}{2\,!}\xi^2 + \frac{(5-a)(1-a)}{4\,!}\xi^4 + \frac{(9-a)(5-a)(1-a)}{6\,!}\xi^6 + \cdots$$

$$f\,\text{Odd}(\xi) = C_1\xi + C_3\xi^3 + C_5\xi^5 + C_7\xi^7 + \cdots$$

$$= \xi + \frac{3-a}{3\,!}\xi^3 + \frac{(7-a)(3-a)}{5\,!}\xi^5 + \frac{(11-a)(7-a)(3-a)}{7\,!}\xi^7 + \cdots$$

So there are two answers for $f(\xi)$, right?

In addition, since we know $f(\xi)$,

$$\Phi(\xi) = e^{-\frac{\xi^2}{2}} \cdot f(\xi)$$

is also known. Let's divide this into odd-numbered and even-numbered terms, too.

$$\Phi \text{ Even}(\xi) = e^{-\frac{\xi^2}{2}} \cdot f \text{ Even}(\xi)$$

$$= \left\{ 1 + \frac{1-a}{2\,!}\xi^2 + \frac{(5-a)(1-a)}{4\,!}\xi^4 + \frac{(9-a)(5-a)(1-a)}{6\,!}\xi^6 + \cdots \right\} e^{-\frac{\xi^2}{2}}$$

$$\Phi \text{ Odd}(\xi) = e^{-\frac{\xi^2}{2}} \cdot f \text{ Odd}(\xi)$$

$$= \left\{ \xi + \frac{3-a}{3\,!}\xi^3 + \frac{(7-a)(3-a)}{5\,!}\xi^5 + \frac{(11-a)(7-a)(3-a)}{7\,!}\xi^7 + \cdots \right\} e^{-\frac{\xi^2}{2}}$$

With this we have found what we were looking for, the electron wave $\Phi(\xi)$. $\Phi(\xi)$ is defined as

$$\Phi(\xi) = \Phi \text{ Even}(\xi) + \Phi \text{ Odd}(\xi)$$

and is made up of even-numbered terms and odd-numbered terms. We have also solved the forms of Φ Even (ξ) and Φ Odd (ξ)!!!

Could it be true? Somehow it's hard to believe. . .

Now, let's confirm whether we have really found the electron wave $\Phi(\xi)$ we've been looking for.

Since a Hooke field is a space with a force pulling toward the center, $\Phi(\xi)$ would have to be 0 in places far from the center.

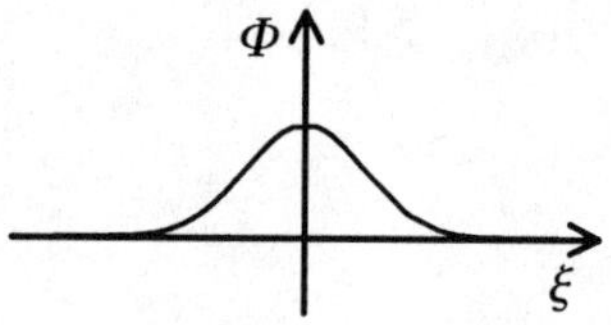

Expressing this as an equation, we get $\Phi(\xi) = 0$ when $\xi \to \pm\infty$.
Now then, let's see what happens.

First let's look at what happens to Φ Even (ξ) when $\xi \to \infty$.

$$\Phi \text{ Even}(\xi) = e^{-\frac{\xi^2}{2}} \cdot f \text{ Even}(\xi) = \frac{f \text{ Even}(\xi)}{e^{\frac{\xi^2}{2}}}$$

When $\xi \to \infty$, both the denominator $e^{-\frac{\xi^2}{2}}$ and the numerator $f(\xi)$ of Φ Even (ξ) are infinite.

But, even if they are both infinite,

when $\left| f \text{ Even}(\xi) \right| > e^{\frac{\xi^2}{2}}$ then $\left| \Phi \text{ Even}(\xi) \right|$ will be infinite;
when $\left| f \text{ Even}(\xi) \right| < e^{\frac{\xi^2}{2}}$ then $\left| \Phi \text{ Even}(\xi) \right|$ will be 0.

Because the final term of the numerator $|f$ Even (ξ)$|$ when $\xi \to \infty$ is

$$f \text{ Even}(\xi \to \infty) = 1 + \frac{1-a}{2\,!}\infty^2 + \cdot\cdot\cdot + \frac{(\ )(\ )\cdot\cdot\cdot(\ )}{\square\,!}\infty^{\infty}$$

we come up with ∞^{∞}. When the denominator is $\xi \to \infty$, we have

$$e^{\frac{\xi^2}{2}} \quad \to \quad e^{\frac{\infty^2}{2}}$$

The result is that $\infty^{\infty} > e^{\frac{\infty^2}{2}}$

This means that when $\xi \to \pm\infty$, $|\Phi(\xi)| = \infty$.

I've got to do something about that. . .

thought Schrödinger.

◆ FINDING CONDITIONS THAT MATCH NATURE!

Remember that the equation for the relationship of the coefficients is

$$C_{n+2} = \frac{2n+1-a}{(n+2)(n+1)} C_n$$

When we refer to conditions that match nature, let's call them boundary conditions.

In this equation, coefficient C_{n+2} is determined by the previous coefficient C_n. This means that if the coefficient is 0 at some point, all subsequent coefficients will be 0.

Although $f(\xi)$ was a series continuing to infinity, if at some point the coefficient becomes 0, then it will be a finite series. In that case, even when $\xi \rightarrow \pm\infty$, $\Phi(\xi)$ will never approach infinity.

$$\Phi \ \mathrm{Odd}(\xi) = C_1\xi + C_3\xi^3 + C_5\xi^5 + 0 + 0 + 0 \cdots$$

I see. We bring it to an end, don't we?

This means

$$\frac{(2n+1-a)}{(n+1)(n+2)} = 0$$

will be a condition that brings an infinite series to an end at some point.

Let's look at the above equation. As n changes according to $n = 0, 1, 2, 3, \cdots$ only a can be changed at will. Therefore, if a is such that

$$2n + 1 - a = 0$$

That is,

$$a = 2n + 1 \qquad (n = 0, 1, 2, 3 \cdots)$$

Then C_n will be 0.

Yes, I see. If the above equation is 0 when $n = 1$, then the equation will be 0 from the third term (C_3) onward. And if the previous equation is 0 when $n = 6$, then the equation will be 0 from the eighth term (C_8) onward. Isn't that right?

But C_n determines each subsequent coefficient in the even or odd sequences. So if n is an even number, then only the subsequent even-numbered terms will be 0. Likewise if it is an odd number, then only the odd-numbered terms will be 0, right?

$$\Phi(\xi) = C_1\xi + C_3\xi^3 + C_5\xi^5 + 0 + 0 + 0 + \cdots$$
$$+ C_0\xi^0 + C_2\xi^2 + C_4\xi^4 + C_6\xi^6 + C_8\xi^8 + \cdots$$

That way, if n is an even number, then the odd-numbered terms will end up being infinite, and if n is an odd number, then the even-numbered terms will end up being infinite.

Oh, that's simple. If n is an even number, we just have to set $C_1 = 0$ so that the odd-numbered terms will be 0. Conversely, if n is an odd number, we set $C_0 = 0$ so that the even-numbered terms will be 0.

Finally, we know the form of $\Phi(\xi)$. By applying a condition so that the results will match what is found in nature, we know that a must be

$$a = 2n + 1 \qquad (n = 0, 1, 2, 3 \cdots)$$

By recalling what a was, we see that it is a constant containing ν. This means that eigenvalue ν is also known. As might be expected, once we know $\Phi(\xi)$, we can also know ν.

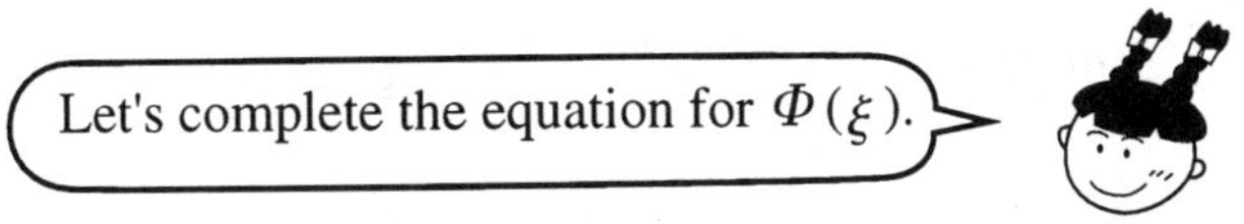

WHEN n IS AN EVEN NUMBER

$$\Phi\ \text{Even}(\xi) = \left\{1 + \frac{1-a}{2\,!}\xi^2 + \frac{(5-a)(1-a)}{4\,!}\xi^4 + \frac{(9-a)(5-a)(1-a)}{6\,!}\xi^6 + \cdots\right\}e^{-\frac{\xi^2}{2}}$$

For example, $a = 9$ when $n = 4$ and therefore the coefficients from C_6 onward will all be 0. In this case, because Φ Even(ξ) corresponds to n, we'll call it $\Phi_n(\xi)$. So $\Phi_4(\xi)$ will be

$$\Phi_4(\xi) = \left(1 + \frac{-8}{2\,!}\xi^2 + \frac{-4\cdot -8}{4\,!}\xi^4\right)e^{-\frac{\xi^2}{2}}$$

$$= \left(1 - 4\xi^2 + \frac{4}{3}\xi^4\right)e^{-\frac{\xi^2}{2}}$$

WHEN n IS AN ODD NUMBER

$$\Phi\ \text{Odd}(\xi) = \left\{\xi + \frac{3-a}{3\,!}\xi^3 + \frac{(7-a)(3-a)}{5\,!}\xi^5 + \frac{(11-a)(7-a)(3-a)}{7\,!}\xi^7 + \cdots\right\}e^{-\frac{\xi^2}{2}}$$

For example, $a = 11$ when $n = 5$ and the coefficients from C_7 onward will all be 0. In this case, because Φ Odd(ξ) corresponds to n, we'll call it $\Phi_n(\xi)$. So $\Phi_5(\xi)$ will be

$$\Phi_5(\xi) = \left(\xi + \frac{-8}{3\,!}\xi^3 + \frac{-4\cdot -8}{5\,!}\xi^5\right)e^{-\frac{\xi^2}{2}}$$

$$= \left(\xi - \frac{4}{3}\xi^3 + \frac{4}{15}\xi^5\right)e^{-\frac{\xi^2}{2}}$$

◆ LET'S FIND EIGENVALUE ν!

$$a = 2n + 1 \qquad (n = 0, 1, 2, 3 \cdots)$$

The a determined according to the boundary condition has been transposed many times. Let's return it to its original state and find eigenvalue ν.

Eigenvalue ν corresponds to integer n. So we'll call it ν_n.

$$a = 2n + 1$$

Transposition 3

$$k_x = \frac{2\pi}{L}$$

$$\frac{\lambda}{\alpha} = 2n + 1$$

Transposition 1

$$\begin{cases} \lambda = 8\pi^2\mathfrak{M}\nu \\ \alpha^2 = \dfrac{4\pi^2\mathfrak{M}k}{h} \end{cases}$$

$$\frac{8\pi^2\mathfrak{M}\nu_n}{\sqrt{\dfrac{4\pi^2\mathfrak{M}k}{h}}} = 2n + 1$$

$$\frac{8\pi^2\mathfrak{M}\nu_n}{2\pi\sqrt{\dfrac{\mathfrak{M}k}{h}}} = 2n + 1$$

Is a so complicated?

$$4\pi\nu_n\sqrt{\frac{\mathfrak{M}h}{k}} = 2n + 1$$

There sure were a lot of transpositions.

$$\nu_n = \frac{2n+1}{4\pi}\sqrt{\frac{k}{\mathfrak{M}h}}$$

$$= \frac{1}{2\pi}\left(n + \frac{1}{2}\right)\sqrt{\frac{k}{\mathfrak{M}h}}$$

$$\boxed{\nu_n = \frac{1}{2\pi}\sqrt{\frac{k}{\mathfrak{M}h}}\left(n + \frac{1}{2}\right) \qquad (n = 1, 2, 3 \cdots)}$$

◆ LET'S FIND THE ENERGY!!

Now that you mention it, Heisenberg was also seeking the energy for harmonic oscillation. I think I'll try and find energy based on my theory that the electron is a wave.

Harmonic oscillation correlates to Hooke fields. You see, in the case of particles, we speak of harmonic oscillation whereas in the case of waves, we refer to Hooke fields.

The energy can be found by multiplying eigenvalue ν by Planck's constant h.

$$E = h\nu_n$$

Let's insert the eigenvalue for Hooke fields into this.

$$E = h\nu_n = \frac{h}{2\pi}\left(n + \frac{1}{2}\right)\sqrt{\frac{k}{h\mathfrak{M}}}$$

Since $m = h\mathfrak{M}$,

$$= \frac{h}{2\pi}\left(n + \frac{1}{2}\right)\sqrt{\frac{k}{m}}$$

$\sqrt{\frac{k}{m}} = 2\pi\nu$. This came up in the section on Heisenberg, too!

$$= \frac{h}{2\pi}\left(n + \frac{1}{2}\right)2\pi\nu$$

Point

$$E = \left(n + \frac{1}{2}\right)h\nu$$

How about that!! This is exactly the same as the energy obtained by Heisenberg, who said, **"LET'S THROW OUT VISUAL IMAGES!"** The energy values Heisenberg found have already been confirmed to be true, corroborating my theory even more. Moreover, my theory has a clear

VISUAL IMAGE of a wave. Ha ha ha!!!

**THE ENERGY WORKS OUT, TOO.
THE ELECTRON IS A WAVE AFTER ALL!**

SUMMARIZING WHAT WE'VE DONE SO FAR

$\Phi_n(\xi)$ is divided into cases where n is an even number and where n is an odd number.

1. When n is an even number

$$\Phi_n(\xi) = \left\{ 1 + \frac{1-a}{2\,!}\,\xi^2 + \frac{(5-a)(1-a)}{4\,!}\,\xi^4 + \frac{(9-a)(5-a)(1-a)}{6\,!}\,\xi^6 \cdots \right\} e^{-\frac{\xi^2}{2}}$$

2. When n is an odd number

$$\Phi_n(\xi) = \left\{ \xi + \frac{3-a}{3\,!}\,\xi^3 + \frac{(7-a)(3-a)}{5\,!}\,\xi^5 + \frac{(11-a)(7-a)(3-a)}{7\,!}\,\xi^7 \cdots \right\} e^{-\frac{\xi^2}{2}}$$

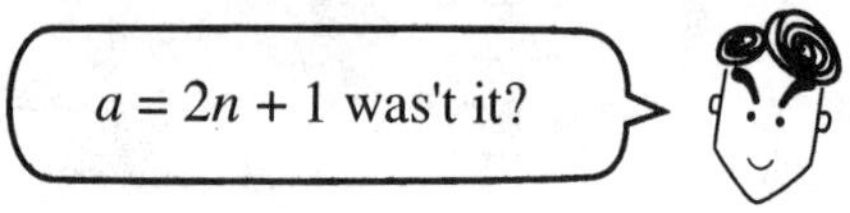

ν_n is

$$\nu_n = \frac{1}{2\pi}\sqrt{\frac{k}{\mathfrak{M}h}}\left(n + \frac{1}{2}\right) \qquad (n = 0, 1, 2, 3 \cdots)$$

The movement Ψ of an electron wave is

$$\Psi_n = \Phi_n e^{-i2\pi\nu_n t}$$

The energy of an electron is

$$E = \left(n + \frac{1}{2}\right)h\nu \qquad (n = 0, 1, 2, 3 \cdots)$$

Now then, let's finally look at the form of the electron wave using the $\Phi(\xi)$ that we actually found!

When $n = 0$ $\quad \Phi_0(\xi) = e^{-\frac{\xi^2}{2}}$

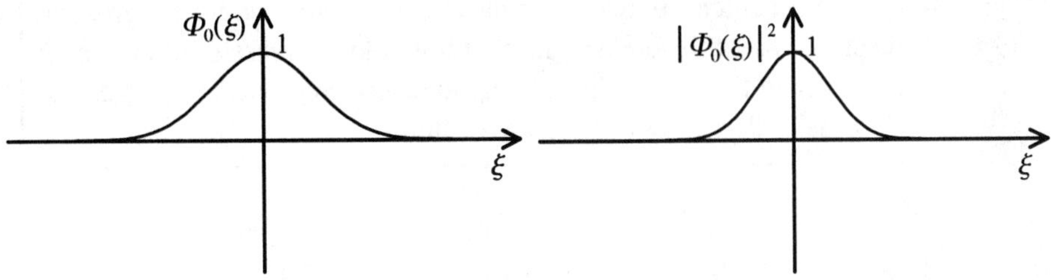

When $n = 1$ $\quad \Phi_1(\xi) = \xi e^{-\frac{\xi^2}{2}}$

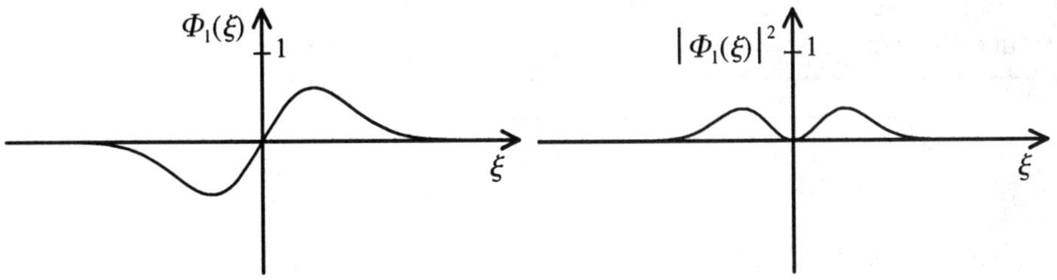

When $n = 2$ $\quad \Phi_2(\xi) = (1 - 2\xi^2)e^{-\frac{\xi^2}{2}}$

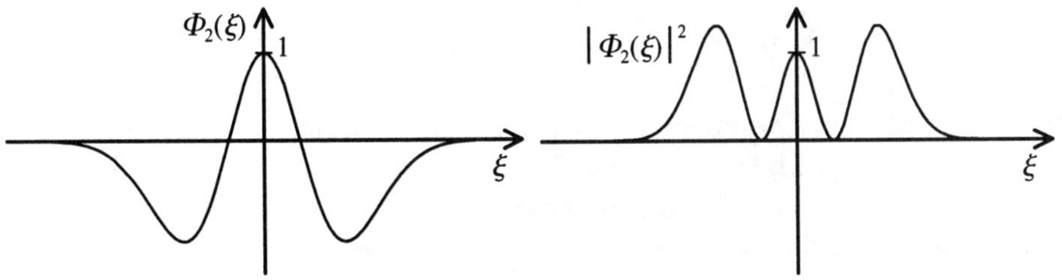

When $n = 3$ $\quad \Phi_3(\xi) = \left(\xi - \frac{2}{3}\xi^3\right)e^{-\frac{\xi^2}{2}}$

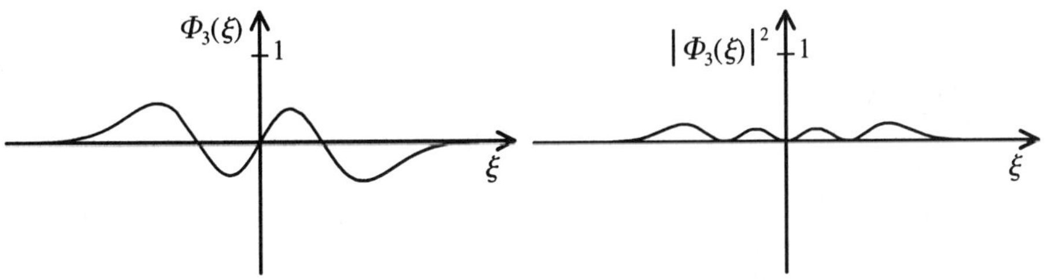

The graph shows that the only time the result agrees with the initial predictions is when $n = 0$. When n does not equal 0, when $\xi \to \pm\infty$, we come up with $|\Phi_n(\xi)|^2 = 0$ as predicted.

When the initial predictions were made, we assumed an electron wave was being acted upon by a force trying to pull it toward a center. It was thought that the force would be greatest when Φ was at the center, and that it would decrease gradually as it approached the outer edges. But we discovered that in some cases, Φ actually decreases even at the center.

I DID IT! I KNOW THE FORM FOR THE ELECTRON WAVE!

Were the calculations fun to do? I liked "DA + AD" and the Taylor expansion and the way C_n gets divided into odd and even numbers just fine. The derivative of a compound function using a snowman was intriguing as well, wasn't it?

What did everyone else find interesting?

Now, let's look quickly again at the similarities between the father's behavior and the behavior of the electron!

The Father

Not knowing whether he would be understood or not, Dad tried reciting some Chinese he learned from the Hippo tapes to a Chinese person. The response Dad received reassured him that he was understood.

The Electron

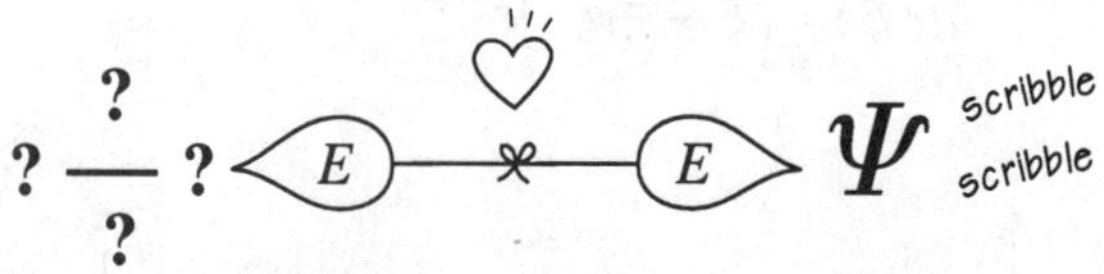

We used the wave equation to find the energy of electrons in conditions similar to those in nature. A visual image of the electron was produced which was then corroborated.

Brimming with confidence, let's now go on to Step 4!

Vamos!

4. 4. 4 STEP 4: THE HYDROGEN ATOM

THE FATHER'S CASE

Dad is in his study. Inside the room, brightly lit by the morning sun, a large, black suitcase is spread open.

1 0 3 . . . 1 0 3 . . . 1 0 3 . . .

He repeats the number to himself again and again. 1 0 3 is the combination of the lock on Dad's suitcase. The day he bought the suitcase, he couldn't decide what combination to use, whereupon his daughter Sonoko said,

"Since it's for you, Dad, why not make it 1 0 3 for October 3, your birthday?" It was easy to remember, and so he made it 1 0 3. The door opens and his wife Kanoko enters the room.

"Do you have your passport, dear?"

"Oh."

"You won't be able to go to China without it."

"I know."

Dad is leaving today for Qinghai, China, as part of the Hippo Homestay Program. While packing his suitcase, Dad reflects a bit on his Hippo experiences which have led up to this trip.

Since the night of the Hippo Family Club's special meeting for fathers, I have become very interested in the Hippo method of language acquisition and have gone to the group meetings every week to improve my skills. By now I am completely comfortable with the Hippo way of learning, that is, learning in a natural setting while having fun. I have even come to enjoy activities such as singing and dancing with others in the group.

I have heard that people who practice speaking foreign languages using the Hippo tapes and who then go abroad all come back with the ability to speak the target language fluently. Of course, you can learn to speak a foreign language well without going abroad, but the thought of using natural methods to learn a language while abroad sounds really fascinating and fun. Besides, imagine the joy of becoming fluent in another language. . .

And so, today I'm off!

When I arrived at Qinghai, a man my age came running up to me speaking in rapid fire Chinese. Just as I was thinking, "What in the world am I going to do?" these words tumbled out of my mouth from nowhere.

"To e puchee, chin neeshu maeiah!"

The man then said, a little more slowly,

Ah to e pucheei. Ni jiu shi Ogura shen shang. Fan-ying ni. Rui la ba?
[Oh, sorry. You are then Ogura-sensei. Welcome. Are you tired?]

The words out of my mouth were the words off one of the Hippo story tapes. What I had just said was a phrase I remembered from a lesson called "At the Airport."

"Well, what do you know. These phrases really do come in handy in situations like this," I thought to myself. "This must surely be a case of a sound taking on meaning the moment it initiates a response."

When Dad returned home to Japan, he couldn't stop talking about his wonderful homestay experience. While relating his adventures, he used a number of Chinese words that came spilling out of his mouth.

"My, you've become just like a native Chinese, haven't you?" teased his wife Kanoko.

Dad was already planning ahead to his next trip. Where should he go next?

This is the end of Dad's story. In listening to it, many of you can probably relate to Dad. In Step 4, instead of limiting himself to staying at home, he ended up traveling abroad. He came back chattering away in Chinese, full of lively tales of his travels.

> This spring I went to Mexico, and when I came back I was just like Dad. We should all go overseas!
> ¡Cruza los mares!

THE CASE OF THE ELECTRON

Let's again compare the father to the electron and see what we come up with this time.

The Father

Dad went to China, where Chinese is actually spoken, to see whether he would be understood by the natives there.

The Electron

? ? Minus? ? ? ?

Let's see if the hydrogen atom can really be explained with Schrödinger's equation for electron waves.

In Steps 1-3, we looked at what happened to the electron under certain conditions using Schrödinger's equation. We were able to confirm that it provided a visual image, and that it neatly explained experimental results. Thus, it is very solid as a theory. You could even say that it's almost flawless.

Now, in Step 4, we will finally find out what is happening to the electron within the atom!

We'll be able to rid ourselves of those unforgivable words of Heisenberg telling us to throw out the visual image.

But we still have to solve the equation.

Having come this far, consider it solved! From here on, we just have to work through the calculations!!

scribble scribble scribble

Oh my, Mr. Schrödinger has already started doing his calculations. We've got to hurry to catch up. . .

But the hydrogen atom is more complex than Hooke fields. So it's really difficult for someone like me, who only met Mr. Schrödinger six months ago, to explain this in a way that even a beginner can understand. This being the case, can you just let me skip the calculations this time around? For those of you who are saying, "I've just got to solve it for myself!" go ahead and work the calculations out on your own.

By the way, the $\mathfrak{V}$ for a hydrogen atom is

$$\mathfrak{V} = -\frac{e^2}{h}\frac{1}{r}$$

e represents the electrical charge and is a constant with a fixed value, so it is different from the natural logarithm e that we have seen before.

Let's make a graph of $\mathfrak{V}$ inside the hydrogen atom.

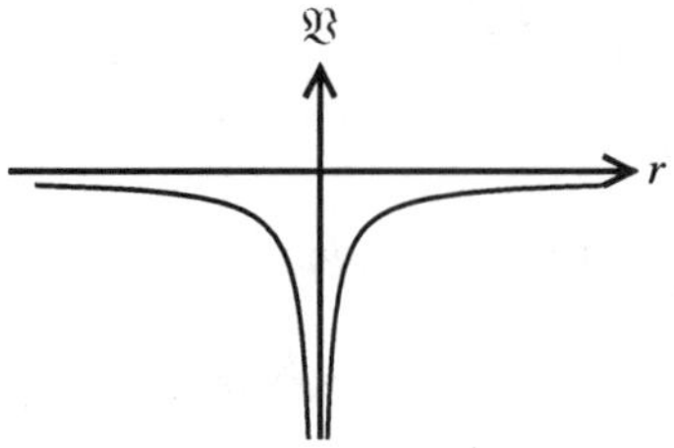

Since h and e are both constants, $\mathfrak{V}$ is something like this. As in Hooke fields, there is a force pulling toward the center. Thus, as one moves away from the center, $\mathfrak{V}$ becomes larger.

Therefore, the equation for electron waves inside the hydrogen atom will be

$$\nabla^2 \Phi + 8\pi^2 \mathfrak{M}\left(\nu + \frac{e^2}{h}\frac{1}{r}\right)\Psi = 0$$

Hey, if we can solve this, we'll know what form the electron wave takes inside the hydrogen atom! Scribble scribble scribble. . .

It's solved!!

At long last, Schrödinger unraveled the mystery of the hydrogen atom.

$$\boxed{\Phi(r, \theta, \phi) = AP_l^m(\cos\theta)e^{im\phi}F_n^l(r)}$$

He was also able to confirm that his theory matched the experimental results. He did all that and obtained a visual image, through a simple method, no less. . .

Bohr and Heisenberg were both amazed at the simple results. They were amazed because understanding the hydrogen atom using Heisenberg's matrix mechanics was a process so incredibly difficult that the only person who could successfully do it was a great mathematical genius named Pauli.

Even Heisenberg couldn't understand it, and he was the one who created it!!

By comparison, working out the hydrogen atom using Schrödinger's equation for waves is so easy that even we can do it with a little effort.

BACKTRACKING

As we have seen in Steps 1-4, the energy values derived from Schrödinger's equation agreed with the experimental results. We have seen how Schrödinger's flawless theory provided a visual image of how and in what form electron waves existed while correctly accounting for experimental results.

In addition, with Schrödinger's equation, if we know under what conditions the electron exists, we will be able to determine how it behaves as a wave. With that in mind, we thought it would be interesting to consider the conditions affecting electrons by comparing them to the situation of a father who joins the Hippo Club.

We went through Steps 1-4 and placed the electron in progressively more complicated situations, checking to see if we could really describe its behavior using Schrödinger's equation. We learned that this process was exactly the same as what happens to a father who has just entered the Hippo Club and who quickly learns to speak a foreign language the way a young child does.

The behavior of the electron varies depending on the environment in which it exists. Keeping that fact in mind as we solve Schrödinger's equations, we found that the environment in which language acquisition is nurtured is determined by the surrounding relationships between people.

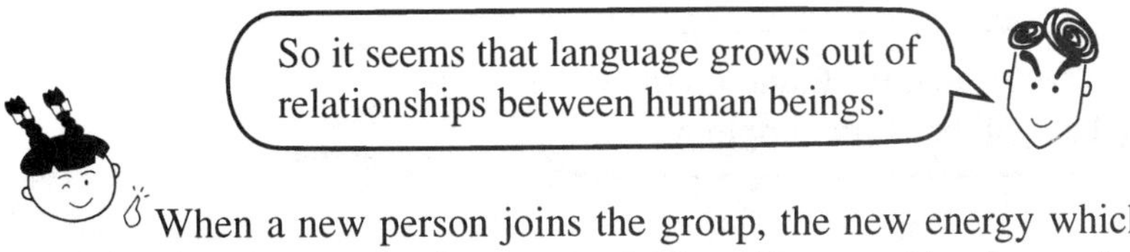

When a new person joins the group, the new energy which he brings in sparks the energy of others around him. Due to this change in dynamics, everyone is motivated to speak the language better. This is echoed in Schrödinger's equation, where the behavior of an electron can be deduced from its environment.

Well, now that you have come this far with us, let's see how you would answer this question. . .

Which would you choose? To think of electrons as particles, which means losing your visual image after working through some difficult matrix mechanics, or to think of electrons as waves, which means being able to retain a visual image after solving Schrödinger's simple wave equation?

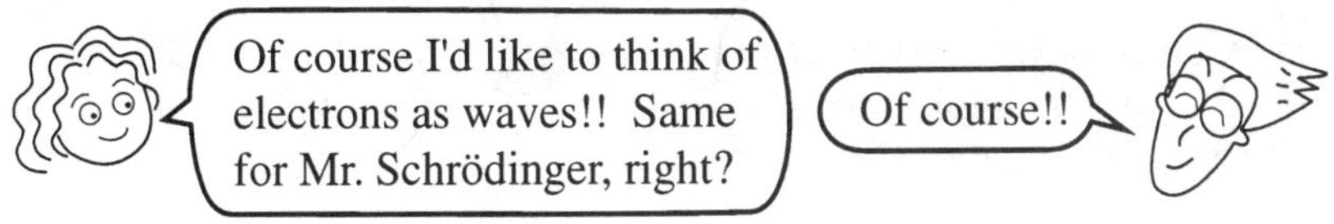

All right then, let's all say it together.

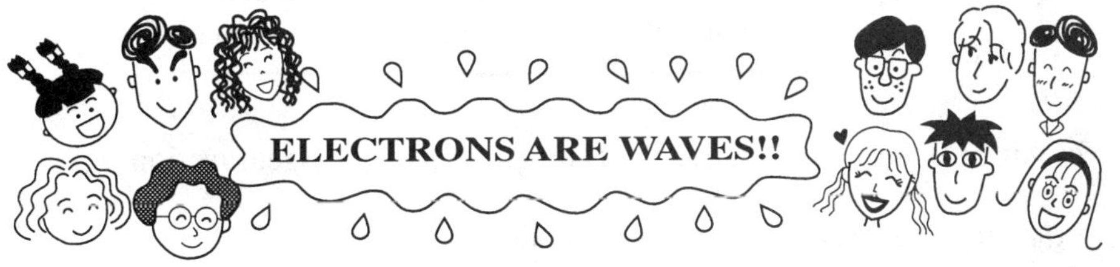

However, Schrödinger was far from satisfied.

4. 5 COMPLICATED ELECTRON WAVES

We have solved equations relating to electron waves in various conditions such as in free space, the inside of a box, in Hooke fields, and inside the hydrogen atom.

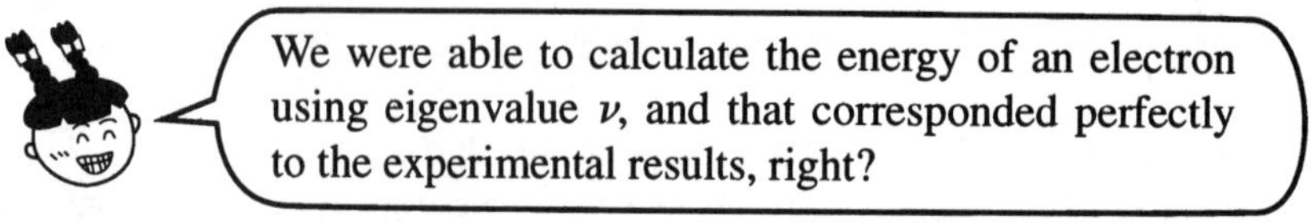

Now, we can say, "It's perfect." But Schrödinger still wasn't satisfied.

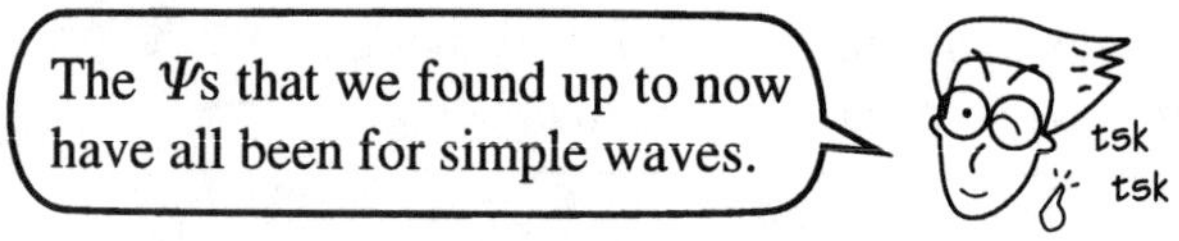

Well, that's true. A simple wave is a wave that oscillates at a specific frequency. In all of the wave equations we've solved so far, Ψ was always

$$\Psi = \Phi e^{-i2\pi \nu t}.$$

And since frequency ν was fixed at a certain value, they were simple waves.

Fourier, Jean Baptiste Joseph, Baron de
[1768-1830]

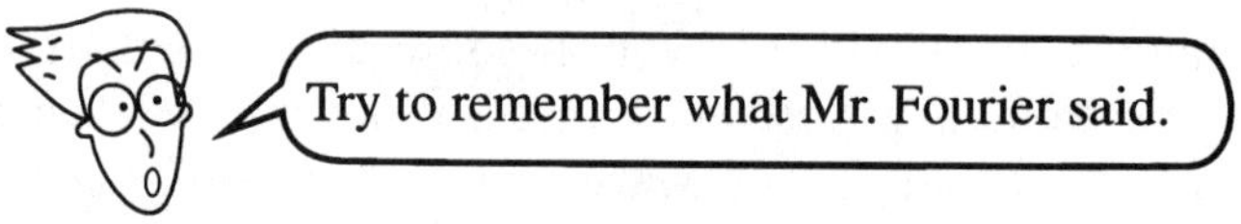

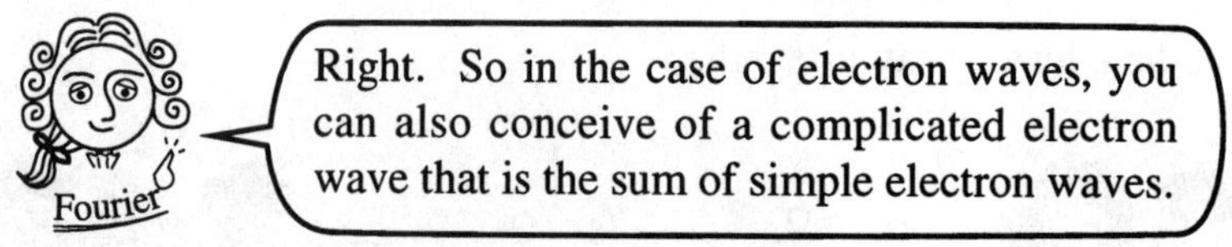

In this case, because Φ corresponds to ν_n, we'll call it eigenfunction Φ_n.

I see. So let's add the simple waves together.

For all of the Ψs we found so far, eigenvalue ν has had various discrete values. If we take one of these eigenvalues and call it ν_n, it will determine the Φ for the electron wave. In this case, because Φ corresponds to ν_n, we'll call it eigenfunction Φ_n.

Eigenvalue		Electron wave
ν_1	......	Φ_1
ν_2	......	Φ_2
ν_3	......	Φ_3
ν_4	......	Φ_4
•	......	•
•	......	•
•	......	•
ν_n	......	Φ_n

Letting Ψ for frequency ν_n be Ψ_n, and letting the corresponding amplitude be A_n, Ψ_n may be expressed as

$$\Psi_n = A_n \Phi_n e^{-i2\pi \nu_n t}$$

In this case, all we have to do is sum up Ψ_n!

Taking Ψ for a complicated electron wave, we have

$$\begin{aligned} \Psi &= \Psi_1 + \Psi_2 + \Psi_3 + \cdots \\ &= A_1 \Phi_1 e^{-i2\pi \nu_1 t} + A_2 \Phi_2 e^{-i2\pi \nu_2 t} + A_3 \Phi_3 e^{-i2\pi \nu_3 t} + \cdots \end{aligned}$$

Expressing this using the symbol for sum Σ, we get

$$\Psi = \sum_n A_n \Phi_n e^{-i2\pi \nu_n t}$$

This is it!

Wait a minute! It's not that easy. You can talk about summing up, but we still have to see if summation can describe any sort of complicated wave. If it can't, then we can't say that a complicated wave is the sum of simple waves.

How do we confirm that?

All we have to do is explain that a complicated wave Ψ can be expanded.

Talking about expansion reminds me of the Fourier coefficients.

The Fourier coefficients

Fourier Series

$$f(t) = a_0 + a_1\cos\,\omega t + b_1\sin\,\omega t + a_2\cos\,2\omega t + b_2\sin\,2\omega t + \cdots$$

$$= a_0 + \sum_{n=1}^{\infty} (a_n\cos\,n\omega t + b_n\sin\,n\omega t)$$

The summation of sine waves and cosine waves (the Fourier series), can describe any complicated wave. This means that, conversely, any complicated wave **CAN BE ANALYTICALLY DECOMPOSED** into sine waves and cosine waves.

That's the Fourier coefficients.

In the Fourier series, frequencies are set at integral multiples. So if we can find the amplitudes of the sine waves and cosine waves, we will be able to decompose the wave.

In Fourier coefficients, if one wants to know the amplitude of simple wave $\sin 1\omega t$ contained in complicated wave $f(t)$, one may find it by multiplying complicated wave $f(t)$ by the wave that you want to extract (in this case, $\sin 1\omega t$). Ultimately, this is the same thing as multiplying, one at a time, the simple waves that make up $f(t)$ by $\sin 1\omega t$. The illustration below will make this easier to understand.

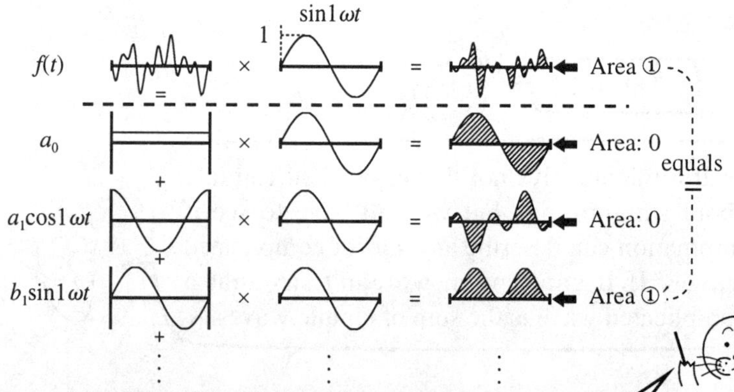

This means that Area ① of $f(t) \times \sin 1\omega t$ will be the same as Area ①′ of $b_1 \sin 1\omega t \times \sin 1\omega t$, which are contained in $f(t)$.

When we find the Fourier coefficients, the area will not be zero when waves of the same form are multiplied; the area can only be zero when waves of different forms are multiplied. When waves are multiplied by something other than themselves and the area that results is zero, the waves are said to be mutually **ORTHOGONAL.**

In short,

1. $f(t)$ is multiplied by a simple wave with an amplitude of 1 and the area is calculated.
2. Because each wave is orthogonal, the area will be 0 for all cases other than when the frequency is the same as the wave that is the multiplier.
3. Thus, waves having the same frequency as the multiplier may be extracted.

By multiplying $f(t)$ by various frequencies of simple waves one at a time, it is possible to decompose $f(t)$.

Yes, I see. In order to confirm whether the sum Ψ

$$\Psi = \sum_n A_n \Phi_n e^{-i2\pi \nu_n t}$$

of simple electron waves Ψ_n can really describe any complicated wave, we must explain why the various simple electron waves are all orthogonal.

But it's difficult to consider the functions of both time and space

$$\Phi_n e^{-i2\pi \nu_n t}$$

at the same time. So, to start, let's find out if the function for space, $\boldsymbol{\Phi_n}$, **IS ORTHOGONAL.**

DETERMINING WHETHER Φ_n IS ORTHOGONAL

In order to say that two waves, Φ_n and $\Phi_{n'}$ ($n \neq n'$), are orthogonal, we must show that when Φ_n and $\Phi_{n'}$ are multiplied, the area is zero. Let's write this in the language of equations.

$$\int_A^B \Phi_n \Phi_{n'}^* \, dx \begin{cases} = 0 & (n \neq n') \\ \neq 0 & (n = n') \end{cases}$$

$\int \square \, dx$ is an integration symbol which indicates "determine the area."

I have a question. What is that * mark on Φ_n?

In some cases, Φ_n is a complex-numbered wave (a wave that contains i). When you deal with an i, or a complex-numbered wave, the area can't be determined without introducing a complex conjugate. The * mark indicates that the complex conjugate has been applied.

When you use a complex conjugate, you change the sign in front of i. For example, the complex conjugate of $2 + 3i$ will be $2 + (-3i) = 2 - 3i$; the complex conjugate of $e^{-i2\pi\nu t}$ will be $e^{-(-i2\pi\nu t)} = e^{i2\pi\nu t}$. Now then, what is the complex conjugate of 1? The answer is 1 because there isn't an i contained in 1!!

When referring to the * mark, let's call it a "star."

There's no need to overthink this. Just consider it a magical formula.

Next, let's begin proving all this!

Let's prove that the two different waves Φ_n and $\Phi_{n'}$ are in fact orthogonal.

This is the result we want to obtain!

$$\int_A^B \Phi_n \Phi_{n'}^* \, dx \begin{cases} = 0 & (n \neq n') \\ \neq 0 & (n = n') \end{cases}$$

From here on, we will assume that everything is one dimensional. First, Φ_n must work in the equation for electron waves.

$$\frac{d^2\Phi_n}{dx^2} + 8\pi^2\mathfrak{M}(\nu_n - \mathfrak{V})\Phi_n = 0 \quad \cdots\cdots ①$$

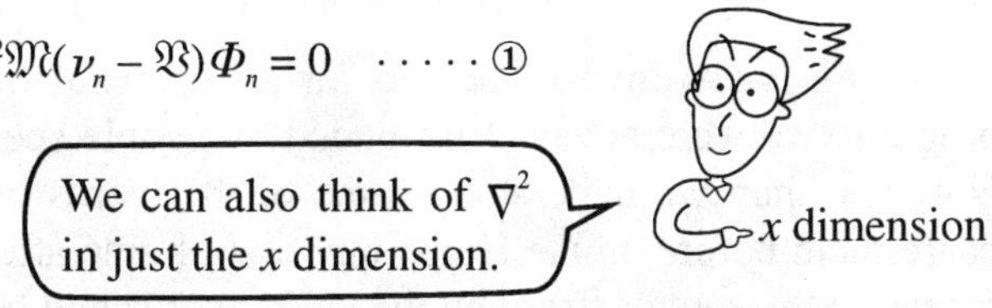

The same applies to $\Phi_{n'}$.

$$\frac{d^2\Phi_{n'}}{dx^2} + 8\pi^2\mathfrak{M}(\nu_{n'} - \mathfrak{V})\Phi_{n'} = 0$$

In order to come up with the desired result, we take the complex conjugate for $\Phi_{n'}$ in this equation.

$$\frac{d^2\Phi_{n'}^*}{dx^2} + 8\pi^2\mathfrak{M}(\nu_{n'} - \mathfrak{V})\Phi_{n'}^* = 0 \quad \cdots\cdots ②$$

Now then, do you think we can manipulate ① and ② into the desired form? Let's rewrite equations ① and ②.

$$① : \quad \frac{d^2\Phi_n}{dx^2} = -8\pi^2\mathfrak{M}(\nu_n - \mathfrak{V})\Phi_n$$

$$② : \quad \frac{d^2\Phi_{n'}^*}{dx^2} = -8\pi^2\mathfrak{M}(\nu_{n'} - \mathfrak{V})\Phi_{n'}^*$$

Next, multiply both sides of equation ① by $\Phi_{n'}$, and both sides of equation ② by Φ_n.

$$\frac{d^2\Phi_n}{dx^2}\Phi_{n'}^* = -8\pi^2\mathfrak{M}(\nu_n - \mathfrak{V})\Phi_n\Phi_{n'}^* \quad \cdots\cdots ①'$$

$$\frac{d^2\Phi_{n'}^*}{dx^2}\Phi_n = -8\pi^2\mathfrak{M}(\nu_{n'} - \mathfrak{V})\Phi_{n'}^*\Phi_n \quad \cdots\cdots ②'$$

This will involve a bit of work, but in order to obtain the desired form, we will need to subtract equation ②′ from equation ①′.

At the Hippo Family Club, we have created a multilingual environment where foreign language tapes are played everywhere, all the time, much like background music. It is a multilingual amusement center where many different people and families gather together as one big family to play fun-filled games with language. After being immersed in this environment for a few months, you find yourself beginning to recognize what languages are being played. By repeating the sounds on the tapes over and over again, you soon are able to say them perfectly.

The Hippo method of language acquisition involves repeating or "singing" the sounds heard on the tapes, without always knowing exactly what they mean word for word.

Vocalizing is important when learning
to speak a language.

When we went to Mexico on an international exchange program, we were always surrounded by people speaking Spanish. Now and then we understood some of the words because we had heard them before on the Hippo tapes. At home after listening and repeating the sounds heard on the tapes, words had begun to tumble forth naturally from our mouths. The words we learned in this way were the ones we were able to pick out in conversations in Mexico.

When you find yourself in a situation similar to one presented on the tapes, you will instantly make the connection in your head. In an actual situation, you will find yourself instinctively using the words heard on the tapes. The words will come to you naturally and easily, and you will find yourself knowing exactly what they mean. As long as you have a good repertoire of sounds in your head, you are bound to hear them verbalized when the situation calls for them. As you try these sounds out, you find they take on meaning, becoming part of your ever growing vocabulary.

We apply the above method of language learning to the language of mathematics. In the language of mathematics, we initially start by absorbing the forms of the equations without really understanding what they mean. I already know, however, that the meaning will come soon enough as I work with the equations. For now, don't worry too much about the details. We can work on them later. The important thing is to keep on working to absorb the language of equations!

Let's calculate ①′ − ②′.

$$\frac{d^2\Phi_n}{dx^2}\Phi_{n'}^* = -8\pi^2\mathfrak{M}(\nu_n - \mathfrak{V})\Phi_n\Phi_{n'}^* \qquad \cdots\cdots ①'$$

$$-\Big)\quad \frac{d^2\Phi_{n'}^*}{dx^2}\Phi_n = -8\pi^2\mathfrak{M}(\nu_{n'} - \mathfrak{V})\Phi_{n'}^*\Phi_{n'} \qquad \cdots\cdots ②'$$

$$\frac{d^2\Phi_n}{dx^2}\Phi_{n'}^* - \frac{d^2\Phi_{n'}^*}{dx^2}\Phi_n = -8\pi^2\mathfrak{M}\nu_n\Phi_n\Phi_{n'}^* + 8\pi^2\mathfrak{M}\mathfrak{V}\Phi_n\Phi_{n'}^*$$

$$+ 8\pi^2\mathfrak{M}\nu_{n'}\Phi_{n'}^*\Phi_n - 8\pi^2\mathfrak{M}\mathfrak{V}\Phi_{n'}^*\Phi_n$$

$$= -8\pi^2\mathfrak{M}\nu_n\Phi_n\Phi_{n'}^* + 8\pi^2\mathfrak{M}\nu_{n'}\Phi_n\Phi_{n'}^*$$

$$= -8\pi^2\mathfrak{M}(\nu_n - \nu_{n'})\,\underline{\Phi_n\Phi_{n'}^*}$$

This looks a bit like the form we're after.

For the next step, we wish to integrate Φ_n and $\Phi_{n'}$ from A to B with respect to x. So we integrate both sides of the equation.

> $\int_A^B \square\, dx$:means to integrate the function $\square$ from A to B and find the area.

$$\int_A^B \left(\frac{d^2\Phi_n}{dx^2} \Phi_{n'}^* - \frac{d^2\Phi_{n'}^*}{dx^2} \Phi_n \right) dx = \underline{-8\pi^2\mathfrak{M}(\nu_n - \nu_{n'})} \int_A^B \Phi_n \Phi_{n'}^* \, dx$$

This is a constant that bears no relation to the integration so we moved it to the front.

$$\underbrace{\int_A^B \frac{d^2\Phi_n}{dx^2} \Phi_{n'}^* \, dx}_{\boxed{\alpha}} - \underbrace{\int_A^B \frac{d^2\Phi_{n'}^*}{dx^2} \Phi_n \, dx}_{\boxed{\beta}} = -8\pi^2\mathfrak{M}(\nu_n - \nu_{n'}) \int_A^B \Phi_n \Phi_{n'}^* \, dx \quad \cdots\cdots \blacktriangle$$

Whee! The right side is coming close to the target equation. But the left side is still hard to recognize. Is that all right, Mr. Schrödinger?

Don't worry. It'll still work. We just need to use a method called partial integration.

Formula for partial integration

$$\int_A^B f(x) \frac{d}{dx} g(x)\, dx = \Big[f(x) \cdot g(x) \Big]_A^B - \int_A^B \frac{d}{dx} f(x) \cdot g(x)\, dx$$

We can continue the proof using this formula!
Let's start our calculations from $\boxed{\alpha}$ on the left side of ▲.

$$\boxed{\alpha} : \int_A^B \frac{d^2\Phi_n}{dx^2} \Phi_{n'}^* \, dx$$

We rearrange the elements of the equation just a bit and we get

$$\int_A^B \Phi_{n'}^* \frac{d^2\Phi_n}{dx^2} \, dx$$

Even if we change the order, the meaning of the equation is still the same.

Comparing this to the formula for partial integration, we see that we can express it as

$$f(x) = \Phi_{n'}^*, \qquad g(x) = \frac{d\Phi_n}{dx}$$

We'll then apply it to the formula.

$$\boxed{\alpha}: \int_A^B \Phi_{n'}^* \frac{d\Phi_n}{dx}\, dx = \left[\Phi_{n'}^* \frac{d\Phi_n}{dx}\right]_A^B - \int_A^B \frac{d\Phi_{n'}^*}{dx} \cdot \frac{d\Phi_n}{dx}\, dx$$

What happens to formula $\boxed{\beta}$ on the left side of ▲?

$$\boxed{\beta}: \int_A^B \frac{d^2\Phi_{n'}^*}{dx^2} \Phi_n\, dx$$

Again, we first rearrange the elements in the formula.

$$\int_A^B \Phi_n \frac{d^2\Phi_{n'}^*}{dx^2}\, dx$$

Comparing this to the formula for partial integration, we see that we can express it as

$$f(x) = \Phi_n, \quad g(x) = \frac{d\Phi_{n'}^*}{dx}$$

Then let's apply this to the formula and do the calculation. We get

$$\boxed{\beta}: \int_A^B \Phi_n \frac{d\Phi_{n'}^*}{dx}\, dx = \left[\Phi_n \frac{d\Phi_{n'}^*}{dx}\right]_A^B - \int_A^B \frac{d\Phi_n}{dx} \cdot \frac{d\Phi_{n'}^*}{dx}\, dx$$

We calculate the entire left side of ▲.

$$\text{left side of } ▲ = \left[\Phi_{n'}^* \cdot \frac{d\Phi_n}{dx}\right]_A^B - \int_A^B \frac{d\Phi_{n'}^*}{dx} \cdot \frac{d\Phi_n}{dx}\, dx$$

$$- \left[\Phi_n \cdot \frac{d\Phi_{n'}^*}{dx}\right]_A^B + \int_A^B \frac{d\Phi_n}{dx} \cdot \frac{d\Phi_{n'}^*}{dx}\, dx$$

$$= \left[\Phi_{n'}^* \cdot \frac{d\Phi_n}{dx}\right]_A^B - \left[\Phi_n \cdot \frac{d\Phi_{n'}^*}{dx}\right]_A^B$$

$$- \underbrace{\int_A^B \frac{d\Phi_n}{dx} \cdot \frac{d\Phi_{n'}^*}{dx}\, dx}_{\boxed{A}} + \underbrace{\int_A^B \frac{d\Phi_{n'}^*}{dx} \cdot \frac{d\Phi_n}{dx}\, dx}_{\boxed{B}}$$

Since we can change the order of multiplication within the $\int$ sign without changing the meaning, the result is that "A" = "B". It follows that the left side of ▲ is

$$\text{left side of } \blacktriangle = \left[\Phi_{n'}^{*} \cdot \frac{d\Phi_n}{dx}\right]_A^B - \left[\Phi_n \cdot \frac{d\Phi_{n'}^{*}}{dx}\right]_A^B$$

Next, we apply a boundary condition to Φ_n in the A and B terms of this equation, such that $\Phi_n(A) = 0$, and $\Phi_n(B) = 0$, and we get

$$\left[\Phi_{n'}^{*} \cdot \frac{d\Phi_n}{dx}\right]_A^B = 0, \quad \left[\Phi_n \cdot \frac{d\Phi_{n'}^{*}}{dx}\right]_A^B = 0$$

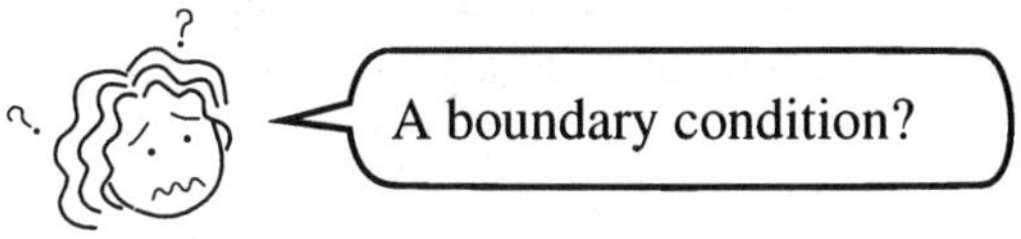

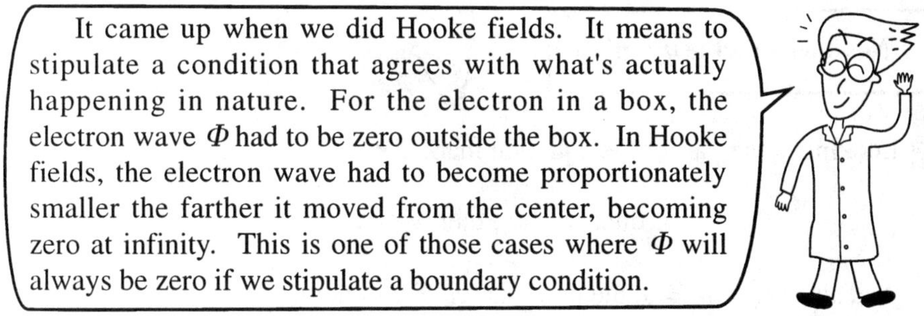

All right, since the left side of ▲ = 0,

$$0 = \underline{-8\pi^2\mathfrak{M}(\nu_n - \nu_{n'})\int_A^B \Phi_n\Phi_{n'}^{*}\,dx}$$

Since $-8\pi^2\mathfrak{M}$ is a constant, if we multiply both sides by $-\frac{1}{8\pi^2\mathfrak{M}}$, we get

$$(\nu_n - \nu_{n'})\int_A^B \Phi_n\Phi_{n'}^{*}\,dx = 0$$

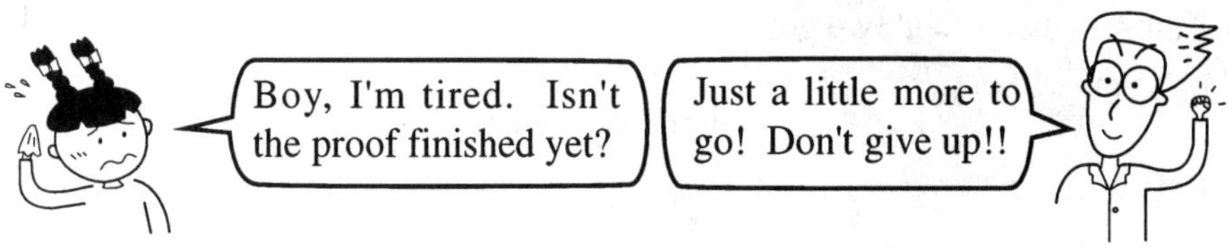

Let's consider this equation after dividing it into two parts.

$$\underbrace{(\nu_n - \nu_{n'})}_{\spadesuit}\ \underbrace{\int_A^B \Phi_n\Phi_{n'}^{*}\,dx}_{\heartsuit} = 0$$

First, the case when $n \neq n'$.

As for the place marked ♠ when $n \neq n'$,

$$\text{Since } \nu_n \neq \nu_{n'}, \text{ then } \nu_n - \nu_{n'} \neq 0.$$

So if the whole left side is 0, the part of the equation marked ♥ will have to be 0, too. This means that when $n \neq n'$, we get

$$\int_A^B \Phi_n \Phi_{n'}^* \, dx = 0$$

Hey!! We've already managed to come up with a proof for $n \neq n'$.

Next, let's tackle $n = n'$.

Looking at the part of the equation marked ♠,

$$\text{Since } \nu_n = \nu_{n'}, \text{ then } \nu_n - \nu_{n'} = 0.$$

And since $\nu_n - \nu_{n'} = 0$, the part marked ♥ will not be 0.

$$\int_A^B \Phi_n \Phi_{n'}^* \, dx$$

Yes, but isn't it all right if the part marked ♥ is 0, since $0 \times 0 = 0$?

That's true. But in that case, Φ will end up being 0 everywhere. Right now, we're thinking of the Φs that have some value, so in this case, Φ will not be 0.

That is, when $n = n'$, we get

$$\int_A^B \Phi_n \Phi_{n'}^* \, dx \neq 0$$

With this, we're able to prove

$$\int_A^B \Phi_n \Phi_{n'}^* \, dx \begin{cases} = 0 & (n \neq n') \\ \neq 0 & (n = n') \end{cases}$$

Up until now, we've only been thinking in one dimension, but we can also prove the same thing in three dimensions.

> We can say that simple waves Φ_n found by solving Schrödinger's equation for electron waves
>
> $$\nabla^2\Phi + 8\pi^2\mathfrak{M}(\nu - \mathfrak{V})\Phi = 0$$
>
> **ARE MUTUALLY ORTHOGONAL IN ANY AND ALL CASES.**

Point

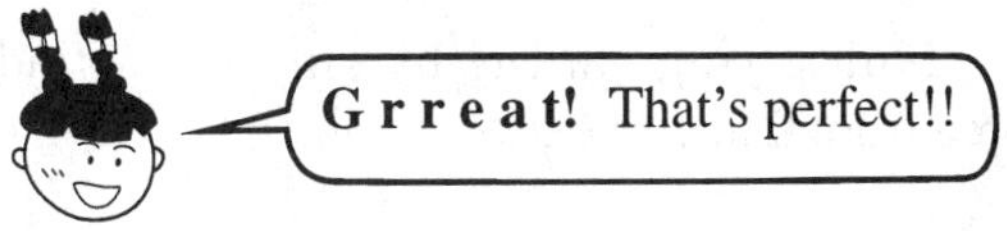

LET'S NORMALIZE IT!

The equation will appear more elegant if we use a technique called normalization.

Don't look so worried. Normalization is not as difficult as it sounds.

In Fourier math, when we wanted to find out how much of simple wave sin $1\omega t$ was contained in complicated wave $f(t)$, what did we do?

Finding out how much of simple wave sin $1\omega t$ is contained in a complicated wave

1. A complicated wave $f(t)$ is multiplied by the simple wave you want to extract, sin $1\omega t$.

$$f(t)\cdot\sin 1\omega t$$

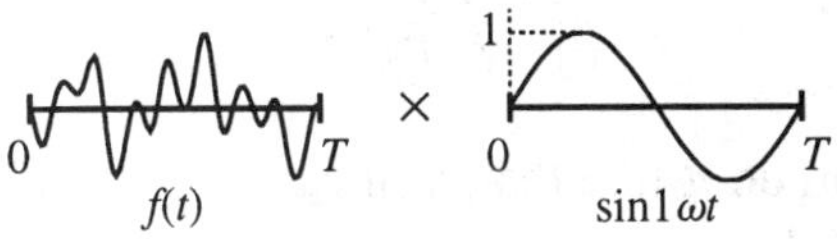

2. Determine the area from 0 to T.

$$\int_0^T f(t)\cdot\sin 1\omega t\, dt$$

3. The amplitude b_1 of sin $1\omega t$ (the part taken up by the simple wave) is found by dividing by $T/2$ (multiplying by $2/T$)

$$b_1 = \frac{2}{T}\int_0^T f(t)\cdot\sin 1\omega t\, dt$$

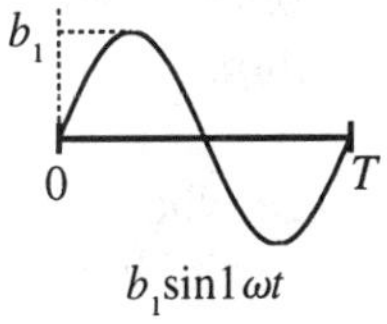

By separating out one simple wave from the complicated wave, you can know how much of the complicated wave (amplitude) is occupied by the simple wave.

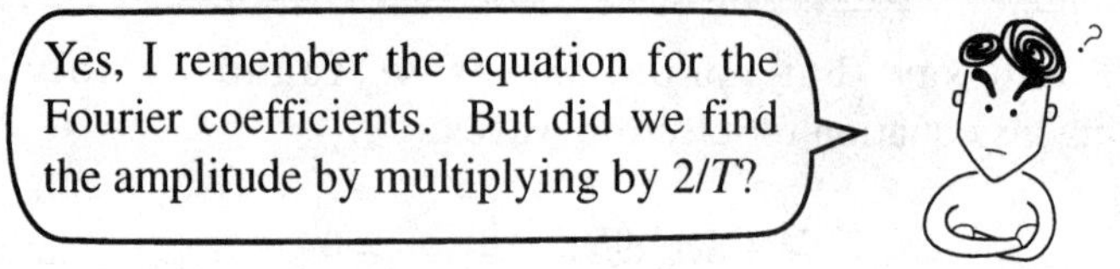

It's easy to figure out if you think about what the answer to $\int_0^T \sin 1\omega t \cdot \sin \omega t \, dt$ will be.

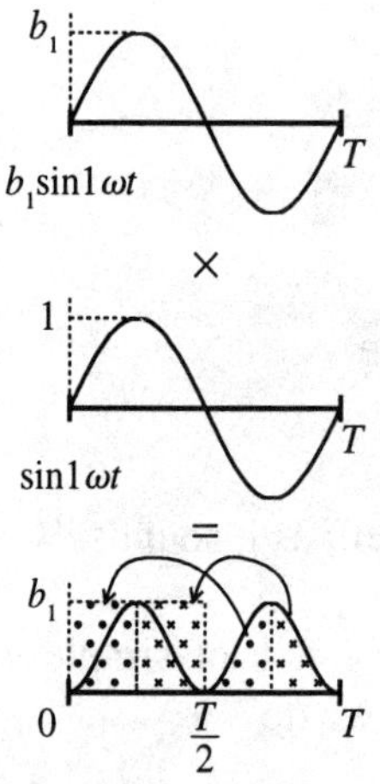

Multiplying $\sin 1\omega t$ by $\sin 1\omega t$ to find the area from 0 to T, we get

$$\int_0^T \sin 1\omega t \cdot \sin 1\omega t \, dt = \frac{T}{2}$$

So, to find the amplitude of a simple wave using Fourier, you multiply the area you found by $2/T$.

$$\frac{2}{T}\int_0^T b_1 \sin 1\omega t \cdot \sin 1\omega t \, dt = b_1$$

At this point, instead of multiplying by $2/T$ each time after finding the area, you multiply each of the two waves by $\sqrt{\frac{2}{T}}$ before multiplying them together. That way you get

$$\int_0^T \sqrt{\frac{2}{T}}\, b_1 \sin 1\omega t \cdot \sqrt{\frac{2}{T}} \sin 1\omega t \, dt = b_1$$

If you do it like that, you can find the amplitude without having to multiply by $2/T$ at the end.

Then if we manipulate the Φ_n in

$$\int_A^B \Phi_n \Phi_n^* dx$$

the same way, we come up with the answer 1. We call this manipulation of the formula **normalization.**

In this case, since what is set up to be multiplied changes as the conditions change, we cannot predict what Φ_n is to be multiplied with.

Here we want to indicate this is something that has been normalized. To do that, we'll use ϕ (the lower case form of Φ) instead of Φ. With that, **the normalized equation for orthogonality becomes:**

$$\int \phi_n \phi_{n'}^* dx \begin{cases} = 0 \ (n \neq n') \\ = 1 \ (n = n') \end{cases}$$

Point

From now on, we will omit the A and B in $\int_A^B$.

If we use the normalized ϕ_n, we can also find amplitude A_n of ϕ_n from complicated wave $f(x)$ with only step.

$$A_n = \int f(x)\phi_n^* dx$$

Whoa! It has become a symphony of elegance! Three cheers!

THE EXPANSION THEOREM

So far the question has been, "Is it really possible to express complicated wave Ψ as the sum of simple waves Ψ_n?"

You only need to be absolutely sure that whatever Ψ you bring in, it can be decomposed into Ψ_n. For decomposition, it will suffice if our Ψ_n are orthogonal. Because it is difficult to examine the function Ψ_n with respect to both time and space, we looked only at the function for space Φ_n to see if it was orthogonal.

And we proved that it was orthogonal.

Right. That means that with respect to space, any complicated wave can be expressed as the sum of normalized simple waves ϕ_n. Since

$$f(x) = \sum_n A_n \phi_n(x)$$

we can find amplitude A_n in the same manner as the Fourier coefficients.

$$A_n = \int f(x)\phi_n^*(x)dx$$

But, there is one thing that you should remember. In order to expand a complicated Ψ, all of the necessary integrations of ϕ must be included. This rule is called the expansion theorem.

That's fine, but would you please explain it so that we can understand, too?

All right. Think back to the Fourier series. We expressed complicated waves with the following equation, remember?

$$f(t) = a_0 + \sum_{n=1}^{\infty} (a_n \cos n\omega t + b_n \sin n\omega t)$$

Take an example like the one in the diagram below. When no part of a complicated wave drops below 0, the simple wave a_0 becomes very important.

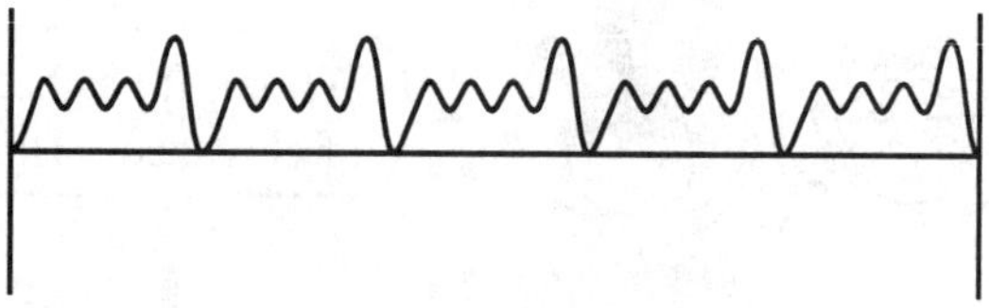

No matter how you manipulate the amplitude of other simple waves, it is impossible to make a complicated wave like this without a_0. In the physical world there are an enormous number of different complicated wave forms. We were able to describe complicated waves using Fourier math by summing simple waves, but that was possible only because we used all of the types of simple waves.

I've got it! The same is true of Ψ and ϕ as well!

You're absolutely right! Just like you were saying, in order to express all complicated waves Ψ, we have to have already accounted for every type of simple wave ϕ.

Does that mean if just one ϕ is missing, it won't work?

If even one is missing, you won't be able to express all of the complicated wave forms.

All we have left to do now is determine whether the functions Ψ of time and space can be expressed as the sum of simple waves.

$$\Psi(x, y, z, t) = \sum_n A_n \phi_n(x, y, z) e^{-i2\pi \nu_n t}$$

That, then, is our next task.

CAN A COMPLICATED ELECTRON WAVE REALLY BE MADE BY SUMMING SIMPLE WAVES ϕ?

Is it really true that the function Ψ of time and space can be described by this equation?

$$\Psi(x, y, z, t) = \sum_n A_n \phi_n(x, y, z) e^{-i2\pi \nu_n t}$$

Let's try to prove it, starting from the assumption that ϕ_n are mutually orthogonal! Before that, you should note one thing. Because we will use a normalized ϕ from here on, the equation for complicated electron waves Ψ will be the sum of normalized ϕ. Thus we will use Ψ in the lower case (ψ), as below.

$$\psi(x, y, z, t) = \sum_n A_n \phi_n(x, y, z) e^{-i2\pi \nu_n t}$$

First, we don't know whether the term for time ψ is correctly expressed as $e^{-i2\pi\nu_n t}$, so for the moment we'll gather all the terms that include time, except those that include space, and call them $C_n(t)$.

If we do that, ψ will be

$$\psi(x, y, z, t) = \sum_n \phi_n(x, y, z) C_n(t)$$

Since ψ refers to a complicated electron wave, it must satisfy the equation for complicated electron waves

$$\nabla^2 \psi + 4\pi i \mathfrak{M} \frac{\partial \psi}{\partial t} - 8\pi^2 \mathfrak{M}\mathfrak{B}\psi = 0$$

When we rewrite each ψ in the above equation, we obtain

$$\nabla^2 \sum_n \phi_n C_n(t) + 4\pi i \mathfrak{M} \frac{\partial}{\partial t}\left\{\sum_n \phi_n C_n(t)\right\} - 8\pi^2 \mathfrak{M}\mathfrak{V} \sum_n \phi_n C_n(t) = 0$$

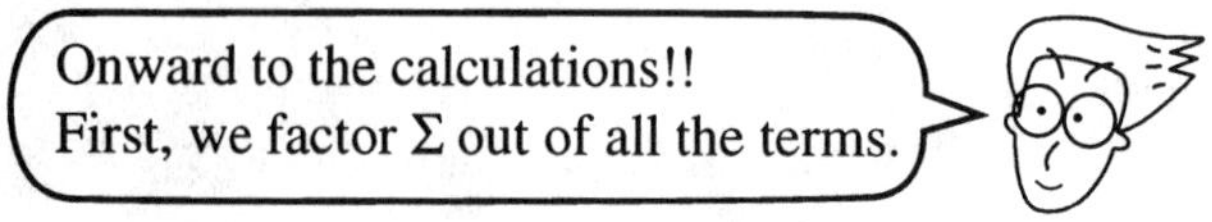

$$\sum_n \left[\underbrace{\nabla^2 \phi_n C_n(t)}_{1^{st}\ \text{term}} + \underbrace{4\pi i \mathfrak{M} \frac{\partial}{\partial t}\left\{\phi_n C_n(t)\right\}}_{2^{nd}\ \text{term}} - \underbrace{8\pi^2 \mathfrak{M}\mathfrak{V}\phi_n C_n(t)}_{3^{rd}\ \text{term}} \right] = 0$$

Next, ∇^2 in the first term is a derivative with repect to x, y, z. So we remove $C_n(t)$, which is a function of time and thus has no relationship to x, y, z, and place it outside, combining it with the third term. Then since the second term $\delta/\delta t$ is a derivative with repect to time, we take ϕ_n, which has no relationship to time, out of the derivative.

$$\sum_n \left\{ C_n(t)\,(\underbrace{\nabla^2 \phi_n - 8\pi^2 \mathfrak{M}\mathfrak{V}\phi_n}_{①}) + 4\pi i \mathfrak{M} \frac{\partial C_n(t)}{\partial t}\phi_n \right\} = 0 \qquad (\bigstar)$$

This may come as a surprise, but it's time now for a quiz!

Question: Term ① may be rewritten in which of the following forms?

1. $4\pi i \mathfrak{M} \frac{\partial A_n(t)}{\partial t}\phi_n$
2. $-8\pi^2 \mathfrak{M}\nu_n \phi_n$
3. $(\nabla^2 - 8\pi^2 \mathfrak{M})\phi_n$

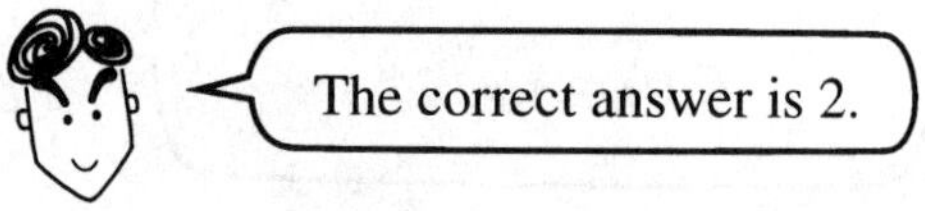

You'll see why if you look at the following equation for electron waves.

$$\nabla^2 \phi_n + 8\pi^2 \mathfrak{M}(\nu_n - \mathfrak{V})\phi_n = 0$$

If we break up this equation and then calculate,

$$\nabla^2\phi_n + 8\pi^2\mathfrak{M}\nu_n\,\phi_n - 8\pi^2\mathfrak{M}\mathfrak{V}\phi_n = 0$$

$$\underbrace{\nabla^2\phi_n - 8\pi^2\mathfrak{M}\mathfrak{V}\phi_n}_{①} = -8\pi^2\mathfrak{M}\nu_n\,\phi_n$$

The left side takes the same form as ①, which means that ① will be

$$-8\pi^2\mathfrak{M}\nu_n\phi_n$$

and the previous equation ★ becomes

$$\sum_n\left\{-8\pi^2\mathfrak{M}\nu_n\phi_nC_n(t) + 4\pi i\mathfrak{M}\,\frac{\partial\,C_n(t)}{\partial\,t}\,\phi_n\right\} = 0$$

We multiply both parts by $\frac{i}{4\pi\mathfrak{M}}$ and factor out ϕ_n.

$$\sum_n\left\{-8\pi^2\mathfrak{M}\nu_n\,\frac{i}{4\pi\mathfrak{M}}\,\phi_nC_n(t) + \frac{i}{4\pi\mathfrak{M}}\cdot 4\pi i\mathfrak{M}\,\frac{\partial\,C_n(t)}{\partial\,t}\,\phi_n\right\} = 0$$

$$\underbrace{\sum_n\left(-i2\pi\,\nu_nC_n(t) - \frac{\partial\,C_n(t)}{\partial\,t}\right)}_{②}\phi_n = 0$$

Now, then let's consider this equation. The right side is 0, but when will the left side be 0? In terms of Fourier, ϕ_n is a simple wave. In that case, the part marked ② in the equation above may be thought of as the amplitude of ϕ_n. We can think of this in the same way as the equation for the Fourier series. Now then, when we take simple waves and keep adding them, they become a complicated wave. But in this equation, no matter how many simple waves are added, the result is 0.

Now then let's consider this equation a bit. The right side is 0, but at just what times will the left side be 0?

A wave of 0 is

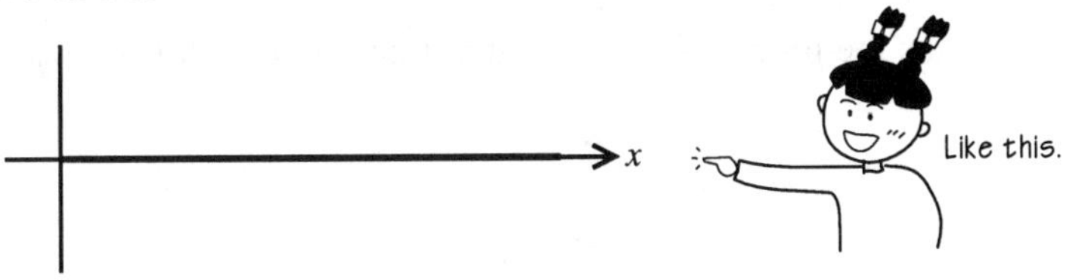

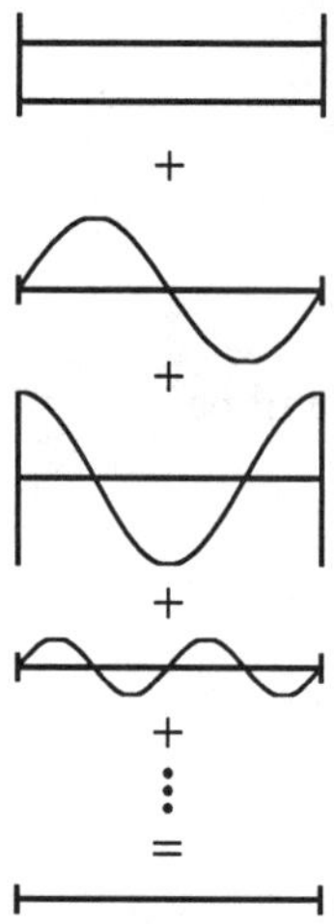

Can you really get a wave of 0 by taking the sum of simple waves? You're right. With the exception of one special case, it is impossible! That special case is when the respective simple waves are all 0. That is to say, when their amplitudes are 0. In that case, for the equation

$$\sum_n \left(-i2\pi\,\nu_n C_n(t) - \frac{\partial\, C_n(t)}{\partial\, t} \right) \phi_n = 0$$

to be true, the amplitude of ϕ_n must be 0. Therefore, we have

$$-i2\pi\,\nu_n C_n(t) - \frac{\partial\, C_n(t)}{\partial\, t} = 0$$

Some of you may have forgotten what we've done so far, so let's take a moment to review. We used $C_n(t)$ to initially express the terms for time in order to confirm whether the terms for time in ψ really were in the form $e^{-i2\pi\nu_n t}$, but in fact we already know $C_n(t)$ from the above equation!

If we transpose $-i2\pi\nu_n\, C_n(t)$ and then multiply both sides by –1, we get

$$\frac{\partial\, C_n(t)}{\partial\, t} = -i2\pi\,\nu_n C_n(t)$$

What this equation says is that when the first derivative of $C_n(t)$ with respect to time is taken, the $-i2\pi\nu_n$ in front will emerge once more to resume a form of its own. Then if $C_n(t)$ is to satisfy this equation, it becomes. . .

$$\boxed{C_n(t) = A_n e^{-i2\pi\,\nu_n t}}$$

A_n is the appropriate real number, and it will be the amplitude when the equation is normalized.

After all, $\dfrac{\partial e^{\square t}}{\partial t} = \square\, e^{\square t}$

This completes the proof. We have found that the term for time ψ really is

$$e^{-i2\pi\,\nu_n t}$$

In other words, whatever the complicated electron wave ψ may be, it can be expressed as

$$\psi(x, y, z, t) = \sum_n A_n\phi_n(x, y, z, t) \cdot e^{-i2\pi\nu_n t} \quad !$$

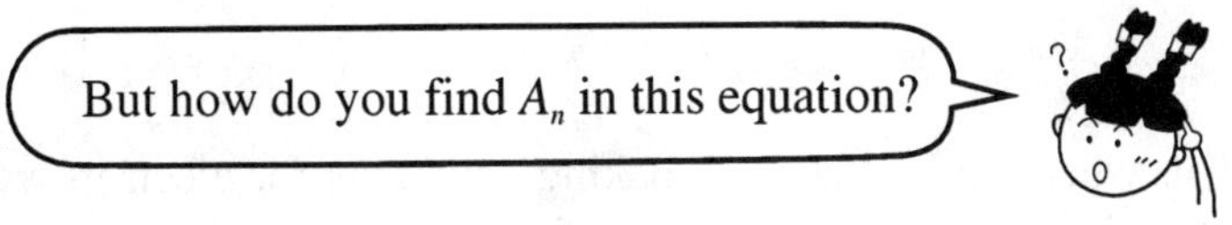

LET'S FIND AMPLITUDE A_n

Having found the term for time ψ, let's find amplitude A_n from ψ for a complicated electron wave. As we saw earlier in the expansion theorem, no matter what form $f(x)$ takes, the amplitude A_n of $\phi_n(x)$ may be extracted in the following manner.

$$A_n = \int f(x)\phi_n^* dx$$

We can do that because $f(x)$ is the sum of simple waves ϕ_n, and may be expressed as

$$f(x) = \sum_n A_n\phi_n$$

Now then, it may be a bit abrupt, but let's look at how $\psi(x, t)$ can be expressed when $t = 0$.

$$\psi(x, 0) = \sum_n A_n\phi_n \cdot e^{-i2\pi\nu_n \cdot 0} = \sum_n A_n\phi_n$$

$$\psi(x, 0) = \sum_n A_n\phi_n = f(x)$$

This means that although in general $\psi(x, t)$ is a function of both time and space, here $\psi(x, 0)$ is a function of space only. Thus we can think of it in the same way as we did the previous $f(x)$.

In that case

$$A_n = \int f(x)\phi_n^* dx$$
$$= \int \psi(x, 0)\phi_n^* dx$$

we have found that amplitude A_n of eigenfunction ϕ_n at this time $t = 0$ can be expanded from $\psi(x, 0)$ of a complicated electron wave.

LET'S REVIEW!

Let's look back over what we have done up until this point. First, we found ν and ϕ from

$$\nabla^2\phi + 8\pi^2\mathfrak{M}(\nu - \mathfrak{V})\phi = 0$$

Next, we found complicated electron wave ψ by obtaining a sum in the following way.

$$\psi = \sum_n A_n \phi_n e^{-i2\pi\nu_n t}$$

Come to think of it, when we first started making equations for electron waves, we went to great trouble to produce the equation for complicated electron waves.

$$\nabla^2\psi + 4\pi i\mathfrak{M}\frac{\partial \psi}{\partial t} - 8\pi^2\mathfrak{M}\mathfrak{V}\psi = 0$$

In the end, however, we ended up not using it.

Why didn't we use the equation for complicated electron waves in Steps 1-4, instead of only using the equation for simple electron waves? Others may be wondering the same thing. The reason is that

COMPLICATED WAVES ARE THE SUM OF SIMPLE WAVES!!

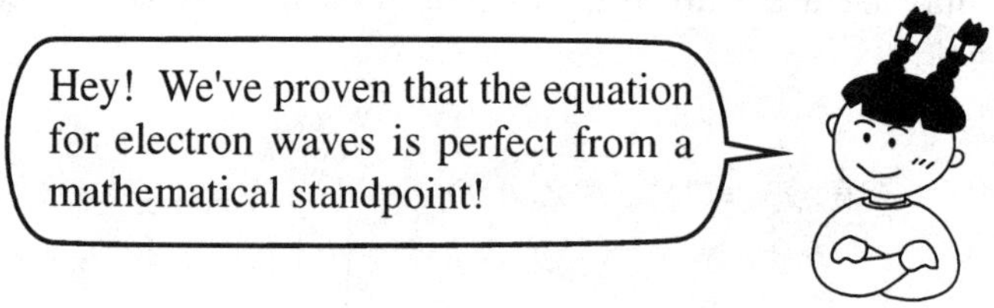

CONCLUDING WITH DE BROGLIE AND SCHRÖDINGER

To conclude, let's look back over what de Broglie and Schrödinger accomplished. Starting from the inspired thought, "Could electrons, which have been considered particles up until now, be described in the language of waves?" De Broglie hammered together a theory stating that electrons are waves.

Using that theory as a base, Schrödinger developed an equation for electron waves. Then, in order to confirm that his equation described what occurs in nature, he succeeded in figuring out the hydrogen atom. In doing all this, the mathematics used in his equation was beautifully concise.

But that was not all. An important consideration was whether a mental image of the electron's behavior inside the atom could be produced. This was not possible with the knowledge available at the time, but Schrödinger's theory made it possible to **HAVE A VISUAL IMAGE!!**

IT WAS MATHEMATICALLY PERFECT,
THE CALCULATIONS WERE CONCISE
AND A VISUAL IMAGE COULD BE PRODUCED.

Schrödinger built a perfect **EQUATION FOR ELECTRON WAVES!**

Schrödinger started with the premise that a visual image was necessary. With that firmly in his mind, he went boldly ahead to construct a theory that fulfilled the basic premise. By now there can be no doubt that electrons are waves. So indeed,

DE BROGLIE'S LAGNIAPPE

BASIC PREMISE OF THE NICOTINE EFFECT

The people around you are more affected by nicotine than you, the smoker.

HIPPO MULTILINGUAL ACTIVITIES AND THE NICOTINE EFFECT

People within earshot of a language tape playing in the background unconsciously absorb more of the sounds than people who are listening intently to the tape. This is because people who are intently listening are often driven to distraction by the effort of learning the words.

THE NOBEL PRIZE AND THE NICOTINE EFFECT

I, Louis de Broglie, got the idea of the nicotine effect for physics from my elder brother Maurice, who was a physicist. I approached physics as a hobby and ended up winning the Nobel Prize. Incidentally, although my elder brother was a co-researcher, he did not receive the prize.

Later, after my brother's death, the title of duke came rolling along, too.

That's marvelous. . .

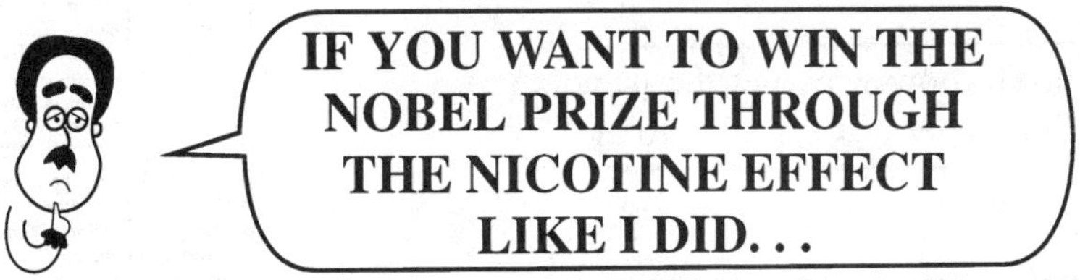

Step 1. You need something to act as the "nicotine". Without it there can be no "nicotine effect". Walk right into a place like TCL where you are likely to get such an effect, and just stay there!

Step 2. It's important to speak out, and you've nothing to lose. So don't be shy!

Like saying, "Electrons are waves!"

Warning:

If you start with some outlandish notion such as, "I'm going to win the Nobel Prize through the nicotine effect theory!" you will not meet with success.

You need to be cool and unfazed to the bitter end!

P. S.

For those who still want a Nobel Prize, going all out like Schrödinger isn't a bad idea!!

THE ADVENTURES OF THE DE BRO(GLIE)–SCHRÖ(DINGER) TEAM

The adventure of quantum mechanics started when a team formed. In the Paris-Dakar motor race, the mechanic, driver, navigator, support personal, etc. are all part of a team. No one can make it through the desert unless the team stays together. Teamwork is everything. In fact, the adventure has already started when the team is formed.

But the difference between us and the Paris-Dakar race is that our teams are determined purely by chance. Practically all TCL students choose their groups by whim. At any rate, when the project announcements are put up on the walls of the school, the students form groups as they please.

Planck, Einstein	Boxer, Ken, Miki, Goyuri, Kanoko, Manju
Bohr	Chibo, Mitoyo, Gotaro, Meenyo, Otake, Penpen
Heisenberg	San-chan, Pero, Yuko, Ricky, Hyon
de Broglie Schrödinger	Dorami, Tamayan, Jirusa, Bucci, Tomakomai, She-chan
Schrödinger	Hana, Jun'O, Osamu, Mari-e, Shenbei
Born Heisenberg	Saru, Ko'shee, Miyaki, Kiyomi, Furuta, Chiyon'mi

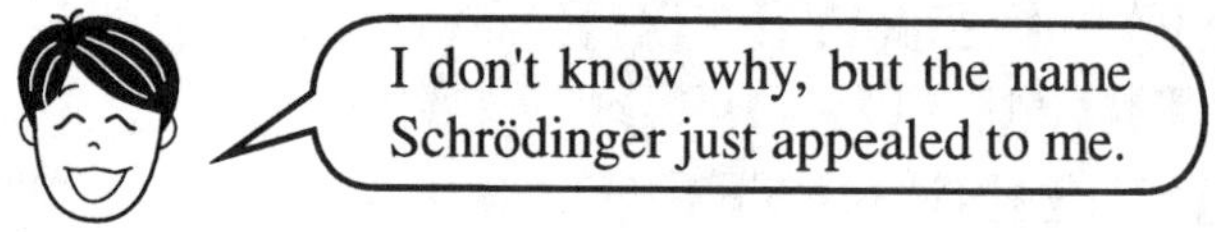

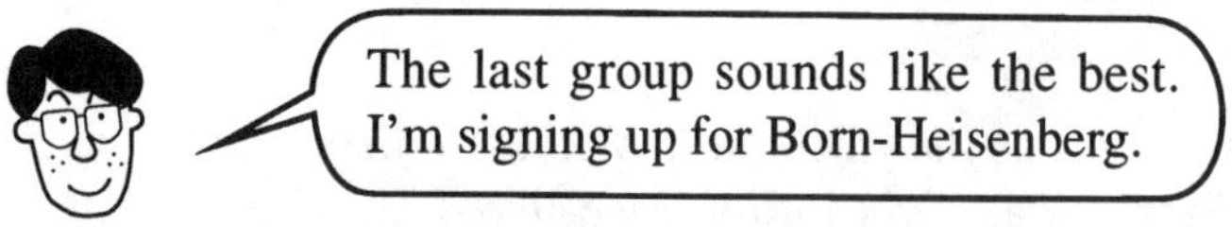

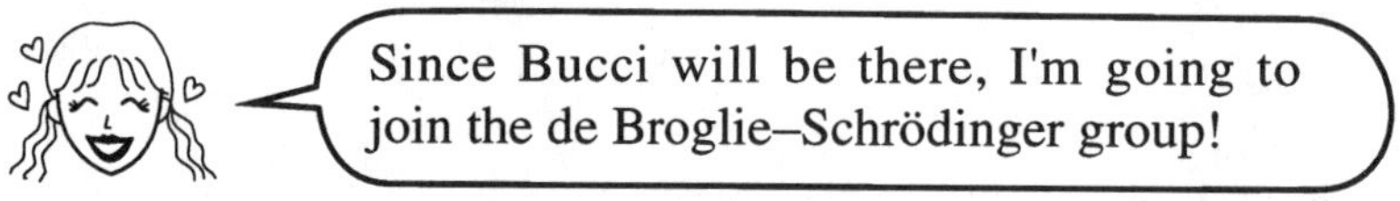

I decided to join the de Broglie–Schrödinger group this time.

By the way, students at TCL love abbreviations.

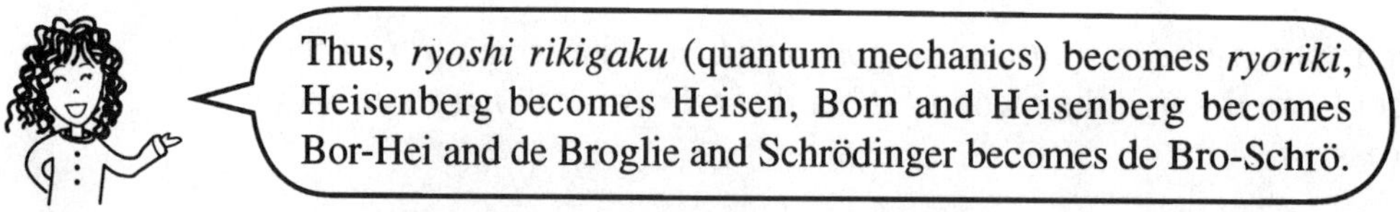

Our de Bro–Schrö group consisted of the students She-chan, from TCL's first class in 1984; Penpen, who entered in 1985; Shenbei and Soyurita, who entered TCL in 1986; Patti (myself), who entered in 1987; Tamyan, who entered in 1988; Jirosa and Muño, who entered in 1989; Doctor Bucci and Dorami, who entered in 1990; and our coordinators, Mr. Senbe and Ms. Tomakomai.

Despite the fact that all of us – from the first-term students to the coordinators – were placed together simply by chance, we launched ourselves into the project as a unified team.

The members began by deciphering some explanatory material on racing cars written in a foreign language. That is, we began deciphering the official guidebook, the pilot edition of *What is Quantum Mechanics? A Physics Adventure*, written by students who had preceeded us at TCL. We understood some parts, but there were a great many things we didn't understand. In fact, it would probably be more accurate to say we didn't understand most of it.

After reading the material, we set about making a car, that is, making our own equations. It was a matter of going by the explanations provided to see what fit and what didn't. We discussed what each of us believed he or she had found.

One of us might demonstrate the de Broglie wave in free space, while another would talk about the diffraction of light. It was as if one were rolling tires around while someone else was trying to explain how to make an engine. I wondered if an automobile actually can be made like this, with no formal guidelines.

After a while. . .

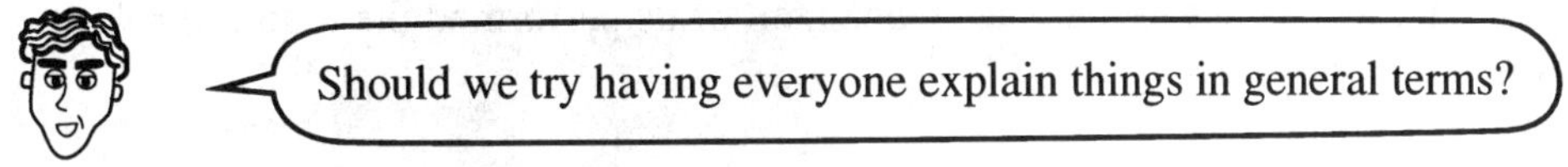

For the time being, let's try to form an image of the de Bro–Schrö racer.

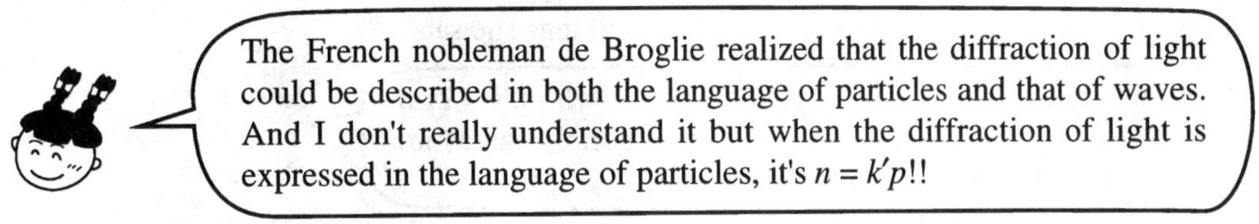

That's the kind of explanations people gave. Statements like "Although I don't really understand," or "Let's assume the calculations have been done," or "Skip this part," were all common. To make an analogy, it was like having a car without a tire or a steering wheel.

In spite of that, through everyone's efforts we gradually come to form an image of de Broglie–Schrödinger. Though we may have encountered many difficulties along the way, they were all happily challenged!

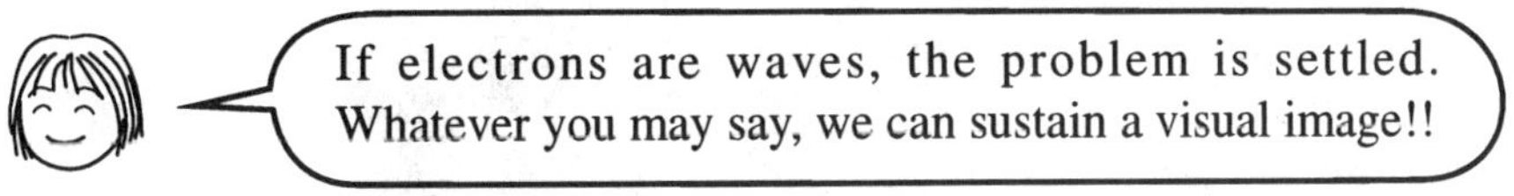

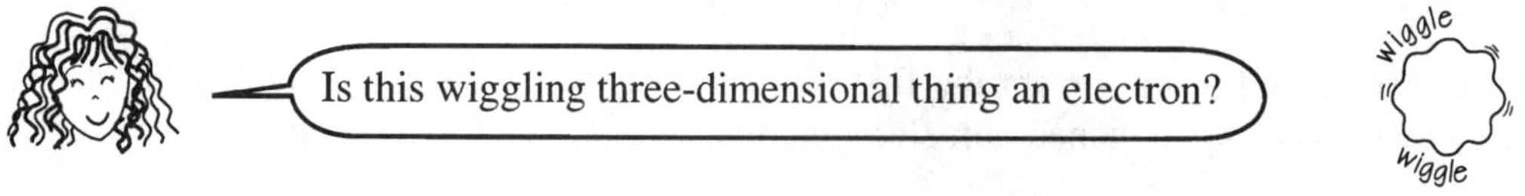

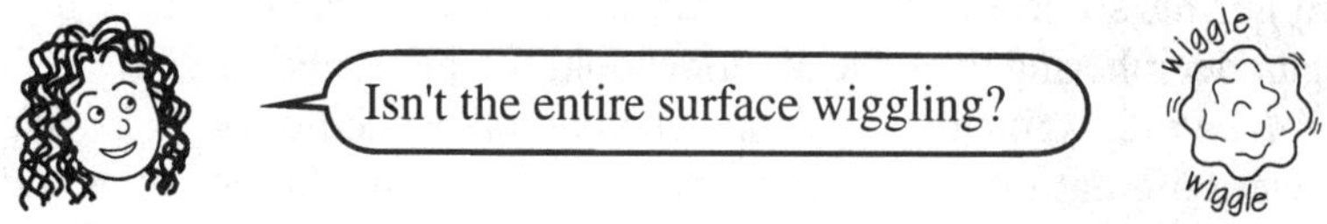

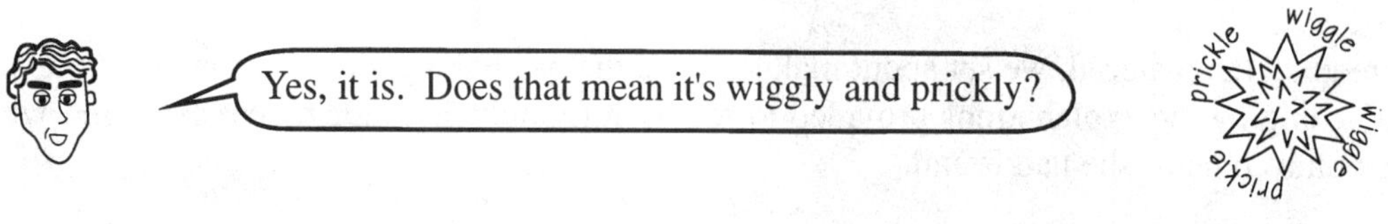

It's not like this and it's not like that. Yak yak blab blab. . . Problems were solved step by step, and we eventually formed a complete picture of what de Broglie and Schrödinger attempted. From the driver, navigator and mechanics to the Race Queen, all of us performed the required roles. We could run this car in a real race. . .

And now for the real thing.

Ms. Tomakomai urged us on, doing cheers and leading pep rallies. She actually started at Paris as one of the drivers. Wearing a swimsuit with high-cut legs she sang,

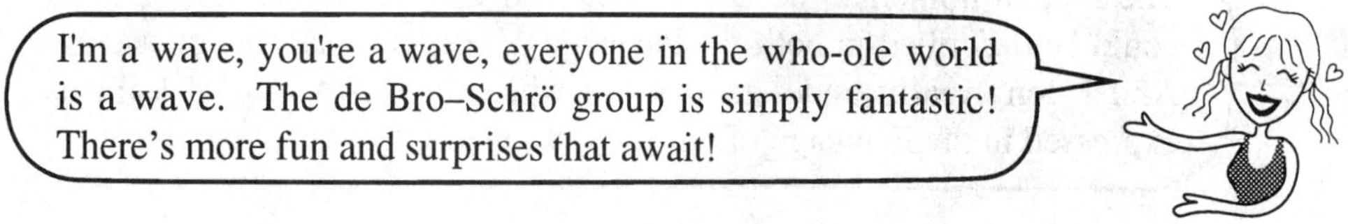

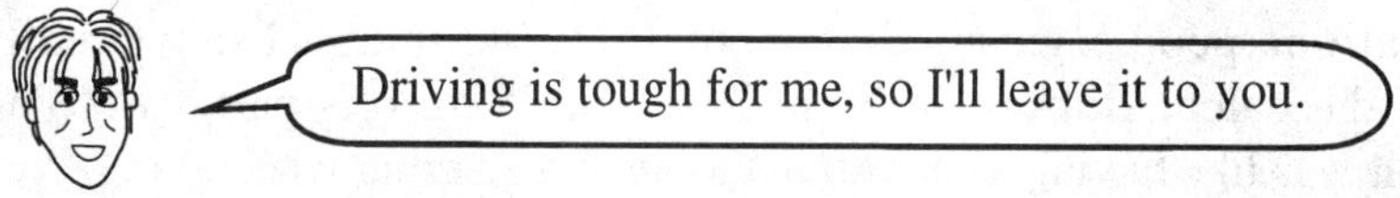

Even Dr. Bucci, who knew very little about mechanics, made it across difficult spots in the desert demonstrating exquisite driving technique. At first he was quite surprised to find himself suddenly thrown onto the unfamiliar race course.

Even Tamayan, who was practically forced into handling the steering wheel, ran beautifully. When it came time for second-termer Jirosa and first-termer Dorami to run, their daring was brilliant. As for my role in all this, I also got to handle the steering wheel. On the appointed day, I was able to slither across that daunting desert. We had so much fun because we were riding in the de Bro–Schrö racer that we had all built together with everyone cheering us on.

The process by which our de Bro–Schrö group went about our adventure is actually quite similar to what happens in a Hippo Family Club. During Hippo Club gatherings, languages are learned in a fun-filled atmosphere where everyone sings and dances and sends words flying about. When one person learns to say new words, it follows that everyone else learns to say them too. Language is something which naturally develops between people as they interrelate with one another. Since quantum mechanics is also a language – an exquisite language that explains nature – it should come as no surprise that this language is learned in the same way.

The only sad thing about our adventure in quantum mechanics is that the de Bro–Schrö group will be dissolved once the project comes to an end!!

The words of first year student Dorami expressed everyone's feelings. That's how wonderful the de Bro–Schrö team was. We will be very happy if all of our readers have this much fun when they read about our adventures with de Broglie and Schrödinger in *What is Quantum Mechanics? A Physics Adventure*.

CHAPTER 5

Erwin Schrödinger

SO LONG, MATRIX!

Schrödinger could not accept Heisenberg's conclusion that it was impossible to form a visual image of electrons. To refute it, he used the idea that electrons are waves to construct a language that would describe their behavior. Schrödinger's hard work and determination bore fruit, and with his marvelous new language, Heisenberg's matrix mechanics was no longer needed.

5.1 SEEKING A VISUAL IMAGE

INTRODUCTION

I'm a Transnational College of LEX (TCL) student, too. I love Hippo! It's wonderful! With just eleven new words I can sing the language of math just fine. Of course it wasn't like that from the start. Before I entered TCL, I was a common, ordinary girl and like so many other people, disliked physics and mathematics. "So how did you come to like them?" you ask. I think you'll understand if you go through this adventure with me. Along the way, you'll probably have many of the same feelings that I had.

Well, let's get going!

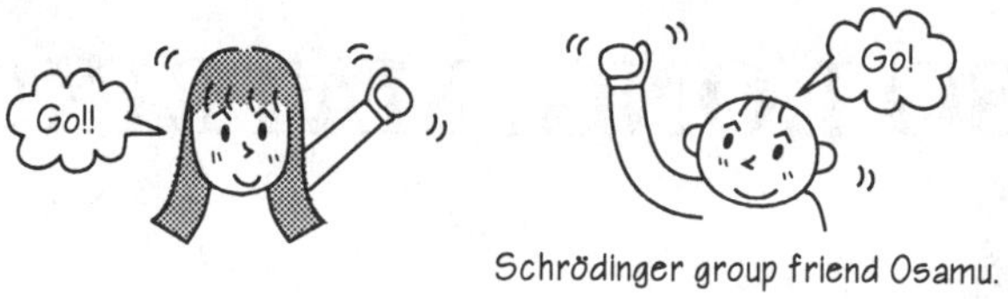

First take a look at this. It's a map of where we've been so far. We've certainly met a lot of different people.

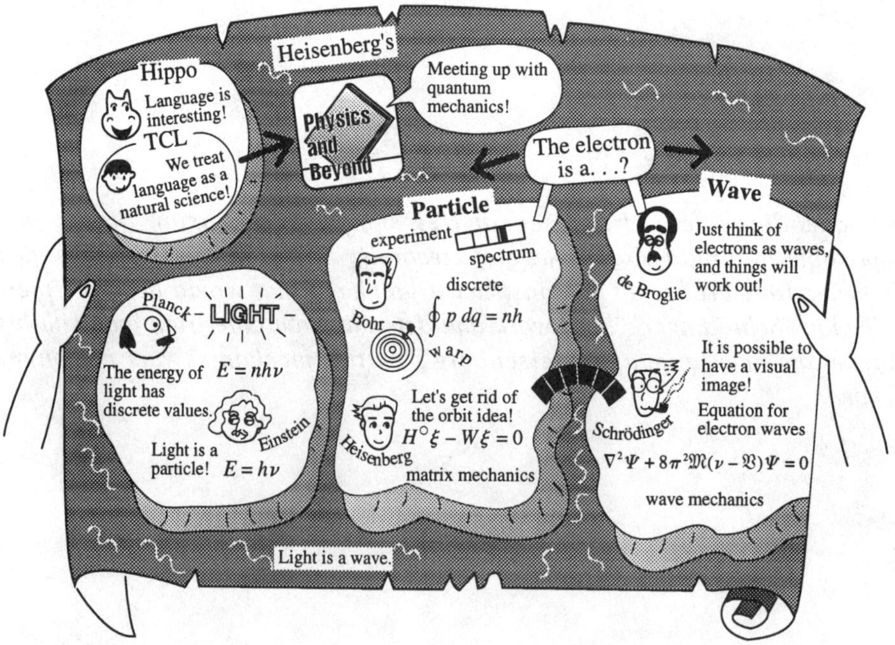

What in the world got us started on quantum mechanics at TCL? Well, it all began with a book by Heisenberg called ***Physics and Beyond.***

You don't have to take any tests or anything to enter TCL, but there is one book called *Physics and Beyond* that our Dean asks us to read.

The conversations between Heisenberg, who formulated matrix mechanics, and the physicists he encountered in the course of constructing quantum mechanics, such as Bohr and Einstein, are recorded in this book.

When I started it, knowing nothing about quantum mechanics, I was totally lost. But after reading and rereading it bit by bit, I got interested. I wanted to know what Heisenberg and the other physicists did, and what quantum mechanics was. That was the beginning.

But why would they read a book written about quantum mechanics at TCL?

That's a good question. Even I feel like I've only recently begun to understand.

Apparently, the thrust at both Hippo and TCL is **treating language as a natural science** — something that left me completely baffled. Only after entering TCL did I begin to see that natural science is the search for a language to describe nature. And physics is certainly a part of natural science.

Newton, Galieo Galilei and all the others were looking for a language that could explain natural occurrences in a single expression.

Galilei, Galieo
[1564-1642]

"Why do apples fall?"

"How and why does the earth revolve around the sun?"

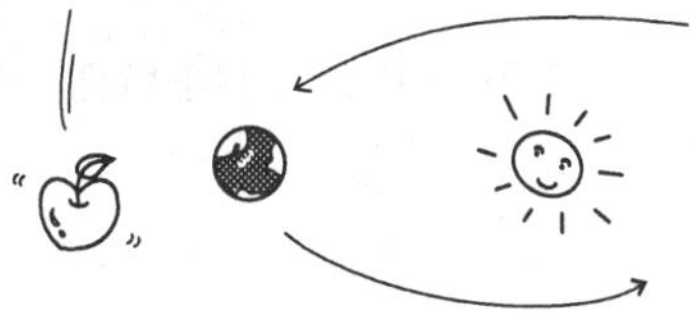

It was a matter of doing experiments and making observations over and over again and identifying an underlying regularity or order, and then expressing that order in terms that would make sense to anyone, anywhere in the world.

Things fall because the earth has a force that pulls them toward its center!

When you consider that everything on this earth is being pulled by that force, then you can express the movements of everything by that one term.

$$F = m\ddot{q}$$

$\ddot{q}$ is the acceleration.
In other words,
Force = mass × acceleration

This language used in physics is **the language of MATHEMATICS**, common to all nations and understood by anyone. What a surprise that mathematical equations have turned out to be the language used to describe nature! My image of math was a collection of meaningless formulas, and memorizing them was just a dull chore. But when I realized that math is a human language shared by all nations, created to describe nature, it quickly acquired a strong, personal importance for me. Math is also something that many people have struggled hard to develop. It has a drama all its own!

It's the same with quantum mechanics. What you discover after studying

is that *What is Quantum Mechanics? A Physics Adventure* is about the search for a language to describe the natural world of light and electrons, a world we cannot see with our eyes alone. And we are now right in the middle of the adventure.

I see what you mean. I think I understand a little better why we're doing quantum mechanics at TCL. Quantum mechanics is the search for a language to explain the electron. We're trying to understand how language itself is constituted so that we can identify the underlying order and find a way to express it in a single term.

"How do babies learn to talk? What is the process of that natural development?"

"I wonder why Japanese has five vowels."

How wonderful if we could describe these things using a single expression! Just as people are creations of nature, language too is a natural phenomenon. So they are really the same thing:

THE SEARCH FOR A LANGUAGE TO DESCRIBE NATURE.

At any rate, if we can relive, even a little, the way physicists discovered a language to describe nature, it will be a great help later when we are thinking about **LANGUAGE** at TCL and Hippo. More than anything else, however, the idea of searching for a language together with the physicists is to me one of the most exciting and interesting adventures anyone could hope for.

Now we are going to go on a search for language with none other than Mr. Schrödinger. We're going with him to find a language that describes the behavior of atoms.

I'm coming along too! . . . But before that, I'd like to look back at that map of our adventure to see the path we've traveled so far.

OUR PATH SO FAR

Before the door to quantum mechanics was opened, physicists believed that the phenomena we observe — a ball being thrown, an apple falling, sound being transmitted, iron sticking to a magnet, and so on — could be completely explained by the language of Newtonian mechanics and Maxwell's electromagnetics. Even if some things could not be clearly explained, the physicists believed that eventually they would be understood.

But no matter how they tried, **TWO** things remained that could not be neatly explained using that language.

One was **LIGHT;** the other was the **ATOM.**

Planck and Einstein came up with various theories regarding light. We won't be discussing those here in detail. But Schrödinger, who we're accompanying in our search for a language, took up the matter of the atom. Let's look at how physicists regarded atoms until then.

At that time, physicists wanted to find a language to explain the **behavior of the electrons inside an atom,** but the problem was that the electron could not be observed by the human eye. They wanted to find out about things that you can't see directly, and they wondered how to do it. Actually, there was a way to discover things about atoms. That was the spectrum of the light emitted by an atom.

The spectrum of the hydrogen atom

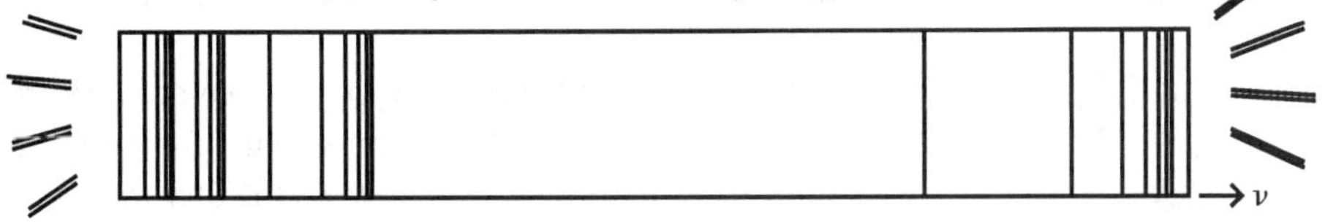

In short, when energy is applied to an atom, light is emitted.

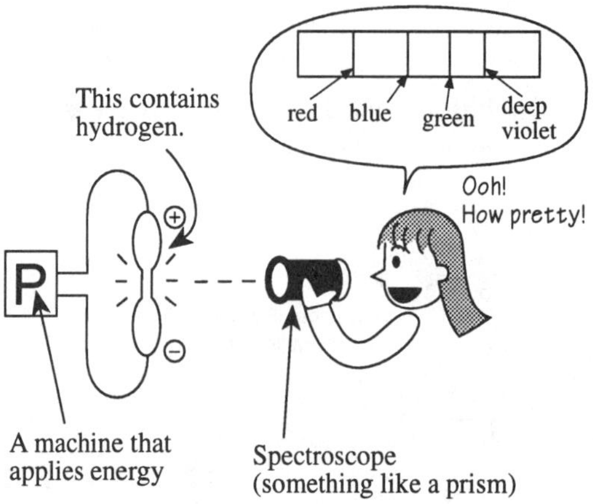

I actually saw this in an experiment. When energy is added to a glass tube containing hydrogen, oxygen or helium inside, hydrogen glows pink, oxygen glows pale violet, and helium glows whitish or yellowish.

When you look at it through a spectroscope, the light that you thought was one color appears to be divided into a number of colors. Those colors are the spectrum of the light emitted by the atom.

Based on the premise that **ELECTRONS ARE PARTICLES,** first Bohr and then Heisenberg were able to find a "language" that could describe the spectrum.

That turned out to be the famous **HEISENBERG'S MATRIX MECHANICS.**

$$H(P^{\circ}, Q^{\circ})\xi - W\xi = 0$$

Using this equation, they could accurately calculate the frequencies and intensities of the spectrum of the light emitted by an atom. That's pretty great!!

However, Heisenberg had this to say:

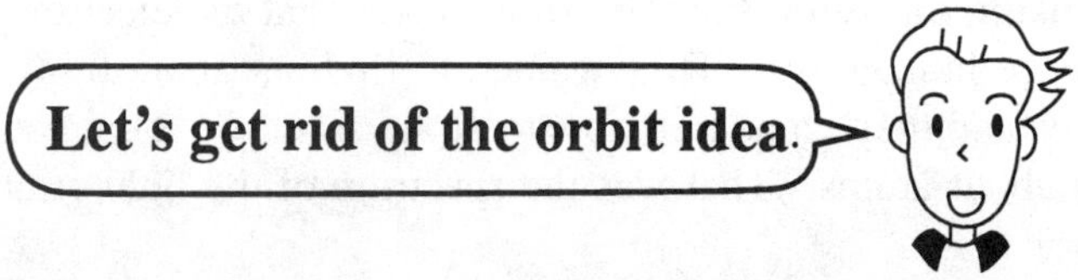

That is to say, **"DON'T TRY TO ENVISION THE FORM AN ELECTRON TAKES, OR THE MANNER IN WHICH IT MOVES!"**

What a thing to say! From the start, our purpose in trying to explain spectra was to find a language to describe the behavior of electrons. Just as we were finally on the verge of being able to explain spectra, how could anyone even suggest that we toss out all thought of how electrons behave?

But Heisenberg defended himself.

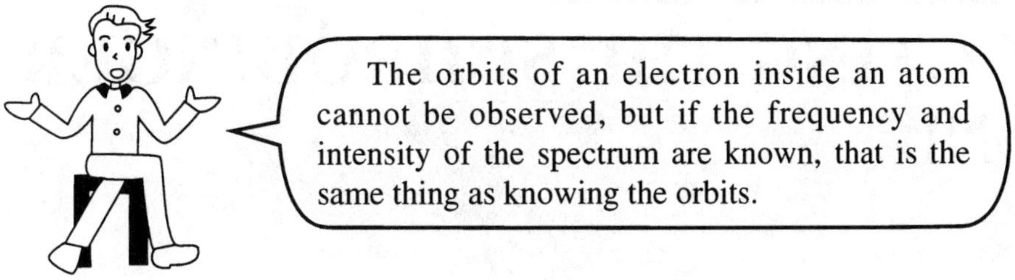

BUT, that statement is absolutely not acceptable!

As we said in the beginning, the intent of physics is to find a language that can express the behavior of things at a certain time.

However, if we were to accept Heisenberg's words,

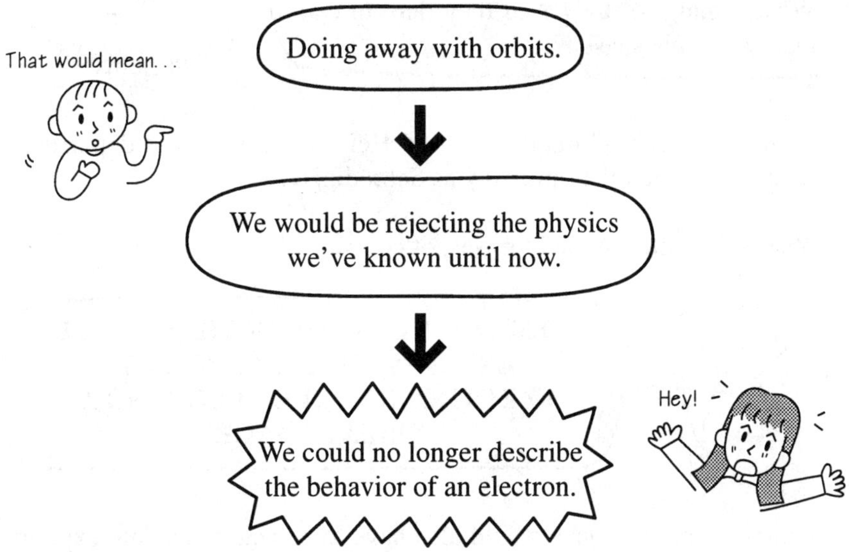

This is just not acceptable! We can't simply toss out accepted knowledge of physics.

5. 2 CONSTRUCTING THE SCHRÖDINGER EQUATION!

DOING AWAY WITH HEISENBERG

The one person who would not allow such a thing was **ERWIN SCHRÖDINGER**.

I simply **can't understand** Bohr's thinking on atomic spectra!
Jumping electrons?
Nonsensical! And according to Heisenberg, **we can't have a visual image!?** Ridiculous! What a thing to say! And they dare to call themselves physicists!?

In this way Schrödinger overruled Heisenberg's absurd departure from common sense. I felt the same way as Schrödinger.

What Schrödinger hoped for was, of course,

TO MAKE A LANGUAGE THAT COULD EXPRESS THE BEHAVIOR OF ELECTRONS WHILE ALLOWING A VISUAL IMAGE!

Naturally, that language would also have to be able to explain experiments. After all, experiments are the only method we have to confirm whether or not a language conveys reality. But no matter how well it might explain experiments, or anything else, physics that does not allow one to form visual images is not necessarily valid. . .

Nevertheless, why do you suppose Schrödinger was so concerned with visual images?

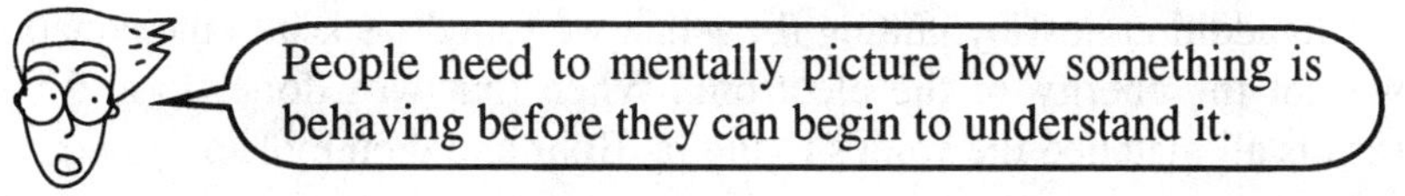

This is what Schrödinger said. In other words,

TO HAVE A VISUAL IMAGE (FORM A MENTAL PICTURE) = TO UNDERSTAND

NOW, in the previous chapter we saw that as long as Schrödinger held to de Broglie's novel way of thinking that

his efforts to produce an equation to describe the state of an electron proceeded admirably. Let's look again at the splendid equation formed by Schrödinger, based on the idea of electrons as waves.

$$\nabla^2\phi + 8\pi^2\mathfrak{M}(\nu - \mathfrak{V})\phi = 0$$

If everything in the world is thought of in terms of waves, then this equation can be applied to any of these waves. If this equation is solved,

THE FORM, THE MOVEMENT AND THE BEHAVIOR OF ANY ELECTRON WAVE WHATSOEVER MAY BE PERFECTLY DESCRIBED.

So this is a very special equation! By using it, we really did succeed in deriving ϕ (the form) and ν (the frequency) for electrons in free space, within a box, and in a field which is ruled by Hooke's law. In other words, this equation succeeded in explaining the behavior of an electron, something that Heisenberg failed to do!!

In addition, just by putting the ν that we found back into the equation $E = h\nu$, we got the energy of the electron. When that was done, lo and behold, the results all matched the values found by Bohr and then by Heisenberg.

Everyone recognized that the values found for energy from Heisenberg's and Bohr's equations were undoubtedly correct. And since it produced the same answers, the language Schrödinger devised — his mathematical expressions — was also correct!

We did it!

It's exactly what we predicted!

This is the road we have traveled so far...

So in other words, by using either Schrödinger's equation or Heisenberg's equation, **the values found for energy are the same.** That means that both Schrödinger's and Heisenberg's equations are correct!

Wait! Hold on a second. That's a bit strange. When I think back carefully, Heisenberg's equation ended up being unable to sustain a visual image, and thus it was impossible to say that electrons are particles. But his equation started from that idea that **electrons are particles.** In contrast, Schrödinger's equation started from the idea that **electrons are waves.**

WAVE and **PARTICLE** are two utterly incompatible ways of thinking. When you think about it, it's strange that the energy found by either one of these approaches is the same.

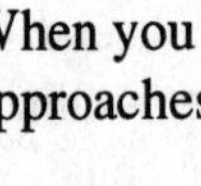

That's true, isn't it? One would think that either Heisenberg's equation, which used the language of particles, or Schrödinger's equation, which used the language of waves, is the true language describing electrons.

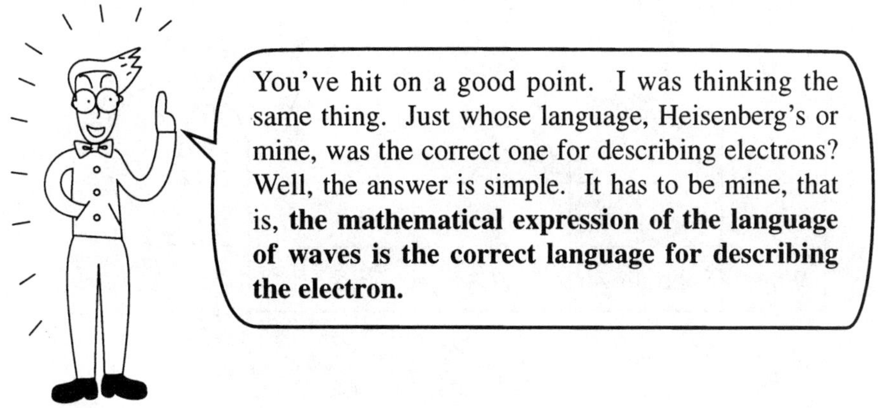

 Gasp. How can you say such a thing?

 Because I can form a **VISUAL IMAGE.** That means I can describe the behavior of the electron.

 Hmm, I see. We want to know what's happening with an electron, but we can't mentally picture its behavior with Heisenberg's equation. No matter how well it matches the experimental results, if it can't explain anything about the electron itself, such a language is meaningless and has some serious deficiencies.

 I agree. On the other hand, Schrödinger's equation really does describe the state of an electron inside an atom. In other words, Schrödinger's equation, which uses the language of waves, is correct!

 You guys are pretty good. Try figuring out for yourselves what we should do next. I'll excuse myself for a while.

 Wa-ait! . . . Oh well, he's gone already. So what we've got to do now is pretend that we're Schrödinger and think about the next step.

 Let's put the story in order. At present there are two equations that can describe the behavior of electrons. One is Schrödinger's, which uses the language of waves; the other is Heisenberg's, which uses the language of particles. Either one will produce the same value for energy.

When we look at this in the form of a table. . .

		Visual image	Energy
Particle	Heisenberg	NO	YES W
Wave	Schrödinger	YES	YES E

The correct language is most certainly Schrödinger's equation, the one that allows a visual image.

Somehow Heisenberg's equation now seems like a nuisance, doesn't it? I wonder if we can do away with it somehow.

What are you saying? You do recall that Heisenberg's equation describes the experimental results perfectly.

Gosh, this is tough. With my brain, I haven't got a clue. Maybe we should give up the search for a language describing electrons and leave this to the physicists.

What are you saying? If you think that way, we'll end up not being able to find a language to describe "language" here at TCL. We are all involved in thinking about language, so we're natural scientists too, in a small way. We shouldn't give up.

You're right. So let's study the table once again. Let's see, what if. .

Huh. . .?

Looking at the table, Heisenberg's equation seems to work well only when it expresses the part of Schrödinger's equation that relates to energy.

Mmm, right. What it means is that **the language of particles is subsumed in the language of waves,** and as a result, everything is expressed in the language of waves!

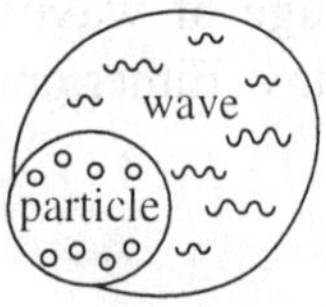

If we can say that, then we can also say

WE DON'T NEED HEISENBERG'S EQUATION.

We'll be able to proudly state that, as a language for describing electrons, Schrödinger's equation alone is more than sufficient. Can we say, then, that the reason why energy W derived from Heisenberg's equation is the same as Schrödinger's energy E is because Heisenberg's equation can be placed inside Schrödinger's equation?

That's a good idea, but I wonder if it'll work.

Heisenberg's equation	Schrödinger's equation
$H(P^{\circ}, Q^{\circ})\xi - W\xi = 0$	$\nabla^2\phi + 8\pi^2\mathfrak{M}(\nu - \mathfrak{V})\phi = 0$

Can we at least find the relationship between the two equations?

Just how are we to take these apparently dissimilar equations and state that Heisenberg's equation can be placed inside Schrödinger's?

Boy, I'd like to discuss this with someone very smart.

You're working at it, aren't you?

Well, Mr. Schrödinger.

I thought the same thing. One of my close friends, Hermann Weyl, is a mathematical genius. He helps me out whenever I run into differential equations. Let's discuss it with him.

Weyl, Hermann
[1885-1955]

It is said that Schrödinger asked Weyl to clarify the relationship between these two equations.

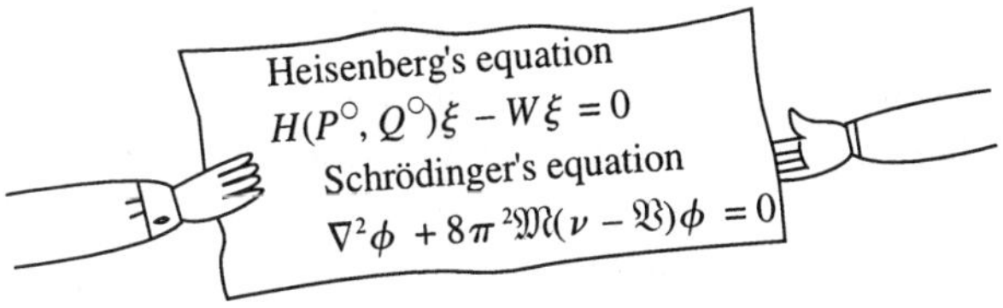

However, genius Weyl's reply was, "I hate to say it, but I couldn't do it either. I apologize for being unable to help." Exactly what he said is not known, but in any event, he was unable to please Schrödinger.

Even the genius Weyl can't do it. Sniff.

It's too much for us after all. Darn.

Are you people going to be deterred by something like that!? If you were natural scientists who gave up so easily, you'd never find a true theory! My esteemed teacher, the great Professor Einstein, would have said the same thing.

WHEN A QUESTION IS POSED THE RIGHT WAY, THE PROBLEM IS HALFWAY SOLVED.

This is a cardinal principle in natural science, and as you continue to think about language, this will be very important. If the question is not properly posed, you will not find the right answer no matter what you do.

You can say that about anything, you know. Thinking about language, for example, very few people learn to speak English just by studying the grammar that is taught in classes at schools. The students get depressed and start to hate English. You could say it's a matter of approaching the problem the wrong way. Schools have lost sight of the way children naturally acquire language. If they would follow the path of nature, anyone ought to be able to learn it.

Absolutely. At Hippo Family and TCL the way a problem is approached is indeed important, isn't it?

That's right. With that in mind, if we recall the way we asked the question, the problem that we posed to ourselves was:

HOW DO WE DESCRIBE THE BEHAVIOR OF ELECTRONS?

There's no mistaking it. No matter how you approach it, the relationship between my equation and Heisenberg's will be discovered, and it will become clear that Heisenberg's equation can be included in my equation. And then we ought to be able to do away with Heisenberg's equation. I know that's what will happen. We just have to forge ahead with that belief.

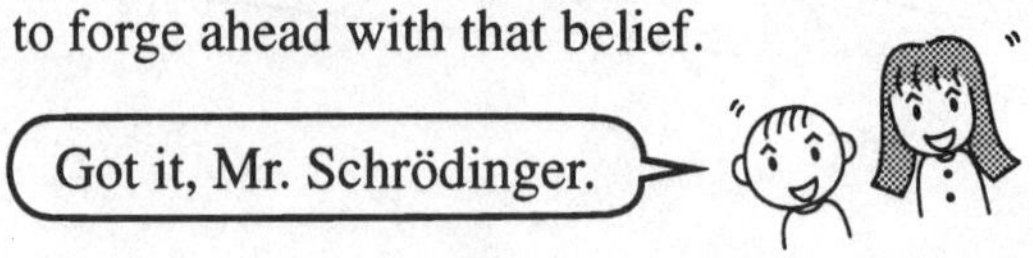

Okay, I think you already have it down, but let's state our objective. Go ahead, say it again.

Right. Okay, let's press on!

THE FORM OF THE EQUATIONS WILL BECOME THE SAME!

Even as we say it, I wonder how we can find the relationship between these two apparently dissimilar equations:

$$H(P^{\circ}, Q^{\circ})\xi - W\xi = 0 \qquad \nabla^2\phi + 8\pi^2\mathfrak{M}(\nu - \mathfrak{B})\phi = 0$$

You get dizzy looking at them.

To repeat, we're looking at two languages here. And we know that Heisenberg's equation is insufficient. But the ***E* and *W* found in the two equations are the same.**

The way things stand, it looks hopeless. That makes me feel even dizzier.

That's it. Everything is much too vague as it is now. What if we think in terms of a concrete situation?

Huh!?

We can imagine various situations, like inside a box or in free space. How about it?

Let's consider **THE CASE WHEN AN ELECTRON FOLLOWS A HOOKE FIELD** (that is, when there is a force being applied that draws toward the center), or in the language of particles, **HARMONIC OSCILLATION**.

The reason we do this is that the *E* derived from Schrödinger's equation is not the same as the *W* derived from Bohr's equation, which is now held to be incorrect. Instead, it agrees with the correct *W* derived from Heisenberg's equation.

Hmm. I don't really understand, but I think it's good to consider the energy in Schrödinger's and Heisenberg's equations, and how they are the same, by looking at concrete examples. By the way, this has been bothering me for a while, but why do *W* and *E* have different symbols, when they mean the same thing, energy?

Don't worry about that. I think that's just how they distinguish the energy found from Schrödinger's equation, called *E*, from Heisenberg's energy, *W*. Anyway, we shouldn't let trivial things like this hold us up.

All right, now we're going to put both equations in the form of Hooke fields, or harmonic oscillation!

For those of you who get dizzy when looking at mathematical expressions, there's no need to feel overwhelmed. As you try repeating them while thinking of them as words of a language, you will gradually be able to "recite" them just like you do with the Hippo tapes. It's a wonderful feeling to be able to "recite" them. I know, because I've done it! Just "recite" the language of mathematical expression along with us. The meaning will eventually dawn on you, out of the blue. Anyway, let's look at things from the broad point of view and work our way through them.

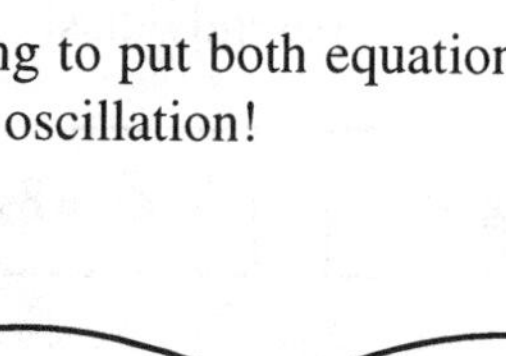

APPLYING HEISENBERG'S EQUATION TO THE FORM FOR HARMONIC OSCILLATION

Heisenberg's equation

$$H(P^{\circ}, Q^{\circ})\xi - W\xi = 0$$

H (the Hamiltonian) is a method of describing the energy using P (momentum) and Q (location). Writing this in detail, we get:

$$H(P^{\circ}, Q^{\circ}) = \frac{1}{2m} P^{\circ 2} + V(Q^{\circ})$$

V is potential energy. Potential energy changes with location; in other words, it is a function of position Q°.

So, writing it out, Heisenberg's equation at the top of the page becomes:

$$\left\{\frac{1}{2m} P^{\circ 2} + V(Q^{\circ})\right\}\xi - W\xi = 0$$

The potential energy in the case of harmonic oscillation $V(Q^{\circ})$ is $\frac{1}{2} kQ^{\circ 2}$. Thus Heisenberg's equation may be rewritten in the following way:

$$\left(\frac{1}{2m} P^{\circ 2} + \frac{k}{2} Q^{\circ 2}\right)\xi - W\xi = 0$$

APPLYING SCHRÖDINGER'S EQUATION TO THE FORM FOR HOOKE FIELDS

Schrödinger's equation

$$\nabla^2\phi + 8\pi^2\mathfrak{M}(\nu - \mathfrak{V})\phi = 0$$

First, using $\mathfrak{V} = \frac{V}{h}$, $\mathfrak{M} = \frac{m}{h}$ and $\nu = \frac{E}{h}$, we replace the potential energy V above with an equivalent term. When we do so, we get:

$$\nabla^2\phi + 8\pi^2\frac{m}{h}\left(\frac{E}{h} - \frac{V}{h}\right)\phi = 0$$

Factoring out $\frac{1}{h}$, we get:

$$\nabla^2\phi + 8\pi^2\frac{m}{h^2}(E - V)\phi = 0$$

V is the same for Hooke fields and harmonic oscillation. In other words, whether an electron is a particle or a wave, the energy applied to it is the same. Thus when we substitute, in the same way as before, $\frac{1}{2}kx^2$ in place of V, we get:

$$\nabla^2\phi + 8\pi^2\frac{m}{h^2}\left(E - \frac{1}{2}kx^2\right)\phi = 0$$

Let's compare Schrödinger's equation, rewritten in this way, with Heisenberg's equation as we just rewrote it:

$$\left(\frac{1}{2m}P^{\circ 2} + \frac{k}{2}Q^{\circ 2}\right)\xi - W\xi = 0$$

Looking at them like this, I still don't see that we've clarified the relationship between these two. It has turned out to be difficult after all.

I don't think we can compare the relationship between these two unless we somehow place them in a more **SIMILAR FORM.** I'm not sure if that's possible, but if we fiddle around with Schrödinger's equation as we just rewrote it, then perhaps we can put it into a comparable form.

All right. Let's try and see if we can do it. We're going to bring Schrödinger's equation into a form more like Heisenberg's, right? It's interesting, much like trying to solve a quiz or a puzzle.

ALIGNING SCHRÖDINGER'S EQUATION FOR HOOKE FIELDS WITH THE FORM OF HEISENBERG'S EQUATION

Schrödinger's equation for Hooke fields

$$\nabla^2\phi + 8\pi^2\frac{m}{h^2}\left(E-\frac{1}{2}kx^2\right)\phi = 0$$

To make the story simpler, let us think of ∇^2 $\left(=\frac{\partial^2}{\partial x^2}+\frac{\partial^2}{\partial y^2}+\frac{\partial^2}{\partial z^2}\right.$: the second-order derivatives in three dimensions) with respect to the x dimension only.

$$\frac{d^2}{dx^2}\phi + 8\pi^2\frac{m}{h^2}\left(E-\frac{1}{2}kx^2\right)\phi = 0$$

Comparing this equation to Heisenberg's, one notices that E and W are the same and that they have the number $-\frac{k}{2}$ in common. One suspects that by making use of this, they can probably be made into the same form.

Heisenberg's equation for harmonic oscillation

$$\left(\frac{1}{2m}P^{\circ 2}+\frac{k}{2}Q^{\circ 2}\right)\xi - W\xi = 0$$

Here we see a minus sign (–) in front of W, but no coefficient. In the other equation, there is a plus sign (+) and the complicated coefficient $8\pi^2\frac{m}{h^2}$.

So that means, in order to erase the coefficient in front of E and change the sign, we multiply by $-\frac{h^2}{8\pi^2 m}$ and get:

$$-\frac{h^2}{8\pi^2 m}\frac{d^2}{dx^2}\phi - \left(E - \frac{k}{2}x^2\right)\phi = 0$$

Removing the parentheses and changing the order a bit, we get:

$$-\frac{h^2}{8\pi^2 m}\frac{d^2}{dx^2}\phi + \frac{k}{2}x^2\phi - E\phi = 0$$

Now we factor ϕ out of the first two. Hmm. . .
This looks quite a bit like Heisenberg's equation!

$$\left(-\frac{h^2}{8\pi^2 m}\frac{d^2}{dx^2} + \frac{k}{2}x^2\right)\phi - E\phi = 0$$

Looking closely, you see that the symbols used are a bit different, but if we factor $\frac{1}{2m}$ out of one more term, the form becomes even more similar.

Okay, let's factor out $\frac{1}{2m}$. When we do, we come up with:

$$\left\{\frac{1}{2m}\underline{\left(-\frac{h^2}{4\pi^2}\frac{d^2}{dx^2}\right)} + \frac{k}{2}x^2\right\}\phi - E\phi = 0$$

If we make this into (something)^2, then they become even more alike.

$-1 = i^2$, and $\frac{d^2}{dx^2}$ is $\frac{d}{dx}\cdot\frac{d}{dx}$, so the equation above is:

$$\boxed{\left\{\frac{1}{2m}\left(\frac{h}{2\pi i}\frac{d}{dx}\right)^2 + \frac{k}{2}x^2\right\}\phi - E\phi = 0}$$

BANG! Schrödinger's equation has turned into this form!

And when we look and see what Heisenberg's equation is,

$$\left(\frac{1}{2m}P^{\bigcirc 2}+\frac{k}{2}Q^{\bigcirc 2}\right)\xi - W\xi = 0$$

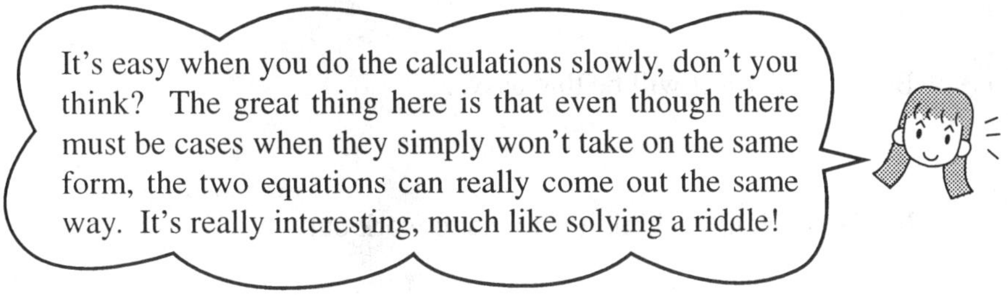

COMPARING SCHRÖDINGER'S EQUATION WITH HEISENBERG'S

Let's look at the contents a little more closely.

$$\left\{\frac{1}{2m}\underline{\left(\frac{h}{2\pi i}\frac{d}{dx}\right)^2} + \frac{k}{2}\underline{x^2}\right\}\underline{\phi} - \underline{E}\phi = 0$$

$$\updownarrow \qquad \updownarrow \qquad \updownarrow \qquad \updownarrow$$

$$\left(\frac{1}{2m}\boxed{P^{\bigcirc}}^2 + \frac{k}{2}\boxed{Q^{\bigcirc}}^2\right)\boxed{\xi} - \boxed{W}\xi = 0$$

When we look at them like this, the symbols are completely different. However, to say something is in the same place but in a different form is the same as tying the two, underlined parts and □ , together as is done above. We know that E and W are the same thing.

Hey, listen. Maybe. . .

If we could say that $\overset{\circ}{P}$, $\overset{\circ}{Q}$, ξ were all originally Schrödinger's $\frac{h}{2\pi i}\frac{d}{dx}$, x, ϕ, then we won't need Heisenberg's equation! Won't Schrödinger's equation alone be sufficient?

 But I wonder if it will be that easy. . .

 It'll be all right! I think it's bound to work out.

 You're probably right. Well then, let's first recall just what all those symbols were. If we don't know what they are, we won't be able to do a thing.

Quiz: Remembering the Symbols ?

Write what you know in the ☐

	Name	What is it?
P°, Q° is?		
ξ is ?		
W and E are?		
ϕ is?		
$\frac{h}{2\pi i}\frac{d}{dx}$ and x are?		

Now just what was the P°, Q° in Heisenberg's equation?

Have you forgotten already? It's a **MATRIX**.

Oh, right. 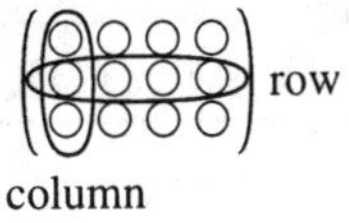

It's numbers gathered together like this in rows and columns.

ξ is a **VECTOR.**

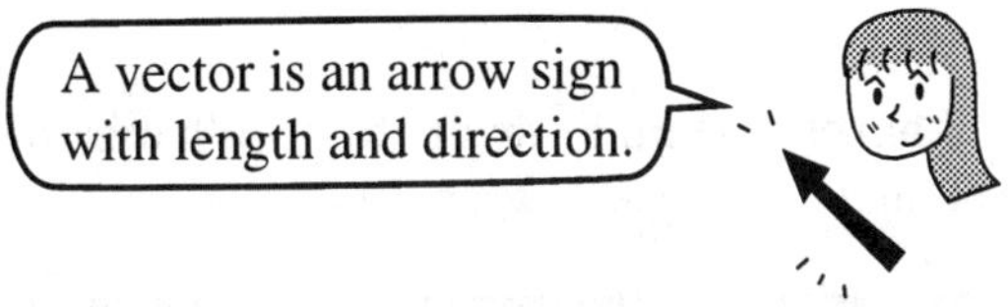

W and *E* are **ENERGIES.** There's no problem there. But what is ϕ?

It was **A FUNCTION OF LOCATION** (x, y, z) although now we're just using x. Anyway, it's a function, something that tells you ϕ if you know x.

I wonder then what the $\frac{h}{2\pi i}\frac{d}{dx}$ and x that correspond to the matrices P°, Q° are? There's probably a way of **EXPRESSING IT IN ONE WORD.**

$\frac{d}{dx}$ is a differentiation symbol, $\frac{h}{2\pi i}$ can be called a number, and x is position. You're now going to put all this together and give it a name? Oh dear, I won't know what's what anymore! How about everyone else? What could that name possibly be? If there is someone who knows, tell me POR FAVOR!

Ha ha ha!! You've come along pretty well, haven't you?

I mulled this over quite a bit too. And then, one particular bit of math that I had heard somewhere before suddenly came to mind.

Well, I've listened to the mathematics tapes a few more times than you folks. Listening to those tapes sure turned out to be a useful thing.

Operator. . ? I haven't heard of that before. What is this operator that Schrödinger is talking about?

What's an OPERATOR?

You take something like $\frac{d}{dx}$ or $\int dx$, and like $A \times$, you

~take the derivative
~take the integral
~multiply by the number A

It's something that only involves an **OPERATION.**
(By themselves operators have no meaning; they first gain meaning when they are applied to a function.)

I see. So an operator is something that is applied to a function.

Now, let's separate them neatly so they're easy to distinguish, and put them in a table!

	Heisenberg		Schrödinger	
Rows and columns	P°	——	$\dfrac{h}{2\pi i}\dfrac{d}{dx}$	Operator
	Q°	——	x	
Vector	ξ	——	ϕ	Function
Energy	W	$=$	E	Energy

As we've said before, since these things are the same, if we can begin with Schrödinger's equation, and from that construct Heisenberg's, then we don't need Heisenberg's equation at all. But it looks like this is a big "if." No matter how you look at it, here's a matrix on one side, and an operator on the other. Here's a vector on one side, and a function on the other, all very different things. It's not going to work like this.

Try looking at all this a little more broadly. If you pay too much attention to the details, you'll lose sight of the whole. If you focus on a single pistil in a field of flowers, you won't sense the beauty in the whole field, but if you step back a bit and gaze over it, you'll appreciate the beauty of all the flowers. It's quite an experience!

FIND THE FEATURES COMMON TO BOTH OPERATORS AND MATRICES!

As is written in the chronicles of our adventure, **AN OPERATOR ACQUIRES MEANING WHEN IT OPERATES ON A FUNCTION.**

I'd like to see what that means in more concrete terms.

OK!

OPERATOR PLAZA

Dramatis personae: Operator $\frac{d}{dx}$ Function x^2

The operator $\frac{d}{dx}$ can't do a thing all by itself.

But, if you try applying it to the function x^2,

$$\frac{d}{dx} x^2 = 2x$$

(a new function called $2x$ is produced)

What this means is, $\frac{d}{dx}$ has the **EFFECT** of turning x^2 into $2x$.
Drawing a graph, we get:

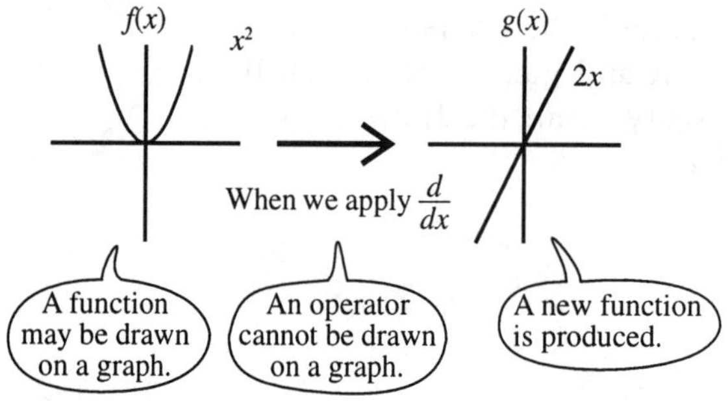

As can be seen,

AN OPERATOR IS SOMETHING THAT, WHEN IT OPERATES ON A FUNCTION, CREATES A NEW FUNCTION.

If we represent the operator as A, the original function as $f(x)$, and the new function as $g(x)$, then the long phrase above can be concisely expressed in mathematical notation as:

$$Af(x) = g(x)$$

In a way, operators are like words. Words by themselves have no effect; you only see their effect if you have an audience present.

For instance, if you say

and no one is around, then nothing happens. Even the meaning of the word "agua" is unclear.

But if you bounce that word off of someone,

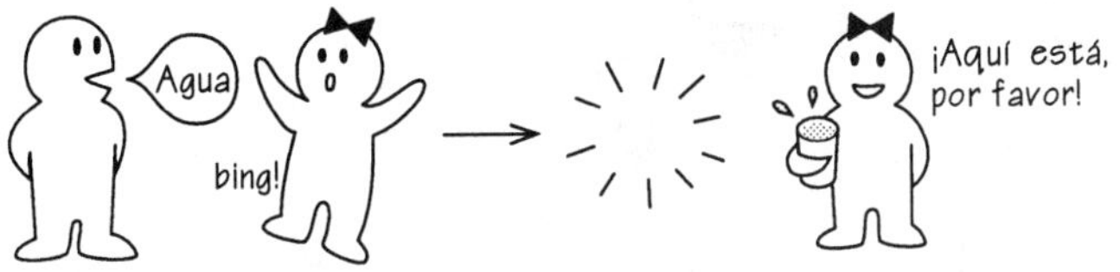

you know from its effect — maybe someone brings you a glass of water  — that agua means water. It's quite similar to an operator.

Be that as it may, the power of **an operator** is that it **produces new functions.**

In Heisenberg's case, matrices worked on vectors. What if we also try looking at matrices?

MATRIX PLAZA

In a nutshell, a matrix is a collection of numbers like this: $\begin{pmatrix} 1 & 5 & 10 & -6 \\ 3 & 2 & -4 & 9 \\ 6 & 4 & 8 & 5 \\ 7 & 14 & 6 & -8 \end{pmatrix}$

A vector is represented by an arrow having length and direction. Its length and direction are extracted and placed within parentheses ( ).

Dramatis personae

Matrix $\begin{pmatrix} 1 & 2 \\ 3 & 4 \end{pmatrix}$ Vector $\begin{pmatrix} 1 \\ 2 \end{pmatrix}$

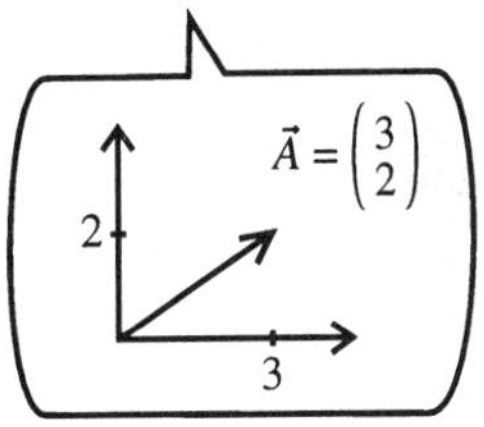

By itself, a matrix is just a collection of numbers whose meaning is unknown.

Only when an operator operates on a function can we tell what its role is.

Let's have this matrix operate on vector $\begin{pmatrix}1\\2\end{pmatrix}$.

$$\begin{pmatrix}1 & 2\\3 & 4\end{pmatrix}\begin{pmatrix}1\\2\end{pmatrix}=\begin{pmatrix}1+4\\3+8\end{pmatrix}$$
$$=\begin{pmatrix}5\\11\end{pmatrix}$$

How about that, a new vector $\begin{pmatrix}5\\11\end{pmatrix}$ has emerged.

The way to multiply rows and columns

$$\begin{pmatrix}A_{11} & A_{12}\\A_{21} & A_{22}\end{pmatrix}\begin{pmatrix}\eta_1\\\eta_2\end{pmatrix}=\begin{pmatrix}A_{11}\eta_1+A_{12}\eta_2\\A_{21}\eta_1+A_{22}\eta_2\end{pmatrix}$$

Incidentally, this can be written as,

$$\zeta_n=\sum_{n'}A_{nn'}\eta_{n'}$$

We need to remember this!

Let's draw a graph just as we did with operators.

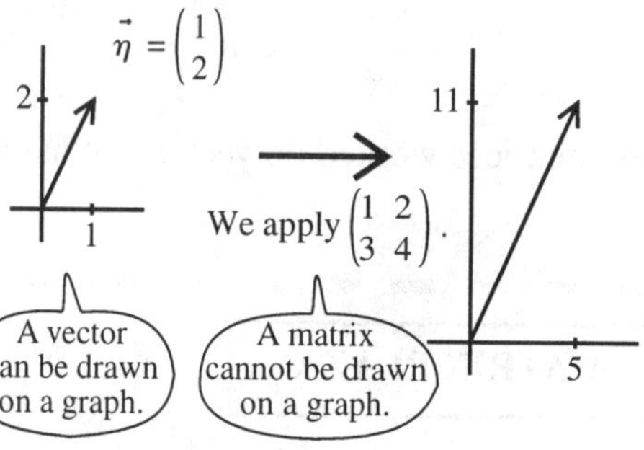

Thus, we may say that,

A MATRIX IS SOMETHING THAT, WHEN IT OPERATES ON A VECTOR, PRODUCES A NEW VECTOR.

When the matrix is set out as A, the vector as η (eta), and the new vector as ζ (zeta), the sentence above turns into the following concise term:

$$A\eta=\zeta$$

So, a matrix has the power to produce a new vector.

At first glance operators and matrices seem to be completely different, but in the sense that they **"BOTH PRODUCE NEW THINGS"**

we can say they're **THE SAME!!**

What that means is,

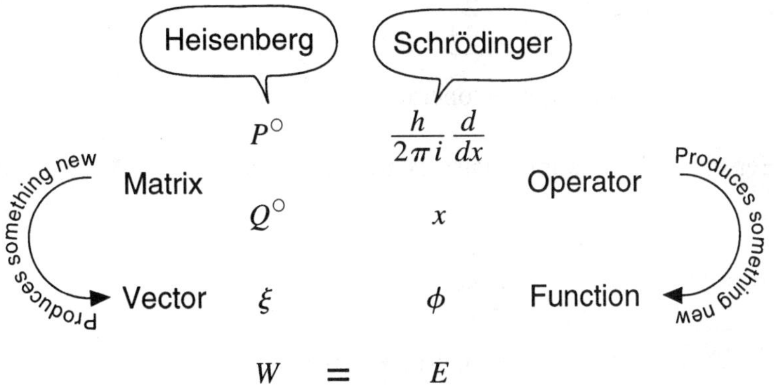

As when we first tackled the question, we have continued to think of Heisenberg's and Schrödinger's languages as totally different, but now we've found a clue suggesting that they are in fact the same. I have a feeling that it will be productive to follow this line of thought.

Yes, but wait a minute. Can we say that so easily? If we compare the two equations,

Schrödinger
$$\left\{\frac{1}{2m}\left(\frac{h}{2\pi i}\frac{d}{dx}\right)^2+\frac{k}{2}x^2\right\}\phi - E\phi = 0$$

Heisenberg
$$\left(\frac{1}{2m}P^{\circ 2}+\frac{k}{2}Q^{\circ 2}\right)\xi - W\xi = 0$$

In both cases, the parts marked by 〰 are multiplied by $\phi(x)$ or ξ.

Looking at each one, we first see that in Schrödinger's equation, the part marked by $\sim\sim\sim$ is a multiplication of operators. That is:

$$\left(\frac{h}{2\pi i}\frac{d}{dx}\right)^2 = \frac{h}{2\pi i}\frac{d}{dx} \times \frac{h}{2\pi i}\frac{d}{dx}$$

$$x^2 = x \times x$$

$$(\text{operator})^2 = \text{operator} \times \text{operator}$$

Besides that, operators are added together:

$$\frac{1}{2m}\left(\frac{h}{2\pi i}\frac{d}{dx}\right)^2 + \frac{k}{2}x^2$$

operator + operator

In Heisenberg's equation, matrices are multiplied:

$$P^{\circ 2} = P^{\circ} \times P^{\circ}$$

$$Q^{\circ 2} = Q^{\circ} \times Q^{\circ}$$

$$(\text{matrix})^2 = \text{matrix} \times \text{matrix}$$

And matrices are added:

$$\frac{1}{2m}P^{\circ} + \frac{k}{2}Q^{\circ}$$

matrix + matrix

If Heisenberg's equation is really contained within Schrödinger's, then the effect of the multiplication and addition of these operators on the function ought to have **THE SAME EFFECT** that the multiplication and addition of the matrices have upon the vector. Don't you agree?

Hmm. . . Is that right? I don't really know, but let's take a look starting from the addition of operators. But wait, how do you add operators?

◆ THE ADDITION OF OPERATORS AND THE ADDITION OF MATRICES

So, you want to **ADD OPERATORS.** Operators are things like $\frac{d}{dx}$ and $\int dx$ that do nothing except operate on, or have **AN EFFECT,** on something else. Can we add them like this?

$$\frac{d}{dx} + \frac{d}{dx} \quad \text{or} \quad \int dx + \frac{d}{dx}$$

Whoa! You know you can't add them together like ordinary numbers. So what do you think we should do?

Look, if you had minded your own business this wouldn't have happened. What are we going to do?

Ha ha ha. It looks like you're in trouble. Actually, I got myself into trouble here, too.

Really? Even you?

Relax. We call it addition of operators, but we don't actually add together a derivative and a derivative, or an integral and a derivative.

Why is it called addition of operators if you don't really add them?

Addition of operators has a specific **DEFINITION.**

Definition?

A definition is something like " ○○○ is □□□." It gives you a fixed meaning for a word.

Well then, what is the definition of "addition of operators"?

Addition of operators A and B
When $(A + B)$ operates on a given function $f(x)$, $(A + B)\,f(x)$, the separate effects of A and B on the function $f(x)$ are added $Af(x) + Bf(x)$.
Thus $(A + B)$ is the sum of the separate effects, not the operators per se.

Hmm. It's a bit tricky, but let me try to explain it. When you see an operator $(A + B)$, you can't calculate anything until it acts upon a function. Then you have to remember that you'll be adding the effects:

$$(A + B)f(x) = Af(x) + Bf(x)$$

Here we are trying to confirm whether the effect on the function in the addition of operators is the same as the effect on the vector in the addition of matrices.

Exactly. Let's look at **ADDITION OF MATRICES.**

Addition of matrices is set up like this:

$$\begin{pmatrix} A_{11} & A_{12} & \cdots \\ A_{21} & A_{22} & \cdots \\ \vdots & \vdots & \end{pmatrix} + \begin{pmatrix} B_{11} & B_{12} & \cdots \\ B_{21} & B_{22} & \cdots \\ \vdots & \vdots & \end{pmatrix} = \begin{pmatrix} A_{11} + B_{11} & A_{12} + B_{12} & \cdots \\ A_{21} + B_{21} & A_{22} + B_{22} & \cdots \\ \vdots & \vdots & \end{pmatrix}$$

You take what's inside the parentheses ( ), which are the elements, and add them up, right?

Yes, it's just as you say. But now we want to know what adding matrices has in common with adding operators, and so we're going to give it a definition, just as we did with addition of operators.

I'll try it. Hmm. . .

> **Addition of matrices A and B**
>
> When $(A + B)$
>
> operates on a given vector η,
>
> $(A + B)\ \eta$,
>
> the individual effects of A and B upon the vector η are added
>
> $A\eta + B\eta$.
>
> Thus $(A + B)$ is the addition of the parts affected by A and B.

Is it something like that?

Beautiful! You've ended up defining it the same way as an operator, didn't you? Which means that, **the effect on a function in addition of operators is the same as the effect on a vector in addition of matrices!**

That's right. Now we're going to do the multiplication too!

◆ MULTIPLICATION OF OPERATORS AND OF MATRICES

Let's attempt a definition for the multiplication of operators, just as we did for their addition.

OK!

Multiplication of operators A and B

When (AB)
acts on a given function $f(x)$,
$(AB)\,f(x)$,
first B is applied to $f(x)$, then A is applied to the resulting function
$A\{Bf(x)\}$.
The two-part operation is condensed into a single operation on $f(x)$.

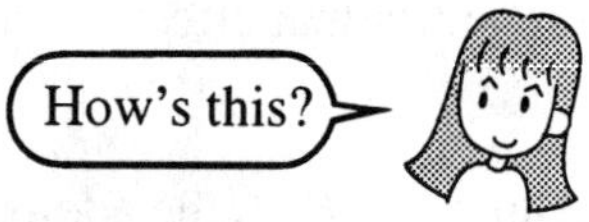

Well done. Indeed it's exactly as you stated.

Now, if we can define the multiplication of matrices in the same way, we'll be in good shape.

That's right. We'll be able to say that the effect on a function in the multiplication of operators is equivalent to the effect on a vector in the multiplication of matrices. I'm going to try it this time.

Multiplication of matrices A and B

When (AB)
is applied to a given vector η,
$(AB)\eta$,
first B is applied to η, then A is applied to the resulting vector
$A(B\eta)$.
Again, the two-part operation is condensed into a single operation on η.

Say, I have a question!

We have defined the multiplication of matrices as

$$(AB)\eta = A(B\eta)$$

but will it work if it is

$$(AB)\eta = B(A\eta)?$$

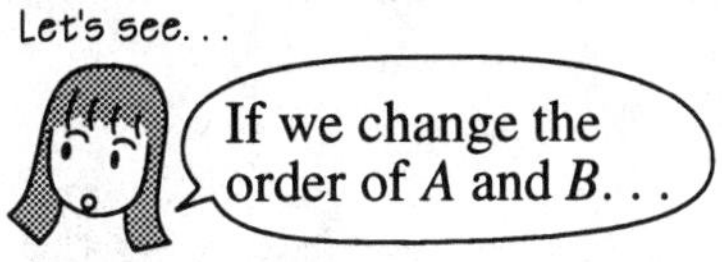

That's a very good point. The order in which operators or matrices are applied is very important. How about trying it out?

Okay. Let's try it first with operators.

When operators $\frac{d}{dx}$ and x act upon the function x^2,

$$\frac{d}{dx}(xx^2) = \frac{d}{dx} \times x^3 = \underline{3x^2}\ .$$

When the order is changed,

$$x\left(\frac{d}{dx}x^2\right) = x \times 2x = \underline{2x^2}\ .$$

That's right. Let's see what happens with matrices.

Apply matrices $\begin{pmatrix}1 & 2\\ 3 & 4\end{pmatrix}$ and $\begin{pmatrix}2 & 1\\ 4 & 3\end{pmatrix}$ to vector $\begin{pmatrix}2\\ 3\end{pmatrix}$ and you get

$$\begin{pmatrix}1 & 2\\ 3 & 4\end{pmatrix}\left\{\begin{pmatrix}2 & 1\\ 4 & 3\end{pmatrix}\begin{pmatrix}2\\ 3\end{pmatrix}\right\} = \begin{pmatrix}1 & 2\\ 3 & 4\end{pmatrix}\begin{pmatrix}4+3\\ 8+9\end{pmatrix} = \begin{pmatrix}1 & 2\\ 3 & 4\end{pmatrix}\begin{pmatrix}7\\ 17\end{pmatrix} = \begin{pmatrix}7+34\\ 21+68\end{pmatrix} = \underline{\begin{pmatrix}41\\ 89\end{pmatrix}}\ .$$

When the order is changed, you get

$$\begin{pmatrix}2 & 1\\ 4 & 3\end{pmatrix}\left\{\begin{pmatrix}1 & 2\\ 3 & 4\end{pmatrix}\begin{pmatrix}2\\ 3\end{pmatrix}\right\} = \begin{pmatrix}2 & 1\\ 4 & 3\end{pmatrix}\begin{pmatrix}2+6\\ 6+12\end{pmatrix} = \begin{pmatrix}2 & 1\\ 4 & 3\end{pmatrix}\begin{pmatrix}8\\ 18\end{pmatrix} = \begin{pmatrix}16+18\\ 32+54\end{pmatrix} = \underline{\begin{pmatrix}34\\ 86\end{pmatrix}}\ .$$

So we find that with matrices also, if you change the order, you get a different result.

I see. Now I know the reason why we made

$$(AB)f(x) = A\{Bf(x)\}$$
$$(AB)\eta = A\{B\eta\}$$

You can't change the order of either one. In other words, **the effect on functions in the multiplication of operators and the effect on vectors in the multiplication of matrices are equivalent!**

With this, we can proudly say that the effect

$$\frac{1}{2m}\left(\frac{h}{2\pi i}\frac{d}{dx}\right)^2 + \frac{k}{2}x^2$$

in Schrödinger's equation has on a function, and the effect

$$\frac{1}{2m}P^{\circ 2} + \frac{k}{2}Q^{\circ 2}$$

in Heisenberg's equation has on a vector, are **THE SAME!**

Now we know that **matrices and operators have the same effect,** but what we really want to know in more detail is whether Heisenberg's matrices P° and Q° and Schrödinger's operators $\frac{h}{2\pi i}\frac{d}{dx}$ and x are the same thing. We know that they're roughly the same thing, but now we have to delve into this a little more deeply.

From generalities to details. . . I think I've heard those words somewhere before.

You definitely have. In any event, let's see if we can really say that $\boldsymbol{P^\circ}$ is the same as $\boldsymbol{\frac{h}{2\pi i}\frac{d}{dx}}$, or that $\boldsymbol{Q^\circ}$ is the same thing as $\boldsymbol{x}$!

Now then, not just any matrix would suffice for Heisenberg's P° and Q°. It had to meet certain **FIXED CONDITIONS.**

LOOKING FOR THE RELATIONSHIP BETWEEN P°, Q° AND $\frac{h}{2\pi i}\frac{d}{dx}$, x

> CONDITIONS FOR HEISENBERG'S P° AND Q°
>
> 1. They satisfy the **canonical commutation relation.**
>
> $$P^\circ Q^\circ - Q^\circ P^\circ = \frac{h}{2\pi i} 1$$
>
> 2. They are **Hermitian.**

In order to claim that Heisenberg's matrices P° and Q°, which fulfill these **two conditions,** were originally the same things as operators $\frac{h}{2\pi i}\frac{d}{dx}$, x, the two operators would naturally have to fulfill the **same conditions,** right? However, since we don't really know what a Hermitian operator is, for the time being let's look at them simply in terms of the canonical commutation relation.

DO THE OPERATORS FULFILL THE CANONICAL COMMUTATION RELATION?

I don't really know what **canonical commutation relation** means. . . But apparently we get this:

$$P^\circ Q^\circ - Q^\circ P^\circ = \frac{h}{2\pi i} 1$$

In Heisenberg's canonical commutation relation, the fact that we had a matrix meant we had to attach unit matrix 1 to $\frac{h}{2\pi i}$. Do you recall this?

For details, please review the Heisenberg section.

Since P° corresponds to $\frac{h}{2\pi i}\frac{d}{dx}$, and Q° to x,

THE EQUATION FOR THE CANONICAL COMMUTATION RELATION IN THE CASE OF OPERATORS

$$\frac{h}{2\pi i}\frac{d}{dx}\cdot x - x\cdot\frac{h}{2\pi i}\frac{d}{dx} = \frac{h}{2\pi i}$$

Isn't it $\frac{h}{2\pi i}1$? So where did the 1 go?

In the case of operators, it simply means "multiply by 1," and so it's all right to omit it.

And if the equation works, it will be all we need. I wonder if it'll work. . .

But that equation has nothing but operators, and so I don't see how we can do any calculations.

Right. We saw in the Operator Plaza (see page 444) that operators only take on meaning when they operate on a function.

Well, in that case, can't we make calculations if we apply $\frac{h}{2\pi i}\frac{d}{dx}\cdot x - x\cdot\frac{h}{2\pi i}\frac{d}{dx} = \frac{h}{2\pi i}$ to a function?

Yes. Now let's first take the left side $\frac{h}{2\pi i}\frac{d}{dx}\cdot x - x\cdot\frac{h}{2\pi i}\frac{d}{dx}$ and apply it to $f(x)$ in such a way that any function will do, and then calculate it.

It would be great if the result turned out to be $\frac{h}{2\pi i}f(x)$ . . .

What's going to happen to $\frac{h}{2\pi i}\frac{d}{dx}\cdot x - x\cdot\frac{h}{2\pi i}\frac{d}{dx}$!?

First, we rewrite it so that we can apply each of the terms to $f(x)$ and then calculate.

$$\left(\frac{h}{2\pi i}\frac{d}{dx}\cdot x\right)f(x) - \left(x\cdot\frac{h}{2\pi i}\frac{d}{dx}\right)f(x)$$

Using the definition of the multiplication of operators, $A\{Bf(x)\} = (AB)f(x)$, we get:

$$= \frac{h}{2\pi i}\frac{d}{dx}\left\{xf(x)\right\} - x\left\{\frac{h}{2\pi i}\frac{d}{dx}f(x)\right\}.$$

Since $\frac{h}{2\pi i}$ is a fixed number, we can factor it out and come up with:

$$= \frac{h}{2\pi i}\left|\underline{\frac{d}{dx}\left\{xf(x)\right\}} - x\left\{\frac{d}{dx}f(x)\right\}\right|.$$

This underlined part is called the derivative of a product!

Formula for the derivative of a product

$$\frac{d}{dx}\left\{f(x)\cdot g(x)\right\} = \frac{d}{dx}f(x)\cdot g(x) + f(x)\frac{d}{dx}g(x)$$

Using this, we have:

$$= \frac{h}{2\pi i}\left|\left(\frac{d}{dx}x\right)f(x) + x\left\{\frac{d}{dx}f(x)\right\} - x\left\{\frac{d}{dx}f(x)\right\}\right|.$$

Since $\frac{d}{dx}x$ (the derivative of x) is 1,

$$= \frac{h}{2\pi i}f(x).$$

This means that,

$$\left(\frac{h}{2\pi i}\frac{d}{dx}\cdot x\right)f(x) - \left(x\cdot\frac{h}{2\pi i}\frac{d}{dx}\right)f(x) = \frac{h}{2\pi i}f(x).$$

Now that we have the results of applying them to a function, if we **extract the actual effect** from our results. . .

$$\frac{h}{2\pi i}\frac{d}{dx}\cdot x - x\cdot\frac{h}{2\pi i}\frac{d}{dx} = \frac{h}{2\pi i}.$$

In other words, we've found that

THE OPERATORS $\frac{h}{2\pi i}\frac{d}{dx}$ AND x BOTH SATISFY THE CANONICAL COMMUTATION RELATION!!

We did it! Doesn't that mean that P° and $\frac{h}{2\pi i}\frac{d}{dx}$, Q° and x, in their essential points, are really the same thing?

We did it!

Hey, you folks are in no position to be celebrating. Our objective here is to determine that

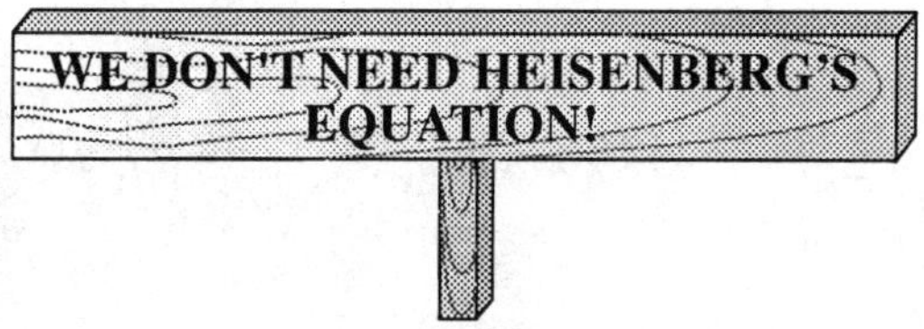

In order to do that, just to say that **their effects are the same** is not enough; we must be able to show that

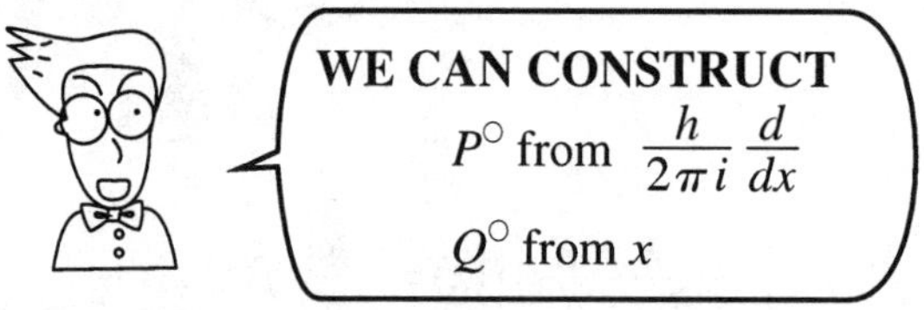

If we can do that, then P° and Q° become unnecessary. Next, we must think about how that can be done. Then, at the end,

I'M GOING TO FORMULATE HEISENBERG'S EQUATION OUT OF MY "SCHRÖDINGER EQUATION"!

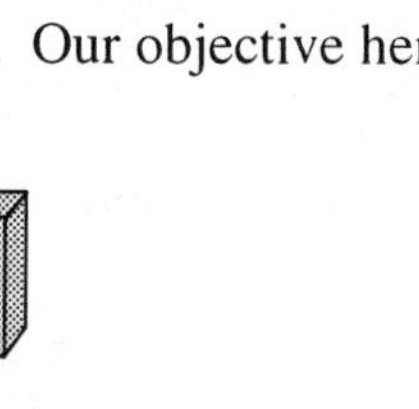

If you say so — but can we really do it?

MAKING VECTORS OUT OF EQUATIONS

What is TCL's *Who is Fourier? A Mathematical Adventure* doing here? I wonder if that's some sort of hint.

You still don't know of a method for making matrices out of operators. Before starting off on this adventure in quantum mechanics, all of you completed the Fourier Adventure, right?

Yes.

Then you must know the chapter in *Who is Fourier? A Mathematical Adventure* called "Projection and Orthogonality" that discusses how to make vectors out of functions.

Oh. . . I guess I've forgotten.

Well then, try to remember **a method for making vectors out of functions** using Fourier mathematics.

When you say Fourier mathematics, that means **a complicated wave is the sum of simple waves.**

Writing this in equation language,

$$f(x) = a_0 + a_1 \cos 1\omega t + b_1 \sin 1\omega t$$
$$+ a_2 \cos 2\omega t + b_2 \sin 2\omega t$$
$$+ \cdots\cdots$$

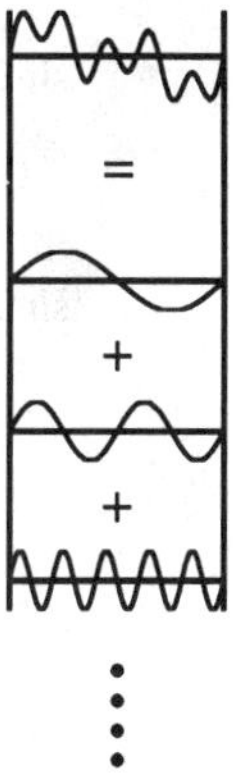

By the way, this means the same thing as
complicated wave = complicated function
simple wave = simple function.

Now then, in each of these simple waves a certain relationship exists between cosine and sine. Do you remember what we call it?

Let's see. . .

They are

Yes, "orthogonal," but it still doesn't ring a bell. The word means that things form a 90 degree angle. But how can two functions (waves) be orthogonal?

Could it be something like this?

No, no. That's not quite right. To say that two **functions are orthogonal** means that "when a certain function is multiplied by a certain other function, **the area of the resulting function is 0.**" Let's take a look.

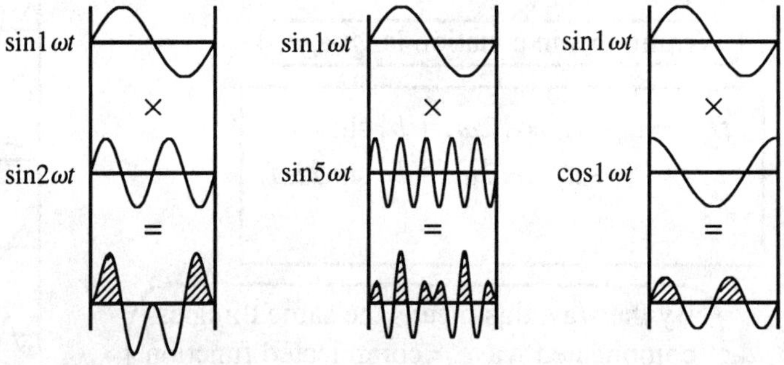

Area = 0
They are orthogonal.

Area = 0
They are orthogonal.

Area = 0
They are orthogonal.

I see. So any kind of a simple wave is orthogonal.

But there is a simple wave that is not orthogonal. Do you know which one that is?

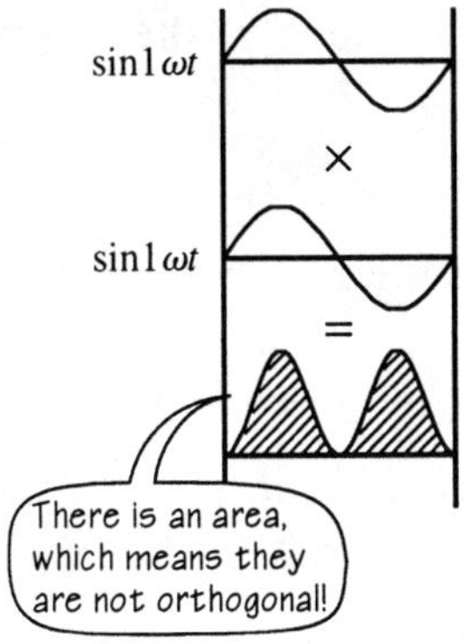

As the diagram at the left shows, simple waves are not orthogonal when they are multiplied by themselves. In other words, when a simple wave is multiplied by itself, the resulting area does not equal zero. So we know that **they are not orthogonal to themselves.**

In this manner, sine and cosine are functions that are orthogonal to everything but themselves. To put it briefly, they are called

A SYSTEM OF ORTHOGONAL FUNCTIONS.

Point

But you can't tell if those functions are orthogonal just by looking at them. Can we write them in such a way that you can tell **at a glance** if they're orthogonal?

Yes, easily. Just put these orthogonal functions on a graph. We place each wave along an axis. As they are mutually orthogonal,

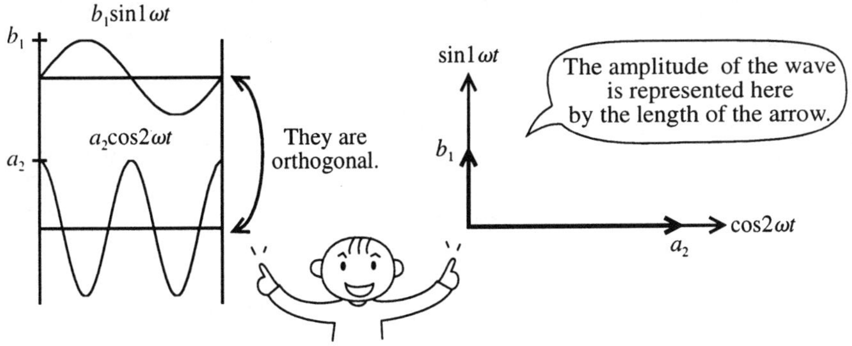

Somehow it seems too easy. But that arrow on the previous graph . . . I mean, isn't it a **VECTOR?!!**

Besides the amplitude of each wave is the length of one of the respective orthogual vectors!

I know how to find the amplitude of waves. That's **Fourier coefficients,** right?

FOURIER COEFFICIENT $a_n = \frac{2}{T}\int_0^T f(t)\cos n\omega t\, dt$

A complicated wave is multiplied by the wave that is to be extracted, and the area is found and divided by $\frac{T}{2}$.

Using this method, we can find the amplitude of any simple wave and we'll be able to find

the length of orthogonal arrows (= vectors).

The sum of the two previous waves makes a complicated wave $f(t)$. Let's try drawing it on this orthogonal graph. I wonder if it'll all work out.

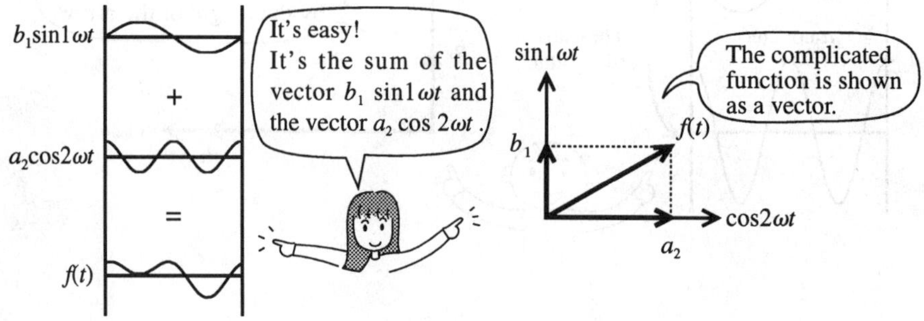

The resulting vector is shown by **lining up their length vertically and attaching parentheses** ( ) as follows:

$$\overrightarrow{f(t)} = \begin{pmatrix} a_2 \\ b_1 \end{pmatrix}$$

If this is 5, enter 5; if it is 3, enter 3.

In other words, when the amplitude of simple waves are aligned vertically and surrounded by parentheses, they become a complicated wave expressed in vectors.

Here we were using the Fourier transformation, and so the system of orthogonal functions was sine and cosine, but there are other systems of orthogonal functions. As long as they are a system of orthogonal functions, they may be anything, so let's put them in a more general form.

In order to turn the ordinary equation for transformation into something that can be used with any system of orthogonal functions. . .

$$a_n = \frac{2}{T}\int_0^T f(t)\cos n\omega t\, dt$$

This is the amplitude of the cosine, so it's a_n.

We make η the amplitude in the case of orthogonal functions.

Here these range are $-\infty \sim \infty$ so we don't have to write anything.

This is now $f(x)$.

We let the general form of systems of orthogonal functions be $\chi_n(x)$. This $\chi_n(x)$ has been normalized, and so it can include $\frac{2}{T}$.

So. . .

If we change the order a bit. . .

THE METHOD OF FINDING ONE OF THE ELEMENTS η_n OF A VECTOR PRODUCED FROM $f(x)$

$$\eta_n = \int \chi_n^*(x) f(x)\, dx$$

The orthogonal function is multiplied by the complicated function whose vector is to be found, and the area is determined.

Here the * symbol indicates that $\chi_n(x)$ can be used when $f(x)$ is a complex function, so you can just disregard it.

When we insert 1, 2, 3 · · · as n, the length of the respective vectors emerge. And when they are surrounded by parentheses,

$$\int \chi_1^*(x) f(x)\, dx = \eta_1$$

$$\int \chi_2^*(x) f(x)\, dx = \eta_2 \quad \rightarrow \quad \begin{pmatrix} \eta_1 \\ \eta_2 \\ \eta_3 \end{pmatrix} = \vec{\eta}$$

$$\int \chi_3^*(x) f(x)\, dx = \eta_3$$

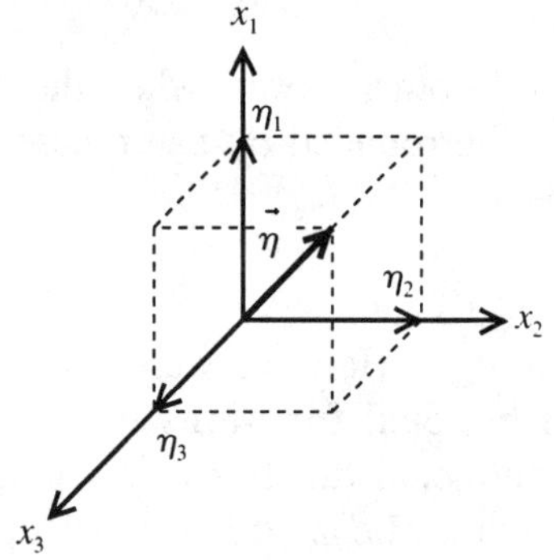

WE DID IT! WE WERE ABLE TO PRODUCE VECTOR $\vec{\eta}$ FROM A GIVEN FUNCTION $f(x)$!

As in the case of vector η from a given function $f(x)$ or vector ζ from a given function $g(x)$, a certain vector can be produced from a single function. By the way, if this is applied in reverse,

A COMPLICATED FUNCTION $f(x)$ IS THE SUM OF SIMPLE FUNCTIONS:

$$f(x) = \sum_n \eta_n \chi_n(x)$$

We were able to make vectors from functions, but we mustn't forget that, in order to do away with Heisenberg's ideas, we have to be able to show that

$$\frac{h}{2\pi i}\frac{d}{dx} \rightarrow P^{\circ} \qquad x \rightarrow Q^{\circ}$$

In other words,

WE WANT TO PRODUCE A MATRIX FROM AN OPERATOR!

That's exactly right. Let's challenge ourselves and produce a matrix from an operator, using the method that we just used to create a vector from a function.

PRODUCING A MATRIX FROM AN OPERATOR

A vector can be produced from a function. You tell us to use this method, but. . . I've got it! For example, we see in

$$Af(x) = g(x)$$

that since we have produced vector η from $f(x)$, it is possible to produce a different vector from $g(x)$. Let us call this new vector ζ(zeta).

$$\zeta_n = \int \chi_n^*(x) g(x)\, dx$$

This $g(x)$ is $Af(x)$,

So we get

$$\zeta_n = \int \chi_n^*(x) A f(x)\, dx$$

If we changed the form of this equation, we might be able to understand the relationship between operators and matrices. Let's try it! This ζ_n is the equation we saw before:

$$f(x) = \sum_n \eta_n \chi_n(x)$$

If we apply the sum of simple orthogonal functions to complicated functions,

$$\zeta_n = \int \chi_n^*(x) A \sum_{n'} \eta_{n'} \chi_{n'}(x)\, dx$$

(To distinguish this from the earlier n, we add a $'$ and read it "n prime.")

Here it's the same thing whether the summation is made with operator A applied to the terms taken as a whole or individually. Thus we can place A inside Σ.

$$\zeta_n = \int \chi_n^*(x) \sum_{n'} A \eta_{n'} \chi_{n'}(x)\, dx$$

Since it doesn't matter whether we do the addition and then the integration, or do the integration and then the addition, we bring Σ to the front.

$$= \sum_{n'} \int \chi_n^*(x) A \eta_{n'} \chi_{n'}(x)\, dx$$

Here we are taking the integral of x, and since $\eta_{n'}$ has no relationship to x, we take it outside of the integration $\int dx$. Then we have. . .

$$= \sum_{n'} \underline{\int \chi_n^*(x) A \chi_{n'}(x)\, dx}\, \eta_{n'}$$

What we've been doing is calculating the magnitude ζ_n of the vector. In other words, the magnitude ζ_n of a vector is:

$$\zeta_n = \sum_{n'} \underline{\int \chi_n^*(x) A \chi_{n'}(x)\, dx}\, \eta_{n'}$$

What? I know I've seen this somewhere before.

I don't remember it at all.

Don't you recall doing the multiplication of matrices and vectors in the Matrix Plaza (see page 445)? This was the one they said was a good thing to remember.

I just looked at what we were encouraged to remember but it was

$$\zeta_n = \sum_{n'} A_{nn'} \eta_{n'}$$

But this one is

$$\zeta_n = \sum_{n'} \underline{\int \chi_n^*(x) A \chi_{n'}(x)\, dx}\; \eta_{n'}$$

They're totally different.

Let's close our eyes to the underlined part and we'll see. . .

$$\zeta_n = \sum_{n'} \underline{\qquad\qquad} \eta_{n'}$$

Hmm. . . If you say they're alike, maybe they are alike.

Couldn't you perhaps consider that the underlined part is one element in matrix $A_{nn'}$? In other words, that it's a certain number?

I suppose so.

In that case, since the underlined part is an integral, it's a value for area. Let's think about what determines that value.

You say area, but the area of what?

If you look at the underlined part, $A\chi_{n'}(x)$ is a new function that results from applying operator A to function $\chi_{n'}(x)$.

$$\underline{\int \chi_n^*(x) A \chi_{n'}(x)\, dx}$$

In other words, it is a new function that resulted from multiplying a complicated function by a simple function. Now then, what will determine the final form of the function? That the value is determined by operator A goes without saying. After all, the value changes according to whether A is a derivative $\frac{d}{dx}$ or an integral $\int dx$.

Yes, of course.

It also changes with respect to n' of the system of orthogonal functions $\chi_{n'}(x)$. For example, if we take the present case of orthogonal function $\sin n'x$, the forms of $\sin 15x$ and $\sin 3x$ are totally different. It is the same for n in $\chi_n^*(x)$. In other words, if even one of the n and n' pairings is different, the form of the function created from them ends up being totally different, as does the area.

Yes, that's right.

This means that the value of the integral is determined by the combination of A and n and n'. In other words, it's a single number. Since that number is determined by A and n and n', let's write it as,

$$\boxed{A_{nn'}}$$

This form is. . .

!

A MATRIX!
Does this mean that what is determined by the combination of n and n' is

$$\begin{pmatrix} A_{11} & A_{12} & A_{13} & \cdots \\ A_{21} & A_{22} & A_{23} & \cdots \\ A_{31} & A_{32} & A_{33} & \cdots \\ \vdots & \vdots & \vdots & \end{pmatrix}$$

I may be totally deceived, but it really does appear to be a matrix.

So the current underlined part is a method for making a matrix from an operator, isn't it? Super!!

Okay. Now let's summarize the method for making a matrix from an operator.

MAKING A MATRIX FROM AN OPERATOR

$$\int \chi_n^*(x) A \chi_{n'}(x)\, dx$$

If the operator A that is to be made into a matrix is sandwiched between two orthogonal functions and the area is determined, a matrix emerges from A.

Using this method, you can make a matrix from an operator.

No, not yet! We aren't really finished until we can make matrix P° from Schrödinger's $\dfrac{h}{2\pi i}\dfrac{d}{dx}$ and matrix Q° from Schrödinger's x!!

Oh, boy! It seems like the time has finally come. It would be so great if we could really do it!

Don't get too worked up, but let's try it.

AT LAST, MAKING P° and Q°

First, making a matrix out of $\frac{h}{2\pi i}\frac{d}{dx}$ and x is simple. You do it by making a sandwich, like we did before.

$$\int \chi_n^*(x)\,\frac{h}{2\pi i}\frac{d}{dx}\,\chi_{n'}(x)\,dx \quad = \quad \boxed{\text{a certain matrix}}$$

$$\int \chi_n^*(x)\,x\,\chi_{n'}(x)\,dx \quad = \quad \boxed{\text{a certain matrix}}$$

Using this method, one matrix can be made from $\frac{h}{2\pi i}\frac{d}{dx}$, and another matrix can be made from x. If these new matrices can satisfy Heisenberg's special conditions,

> 1. they satisfy the canonical commutation relation
>
> $$P^{\circ}Q^{\circ} - Q^{\circ}P^{\circ} = \frac{h}{2\pi i}1$$
>
> 2. they are Hermitian

then we can definitely say that the two matrices are P° and Q°.

Well, shall we give the name $P^{\triangle}$ to the matrix made from $\frac{h}{2\pi i}\frac{d}{dx}$ and the name $Q^{\triangle}$ to the matrix made from x?

I wonder if $P^{\triangle}$ and $Q^{\triangle}$ really will become P° and Q°! First let's see if $P^{\triangle}$ and $Q^{\triangle}$ satisfy the canonical commutation relation.

CONDITION 1. DO MATRICES $\overset{\Delta}{P}$, $\overset{\Delta}{Q}$, DERIVED FROM OPERATORS $\frac{h}{2\pi i}\frac{d}{dx}$ AND x, SATISFY THE CANONICAL COMMUTATION RELATION?

Previously we confirmed that $\frac{h}{2\pi i}\frac{d}{dx}$ and x satisfy the canonical commutation relation.

$$\boxed{\frac{h}{2\pi i}\frac{d}{dx}\cdot x - x\cdot\frac{h}{2\pi i}\frac{d}{dx} = \frac{h}{2\pi i}}$$

Yes, but here we are confirming whether the matrices made from $\frac{h}{2\pi i}\frac{d}{dx}$ and x satisfy the canonical commutation relation.

Exactly.

How do we go about confirming this?

We just stick the matrices into the left and right sides of the equation for the canonical commutation relation:

$$\boxed{\frac{h}{2\pi i}\frac{d}{dx}\cdot x - x\cdot\frac{h}{2\pi i}\frac{d}{dx} = \frac{h}{2\pi i}}$$

Can we do that?

Think about it. If you take the left side $\left(\frac{h}{2\pi i}\frac{d}{dx}x - x\frac{h}{2\pi i}\frac{d}{dx}\right)$ and apply a function to it, you can make the whole thing into an operator; and $\frac{h}{2\pi i}$ naturally is a number. If you apply a function to it, it falls into the category of operators. If you start with an operator, you can always make a matrix by using the "sandwich method" attack. Anyway, let's do it!

But can you do such a thing? Never mind. Let's just do it! The right side is simple, so let's start with that.

LET'S MAKE THE RIGHT SIDE, $\dfrac{h}{2\pi i}$, INTO A MATRIX.

Now we initiate the "sandwich method" attack!

$$\int \chi_n^*(x)\, \frac{h}{2\pi i}\, \chi_{n'}(x)\, dx$$

This is simply a number, so we can remove it from the integration.

$$= \frac{h}{2\pi i} \int \chi_n^*(x) \chi_{n'}(x)\, dx$$

What will the integral of this be?

$\chi_n(x)$ is a system of orthogonal functions.

Let's see, if you multiply a function by a function and take the integral. . . Oh! That's the method that we used to confirm orthogonality, isn't it?

This means that there is an elegant way of writing this integral. You take the area and,

- When $n \neq n'$, it is 0. — When multiplying a pair of unlike things, the resulting area is 0.
- When $n = n'$, it is 1. — When multiplying a pair of like things, we come up with an area. Here we've set things up so that the area will be 1.

You can write it as a matrix.

$$\delta_{nn'}$$

This is read as "Kroneckers delta."

You can change those long sentences above into single mathematical expressions.

It's so compact!

What sort of matrix is this?

$$
\begin{array}{c} \\ n=1 \\ =2 \\ =3 \\ =4 \\ \vdots \end{array}
\begin{array}{c} n'=1\ \ 2\ \ 3\ \ 4\cdots \\ \begin{pmatrix} 1 & 0 & 0 & 0\cdots \\ 0 & 1 & 0 & 0\cdots \\ 0 & 0 & 1 & 0\cdots \\ 0 & 0 & 0 & 1\cdots \\ \vdots & \vdots & \vdots & \vdots \end{pmatrix} \end{array}
$$

Of course! The vertical columns are n' and the horizontal rows are n.

Only the elements along a diagonal line become 1. I'm positive this is called a **unit matrix.** Am I right?

Hey, that's great. You've been gradually learning the language of equations, haven't you? Just as you say, it's a unit matrix. We express it with the numeral 1.

$$1 = \begin{pmatrix} 1 & 0 & 0 \\ 0 & 1 & 0 \\ 0 & 0 & 1 \end{pmatrix}$$

So the continuation of the previous calculation is:

$$\frac{h}{2\pi i}\delta_{nn'} \rightarrow \frac{h}{2\pi i}\begin{pmatrix} 1 & 0 & 0 \\ 0 & 1 & 0 \\ 0 & 0 & 1 \end{pmatrix} = \underline{\frac{h}{2\pi i}1}$$

This is the form of the right side when it is made into a matrix, right?

LET'S TURN THE LEFT SIDE INTO A MATRIX!!

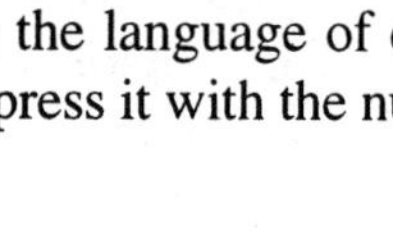

We're going to take the left side

$$\frac{h}{2\pi i}\frac{d}{dx}\cdot x - x\cdot\frac{h}{2\pi i}\frac{d}{dx}$$

and gather it up into a matrix?? It looks difficult.

Don't worry. It probably can be done. The method for turning an operator into a matrix is. . .

The "sandwich method" attack! Leave it to me! We need to place the operator between two orthogonal functions of $\chi_n(x)$, so we have to do this.

$$\int \chi_n^*(x)\left(\frac{h}{2\pi i}\frac{d}{dx}x - x\frac{h}{2\pi i}\frac{d}{dx}\right)\chi_{n'}(x)\,dx$$

Yes. I'm going to use the definition of the addition of operators and break up what is in the parentheses, okay?

$$=\int \chi_n^*(x)\left\{\left(\frac{h}{2\pi i}\frac{d}{dx}\cdot x\right)\chi_{n'}(x) - \left(x\cdot\frac{h}{2\pi i}\frac{d}{dx}\right)\chi_{n'}(x)\right\}dx$$

We can break it up further, since taking the area of the integral all at once and taking the areas piece by piece are the same thing.

$$=\int \chi_n^*(x)\left(\frac{h}{2\pi i}\frac{d}{dx}\cdot x\right)\chi_{n'}(x)\,dx - \int \chi_n^*(x)\left(x\cdot\frac{h}{2\pi i}\frac{d}{dx}\right)\chi_{n'}(x)\,dx$$

When we rearrange what is in the parentheses again, according to the multiplication of operators, we have this.

$$=\int \chi_n^*(x)\,\frac{h}{2\pi i}\frac{d}{dx}\left\{x\cdot\chi_{n'}(x)\right\}dx - \int \chi_n^*(x)\,x\left\{\frac{h}{2\pi i}\frac{d}{dx}\cdot\chi_{n'}(x)\right\}dx$$

What happens next?

Next we can use a trick.

What sort of trick?

It's simple. We rewrite $x\chi_{n'}(x)$ and $\frac{h}{2\pi i}\frac{d}{dx}\chi_{n'}(x)$. To do that, we first make matrices from the individual operators $\frac{h}{2\pi i}\frac{d}{dx}$ and x.

That is to say:

$$P^{\triangle}_{nn'} = \int \chi_n^*(x)\frac{h}{2\pi i}\frac{d}{dx}\chi_{n'}(x)\,dx$$

$$Q^{\triangle}_{nn'} = \int \chi_n^*(x)x\chi_{n'}(x)\,dx\,.$$

Then we use the method of making a vector from a function, and of making a function from a vector. That is, we use the summation equation.

In order to make a function from a vector,

$$\eta_n = \int \chi_n^*(x)f(x)\,dx\,.$$

This corresponds to the so-called Fourier series.

In order to make a vector from a function,

$$f(x) = \sum_n \chi_n(x)\eta_n\,.$$

This corresponds to the so-called Fourier coefficients.

If you look closely, making a matrix from an operator and making a vector from a function are very similar. Let's compare them.

$$P^{\triangle}_{nn'} = \int \chi_n^*(x)\,\underline{\frac{h}{2\pi i}\frac{d}{dx}\chi_{n'}(x)}\,dx$$

$$\eta_n = \int \chi_n^*(x)\,\underline{f(x)}\,dx$$

$$Q^{\triangle}_{nn'} = \int \chi_n^*(x)\,\underline{x\chi_{n'}(x)}\,dx$$

$$\eta_n = \int \chi_n^*(x)\,\underline{f(x)}\,dx$$

Only the underlined parts are different. $f(x)$ is a complicated function. Because an operator is being applied to the function, the newly created equation should be a complicated function.

Hmm.

Think of $x\chi_{n'}(x)$ and $\frac{h}{2\pi i}\frac{d}{dx}\chi_{n'}(x)$ as $f(x)$ and use the method for producing a function from a vector.

So that means,

$$f(x) = \sum_{n} \chi_n(x)\eta_n$$
$$\frac{h}{2\pi i}\frac{d}{dx}\chi_{n'}(x) = \sum_{n} \chi_n(x)P^{\triangle}_{nn'}$$
$$x\chi_{n'}(x) = \sum_{n} \chi_n(x)Q^{\triangle}_{nn'}\,.$$

Is this right?

Yes. And then we insert this into the underlined part of this equation that appeared previously.

$$\int \chi_n^*(x)\frac{h}{2\pi i}\frac{d}{dx}\underline{\left\{x\cdot\chi_{n'}(x)\right\}}\,dx - \int \chi_n^*(x)\,x\,\underline{\left\{\frac{h}{2\pi i}\frac{d}{dx}\cdot\chi_{n'}(x)\right\}}\,dx$$

OK! Now, since there are two n's, we replace the n inside the parentheses with n''. When we do that, we get

$$= \int \chi_n^*(x)\frac{h}{2\pi i}\frac{d}{dx}\sum_{n''}\chi_{n''}(x)Q^{\triangle}_{n''n'}\,dx - \int \chi_n^*(x)x\sum_{n''}\chi_{n''}(x)P^{\triangle}_{n''n'}\,dx$$

That's right. We can place Σ outside the integral. You get the same thing whether you add after taking the integral or take the integral after adding. From there, $P^{\triangle}{}_{n''n'}$ and $Q^{\triangle}{}_{n''n'}$ have no relation to x, and so they'll have no relation to the integral. Therefore, these can also be taken out of the integration. When we do that,

$$= \sum_{n''}\underline{\int \chi_n^*(x)\frac{h}{2\pi i}\frac{d}{dx}\chi_{n''}(x)\,dx}\cdot Q^{\triangle}_{n''n'} - \sum_{n''}\underline{\int \chi_n^*(x)x\,\chi_{n''}(x)\,dx}\cdot P^{\triangle}_{n''n'}\,.$$

What!? Doesn't that mean that the underlined part, which started as the integral of $\frac{h}{2\pi i}\frac{d}{dx}$ sandwiched between orthogonal functions, is now matrix $P^{\triangle}{}_{nn''}$? What is more, the next underlined part is $Q^{\triangle}{}_{nn''}$. Therefore, the above equation can be written in the following way.

$$= \sum_{n''} P^{\triangle}_{nn''} Q^{\triangle}_{n''n'} - \sum_{n''} Q^{\triangle}_{nn''} P^{\triangle}_{n''n'}$$

Could this really be?

It could indeed! This is the type of matrix that we saw in Matrix Plaza. In other words, when

$$\sum P^{\triangle}_{nn''} Q^{\triangle}_{n''n'} = \left(P^{\triangle}Q^{\triangle}\right)_{nn'}$$

$$\sum Q^{\triangle}_{nn''} P^{\triangle}_{n''n'} = \left(Q^{\triangle}P^{\triangle}\right)_{nn'}$$

is placed in accordance with the result previously obtained for the right side, we get

$$\left(P^{\triangle}Q^{\triangle}\right)_{nn'} - \left(Q^{\triangle}P^{\triangle}\right)_{nn'} = \frac{h}{2\pi i}\delta_{nn'}$$

Thus,

$$\boxed{P^{\triangle}Q^{\triangle} - Q^{\triangle}P^{\triangle} = \frac{h}{2\pi i}1}$$

Hey! Isn't this the same as Heisenberg's equation for the canonical commutation relation!?

$$\boxed{P^{\circ}Q^{\circ} - Q^{\circ}P^{\circ} = \frac{h}{2\pi i}1}$$

That's exactly right. In other words,

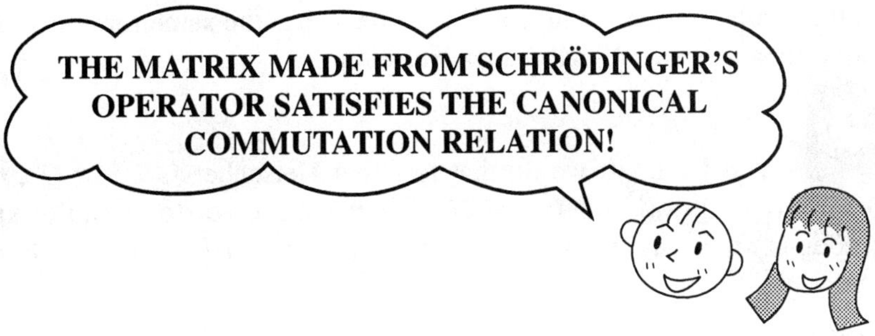

Well then, if it satisfies condition number 2, that it be Hermitian, then it will really and truly be $P^{\circ}\ Q^{\circ}$. In that case, the matrix made from Schrödinger's operator will be $P^{\circ}\ Q^{\circ}$, right?

Yes.

Then Heisenberg's equation will become unnecessary! Quick, let's find out if $P^{\triangle}\ Q^{\triangle}$ is Hermitian and satisfies the condition!

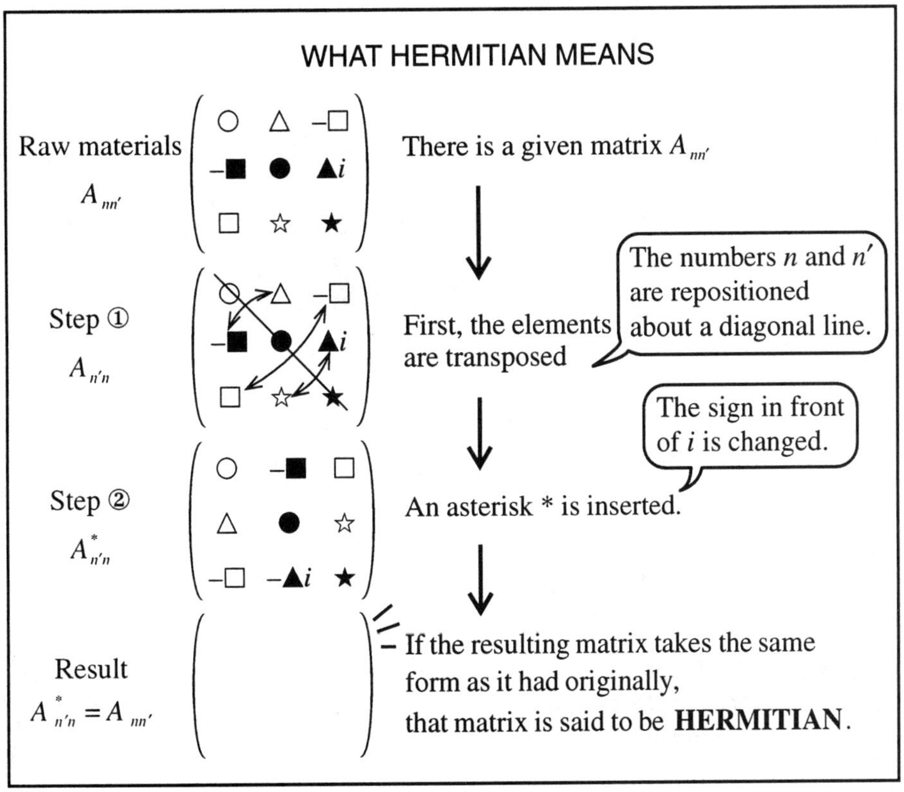

CONDITION 2. CONFIRMING WHETHER MATRIX $P^{\triangle}$, $Q^{\triangle}$, FORMED FROM OPERATOR $\frac{h}{2\pi i}\frac{d}{dx}$, x, IS HERMITIAN

As you can tell from looking at this, when you have a given matrix, and the result after performing steps ① and ② has the same form as the original matrix, then we can call that matrix Hermitian.

Yes, I see. If we do that to either Heisenberg's P° or Q°, they will take their original form, right? All we have to do is make sure that Schrödinger's $P^{\triangle}$ and $Q^{\triangle}$ will go back to their original form if we do them the same way.

All right, let's get right to it.

First, let's CONFIRM THAT $P^{\triangle}$ IS HERMITIAN.

Its original form is

$$P^{\triangle}_{nn'} = \int \chi_n^*(x) \frac{h}{2\pi i} \frac{d}{dx} \chi_{n'}(x)\, dx \ .$$

First, we do step ①. In other words, we transpose n and n'. Thus,

$$P^{\triangle}_{n'n} = \int \chi_{n'}^*(x) \frac{h}{2\pi i} \frac{d}{dx} \chi_{n}(x)\, dx \ .$$

Next, in step ② we add a * (we change the sign in front of i).

$$P^{\triangle *}_{n'n} = \int \chi_{n'}(x) \left(- \frac{h}{2\pi i} \frac{d}{dx} \right) \chi_{n}^*(x)\, dx \, .$$

The asterisk disappears.

There is an i, so we make it negative ⊖.

We add an asterisk.

Let's go on to calculate this.

$-\dfrac{h}{2\pi i}$ is a number so it is placed outside the integration.

$$= \frac{h}{-2\pi i} \int \chi_{n'}(x) \frac{d}{dx} \chi_n^*(x)\, dx$$

You know this part; it's in the form of a **PARTIAL INTEGRATION.**

Formula for partial integration

$$\int f(x)\,\frac{d}{dx}\,g(x)\,dx = \Big[f(x) - g(x)\Big]_{-\infty}^{\infty} - \int \frac{d}{dx}\,f(x)g(x)\,dx$$

$$= -\frac{h}{2\pi i}\left\{\Big[\chi_{n'}(x)\chi_n^*(x)\Big]_{-\infty}^{\infty} - \int \frac{d}{dx}\,\chi_{n'}(x)\chi_n^*(x)\,dx\right\}$$

$\chi_{n'}(x)$ is chosen so that it will be 0 for $x_n(\infty)$ and $x_n(-\infty)$.

$$= -\frac{h}{2\pi i}\left\{0 - \int \frac{d}{dx}\,\chi_{n'}(x)\cdot\chi_n^*(x)\,dx\right\}$$

$$= \frac{h}{2\pi i}\int \frac{d}{dx}\,\chi_{n'}(x)\cdot\chi_n^*(x)\,dx$$

We put this inside.

$$= \int \chi_n^*(x)\,\frac{h}{2\pi i}\,\frac{d}{dx}\,\chi_{n'}(x)\,dx$$

We transpose these.

OH! This is the original form of $P^{\triangle}_{nn'}$!!

Meaning that $P^{\triangle}$ **IS HERMITIAN.**

All right, then $P^{\triangle}$ IS $P^{\bigcirc}$.

Next, let's check to see if $Q^{\triangle}$, which was made from operator x, is Hermitian.

Original form $\quad Q^{\triangle}_{nn'} = \int \chi_n^*(x) x \chi_{n'}(x)\, dx$

Step 1

n and n' are transposed. $\quad Q^{\triangle}_{n'n} = \int \chi_{n'}^*(x) x \chi_n(x)\, dx$

Step 2

* is inserted. $\quad Q^{\triangle *}_{n'n} = \int \chi_{n'}(x) x \chi_n^*(x)\, dx$

Now, all we have to do is see whether this is the same as what we started with. So, when changing the order. . .

$$= \underline{\int \chi_n^*(x) x \chi_{n'}(x)\, dx}$$

Whee! $Q^{\triangle}_{nn'} = Q^{\triangle *}_{n'n}$ are the same.

$Q^{\triangle}_{nn'}$ **is also a Hermitian matrix** after all!!

Now that we've made this clear, **we can also make $Q^{\triangle}_{nn'} = Q^{\bigcirc}_{nn'}$ for the matrix made from x!**

That's right. The matrices made from Schrödinger's operators $\dfrac{h}{2\pi i}\dfrac{d}{dx}$ and x fulfill Heisenberg's two conditions for $P^{\bigcirc}$ and $Q^{\bigcirc}$. This means that in the end we really have

PROVEN THAT IT IS POSSIBLE TO CREATE HEISENBERG'S MATRICES FROM SCHRÖDINGER'S OPERATORS.

Great! If we have Schrödinger's operators, then **we don't need Heisenberg's P° or Q° any more.** Next, if we show that ξ can be made from ϕ, then Heisenberg's equation will no longer be needed!

SCHRÖDINGER'S EQUATION PERFECTED!!

At this point, let's look again at Schrödinger's and Heisenberg's equations.

Schrödinger	$\left\{\frac{1}{2m}\left(\frac{h}{2\pi i}\frac{d}{dx}\right)^2 + \frac{k}{2}x^2\right\}\phi(x) - E\phi(x) = 0$
Heisenberg	$\left(\frac{1}{2m}P^{\circ 2} + \frac{k}{2}Q^{\circ 2}\right)\xi - W\xi = 0$

We've found that P° can be made from $\frac{h}{2\pi i}\frac{d}{dx}$, and that Q° can be made from x. That means

Schrödinger's $\qquad\qquad$ Heisenberg's

$$\left\{\frac{1}{2m}\left(\frac{h}{2\pi i}\frac{d}{dx}\right)^2 + \frac{k}{2}x^2\right\} \quad \text{and} \quad \left(\frac{1}{2m}P^{\circ 2} + \frac{k}{2}Q^{\circ 2}\right)$$

If a system of orthogonal functions is used,

$$\left\{\frac{1}{2m}\left(\frac{h}{2\pi i}\frac{d}{dx}\right)^2+\frac{k}{2}x^2\right\}$$

can always be produced from Schrödinger's equation,

$$\left(\frac{1}{2m}P^{\bigcirc 2}+\frac{k}{2}Q^{\bigcirc 2}\right).$$

Next, if **vector ξ can be produced from function $\phi(x)$, it will be perfect!**

To create a vector from a function, we use a system of orthogonal functions.

We have yet to determine whether ξ can be formed, so for the time being let's say the vector made from $\phi(x)$ is η. Then, when we rewrite Schrödinger's equation,

$$\left\{\frac{1}{2m}\left(\frac{h}{2\pi i}\frac{d}{dx}\right)^2+\frac{k}{2}x^2\right\}\phi(x)-E\phi(x)=0$$

↓ we use the system of orthogonal functions.

$$\left(\frac{1}{2m}P^{\bigcirc 2}+\frac{k}{2}Q^{\bigcirc 2}\right)\eta-E\eta=0$$

This is what we get.

Oh, my! I'm pretty sure that Heisenberg's equation

$$\left(\frac{1}{2m}P^{\bigcirc 2}+\frac{k}{2}Q^{\bigcirc 2}\right)\xi-W\xi=0$$

means that you should take a certain vector out of matrix $\left(\frac{1}{2m}P^{\bigcirc 2}+\frac{k}{2}Q^{\bigcirc 2}\right)$.

That's right, just as you say. Heisenberg's equation, and my equation, altered by using the system of orthogonal functions, both involve taking a vector from the same matrix. Naturally, it's bound to turn out that **ξ and η are the same!**

So does that mean that **the vector made from ϕ is the same as ξ?**

Exactly! If my equation is rewritten using a system of orthogonal functions, it will turn into Heisenberg's equation.

If we think about it, until now we've been using the example of Hooke fields, but there's no reason why we have to be limited to these. Originally, $\left(\frac{1}{2m}P^{\circ 2}+\frac{k}{2}Q^{\circ 2}\right)$ was $H\,(P^{\circ},\,Q^{\circ})$ with the conditions for Hooke fields applied. So, in general terms, it was

$$H(P^{\circ},Q^{\circ})=\frac{1}{2m}P^{\circ 2}+V(Q^{\circ})\ .$$

It so happens that $\frac{h}{2\pi i}\frac{d}{dx}$ and x correspond to the P° and Q° of this equation. Thus, operators $\frac{h}{2\pi i}\frac{d}{dx}$ and x that come up in my equation can be inserted into this equation as P° and Q°.

So Schrödinger's equation may be rewritten like this!

$$H\left(\frac{h}{2\pi i}\frac{d}{dx},\,x\right)\phi\,(x)-E\phi\,(x)=0$$

Point

A NEW EQUATION FOR DESCRIBING THE ELECTRON IS BORN!

We've traveled a long road, but we're done at last.

He did it!! He's incredible, super!!

It's a wonder we got this far!
This most certainly is **a language that describes the electron. It's really splendid!** This equation **ALLOWS A VISUAL IMAGE OF THE ELECTRON, AND EXPLAINS ITS PHENOMENA PERFECTLY!**

When I completed this equation, I felt just as you do now. Now, as for the equation that says you can't have a visual image of the electron. . .

Heisenberg's nonsensical equation is no longer needed!

I don't think Heisenberg ever noticed that my equation was at the root of his. Ha-ha-ha!

Heisenberg's language for describing the electron was incomplete. The electron can be fully described using only the language of waves. My equation does it all! Ha-ha!

Super! We did pretty well too in coming up with this language.

That makes us part of the world of natural scientists.

Do you think there's a chance of receiving the Nobel Prize?

This splendid equation was completed by Schrödinger in 1926. Afterwards, this equation came to be called **THE SCHRÖDINGER EQUATION** in honor of his great achievement.

5.3 SO LONG, MATRIX

FINDING THE SPECTRUM

$$H\left(\frac{h}{2\pi i}\frac{d}{dx}, x\right)\phi(x) - E\phi(x) = 0$$

We've finally come up with the above equation. Not only does it allow a visual image of the electron, it explains the experimental results perfectly.

We no longer need Heisenberg's equation. We did it, Mr. Schrödinger!

Uh, well.

Okay, then let's find the spectrum of an atom!

To find the spectrum, you have to find its **frequencies and intensities.** So, let's try it!

.....

What's the matter, Mr. Schrödinger?

I noticed something dreadful. When you use the Schrödinger equation to find the spectrum of light emitted by an atom, **frequency** ν is found using

$$\nu = \frac{W_n - W_{n'}}{h}.$$

Bohr's equation for the frequency relationship

You see, since $W = E$, it's the same thing as saying

$$\nu = \frac{E_n - E_{n'}}{h}.$$

But when you find the intensity $|Q|^2$, you still need to perform matrix calculations.

Oh, no!

What do you mean? I don't understand.

So far we've found that Heisenberg's equation

$$H(P^{\circ}, Q^{\circ})\xi - W\xi = 0$$

can be produced from my equation, right? But that is all that we know so far. I mean, when we find the frequencies and intensities of the spectrum of light emitted by an atom, we must basically use the same methods that Heisenberg used.

To find frequency ν of a spectrum from Heisenberg's equation, you use

$$\nu = \frac{W_n - W_{n'}}{h}$$

However, some clever maneuvering is necessary to find the intensity.

First of all, you find ξ from Heisenberg's equation. In this case, you have to find not just one ξ, but many of them. For example, if $H(P^{\circ}, Q^{\circ})$ is a matrix of three rows and three columns, then you have to find three ξ's; if there are ten rows and ten columns, then it's ten ξ's, and so on.

As in the following diagram, we gather together all of these ξ's and make them into a single matrix.

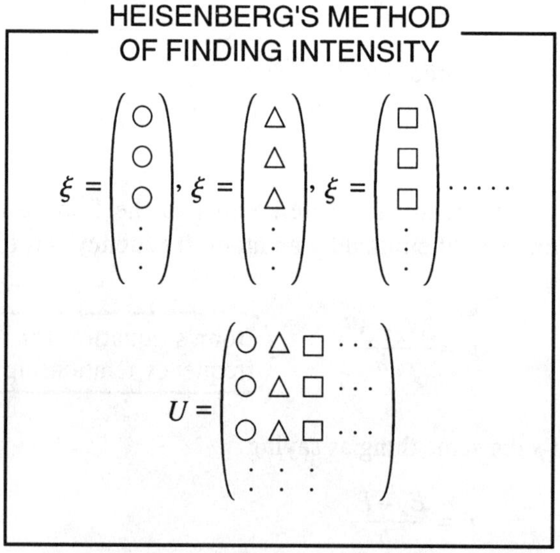

This U is called a **UNITARY MATRIX**.

Unitary matrix? Now what does that do?

I remember. I'm pretty sure that as soon as you clamp these unitary matrices U and $U^\dagger$ around Q°, you can then find Q.

$$Q = U^\dagger Q^\circ U$$

That's right. The square of the absolute value of Q will be the intensity of the light emitted by the atom.

$$\text{Intensity} = |Q|^2$$

I stated before that Q and ξ can be found from my equation, didn't I? But you see, when we go on to derive the intensity. . .

I get it! Since we can derive ξ from the ϕ found from Schrödinger's equation, unless the unitary matrices U and $U^\dagger$ are found from ξ and then applied in a unitary transformation to Q°, the intensity $|Q|^2$ cannot be found!

Summarizing it. . .

Heisenberg	Schrödinger
$H(P^\circ, Q^\circ)\xi - W\xi = 0$	$H\left(\frac{h}{2\pi i}\frac{d}{dx}, x\right)\phi(x) - E\phi(x) = 0$
↓	↓
	$\phi(x)$
ξ ←	┘
↓	
$U, U^\dagger$	
↓	
$U^\dagger Q^\circ U$	
↓	
Q	

Now I see what you mean. When we find the intensity, we can't avoid doing Heisenberg's matrix calculations as part of our other calculations.

What are we going to do, Mr. Schrödinger?

There's nothing we can do, except give up.

Don't let something like this discourage you. Who was it that once said, "If you let every little thing discourage you, you'll never be able to discover a language to describe language"? Wasn't that you, Mr. Schrödinger?

That's right. It was you.

I'm sorry, but can't you folks do something about it for me?

We'll certainly give it a try!

Yeah!

WE DON'T NEED UNITARY TRANSFORMATION!

First of all, let's review how to calculate vector ξ from the function $\phi(x)$ one more time.

Okay. In order to get ξ from $\phi(x)$, you have to do this:

$$\xi_n = \int \phi(x)\chi_n^*(x)\,dx$$

You have to multiply $\phi(x)$ by the system of orthogonal functions $\chi_n(x)$, and then find the area.

By the way, what form does $\phi(x)$ take?

Let's see. Recalling the de Broglie wave for the inside of a box, it's in the form

$$\phi(x) = \sin\frac{n\pi}{L}x \qquad (n = 1, 2, 3, \cdots)$$

Hey, there's an n inside the equation!

You're right. We forgot all about that. Well. . .

$$\phi_1(x) = \sin\frac{1\pi}{L}x$$

$$\phi_2(x) = \sin\frac{2\pi}{L}x$$

$$\phi_3(x) = \sin\frac{3\pi}{L}x$$

$\phi(x)$ is an ordinary thing taking the form of many functions written together. You could say it's a collection of functions.

So we have to make ξ from each one of these functions ϕ_1, ϕ_2, ϕ_3 . . . We apply an orthogonal function to each one and then find the area, so. . .

$$\xi_{n1} = \int \chi_n^*(x)\phi_1(x)\,dx$$

$$\xi_{n2} = \int \chi_n^*(x)\phi_2(x)\,dx$$

$$\xi_{n3} = \int \chi_n^*(x)\phi_3(x)\,dx$$

All of the ξs that result are then gathered together — that is the unitary matrix U.

There's a good way of doing that. Because the subscripts change regularly as in ϕ_1, ϕ_2, ϕ_3. . ., can't we just shorten it all into $\phi_{n'}$? If we do that, then

$$\int \chi_n^*(x)\phi_{n'}(x)\,dx = U_{nn'}$$

will be a unitary matrix just as it is!

Well, aren't you smart!. . . Aaah!

What is it? Why are you suddenly shouting? Is something wrong?

What did we just say $\phi(x)$ was?

We said it was a collection of functions. . . Oh!

$\phi(x)$ is a system of orthogonal functions!

After all, $\phi_n(x)$ were all orthogonal to one another!

But they've been normalized. I'm pretty sure that if $\chi_n(x)$ were a system of orthogonal functions and were normalized, it would have worked. That means. . .

$\phi_n(x)$ can be used in place of $\chi_n(x)$!

This is a brilliant idea! You really live up to your billing as natural scientists.

Mr. Schrödinger, do you already know what's coming next?

I didn't listen to the math language tapes for nothing!

You sure didn't. I can't wait to grow up and be like Mr. Schrödinger.

Let's keep going, okay? Like Mr. Schrödinger says, it's a brilliant idea. All we have to do is keep moving in the same direction.

Can I say something? What if we use $\phi_n(x)$ to make Q° and ξ?

$$Q^{\circ}_{nn'} = \int \phi_n^*(x) x \phi_{n'}(x)\, dx$$

$$U_{nn'} = \int \phi_n^*(x) \phi_{n'}(x)\, dx$$

I have a feeling I've seen the equation for finding $U_{nn'}$ somewhere before. I'm pretty sure it was at the end of the last chapter. . .

I know!!

Don't tell us! I ought to be able to figure it out, too. Hmm. . . I've got it! It's the equation for orthogonality!

That's right. This equation. . .

Wait, let me say it.
When n and n' are different numbers, they are orthogonal and the area will be 0.
When n and n' are the same, the area will be 1.

In other words, the unitary matrix U is

$$U = \begin{pmatrix} \int \phi_1^* \phi_1 \, dx & \int \phi_1^* \phi_2 \, dx \cdots \\ \int \phi_2^* \phi_1 \, dx & \int \phi_2^* \phi_2 \, dx \cdots \\ \vdots & \vdots \end{pmatrix} = \begin{pmatrix} 1 & 0 & 0 & \cdots \\ 0 & 1 & 0 & \cdots \\ 0 & 0 & 1 & \cdots \end{pmatrix}$$

a **UNIT MATRIX!** Then what is $U^\dagger$?

U is a unit matrix.

"$U^\dagger$" can be found by looking back at the definition of "dagger" on page 277. A dagger tells you to switch the positions of rows and columns and then take the complex conjugate. If U is a unit matrix, then even if you switch the position of the rows and columns and take the complex conjugate, the matrix will not change. Therefore,

$$U^\dagger = U = \begin{pmatrix} 1 & 0 & 0 & \cdots \\ 0 & 1 & 0 & \cdots \\ 0 & 0 & 1 & \cdots \end{pmatrix}$$

I'm sure there was an equation $UU^\dagger = U^\dagger U = 1$. We need to think of what will equal 1 when it is multiplied by the unit matrix U, in other words, what will make a unit matrix.

$$\begin{pmatrix} 1 & 0 & 0 & \cdots \\ 0 & 1 & 0 & \cdots \\ 0 & 0 & 1 & \cdots \end{pmatrix} \times \begin{pmatrix} ? \end{pmatrix} = \begin{pmatrix} 1 & 0 & 0 & \cdots \\ 0 & 1 & 0 & \cdots \\ 0 & 0 & 1 & \cdots \end{pmatrix}$$

It's a **UNIT MATRIX** after all!

$U^\dagger$ is a unit matrix, too!

Now that we've found U and $U^\dagger$, let's **apply the unitary transformation to Q°.**

$$Q = U^\dagger Q^\circ U = 1Q^\circ 1 = Q^\circ$$

What? It turned back into $\overset{\circ}{Q}$.

Don't sound so surprised. We have $\boldsymbol{Q} = \boldsymbol{Q}^{\circ}$. Therefore, although we thought that the matrix made from

$$\int \phi_n^*(x)x\phi_{n'}(x)\,dx$$

was Q°, it was in fact none other than **Q ITSELF!**

Point

$$Q_{nn'} = \int \phi_n^*(x)x\phi_{n'}(x)\,dx$$

This is the way to find spectral intensities without using matrix calulations!!

Yes, I see. It's far simpler than Heisenberg's method.

Congratulations! It's done, Mr. Schrödinger.

There's nothing more to say. That's really splendid! You did a great job.

We no longer need any unitary transformation!

We did it! Those matrix calculations were so troublesome and difficult. I hated them!

There's also another great thing. As I've said many times before, Heisenberg's equation could only describe the spectrum. But, if you think about it, the $|\Psi|^2$ that we obtained from

$$\nabla^2\Psi + 4\pi i\mathfrak{M}\frac{\partial\Psi}{\partial t} - 8\pi^2\mathfrak{M}\mathfrak{V}\Psi = 0$$

which we constructed in the previous chapter on de Broglie and Schrödinger

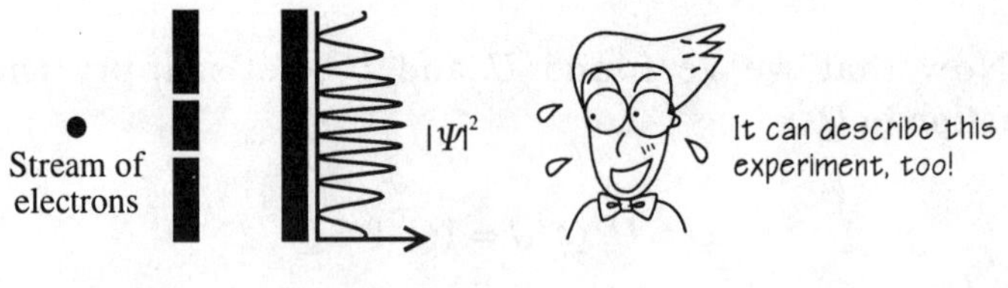

can describe the interference experiment. Besides that, **it can explain how an electron changes over time.**

I'd like to make this a Hermitian equation, too. By doing that, we'll distance ourselves even farther from Heisenberg.

I'll leave out the detailed calculations here, but the equation we come out with is:

Time dependent Schrödinger equation

$$H\left(\frac{h}{2\pi i}\frac{\partial}{\partial x}, \frac{h}{2\pi i}\frac{\partial}{\partial y}, \frac{h}{2\pi i}\frac{\partial}{\partial z}, x, y, z\right)\Psi(x, y, z, t) + \frac{h}{2\pi i}\frac{\partial \Psi}{\partial t} = 0 .$$

This may be gilding the lily, for we have already proven our point: we can now explain the interference experiment, which Heisenberg could not do, and we can describe changes in an electron over time. We have everything we need to **HAVE A VISUAL IMAGE, AND TO DESCRIBE THE PHENOMENA COMPLETELY**.

But the required calculations are far simpler than matrix mechanics. We have just brought a **PERFECT THEORY** into the world of physics!!

Wow, we really did something pretty great.

I feel a lot closer to Mr. Schrödinger.

This is marvelous. You were a big help. Thank you! Now then, let's all say it together. . .

5. 4 SCHRÖDINGER'S EQUATION IN JEOPARDY

THE STRENGTHS OF SCHRÖDINGER'S EQUATION

Not even Schrödinger could suppress his excitement over his brand new equation. We should stop for a minute and review the points that make it brilliant.

$$H\left(\frac{h}{2\pi i}\frac{d}{dx}, x\right)\phi(x) - E\phi(x) = 0$$

THE THREE STRENGTHS OF SCHRÖDINGER'S EQUATION

1. It allows for a visual image.
2. The calculations are simple.

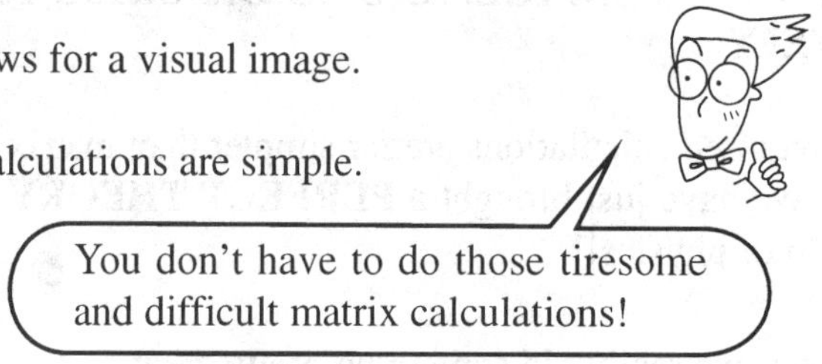

3. It offers a way to explain interference. That may be calculated as $|\Psi|^2$.

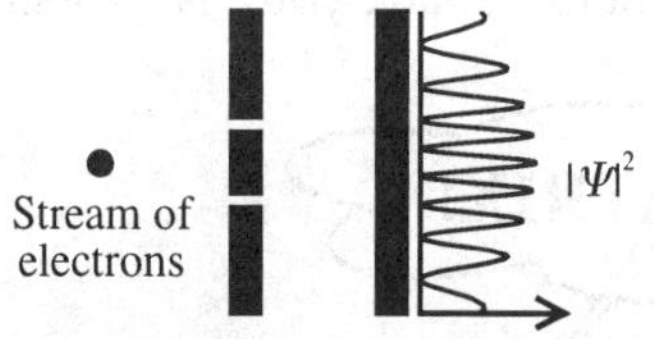

$|\Psi|^2$ precisely matches the effect obtained in experiments by passing an electron through a barrier with two holes in it.
Heisenberg is not able to explain this effect.

It's amazing! If you use this equation, all sorts of things that couldn't be explained by Heisenberg's equation become clear.

CONFRONTATION WITH BOHR

But that wasn't the end of it. . .

Come to think of it, what started us on our physics adventure was the one book that was assigned reading when we entered TCL.

A description of what happened when Schrödinger, super equation in hand, went riding into Heisenberg's encampment appears in the chapter **"FRESH FIELDS."**

In the summer of 1926, Schrödinger lectured on his theory at a seminar in Munich at the invitation of Heisenberg's teacher, Professor Sommerfeld. Naturally Heisenberg was there, too. As Heisenberg later remembered,

"Schrödinger first of all explained the mathematical principles of wave mechanics by using the hydrogen atom as an illustration. All of us were delighted to see his elegant and simple solution by conventional methods of a problem that Wolfgang Pauli had been able to solve only with great difficulty using quantum mechanics."

Schrödinger explained the hydrogen atom so simply that those attending the seminar were speechless. Heisenberg tried to refute him on one point, but it was a minor issue, and by then everybody was convinced that Schrödinger's method would eventually be able to clear up everything.

"Even Sommerfeld, who felt most kindly toward me, succumbed to the persuasive force of Schrödinger's mathematics."

Schrödinger's equation was indeed formidable. But Heisenberg simply refused to accept it. That very evening he wrote to Bohr telling him of the day's events.

> After reading what Heisenberg had to say, Bohr invited Schrödinger to his own home in Copenhagen that autumn in order to discuss the behavior of the electron. Bohr's discussions with Schrödinger began at the railway station and were continued daily from early morning until late at night. Schrödinger stayed in Bohr's house so that nothing would interrupt the conversation. When it came to topics related to quantum mechanics, neither one yielded an inch; they sent sparks flying.

Physics and Beyond

Physics and Beyond

Physics and Beyond

Physics and Beyond

Surely you realize that the whole idea of quantum jumps is bound to end in nonsense. You claim first of all that if an atom is in a stationary state, the electron revolves periodically but does not emit light, when, according to Maxwell's theory, it must. Next, the electron is said to jump from one orbit to the next and to emit radiation. **Is this jump supposed to be gradual or sudden?** If it is gradual, the orbital frequency and energy of the electron must change gradually as well.

In other words, **the whole idea of quantum jumps is sheer fantasy.**

Physics and Beyond

What you say is absolutely correct. **But it does not prove that there are no quantum jumps.**

Physics and Beyond

It only proves that **we cannot imagine them,** that the representational concepts with which we describe events in daily life and experiments in classical physics are inadequate when it comes to describing quantum jumps. Nor should we be surprised to find it so, seeing that the processes involved are not the objects of direct experience.

Physics and Beyond

I don't wish to enter into long arguments about the formation of concepts; I prefer to leave that to the philosophers.

I wish only to know what happens inside an atom.

I don't really mind what language you choose to discuss it.· · ·

The moment, however, that we change the picture and say that **there are no discrete electrons, only electron waves or waves of matter, then everything looks quite different.** We no longer wonder about the fine lines.· · ·

What seemed to be insoluble contradictions have suddenly disappeared.

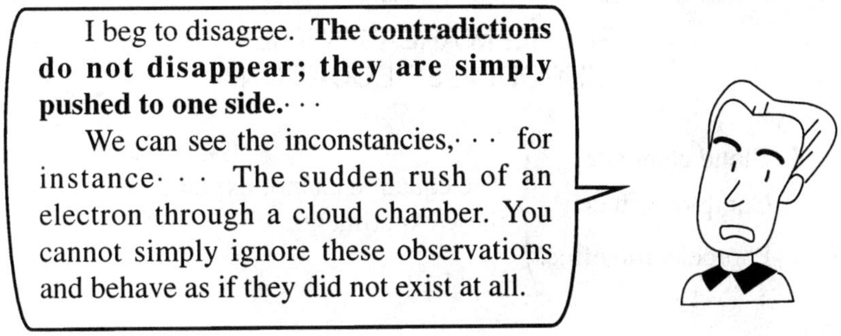

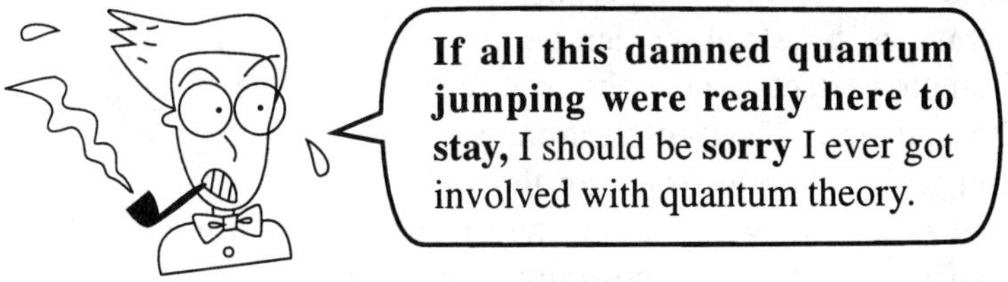

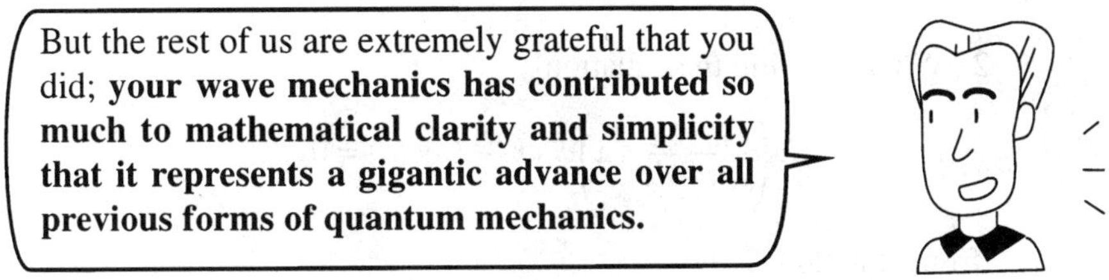

Day after day, from dawn to dusk, their discussion of the atom went on and on.

After a few days Schrödinger fell ill, perhaps as a result of his enormous effort; in any case, he was forced to keep to his bed with a feverish cold.

Niels Bohr kept sitting on the edge of the bed talking at Schrodinger: "But you must surely admit that..." No real understanding could be expected since, at the time, neither side was able to offer a complete and coherent interpretation of quantum mechanics.

In this conversation, Bohr seemed to be saying that there is some sort of problem with Schrödinger's "perfect" equation. Hmm. . . Maybe Schrödinger's equation seemed so complete and perfect because he himself never touched on its problems. That's possible, and I guess it's up to us TCL students to look again at Schrödinger's equation, this time with TCL eyes!

PROBLEM AREAS IN THE SCHRÖDINGER EQUATION

1. Cloud chamber
   Compton effect
   Photoelectric effect

   } The equation cannot explain these experiments.

Cloud chamber

In the cloud chamber experiment, the paths traveled by electrons can be seen. The Compton effect and the photon effect refer to collisions between electrons and light, in which the electrons are thrown back. If electrons were waves, they would keep on going when they collided with light without being thrown back, and the ricocheting phenomenon would not occur.

2. When creating the equation

$$H\left(\frac{h}{2\pi i}\frac{d}{dx}, x\right)\phi(x) - E\phi(x) = 0$$

from equation

$$\nabla^2\phi + 8\pi^2\mathfrak{M}(\nu - \mathfrak{V})\phi = 0$$

why were $\mathfrak{M}$, $\mathfrak{V}$ and ν first changed to

$\mathfrak{M} \to \frac{m}{h}$, $\nu \to \frac{E}{h}$ and $\mathfrak{V} \to \frac{V}{h}$, the language of particles?

This is supposed to be a wave equation. What is going on?

3.

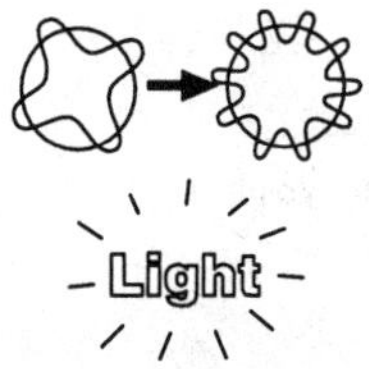

Light is emitted when the number n changes, getting smaller or bigger (left diagram). Not even Bohr suggested how and when this occurs.

Regarding this, Schrödinger said it's hard to imagine an electron jumping about like a flea and that he felt better thinking of it as a wave.

How about that! We thought Schrödinger's equation was perfect, yet there are all these weak points.

Mr. Schrödinger, what are you going to do about all these problems?

. . . .

Mr. Schrödinger! How do you suggest solving these problems?

Hee hee hee. Such concern over a few little things. . . Eventually,

In general, this equation **lets you form a visual image!** That's the basis of physics, the very foundation. As I said before, only when people can conceptualize the image in their heads, can they be said to understand it. Compared to the all important "visual image," these problems are minor.

Schrödinger spoke with strong conviction, stemming from the most crucial element of his equation, which is that

IT ALLOWS A VISUAL IMAGE.

Heisenberg gave up and declared, "Let's get rid of the visual image." Compared to his proposal, Schrödinger's equation is absolutely splendid!

THE LOST IMAGE

However. . . A dreadful discovery was made relating to the source of Schrödinger's self-confidence, the **visual image!!** This happened when Schrödinger's equation, taking the electron as a wave, was used in the case where **there are two electrons.**

Let's see. . . Schrödinger's equation

$$H\left(\frac{h}{2\pi i}\frac{d}{dx}, x\right)\phi(x) - E\phi(x) = 0$$

described the case of **A SINGLE-ELECTRON WAVE.**

I'd like to call your attention to something. At the time we made my equation from the equation for de Broglie fields

$$\nabla^2\phi + 8\pi^2\mathfrak{M}(\nu - \mathfrak{V})\phi = 0$$

do you recall that Ψ was the second derivative of x, y, z, and we decided that we would take just the x dimension because the calculations were so troublesome?

Now that you mention it. . .

$$\nabla^2\Psi = \underline{\frac{\partial^2\Psi}{\partial x^2}} + \frac{\partial^2\Psi}{\partial y^2} + \frac{\partial^2\Psi}{\partial z^2}$$

(We took only this part into consideration when making the equation.)

This means that you can't really describe one electron without considering the y and z dimensions too.

That's correct.

$$\underline{H\left(\frac{h}{2\pi i}\frac{d}{dx}, x\right)\phi - E\phi = 0}$$

Otherwise, you know the movements of the electron only in the x dimension. Now then, ϕ in this equation will be a function of what?

If we look within the brackets, H is determined by $\frac{d}{dx}$ — that is, the derivative with respect to x — and by x. Doesn't that make ϕ a function of x, too?

That's exactly right. H is basically a way of expressing energy as a function of P (momentum) and V (position), and is known as a Hamiltonian. If we look at it closely, it is

$$H(P_x, x) = \frac{P_x^2}{2m} + V(x)$$

But as we already know, any P_x may be expressed in the language of waves as $\frac{h}{2\pi i}\frac{d}{dx}$. So in reality, it is enough to perform this calculation:

$$H\left(\frac{h}{2\pi i}\frac{d}{dx},\, x\right) = \frac{1}{2m}\left(\frac{h}{2\pi i}\frac{d}{dx}\right)^2 + V(x)$$

The point is, since the H is determined by the derivation in respect to x, the wave ϕ of this electron is also determined solely by the one dimension x.

So if we want to describe a single electron properly, we also have to think in terms of the y and z dimensions. That means we must take H, which was determined solely in terms of x, and modify it so that it is determined by y and z as well. Is it something like this?

$$H\left(\frac{h}{2\pi i}\frac{\partial}{\partial x},\, \frac{h}{2\pi i}\frac{\partial}{\partial y},\, \frac{h}{2\pi i}\frac{\partial}{\partial z},\, x, y, z\right)\phi - E\phi = 0$$

Super! That's exactly right. Okay, this time the electron wave is a function of what and what and what?

That's simple. It's $\phi\ (x, y, z)$. In other words, it's a **three-dimensional wave** determined by the three elements x, y and z.

That's right. In sum, **A SINGLE ELECTRON IS A THREE-DIMENSIONAL WAVE.**

There are three-dimensional waves all around us. Sound waves are one example. If you think of them that way, you can picture them in your mind, can't you?

Yes.

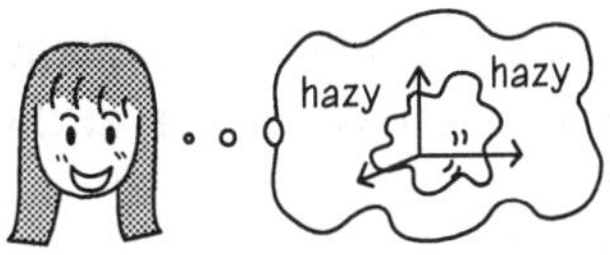

So far, so good. Now what happens when we describe the case of **two-electron waves?**

First, let's think concretely about what happens to H when $H\phi - E\phi = 0$.

The energy of the first electron is described as a Hamiltonian. We call this H_1.

$$H_1\left(\frac{h}{2\pi i}\frac{\partial}{\partial x_1}, \frac{h}{2\pi i}\frac{\partial}{\partial y_1}, \frac{h}{2\pi i}\frac{\partial}{\partial z_1}, x_1, y_1, z_1\right)$$

The energy of the second electron is also described as a Hamiltonian. We call this H_2.

$$H_2\left(\frac{h}{2\pi i}\frac{\partial}{\partial x_2}, \frac{h}{2\pi i}\frac{\partial}{\partial y_2}, \frac{h}{2\pi i}\frac{\partial}{\partial z_2}, x_2, y_2, z_2\right)$$

Next, **the energy in the case of two electrons in three-dimensional space** is described as a Hamiltonian. We call this H.

$$H\left(\frac{h}{2\pi i}\frac{\partial}{\partial x_1}, \frac{h}{2\pi i}\frac{\partial}{\partial y_1}, \frac{h}{2\pi i}\frac{\partial}{\partial z_1}, \frac{h}{2\pi i}\frac{\partial}{\partial x_2}, \frac{h}{2\pi i}\frac{\partial}{\partial y_2}, \frac{h}{2\pi i}\frac{\partial}{\partial z_2}, x_1, y_1, z_1, x_2, y_2, z_2\right)$$

And in this case, $H = H_1 + H_2$.

Therefore, **when you use the Schrödinger equation to describe the fact that there are two electrons,** a very long equation results.

$$H\left(\frac{h}{2\pi i}\frac{\partial}{\partial x_1}, \frac{h}{2\pi i}\frac{\partial}{\partial y_1}, \frac{h}{2\pi i}\frac{\partial}{\partial z_1}, \frac{h}{2\pi i}\frac{\partial}{\partial x_2}, \frac{h}{2\pi i}\frac{\partial}{\partial y_2}, \frac{h}{2\pi i}\frac{\partial}{\partial z_2}, x_1, y_1, z_1, x_2, y_2, z_2\right)\phi \pm E\phi = 0$$

Let's take a good look at this equation. This time ϕ is. . .

Mr. Schrödinger, it's a disaster!! Using your equation, I described the fact that there are two electrons, but please have a look at this. What on earth happened to ϕ this time?

Slow down. You're jumping ahead of yourself.

Looking at what we have so far, this expression ϕ seems to be determined by $x_1\ y_1\ z_1$, $x_2\ y_2\ z_2$, that is, by **six numbers.**

. . . !

At first I thought that $x_1\ y_1\ z_1$ as well as $x_2\ y_2\ z_2$ were subsumed in the same $x\ y\ z$, but in mathematical terms they are describing completely separate dimensions! Doesn't that mean that **when there are two electrons, we will have a six-dimensional wave?**

. . . .

So if we describe a two-electron wave, we get a six-dimensional wave; **for three electrons, we get nine dimensions; for four electrons, twelve dimensions.** With something like this, **there's no way I can picture such waves.** At first, I was worried, thinking that I couldn't picture such waves because I wasn't smart enough, but that wasn't it at all. I mean, **people can only picture up to three dimensions!** So what exactly is going on here?

. . . .

Our bodies are made up of **how many hundreds of millions** of units called atoms? There are many times that number of electrons. If we try to represent them using Schrödinger's equation, won't we end up with

A WAVE IN INFINITE DIMENSIONS!?

No one can picture an electron wave with infinite dimensions.

. . . . I can't picture it either.

At this point, Schrödinger became aware that it was Hamiltonian mathematics itself that had caused such an incomprehensible thing to happen.

But it was too late. All kinds of thoughts went through Schrödinger's head.

Drat. . . I didn't think there was anything wrong with my thinking. Yet it might have been a mistake for me to use Heisenberg's equation as a model by putting

$$\nabla^2\phi + 8\pi^2\mathfrak{M}(\nu - \mathfrak{V})\phi = 0$$

in Hamiltonian form.

I learned when I made the equation

$$H\left(\frac{h}{2\pi i}\frac{d}{dx}, x\right)\phi(x) - E\phi(x) = 0$$

that as long as ϕ and E are known, ν and Q of a spectrum can be found. That is, you can explain the experiments and still retain a visual image. I wonder if ultimately I'll have to abandon the equation that I've worked so hard to create, and just leave things as they are, with the de Broglie-Schrodinger equation

$$\nabla^2\phi + 8\pi^2\frac{m}{h}(E - V)\phi = 0\,.$$

If I stop at finding just ϕ and E from this equation, since there is a ∇ in it, I can mentally picture it as a simple three-dimensional image. Not only that, if ϕ and E are found, then ν and Q can be found also.

But that idea didn't help either. The problem was that Heisenberg's equation and de Broglie's equation agreed in giving the same correct answer **only in the case of one particle.** When there were two or more particles, de Broglie's equation could not produce correct answers. The equation that produced correct answers was, after all, the H form of the equation that Schrödinger developed. There was no turning back.

Schrödinger was deeply discouraged. Indignant at Heisenberg's statement that a visual image of the electron was not possible, he had tried vigorously to prove him wrong, and apparently succeeded. But as it turned out, he too, had ended up creating an equation that could not produce a visual image.

As for Heisenberg, his starting premise was that a visual image was not possible, and he formulated an equation to correspond to that reality, with the objective of describing actual experiments on spectra.

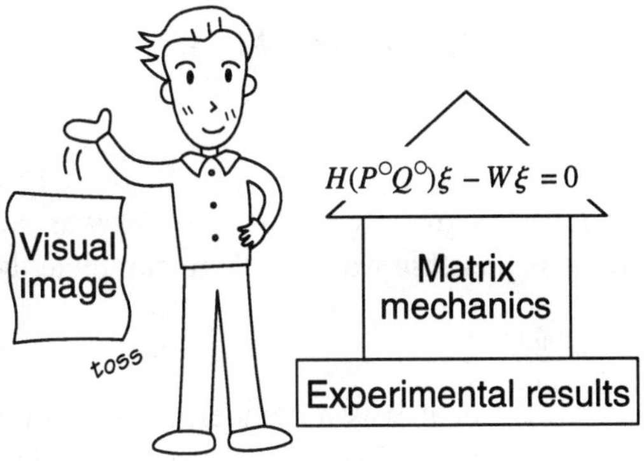

Schrödinger, on the other hand, built up his theory on the cornerstone assumption that we can and must be able to visualize the electron, but when it came time to look at the finished product, the cornerstone wasn't there.

But Schrödinger was not the sort to be daunted by such a thing! He persisted to the bitter end, saying:

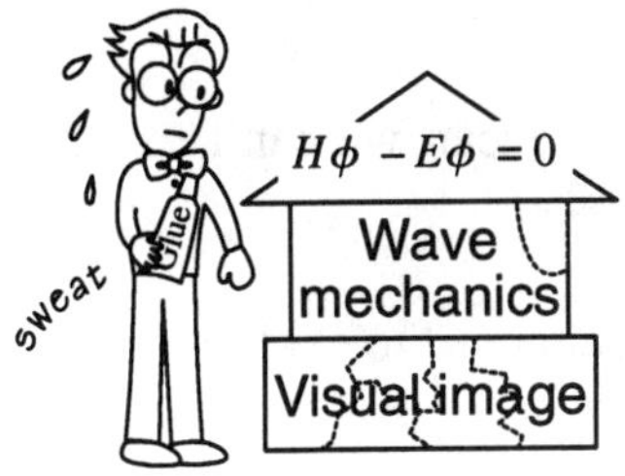

Now that this unintelligible matter of six dimensions has come up, I realize that wave mechanics is only half-developed. Sooner or later, someone is bound to resolve the problems and think up a way to represent the behavior of electron waves in three dimensions. In any event, it seems likely that soon we will achieve a definitive value for $|\Psi|^2$.

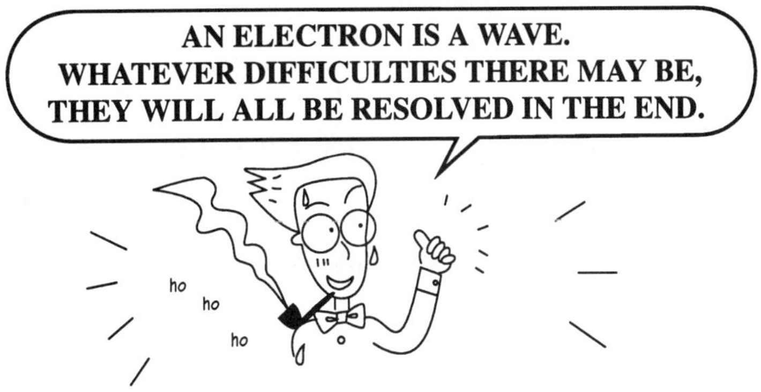

IN CONCLUSION

I feel sorry for Mr. Schrödinger. He struggled so far, only to see his equation end up like this.

I agree. Only because he was so determined to show that **a visual image is possible** was he able to complete the Schrödinger equation.

But it was a wonderful experience creating equations together with Mr. Schrödinger. Because of that, I'm no longer as intimidated by equations. In the end, we truly understood that equations are not complete from the beginning, but are constructed bit by bit. What's more, I somehow feel as if I physically experienced how equations work as language. Heisenberg's equation simply explained phenomena. Schrödinger's equation, on the other hand, had an intimate relationship to language. Creating this equation involved much more than manipulating values; it involved attempting to construct a language that produces a visual image. This **search for a language to describe nature** was a lot of fun!

I agree. Until now we've been looking only at completed things, so we didn't know anything about process. Nevertheless, this electron which we cannot mentally envision. . . what could it be? Normally, we're supposed to be able to produce some kind of visual image with the language that we're using. That's what language is after all, right?

Yes. Language has meaning, and language always produces a mental image. That's why we can transmit meaning to the person to whom we're speaking.

If no visual image is possible, does that mean we can't explain the electron in the language we use?

Come on. If that's so, just how are we supposed to explain it?

That's what I think too, but. . .

I really understand how desperately Schrödinger kept chasing after a visual image.

Right, and I hear that other physicists also gave him a lot of support.

Everyone wanted the reassurance of being able to have a visual image. But in the end we lost the image, and now it seems like we've ended up right back where we started.

It's too bad. Like before, we have a language to explain the results of experiments, but we still don't have one that can explain the behavior of electrons. I don't know how it will turn out, but all we can do is go on. . .

What is going to happen to the electron? Will there really come a day when its mysteries are unraveled? With that tantalizing thought, we're off on the final chapter of our adventure. Let's go!

CHAPTER 6

Max Born and Werner Heisenberg

DEPARTURE TO A NEW WORLD

Bohr and Heisenberg started from the premise that electrons are particles. That approach led to a thesis where a visual image of the electron was not possible. Schrödinger, on the other hand, believed that we can and must always have a visual image. His point of departure was the premise that electrons are waves. But, as it turned out, the theory he worked out couldn't support a visual image either.

And now, here we are, at the climax of our adventure! How, ultimately, will Heisenberg's thesis affect quantum mechanics? Exactly what is this thing called quantum? We now take a step toward a new world.

6.1 HAVING IT OUT

It was Niels Bohr who said:

"We ourselves are · · · both spectators and actors in the great drama of life."

Now that we have started to explore the world of language and of quanta, everything around us — what we hear, see and feel every day — has taken on new meaning as objects of natural science. It's an exciting drama that we want to share with as many people as possible.

One day when we had just about finished quantum mechanics, I turned on the television. As I flipped through the channels, I noticed a program starting on one of the channels that looked interesting. As I began watching, I realized what it was!

10th Anniversary of Hippo:
A TCL SPECIAL
"THE NATURAL SCIENCES IN THE 20TH CENTURY"

Greetings to you all in the television audience. The topic of our special program today is the natural sciences in the 20th century, and we are going to explore the landscape of the micro-world of atoms. My name is Janet Brown and I will be the host of this program. Let me begin by introducing our participants.

The heroes of twentieth-century physics were sitting around a big oval table, along with three guests. Around them sat the audience.

First, on my left, is Max Planck. Mr. Planck discovered Planck's constant h. He is the pioneer who blazed the trail to quantum mechanics. Good evening.

Good evening. Of the various quanta, I am especially interested in talking about light.

Next to him is our old friend who gave us the theory of relativity. Good evening, Mr. Einstein.

Good evening. I've been looking forward to coming here.

Next to him is Niels Bohr. This is a man who constantly surprises us with his innovative ideas.

What a pleasure it is to be able to share with you all the sublime joy of the natural sciences!

Next to him is Werner Heisenberg. Although he is young, his achievements are tremendous.

I have only followed in the path of those who have gone before me.

Sitting proud and erect, Heisenberg stood out among the participants, a refreshing, likable young man.

Next to him is Louis de Broglie. He is the person who first concentrated on the properties of wave motion observed in electrons.

I began to take an interest in the world of physics after reading a thesis that my brother was studying. I hope we can learn more about physics today while having fun and enjoying ourselves.

Next is Erwin Schrödinger. Mr. Schrödinger just recently completed the equation of wave mechanics.

In the process of formulating my equation for wave mechanics, I have made great advances in both mathematics and physics.

Now, coming next after this illustrious parade of people from the physics world is the adventurer Mr. Hippopotamoid. Hippopotamoid makes astute points by asking simple questions. We're looking forward to hearing the questions he will ask today.

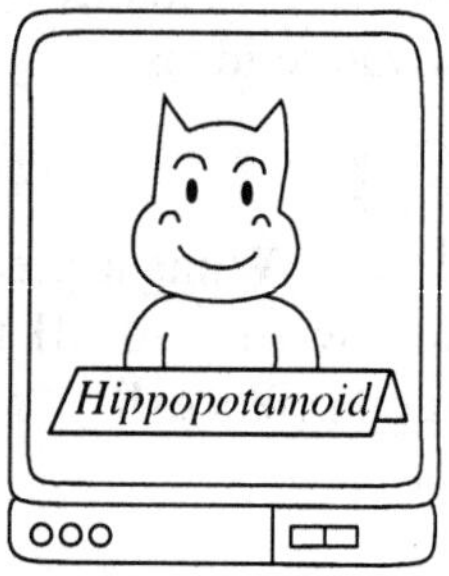

I really enjoy investigating strange things.

Next to him is the critic Aunt Potam, who is none other than Hippopotamoid's aunt. Aunt Potam would like to comment occasionally from the standpoint of a homemaker and mother.

Well, as a homemaker involved in the routines of everyday life, I'd like to find out a few things about natural science.

Finally, to my left, from the Transnational College of LEX , known as TCL, is Ms. Yuka Fujimura.

Physics and Beyond

I will never forget Heisenberg's words: "Science is made by men." Human beings create science and they describe it using language. My interest is exploring the natural sciences from a linguistic point of view.

Well, let's get started. First, will you please look at this diagram?

The diagram was a long and narrow band containing a number of lines.

We are able to determine the atom's size, its weight and also its spectrum. This is the spectrum of the hydrogen atom. I've heard that practically all discoveries in atomic physics were related to the spectrum emitted by an atom.

An atom is too small for us to look directly inside it, but even though we cannot see something, we can still obtain information about it. For instance, when you throw a rock in total darkness and you hear a "kerplunk" sound, where do you suppose the rock landed?

I'd think it was a pond, or some other body of water.

That's right. If you heard glass breaking, you would think you had hit something made of glass. We may not be able to see it, but we can guess what a thing might be by doing something to it and observing the response.

Well then, are we going to hit some atoms?

We cannot actually hit them with anything, but we can place atoms under certain conditions, or limitations, and then observe what happens. That is what it means to perform an experiment.

I once did an experiment in human flight. I attached some banana leaves to myself and tried to fly. I found, however, that I couldn't fly under such conditions.

If we want to find out about atoms, what experiments should we perform?

Do an experiment that applies energy to the atom and observe what happens to the spectrum. The spectrum mentioned earlier is a response that always occurs when energy is applied to an atom.

Mr. Planck, are you able to explain that in more detail?

As we've said, it is impossible to look inside the atom. Nevertheless, the responses to such experiments applying energy to atoms give us certain information. When we talk about applying energy to an atom, we mean passing electricity through it. When that is done, a change in the movement of electrons occurs inside the atom which produces light. The spectrum of an atom is what one sees when that light is passed through a spectroscope, which is something like a prism. Each type of atom produces a distinctive spectrum. Through electromagnetics it was known that electrons give off light when they move, but it was not known how electrons moved within an atom. In order to understand the movements of an electron, we need to understand something about atoms.

So the spectrum is an important key to understanding the structure of the atom.

Before considering the visible spectrum of each type of atom, we had to understand the true nature of the light given off by electrons.

Is it like knowing who the parents are like from looking at the children? Can we think of an electron as a parent who gives birth to light? If the offspring is a hippopotamus, then you know the parent is not an elephant. Human parents give birth to human children. So you can infer things about electrons from your understanding of light, can't you?

What we call light is something that is visible, yet it cannot be seen. Only with light are we able to see things because our eyes see objects by receiving light that is reflected off them. So, although our eyes see light, they do not see what light itself is.

Actually, for some time it has been considered possible that light is something like a wave, something with wave-like properties.

What is the nature of a wave?

We think of a wave as moving, or being transmitted, as its oscillations spread. If you drop something onto the surface of water, you can see the ripples start and spread outward.

Once, when I fell into a pond, the ripples spread out in rings. Is that the same thing?

Right. It was thought that light is transmitted in the form of waves as they spread out from a point of origin. Thus, if we can obtain numbers from light that indicate the speed, the height and the frequency of waves, then we can write about light using wave equations, the language of waves.

What things don't have the properties of waves?

Things called particles. They do not spread; they are not transmitted like ripples are through water. Particles themselves move. The movement of a ball when it is thrown, or the movement of something as it falls are good examples. This kind of thing can be expressed using the laws discovered by Newton. These laws are called Newtonian mechanics, and they are completely different from the behavior of waves. In no way can a particle be a wave, nor a wave be a particle.

The ripples in a pond or the waves in the ocean spread, or are transmitted, across the surface of water. By what medium are light waves transmitted?

Although the properties of light waves and water waves are similar, there is no actual thing, like water in the ocean, that transmits light waves. Light is transmitted even through a vacuum, like the light of the sun that is transmitted to the earth. It is truly a strange thing. Nevertheless, because in certain ways light appears to behave like waves, it was thought that the equations used for waves might be used to describe light.

What characteristics of light resemble the behavior of waves?

Light, like waves on the surface of water, interferes. If Aunt Potam falls into the pond, the ripples, or rings, will simply spread. But, if Hippopotamoid were to jump in also, rings would spread out from both of them and the waves would collide.

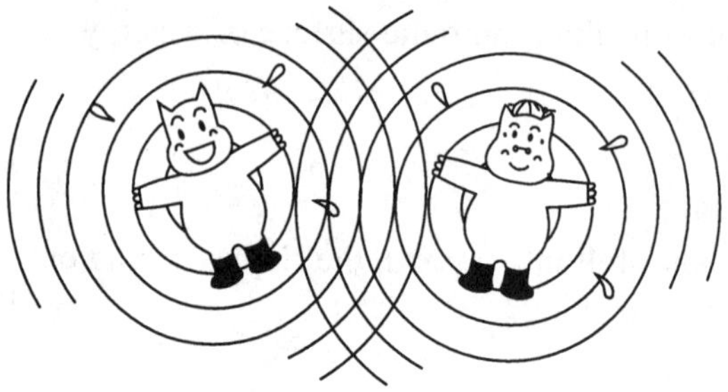

As the waves meet, the places where crests meet become higher, and the places where the valleys meet become lower. Where a crest meets a valley, the waves cancel each other out, creating a place that is neither high nor low. The way that waves meet and influence each other is called wave interference.

The way in which people influence each other — for better or for worse — could be called people interference. Don't you agree?

What do you see when waves interfere?

Wave interference can be demonstrated by passing light through two slits, like this.

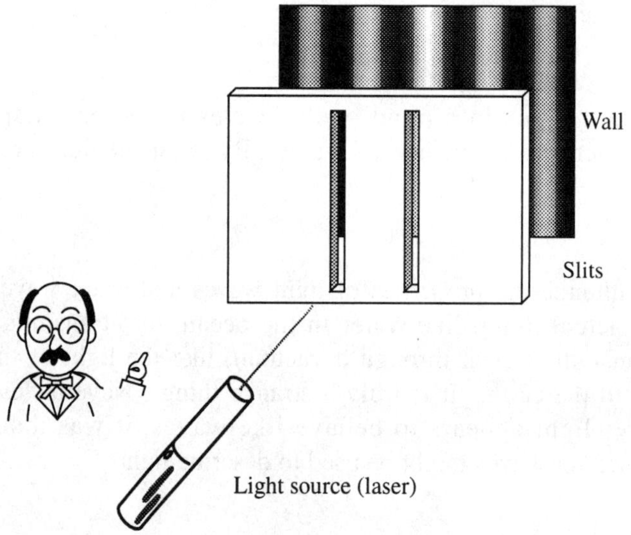

The light that passes through the two slits spreads out from them like waves. Where they collide, they interfere, creating that striped pattern of light and dark on the wall. This would not happen if light behaved like a particle. If light were a particle, it could not pass through both slits at the same time and there would not be any interference. Therefore, light is not a particle, but a wave.

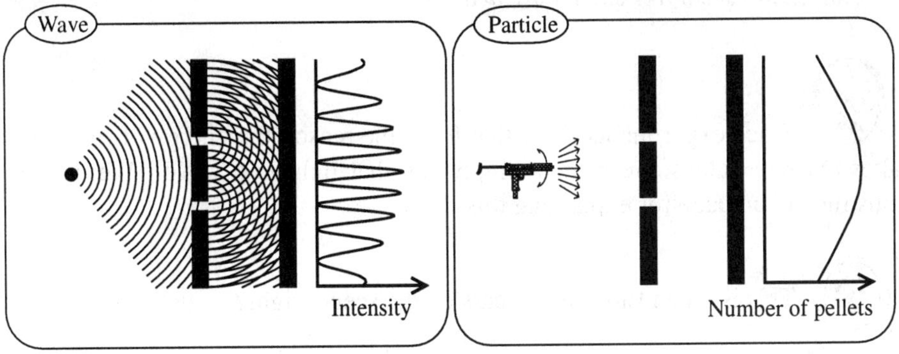

If that's so, saying that light is a wave was correct.

In the end, however, the results of an experiment showed that you couldn't simply call light a wave and leave it at that. The experiment, called blackbody radiation, was designed for measuring the specific heat of light.

What was the meaning of the experiment?

A graph could be made from the experimental results showing the relationship of frequency to energy, but no one could really explain the graph. By all accounts, it was a mystery. People searched for an equation that corresponded to the graph, but many years passed before such an equation was found.

What did that equation tell us about light?

Of course I was glad that an equation had been found, but for a long time I didn't want to believe what it was saying about light. However, after working tirelessly to understand, I came to one conclusion.

Even though it was Planck's own conclusion, he spoke a little regretfully.

The energy of light oscillating at frequency ν only has values which are integral multiples of the value $h\nu$. This is expressed by $E = nh\nu$. It can only have discrete values, and it can never have values in between these multiples. This means that the change in energy levels is not continuous.

That didn't seem like such a big deal to me.

Since experiments show that for some reason the energy of light only takes discrete values, we cannot simply say that light is a wave. We need to construct a language for explaining this.

This is when Einstein appears on the scene, right?

Einstein, who had been thinking hard, now came forward.

There's a ready explanation if you consider light to be a particle.

My, he's bold. Some things can be left only to Einstein.

What difference will it make if we think of light as a particle?

If light is a particle, there is nothing strange about having discontinuous, discrete values.

A particle resembles a coin in that both are counted by jumping from one fixed value to the next. There are no gradations in between these values.

The energy of light has values that are integral multiples of $h\nu$. Thus we can think of n as the number of particles. In other words, each particle of light has energy $h\nu$, and the energy of one particle of light may be written as $E = h\nu$.

I was startled by this radical change of course. As for Einstein, he continued on with his argument.

 I'd like you to recall the photoelectric effect and Compton effect experiments.

These two experiments were inexplicable as long as light was thought of as waves. But as Einstein carefully explained each one, as if by magic I was able to see how light could be regarded as having the characteristics of a particle. And, Einstein said, if you treated light as a particle, you could find its momentum as well. Then he wrote out the two equations in large clear handwriting for us.

Energy of light	$E = h\nu$
Momentum of light	$p = \frac{h}{\lambda}$

By this time, we were just about convinced that light was a particle.

 Wait a minute! What about interference of light? We were just talking about that. If light is a particle, there won't be any interference.

That's true. Didn't we say that light is a wave because it demonstrates interference behavior?

 Also, I can't imagine what the frequency of a particle would be. Isn't frequency a word that relates to waves? Light seems to act like a particle, but talking about that behavior alone does not explain everything about light, does it?

 The logical conclusion is that light has a dual nature; it acts like both a wave and a particle. Further, we have two important equations: one expresses the relationship between momentum and wave length, and the other expresses the relationship between energy and frequency. The development of those equations gives us a connecting link between particle equations and wave equations.

 Those two equations were to become the linchpins in quantum mechanics, and right to the end they were at the crux of questions about the strange behavior of electrons.

A momentary, pained expression on Einstein's face did not escape me.

We talk about a dual nature when something has two contradictory sides, right?

Listening to your conversation has made me think of how much language resembles light. Language also seems to have a dual nature. To me, when language is treated as sounds it has a wave-like character; and when it is treated as meaning, it has a particle-like character. If only there was something that could tie the two together, like an *h* for language!

If light really has a dual nature, then what in heaven's name are those electrons that give off light? Now that we're really determined to find out more about them, let's continue on our way with Bohr's discovery.

First, you look at the movement of an electron as particle motion. If it is particle motion, you can represent a light particle as $E = h\nu$. That was my starting point.

If an electron moves like a particle, how does it move inside an atom?

The electron goes round and round the nucleus of an atom, and that motion is thought to generate light.

But an electron cannot keep rotating and giving off light indefinitely, can it? As it gives off light its energy becomes used up, so the electron will gradually lose centrifugal force and it will be pulled in closer and closer until it is stuck onto the nucleus.

Let us say, then, that the electron gives off light not as it rotates, but when it changes its orbit of rotation.

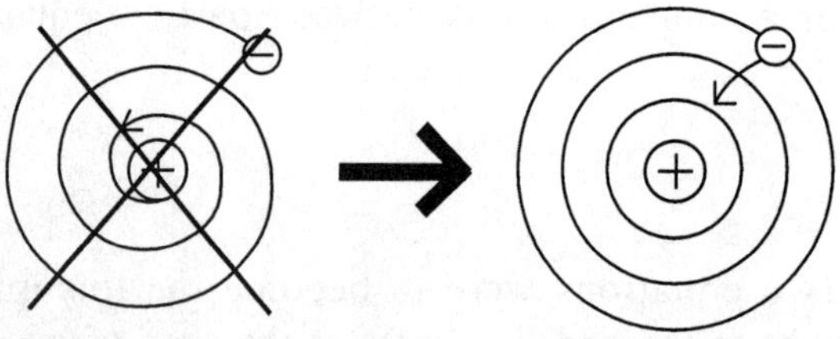

Can you decide such a thing on your own, just like that?

Yes, it's all right. Thinking along the lines of classical mechanics, experimental results on the behavior of electrons could not be properly explained. That is to say, the visual image that could normally be sustained in classical mechanics could not be produced. But I do not think we need to throw out classical mechanics altogether. When we can rewrite classical mechanics for use with quanta, and obtain equations that have no inconsistencies with the results of experiments, then perhaps we will come to understand the atom.

You're saying that if we assume that electrons give off light as they move from one orbit to another, then there is a very good way to explain the atom.

Yes, for the time being. It was a matter of figuring out how an electron works to give off light. When an electron moves from one orbit to another, it releases one light particle with energy $E = h\nu$.

I was astonished at the turn Bohr's discussion was taking.

A violin string produces sound only when it is bowed or plucked. Similarly, electrons give off light only when they move between orbits.

Maybe there's an analogy in language, too. If you utter nothing but the same sound, "aaaa," it won't sound like a word. But as soon as a change is introduced, like "aaaai," then it starts to sound like a word.

How are the spectrum and $E = h\nu$ related?

You remember that we describe spectra using numerical values of frequency and amplitude. Light carries that information. I imagined therefore that I could describe the frequency and amplitude of a spectrum with an equation using h and ν.

Are the numbers for frequency or amplitude arranged in some kind of order?

At first glance, they seem to be a scattered jumble. Now, when I say spectrum, does that remind you of something?

Yes! Fourier.

That's right. Fourier math is a method of describing a complicated wave as the sum of simple waves. It occurred to me that Fourier's method might be of use. For the time being, why not make do with something that appears useful, or at least related. It reminds me of a time I spent living in a shack up in the mountains. Without running water, my dishwater and towels were dirty, but I still managed to get my plates and cups clean.

Did you apply Fourier's method without modification?

If I had been able to do that, it wouldn't have been difficult. But the most important prerequisite for using Fourier math — the requirement that the frequencies have values that are integral multiples — was missing. If the spectrum of light emerging from an atom were a sum of frequencies at regular intervals, I would have used Fourier without giving it a second thought.

Did you think of giving up?

As it happens, when the frequency is very low, it is possible to make calculations using Fourier. Encouraged by this, I decided to proceed using only Fourier.

Could you get those cups and plates clean with Fourier?

No matter what you do, you cannot describe the atom using Fourier alone. That's my conclusion. Since classical mechanics alone could not describe them, I knew that we needed a new quantum language for both electrons and light. When something is lacking, there arises a need to make up for it. Here it is made up for by a special condition that must be applied only in the case of quanta, the quantum condition.

Will the application of the quantum condition solve the problem?

I succeeded in describing things related to frequencies. But with regard to the other element of the spectrum, the amplitude, I could describe nothing.

At this point, Heisenberg begins playing a big role, doesn't he?

That's right. He had the pluck that I did not have, and finally he was able to describe atomic spectra completely in a single equation, without even using the quantum condition.

Oh no, Professor Bohr's pluck and determination are just as admirable. First he tried to express things using only the language that he started with, but with each new barrier he encountered, he changed his course. The method that he developed is now used routinely, although at the time it seemed like a revolutionary new way of thinking about physics. It is a method based on what is called the Correspondence Principle, and one that I also use to tackle the problem.

What I couldn't do was to abandon the idea of orbits. If electrons make transitions, I could see no other way to talk about them except in terms of orbits — that is to say, locations with which to describe motion. Granted, I couldn't say when and how electrons make transitions, but my real regret is that I was unable to say where the electrons went. However, Heisenberg intentionally ignored the idea of orbits producing a breakthrough.

What did you conclude, Mr. Heisenberg?

I came up with Fourier math for use with quanta. I was then able to explain everything about the spectrum of the atom, such as frequency and amplitude. In addition, I could express things without having to use the quantum condition.

That's great. You described the motion of electrons using quantum mechanics.

That's right.

But now we can't mentally picture thc motion of an electron as particle motion any more!

Einstein cut in rather coldly.

That's right. At this stage, if someone asked how an electron moves, all we can do is show the equation and say that it moves as the equation says. It has become impossible to draw a picture of the motion of an electron, or to represent it with some analogy. But I'm really proud of one thing.

What is that? What did you gain by making a visual image impossible?

We were able to describe things using the language of quantum mechanics including classical physics. It became possible to describe high and low frequencies and even amplitude, which changes over time, with just one equation. If the Correspondence Principle is mastered, then anything can be made to correspond with classical theory. The only difference is that the value that represents position in classical mechanics does not refer to position in the case of electrons.

The process of learning a language is also a Correspondence Principle. Toddlers imitate words, don't they? And we imitate the Hippo tapes.

It's like being a voyager who drifts ashore in a strange country. The language of the people who live there is completely strange. To be able to understand each other's intentions, what do you do? You probably start by communicating through body and hand gestures, and then proceed to talk using words as you pick them up. In the end you master a language you had never encountered before.

This is like cooking, I think. At first, it seemed that in order to bring out the flavor of a dish called the atom, an artificial seasoning called the quantum condition had to be added to the basic ingredients of classical mechanics. By flavor, I mean the spectrum. But after the chefs thought and tested for some time, the basic ingredients alone appeared to be giving a good flavor, and they realized that the taste of the atom could be brought out without the use of artificial seasonings.

Mr. Bohr and Mr. Heisenberg, you really boiled down classical mechanics, didn't you?

We boiled it down so much that no traces were left of the original form of the basic ingredients. But the taste is exactly that of the dish called the atom. Since no one has ever seen what the dish called the atom looks like, if the form matches the taste, I suppose it can be established as an atom.

What is the method of cooking?

The dish is made by using the technique known as matrix mechanics. This method of cooking is a very difficult one requiring the skills of a seasoned veteran. It is not something that anyone can do easily at home.

We've seen one dramatic development after another, haven't we? And they seem to lead to the conclusion that it is not possible to have a visual image of the atom!

No, we haven't reached the end yet. We can't do away with a visual image so easily. It is possible, you know, that the initial premise was wrong.

At this point, we come to the story of de Broglie and the wave-like characteristics of electrons.

Bohr tried to associate particle motion with electrons, and ended up with the disadvantage of having to give up on a visual image. But I noticed that one other road remained, which is that light can be treated as a wave. I took up the challenge of writing about electrons in the language of waves. The refraction of light in water can be explained from the standpoint of both waves and particles. I thought that if we described the motion of electrons in terms of waves rather than particles, we wouldn't have to sacrifice the visual image.

De Broglie's equation for electron waves supported a visual image of them.

Of course it did. And it didn't require anything special like a quantum condition. In the end, Schrödinger built up the equation for electron waves for us, calling it wave mechanics.

Do you understand what it means to express the motion of an electron using wave mechanics? It means that the electron is a wave, and we can have a visual image of it.

That is the way I think natural science should be. Moreover, the calculations for the Schrödinger equation of wave mechanics are simple. We've found, in fact, that his equation is fully equivalent to matrix mechanics.

Everything working out smoothly isn't all that is required. You've got to be more rigorous than that. Matrix mechanics may be difficult, and granted it doesn't give you a visual image, but the fact remains that it can be written in a beautiful equation that describes the spectrum of an atom. Matrix mechanics is an elegant language of quantum mechanics. Besides, you say that the equation of wave mechanics lets you have a visual image, but isn't the wave you see in your mind a complex-numbered wave? And how do you explain the fact that when you calculate for two or more electrons, you end up with an equation that gives you more than three dimensions?

Look, those things will be resolved in the end.

Mr. Schrödinger, you are really excited at being able to form a visual image, but to me, the exciting part is something else.

What is that?

The calculations for the matrix mechanics that I came up with are difficult. I am very grateful to you for making it easier to calculate by putting it in the form of a differential equation. It is absolutely magnificent that, starting from either wave equations or particle equations, we were able to arrive at equivalent equations.

In the process of completing Schrödinger's equation, we made one big discovery. Since the "effects" of the differential equations and matrix equations are the same, they can be thought of as the same thing even though they appear to be completely different. That's really fantastic, isn't it? This is true with languages as well. French and Chinese are two completely different languages, but they can have the same effect. For example, either one can convey something like "I want water." Don't you think that's remarkable?

 The Schrödinger equation wins. It has achieved the greatest thing, namely a visual image.

 It isn't possible to sustain a visual image.

 Why is that?

 It is not because of matrix mechanics that a visual image of an electron's movements cannot be drawn. It has been proven that producing this image simply cannot be done.

 Now listen to me. If you think of an electron as a wave, you can mentally picture it. Moreover, you can do without matrix mechanics where equations are difficult to calculate. It becomes possible to describe everything about electrons using just the Schrödinger equation.

Schrödinger's explanations convinced everyone that an electron is a wave. He also stated firmly that electrons are not particles.

 I think he is wrong.

 Even if the characteristics of waves are the premise of an equation expressing the behavior of electrons, there is no reason to expect that we can actually form a visual image. The use of quantum mechanics was important not only because the order of the spectrum could be put into an equation, but also because it gave me reason to conclude that the electron cannot be pictured mentally.

The television program came to an end midway through the debate. I wonder what happened to the atom after that.

6. 2 BORN'S PROBABILITY INTERPRETATION

DEPARTURE TO A NEW WORLD

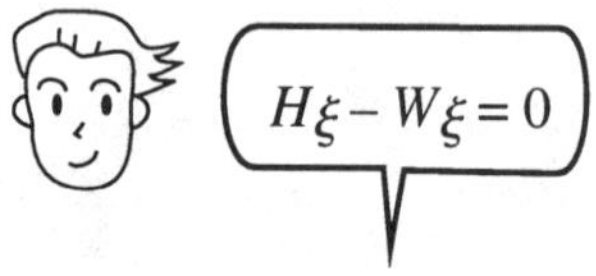

MATRIX MECHANICS, inspired by Newtonian mechanics, treats electrons as particles.

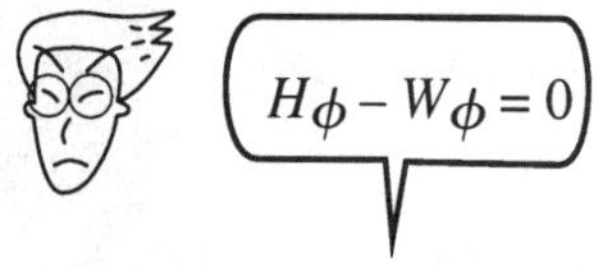

THE SCHRÖDINGER EQUATION, inspired by wave mechanics, envisions the behavior of electrons as waves.

Surprisingly, these two equations, born of two contradictory ways of thinking, express the same things from a mathematical standpoint.

For all the effort Schrödinger invested to formulate an equation that would yield a visual image of the electron, his achievement ultimately suffered the same fate as matrix mechanics.

IT COULD NOT SUPPORT A VISUAL IMAGE FOR A MULTI-ELECTRON ATOM.

WE STILL DON'T KNOW WHETHER THE ELECTRON IS A PARTICLE OR A WAVE!

What will the electron end up being?
Where will the arduous path of quantum mechanics lead?
On we go to our final adventure!

Compared to matrix mechanics, the Schrödinger equation is easy to calculate! It would be a waste to toss it aside just because you can't get a visual image from it.

BORN'S APPROACH OF USING PROBABILITY

Such were the thoughts of Max Born as he pondered a way to rescue the visual image in Schrödinger's equation. Of course Schrödinger was thinking the same thing, but he wasn't getting anywhere. The problem seemed to be that he had become so intent upon finding a wave-like image of electrons that other possibilities were overlooked.

What about Born? Well, he was a determined sort of person. To begin with, he believed that the electron was a particle, but he was also very interested in the Schrödinger equation, which is an equation describing waves.

Jordan, Ernst Pascual [1902-1980]

Biographical Notes on Max Born

Born was born in 1882. Using the theory of relativity as a base, he made contributions to physics in thermodynamics, quantum mechanics and other areas.

In 1925, with Werner Heisenberg and Ernst Jordan, he developed matrix mechanics. He was awarded the Nobel Prize in Physics in 1954 for the probability interpretation of the Schrödinger Equation, which we will discuss here.

Born then went on to work out theoretical ideas on electrons by **TAKING A PARTICLE AS THE VISUAL IMAGE, WHILE USING SCHRÖDINGER'S EQUATION AS THE MATH BASE.**

Born was prompted to try this when he noticed a relationship between the slit experiment and the Schrödinger equation.

UNTIL THEN, Schrödinger had thought that the result of the slit experiment, $|\Psi|^2$, was accounted for by the wave-like characteristics of electrons. For example, an electron was transmitted as a wave, and after passing through two slits, became two waves that interfered.

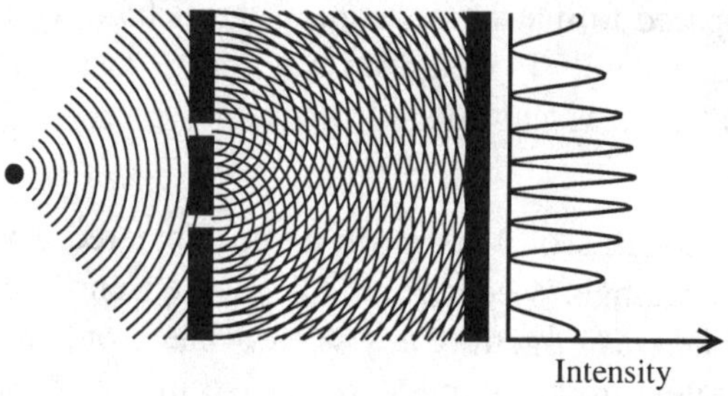

However, Born thought that $|\Psi|^2$ might be explained as **particle behavior.**

There is a detector that can take a count of electrons as particles. It is a simple machine that clicks and makes a tally as each electron is detected. It tallies only whole electrons. If you set up a detector on a wall and release electrons, the total count of electrons that it records corresponds with $|\Psi|^2$.

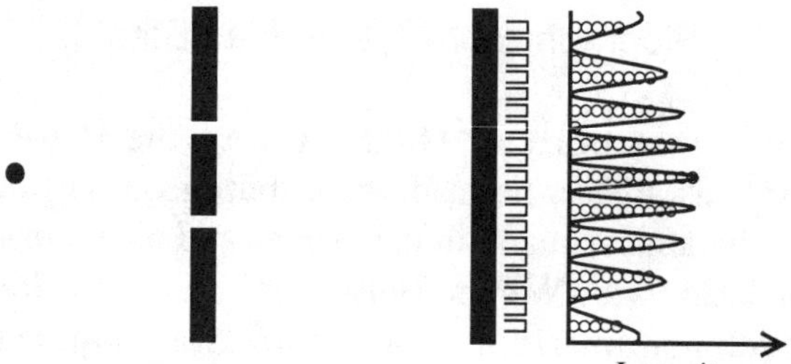

The results of the slit experiment $|\Psi|^2$ can be interpreted in either of two ways, as the **intensity of the wave** or as the **number of electrons,** but only when a great many electrons are released. When just one electron is released, a problem arises.

If, like Schrödinger, you approached electrons as if they were waves, then you would expect the intensity of a wave that has interfered to be visible at the wall even when only a single electron has been released.

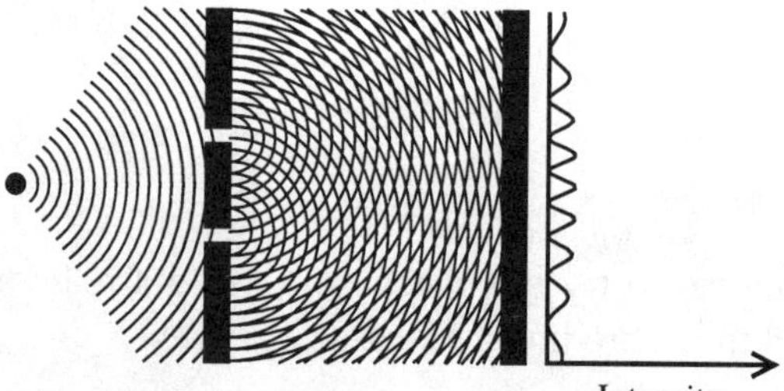

But Born believed **THAT WOULD NOT HAPPEN.**

An electron is no doubt a particle, he thought, and so if only one were projected, it would hit only one spot on the wall.

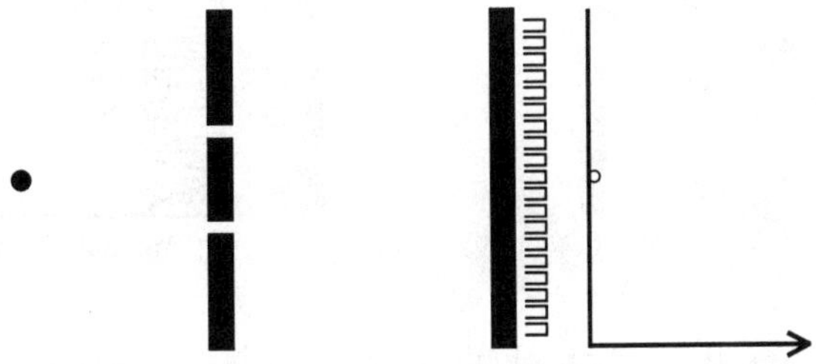

You might think his idea would be easy to confirm, but it really wasn't because no one at the time had the technology for releasing one electron at a time.

RECENTLY it has become possible to actually project single electrons during the slit experiment. When one electron is projected, it does indeed make one spot on the wall. Plop!

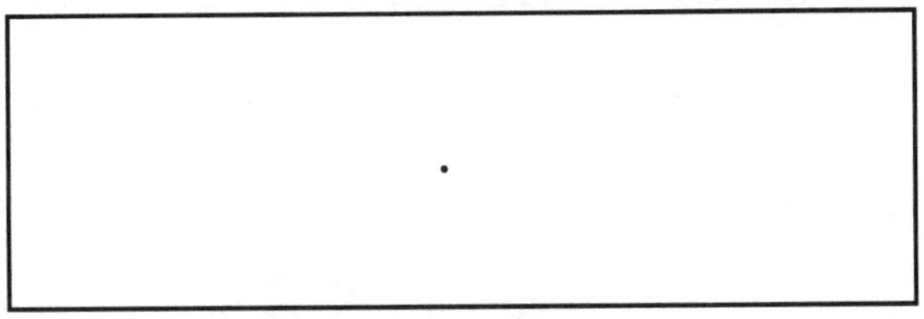

If 50 are projected, we see this.

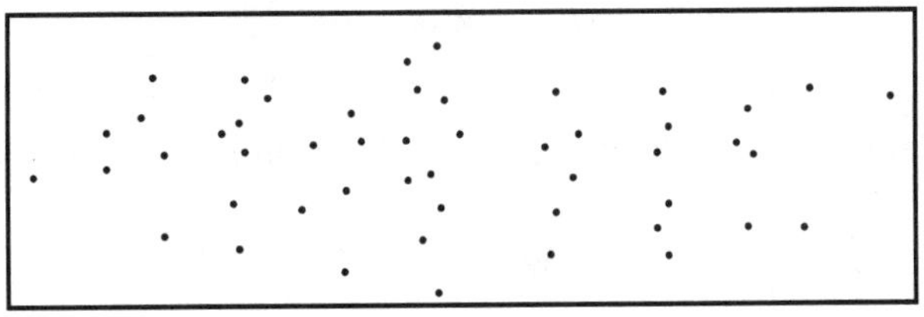

If about 3,000 are projected, then we see something like this.

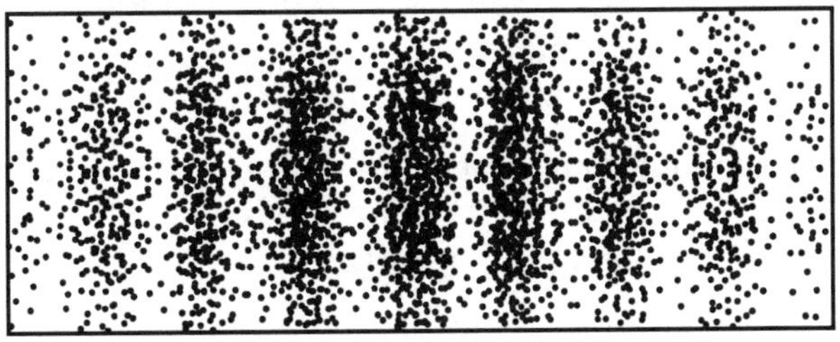

In that way, concentrations of spots are dense or not so dense, showing the places where many electrons came flying and places where they were fewer. Thus it became possible to show experimentally that, just as Born said, Schrödinger's function of wave motion $|\Psi|^2$ describes the distribution of the number of electrons projected one by one.

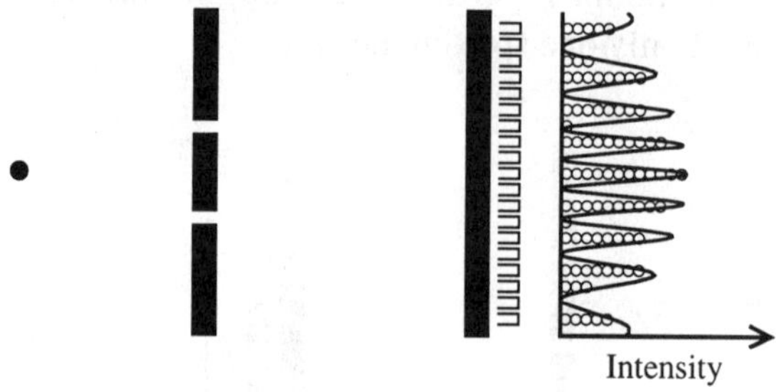

As in cases like this when electrons are projected any number of times, if the square of Schrödinger's function of wave motion Ψ expresses the **number of electrons,** then in the case of a single electron,

THE SQUARE OF Ψ DESCRIBES THE PROBABILITY THAT AN ELECTRON WILL ARRIVE AT A CERTAIN SPOT.

Although it was impossible in Born's time to perform experiments where electrons are released one at a time, other experiments had confirmed that electrons could be "captured one at a time."

Let's see how the meaning of the Schrödinger equation changes when the principles of probability are applied to it.

$$H\phi - W\phi = 0$$

When this equation is solved, it is possible to find the eigenvalues

$$W_1, W_2, W_3, \cdots\cdots W_n, \cdots\cdots$$

as well as the eigenfunctions

$$\phi_1, \phi_2, \phi_3, \cdots\cdots \phi_n, \cdots\cdots$$

Since Ψ is the sum of the eigenfunctions ϕ_n, it may be expressed thus:

$$\Psi(q,t) = \sum_n A_n(t)\phi_n(q)$$
$$= \sum_n A_n \phi_n(q) e^{\frac{i2\pi W_n t}{h}}$$

Adding up these simple waves ϕ_n, we find that electrons have states when their energy is W_1, W_2 and so on, all at the same time.

An electron is a particle, however, and when its energy is measured experimentally, it is always a single value. It would never indicate two or three energy states at the same time.

The problem here is exactly what we ran into before, that is, how to interpret the meaning of Ψ.

According to Schrödinger's way of thinking, the square of Ψ, $|\Psi(q, t)|^2$, is the intensity of a wave at a given location q, and so it has many, continuous values. Nevertheless, in experiments an electron is a particle which can only be measured at one location. Born then came up with the idea that $|\Psi(q, t)|^2$ was the probability of an electron being at a given location q.

What if we take the same approach to the present case?

$$\Psi(q, t) = \sum_n A_n \phi_n(q) e^{\frac{i2\pi W_n t}{h}}$$

According to the equation, the energy turns out to have many values at the same time. But here, we will define the intensity $|A_n|^2$ of the simple wave ϕ_n (which describes the energy of an electron as W_n) as the probability that an electron will have energy W_n.

Differences in Interpretation Between Schrödinger and Born

Schrödinger	→	Born
Material DENSITY of an electron There is density in any position, as if the electron was thinly spread out.	$\lvert\Psi\rvert^2$	**PROBABILITY of an electron being at a given place** Like a particle, an electron exists only in one spot. This expresses the probability of that electron's position.
Simple electron wave n corresponds to the frequency of the electron wave. Simple wave ϕ_n has eigenvalue W_n.	ϕ_n	**State of the electron** n corresponds to the n in W_n. ϕ_n describes the state where the electron particle has the energy W_n.
Value for electron's energy	W_n	**Value for electron's energy**
Wave amplitude When the amplitude is squared, it becomes the intensity of the wave.	A_n	**Probability amplitude** When squared, it becomes the probability of the state ϕ_n, where energy is W_n.

BORN'S EQUATION OF INCLUSION : USEFUL IN FINDING THE PROBABILITY OF PHYSICAL QUANTITIES

Now, how do we find the coefficient A_n? Ψ was the sum of ϕ:

$$\Psi(q, t) = \sum_n A_n(t)\phi_n(q)$$

But the ϕ_n were all orthogonal.

AS FOR THE SUM OF ORTHOGONAL CONDITIONS...

As we found when we were dealing with de Broglie and Schrödinger, we can find amplitudes for ϕ_n by using the same method as the **Fourier coefficients.**

Remember how we multiplied the complicated wave Ψ by the simple wave ϕ_n whose amplitude we wanted to extract, and then did the integration? We do the same thing here.

$$A_n(t) = \int \Psi(q, t)\phi_n^*(q)\, dq\ .$$

Born compared the energy probabilities he calculated this way to actual experimental results. The results were just as he had predicted. Born began thinking about probability in other situations. After considerable trial and error, he arrived at the following equation.

Point

$$\boxed{\Omega\phi - \omega\phi = 0}$$

At TCL, we call this **the Born equation of inclusion.** This equation is very useful in finding all sorts of physical quantities for electrons.

Let's see how it works to find **ENERGY.** If we replace the Ω in the Born equation of inclusion with H (energy operator), and replace ω with the eigenvalue W, we get:

$$H\phi - W\phi = 0\ .$$

This is the Schrödinger equation.

Okay, we're saying that an electron is a particle, right? So let's find the electron's **position** and **momentum.** Because position and momentum are basic physical quantities that describe a particle, they are extremely important when considering electrons as particles.

We can find the position and the momentum the same way we went about finding energy. When we are solving for momentum, we let Ω be momentum operator P, and ω be eigenvalue p_x.

$$\begin{array}{ccccc} \Omega\phi & - & \omega\phi & = 0 \\ \downarrow & & \downarrow & \\ P\phi & - & p_x\phi & = 0 \end{array}$$

(The ϕ in this equation may also be written as ϕ_{p_x}.)

We can get eigenfunction ϕ_{px}, which corresponds to p_x, from this equation. Next, as in the case of energy, the probability of the momentum being in the state ϕ_{px} may be found.

$$A_{p_x} = \int \Psi(q)\phi_{p_x}^*(q)\, dq$$

$$\text{Probability of momentum } P(p_x) = \left|A_{p_x}\right|^2$$

We can also find the probability of position, which is what got us into probability as an approach. To find the position, we let Ω be position operator q, and ω be eigenvalue q_0.

$$q\phi - q_0\phi = 0$$

(The ϕ in this equation may also be written as ϕ_{q0}.)

The ϕ_{q0} found from this equation describes the state of an electron in position q_0. We apply an expansion, and find A_{q0}.

$$A_{q0} = \int \Psi(q)\phi_{q0}^*(q)\, dq$$

Next, if we take the square, we can find the probability of position.

$$\text{The probability that the electron is in position } q_0 \quad P(q_0) = \left|A_{q0}\right|^2 .$$

Up to this point, we've proceeded as we did for energy and momentum. However, if we calculate again to see what sort of value position probability $\left|A_{q0}\right|^2$ takes, we discover something interesting.

The equation of inclusion for finding the position is:

$$q\phi_{q0} - q_0\phi_{q0} = 0 .$$

We factor ϕ_{q0} out of the equation.

$$(q - q_0)\phi_{q0} = 0$$

In an equation such as this, one thing is certain concerning ϕ_{q0} and $(q - q_0)$. When $(q - q_0)$ is 0, ϕ_{q0} may assume a value, but when $(q - q_0)$ is not 0, then ϕ_{q0} must be 0. A relation such as this between ϕ_{q0} and $(q - q_0)$ is called a δ (delta) function.

$$\text{When } (q - q_0) = 0, \ \phi_{q0} \neq 0$$

$$\text{When } (q - q_0) \neq 0, \ \phi_{q0} = 0$$

Such a relationship is expressed in the following equation.

$$\phi_{q0} = \delta\,(q - q_0)$$

When we take the complicated conjugate of ϕ_{q0} and insert it into the equation A_{q0} we get the following.

$$A_{q0} = \int \Psi(q)\phi_{q0}^{*}(q)\, dq$$

$$= \int \Psi(q)\delta\,(q - q_0)^{*}\, dq$$

What sort of values will we get on the right side? At this point, we're going to use a formula for delta functions.

$$\int f(x)\delta\,(x - x_0)dx = f(x_0)$$

Using this, the right side is as follows.

$$\int \Psi(q)\delta\,(q - q_0)^{*}dq = \Psi(q_0)$$

This means that A_{q0} becomes $\Psi(q_0)$.

$$A_{q0} = \Psi(q_0)$$

$$|A_{q0}|^2 = |\Psi(q_0)|^2$$

Do you see? The value for the position probability $|A_{q0}|^2$ found from Born's equation of inclusion is equal to $|\Psi_{q0}|^2$. It's just as Born surmised!

Right up to the end Schrödinger was convinced that electrons were waves. In experiments, however, physicists could observe electrons behaving like particles. So at that point they still didn't know how the results from solving Schrödinger's equation were related to the experimental results. But with Born's use of probability, they found a way to calculate various physical quantities and compare the results with experimental results. The results of the calculations and the results of the experiments matched perfectly!

PROBABILITY THEORY BRINGS BACK THE VISUAL IMAGE BUT...

It turns out that probability provided the tool to reclaim the visual image we lost when we were using Schrödinger's method. The probability that a single electron will be in location x, y, z at time t is expressed in the following equation.

$$P(x, y, z, t) = \left| \Psi(x, y, z, t) \right|^2$$

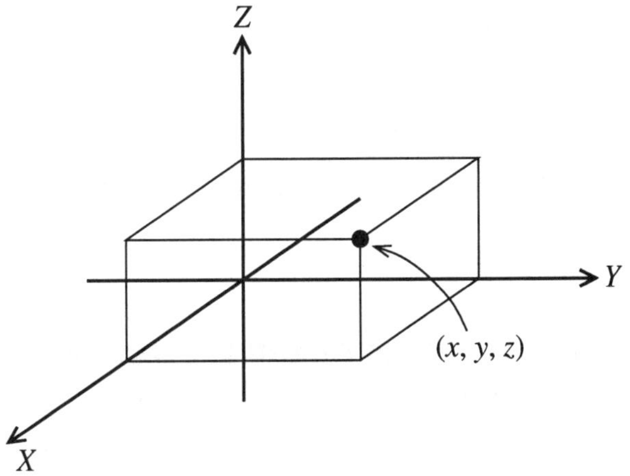

Next, the probability for the positions of two electrons is expressed in the following way.

$$P(x_1, y_1, z_1, x_2, y_2, z_2, t) = \left| \Psi(x_1, y_1, z_1, x_2, y_2, z_2, t) \right|^2$$

This means that one electron is at position x_1, y_1, z_1, and the other is at x_2, y_2, z_2. Seen in a diagram, it looks like this.

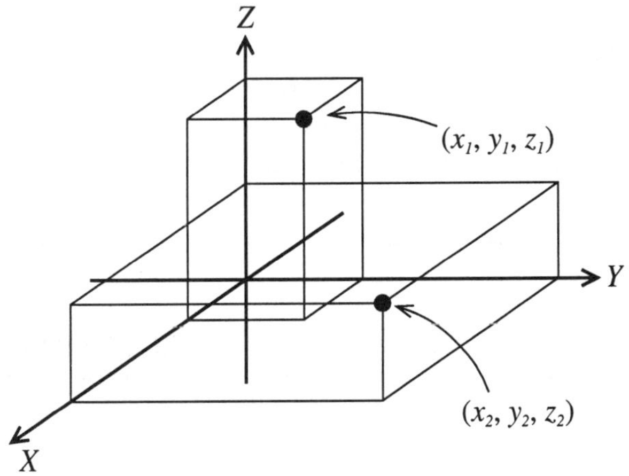

When the case of two electrons is solved using Schrödinger's equation, Ψ ends up with six variables. If these electrons were thought of as waves, the equation would end up describing a six-dimensional wave, something pretty hard to visualize.

BUT, if the two electrons are considered in terms of probability, it becomes a matter of the probability of one electron being in position x_1, y_1, z_1, and the other in position x_2, y_2, z_2. Thus, it is still possible to envision things in three dimensions. Whether there are three, four or however many electrons, it is possible to always make three-dimensional mental constructs. Using probability, no matter how many electrons there are,

A VISUAL IMAGE
IN THREE DIMENSIONS
CAN BE MAINTAINED.

I did it! I got back the visual image of Schrödinger's equation!

SO BORN'S USE OF PROBABILITY GAVE A BOOST TO QUANTUM MECHANICS. . .

Contribution 1:
With probability, electrons could be described using the Schrödinger equation with mathematical expressions far simpler than matrix mechanics.

Contribution 2:
If we take the wave motion function Ψ as expressing the position probability for each electron, then we can describe things within three dimensions even when there are two or more electrons. That restores to us the long cherished visual image.

WHAT NOTEWORTHY CONTRIBUTIONS!
QUANTUM MECHANICS IS COMPLETE!

Meanwhile, back in the lab. . .

Heisenberg and Bohr cut in.

I think Born's probability approach is splendid. But how do you account for the cloud chamber experiment if you're using the Schrödinger equation? The electron tracks running around inside the cloud chamber don't spread out like waves!

THE CLOUD CHAMBER EXPERIMENT

We saw the cloud chamber experiment performed earlier at TCL. Let's look at it again to see what's going on.

At TCL, we used a simple cloud chamber from a set of educational materials. The "cloud chamber" was a round container that could be held in the palms of two hands. As shown in the drawing below, instead of electrons, this set contained an alpha ray generator that emitted alpha particles. Since electrons and alpha particles are both quanta (particles smaller than atoms), they will appear to be almost identical.

At normal temperatures, alcohol fumes are a vapor, but when the temperature drops below a certain level, they turn into liquid. Alcohol is dribbled into a small box cooled by dry ice. As this is done, the alcohol evaporates, but meeting the low temperature, it tries to return to a liquid state. Into this vapor, alpha particles are shot.

When alpha particles are shot into uniformly distributed alcohol vapor, lines appear. What happens is that as the alpha particles pass, the alcohol that had been vapor turns into small droplets of liquid. This occurs continuously along the path traveled by an alpha particle, and a single line of droplets is formed for each alpha particle. You can see this happening with the naked eye. The lines really do look like the tracks made by alpha particles.

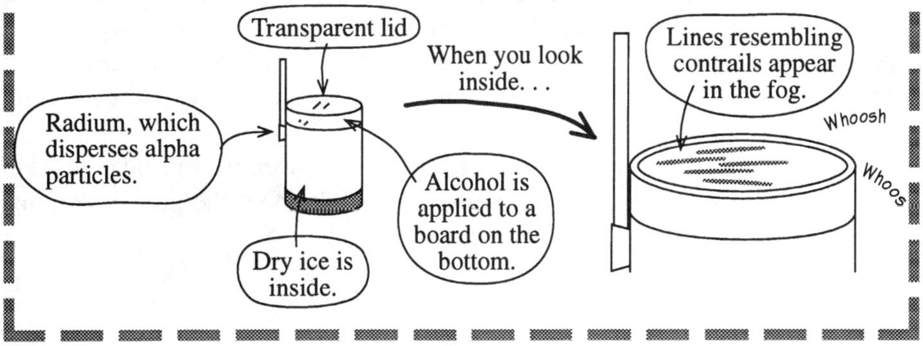

The fact that electrons make tracks in straight lines inside the cloud chamber was originally completely incompatible with the behavior of electrons described by the Schrödinger equation. What I mean is that, as long as Schrödinger's wave motion function Ψ mathematically describes a wave, even if it is thought of as a "probability wave," it ought to keep spreading out over time. But the electrons inside the cloud chamber do not spread out; they fly along in nearly straight lines.

Even though electrons that make tracks like particles and electrons that spread and interfere like waves are one and the same thing, we still need a language that can explain both without inconsistencies.

Despite Born's achievements with probability, the fact remained that Ψ was a wave. For that reason, electrons should theoretically continue to spread when placed in a cloud chamber even if they are initially gathered together in one spot. Since electrons should, therefore, exist randomly somewhere on the surface of the spreading wave, there ought to be randomly spreading spots of electrons, as in the following drawing. (Figure 1)

But in fact, electrons inside the cloud chamber appear to draw a straight track as they fly by. (Figure 2)

(Figure 1)

(Figure 2)

Attempting to resolve these difficulties, Bohr and Heisenberg kept up a running interchange for months. Together they went over every possible experiment concerning electrons in a cloud chamber. They exhausted every avenue to reconcile the electron tracks in the cloud chamber experiment with the Schrödinger equation.

Close to burn out and having failed to find the answer, they decided to take separate holidays. As Heisenberg continued to think about the problem on his own, he remembered something Einstein had said:

"IT IS THE THEORY WHICH DECIDES WHAT WE CAN OBSERVE. "

And then he thought once again about the kind of theory he needed, and what it would yield for him to observe.

So far we've talked fairly casually about

BEING ABLE TO SEE THE TRACKS OF ELECTRONS

inside a cloud chamber.

When we tried to reconcile the electron tracks and the wave Ψ, we got nowhere.

Let's think. When we say "track," we are referring to a thin line running through the vapor. However, what we are really seeing inside the cloud chamber is, in fact,

A ROW OF LIQUID DROPLETS THAT ARE BIGGER AND WIDER THAN ELECTRONS.

So what I'm suggesting is. . .

It just might be that we haven't been looking at electron tracks at all. If those lines in the cloud chamber are not actual electron tracks, then we should change the way we state the problem. Instead of trying to find a way to describe the electrons' tracks using the wave equation Ψ, we need to explain the row of fat liquid droplets that were formed by the electrons.

Once the problem was restated in this way, it became clear that there were limits to how far an electron could be observed. This conclusion was called the uncertainty principle, and it was to be significant in the amazing climax of quantum mechanics.

6. 3 THE UNCERTAINTY PRINCIPLE

THE UNCERTAINTY OF POSITION AND MOMENTUM

Here we will consider an experiment such as the one below. We will examine how an electron wave spreads out when it passes through a slit.

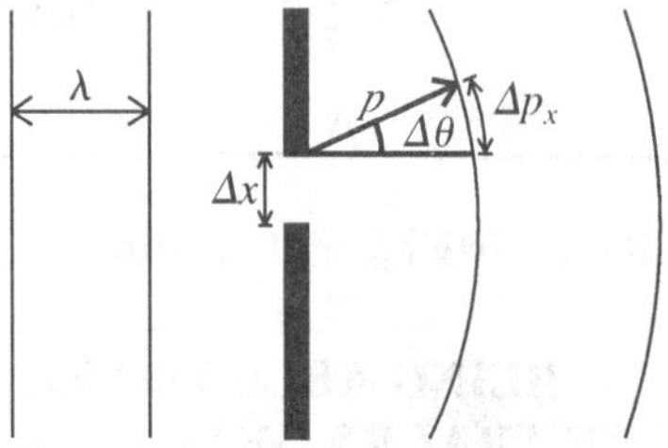

λ : Wavelength λ (lambda) of the wave
Δx : Width Δx (delta x) of the slit
$\Delta\theta$: Angle of dispersion $\Delta\theta$ (delta theta) of the wave after passing through the slit
p : Momentum p of the electron
Δp_x : Dispersion of momentum Δp_x (delta p_x) of the electron for x

We will now look at the relationship among these five values. But since it is difficult to handle the relationships of all the variables at once, we will begin constructing our equation by confirming the relationship among three variables at a time.

1. Relationship between width Δx of the slit and angle of dispersion $\Delta\theta$ of the wave when the wavelength is the same

To find this relationship, we first make sure the wavelengths are the same, and then we observe how the waves spread as the width of the slit is changed. We find, as in the diagram, that when the width Δx of the slit is increased, the angle of dispersion $\Delta\theta$, or spread, of the wave decreases; and when Δx is narrowed, $\Delta\theta$ grows larger. This is an inversely proportional relationship.

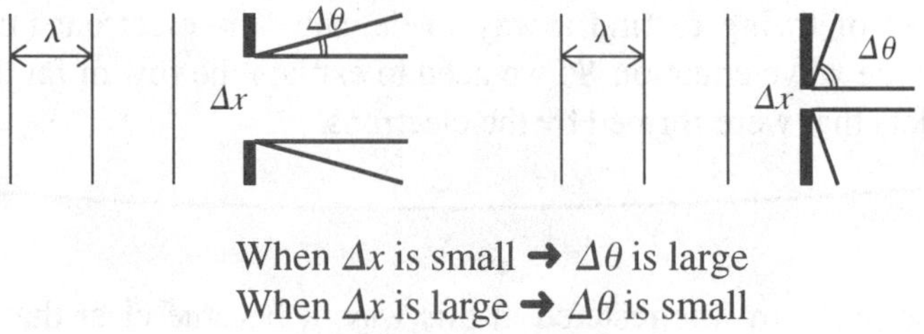

When Δx is small ➔ $\Delta\theta$ is large
When Δx is large ➔ $\Delta\theta$ is small

$\Delta\theta$ AND Δx HAVE AN INVERSELY PROPORTIONAL RELATIONSHIP.

2. Relationship between wavelength λ and the angle of dispersion $\Delta\theta$ of the wave when the slit width is the same

This time we'll keep the width of the slit constant, and we will watch how the wave spreads as we change the wavelength. As in the diagram below, when wavelength λ is large, the angle of dispersion $\Delta\theta$ of the wave is also large; and when λ is small, $\Delta\theta$ is also small. This is a directly proportional relationship.

When the wavelength is long, the wave spreads out more easily than when it is short. This phenomenon also occurs in our immediate surroundings. AM radio waves, which are long, travel between buildings or into valleys more easily than FM waves or television waves, which have short wavelengths.

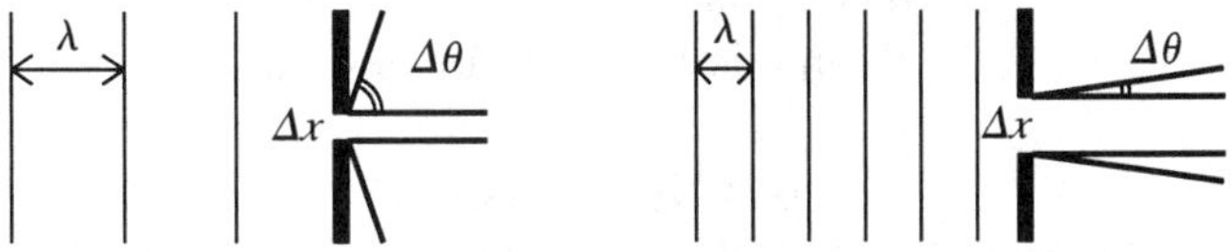

When λ is large ➜ $\Delta\theta$ is large
When λ is small ➜ $\Delta\theta$ is small

$\Delta\theta$ AND λ HAVE
A DIRECTLY PROPORTIONAL RELATIONSHIP.

Now, when we combine the two relationships 1. and 2. above into an equation, we get:

$$\Delta\theta = \frac{\lambda}{\Delta x} \qquad \text{Equation 1-2}$$

3. Relationship between the dispersion of momentum Δp and angle of dispersion $\Delta\theta$ of the wave when the momentum is the same

As the angle of dispersion $\Delta\theta$ of the wave increases, the dispersion of momentum Δp_x also increases.

When $\Delta\theta$ is large ➜ Δp_x is large
When $\Delta\theta$ is small ➜ Δp_x is small

$\Delta\theta$ AND Δp_x HAVE
A DIRECTLY PROPORTIONAL RELATIONSHIP.

4. Relationship between the dispersion of momentum Δp and the momentum p when the angle of dispersion is the same

If the angle of dispersion $\Delta\theta$ of the wave is not changed while the momentum p is increased, as in the diagram, the dispersion of momentum Δp increases. As in 3., this is a directly proportional relationship.

When p is large ➔ Δp_x is large
When p is small ➔ Δp_x is small

p_x AND Δp_x HAVE
A DIRECTLY PROPORTIONAL RELATIONSHIP.

Putting 3. and 4. together into one equation, we get:

$$p\Delta\theta = \Delta p_x$$

We divide both sides by p:

$$\Delta\theta = \frac{\Delta p_x}{p} \qquad \text{Equation 3-4}$$

Now let's put equations 1-2 and 3-4 together. Since both equations take the form $\Delta\theta$ = ∗∗∗∗, they can be placed into a single equation. When we put them together, the result is:

$$\frac{\lambda}{\Delta x} = \frac{\Delta p_x}{p}$$

If the form of the fraction is changed, it can be written as $\Delta x \cdot \Delta p_x = \lambda p_x$.

Here, let's bring out the equation for quanta, the one we have seen when we were talking about Einstein:

$$p = \frac{h}{\lambda}$$

This equation describes the relationship between a quantum's momentum and its wavelength. If we replace p with $\frac{h}{\lambda}$, we get:

$$\Delta x \cdot \Delta p_x = \cancel{\lambda}\frac{h}{\cancel{\lambda}} = h$$

$$\Delta x \cdot \Delta p_x = h$$

With this, we've got a relationship where the product of width Δx of the slit and the dispersion of momentum Δp of the electron equals Planck's constant h. This equation means that the position and the momentum of an electron are uncertain; it is none other than the equation for Heisenberg's uncertainty principle, an idea that caused a big stir in the physics world!

EQUATION FOR THE UNCERTAINTY PRINCIPLE

$$\Delta x \cdot \Delta p_x \approx h$$

Point

≈ : means "approximately equals"

Planck's constant h is a fixed value, so in this equation if Δx becomes small, the equation will not balance out unless Δp_x becomes proportionately that much bigger.

Of course if Δp_x becomes smaller, then Δx must become that much bigger.

As Δx is the width of the slit, one might say that Δx is the "applied position" of the electron, somewhere along the way which the electron has passed. On the other hand, Δp_x is the dispersion of momentum.

To sum up the uncertainty of the electron, "The more precisely you try to determine the position of an electron, the less you will know about its momentum; conversely, the more you know about momentum, the less you will know about the position of the electron."

USING THE UNCERTAINTY PRINCIPLE TO EXPLAIN ELECTRONS IN THE CLOUD CHAMBER

Knowing all we do about the uncertainty of the electron's position and momentum, let's now consider electrons in a cloud chamber. Let's say that at a certain time, a droplet of alcohol forms and its size is Δx. This tells us that the electron is somewhere within the droplet, and therefore **THE POSITION OF THE ELECTRON IS MEASURED AS BEING WITHIN THE LIMITS OF Δx.**

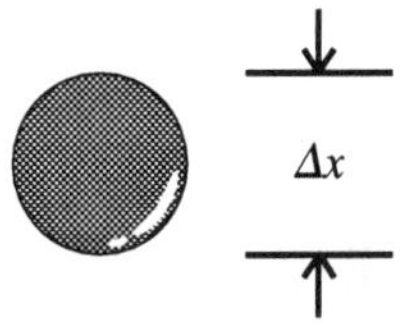

Because $\Delta x \cdot \Delta p_x \approx h$, if Δx can be determined, then dispersion Δp of the electron's momentum p can also be found. Δp describes the way in which a wave spreads, so to say that Δp has a value means that **THE WAVE WILL SPREAD.**

But size Δx of the cloud particle is much greater than the value for Planck's constant h, so dispersion of momentum Δp must therefore be very small. Vitally important is that no matter how small Δp is, it is never 0. Thus each time a cloud particle forms, the probability wave begins to spread again, even if only a little.

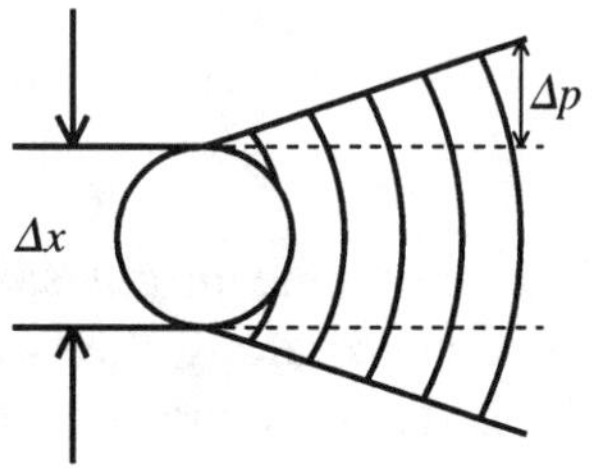

And before the probability wave spreads very much, the next cloud particle soon forms somewhere on the spreading wave surface.

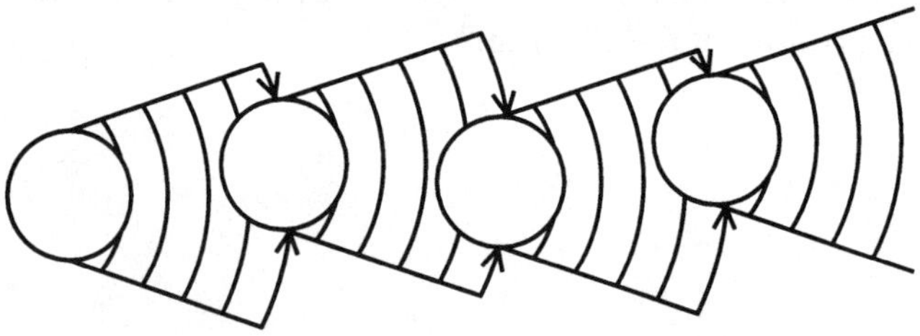

In this way, the formation of a cloud particle clearly indicates the presence of an electron within the range Δx that defines the size of the cloud particle. Since the electron is not outside that range, the probability wave, having once spread out, ends up shrinking to Δx, the size of the cloud particle! Because the probability wave shrinks back each time another cloud particle forms, that can account for why the wave does not continue to spread out, and why instead the cloud particles line up in a roughly straight line.

Still, it probably seems hard to believe that **EACH TIME A CLOUD PARTICLE FORMS, THE PROBABILITY WAVE OF THE ELECTRON STOPS SPREADING** no matter how it is explained.

THE PROBABILITY WAVE SHRINKS!?

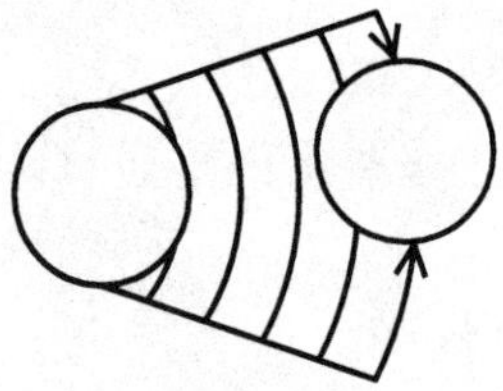

Let's consider this in terms of rolling a die. Whenever you toss a die, there is the possibility that any one of six faces will appear. But after you've tossed it, one possibility is chosen. In other words, in the instant that one of the faces appears, the possibility that any of the other five will appear is gone.

What the probability wave does is describe the possibility that somewhere along the wave surface an electron will be found. You could call it a "possibility wave." As in throwing a die, the instant it is discovered that there is an electron in one place, the possibility of it being in another place is gone, and the possibility wave ends up "shrinking."

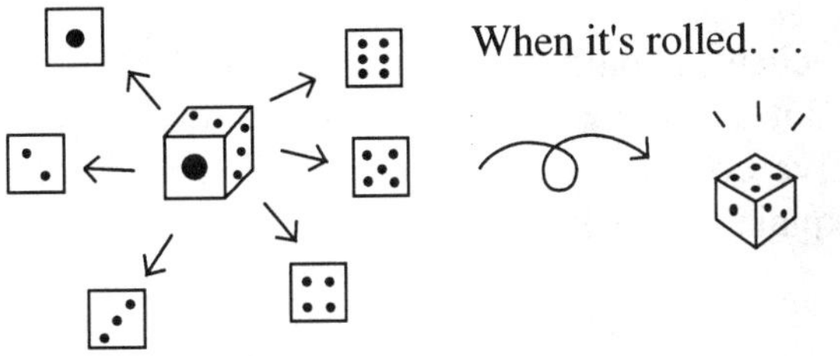

IT IS IMPOSSIBLE TO SEE AN ELECTRON WITH OUR OWN EYES.

LIMITS TO WHAT WE CAN KNOW ABOUT THE ELECTRON

Because we cannot see electrons, we have to resort to techniques such as observing cloud particles that are formed when electrons are present, or examining light as it strikes electrons, if we want to know about their position or momentum. Without such observations, we'd never learn anything about electrons.

However, **the uncertainty of an electron's position and momentum** is established the moment it is observed, resulting in the measured values always being dispersed.

The closer you try to look at position, the more dispersed momentum becomes; and the closer you try to look at the momentum, the more dispersed position becomes.

The formula $\Delta x \cdot \Delta p \approx h$ for the uncertainty principle shows that it is impossible to know the position or the momentum to a more exact degree than Planck's constant h. In other words, it lays out

THE LIMITS TO OBSERVATION OF THE ELECTRON.

The adventure in quantum mechanics started out with Planck's constant h, and may end with it as well.

When Born talked about describing electrons in terms of probability, the meaning of "probability" was unclear. Probability is a technique that is often used. For example, although it is possible to find exactly how a particle is moving, expressing things in terms of probability is useful in that it offers an alternative to dealing with a large number of bothersome variables.

But in the case of electrons, describing them in terms of probability in accordance with Heisenberg's uncertainty principle turned out to be not just an alternative method but the way to a definitive conclusion. It was determined conclusively that position and momentum would always be dispersed, and that the only way they could be described was in terms of probability.

Classical mechanics could never have imagined such an unorthodox, odd development. But accepting the idea finally allowed quantum mechanics to reach a definitive conclusion. Unless one thought in those terms, it was impossible to explain the tracks of the electrons in the cloud chamber.

A DUAL NATURE: PARTICLE AND WAVE

When performing the slit experiment, electrons demonstrate wave-like behavior in their interference. Despite interfering, an electron also demonstrates particle-like behavior in arriving at one spot on the wall. With the uncertainty principle, we can now resolve the inconsistencies of the slit experiment.

If an electron is going to interfere as a wave, it must pass through both slits at the same time. But if the electron is a particle, as it appears to be when it arrives at the wall, then it must pass through one or the other slit, not both. What's going on??

Let's set up the following experiment. We'll place light bulbs near each of the two slits as shown below in the diagrams. When we turn the bulbs on, we can see a flicker as the electron passes through the slit. This way we can actually see which slit the electron has passed through. Because electrons are invisible to the naked eye, we must use props such as this to observe their movements in determining which slit they passed through.

If we leave the light bulbs off and shoot off electrons, they interfere.

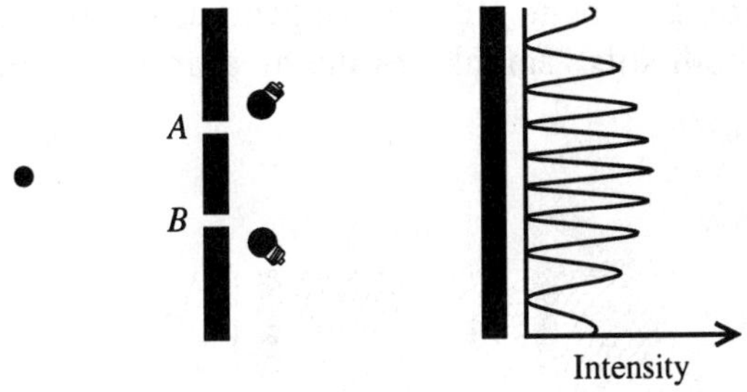

Then we turn on the bulbs and shoot off some more electrons. With the lights on, we can see that a given electron goes through either slit *A* or slit *B*.

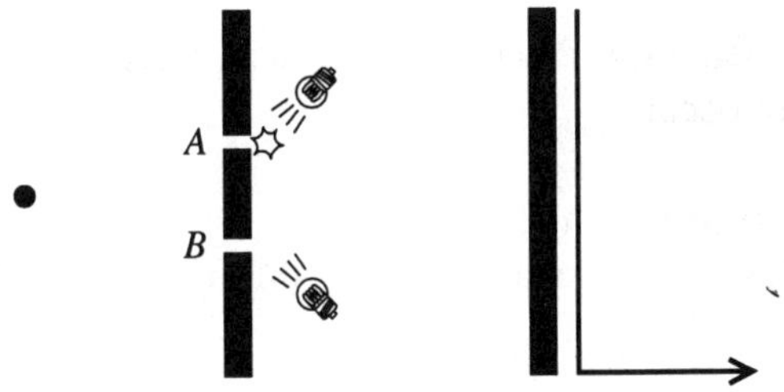

Well, what do you know. An electron went right through one of the slits.

But wait! In experiments where we can tell which slit an electron goes through, it means the electrons don't interfere!!

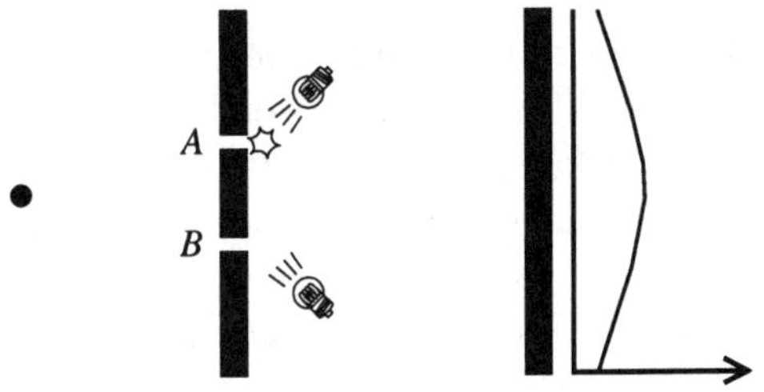

What could have happened? We did the experiment in the first place to learn how the interfering electrons passed through the slits. Now it turns out that such an experiment cannot be done!

We can explain what took place by bringing in the uncertainty principle. Turning on the light bulbs, we were able to observe which slit the electron went through. Let's say we saw it passing through slit *A*. At that instant, the possibility of it going through slit *B* disappeared, meaning that the electron wave arriving at both slits "shrank" to the area around *A* before it could go anywhere further.

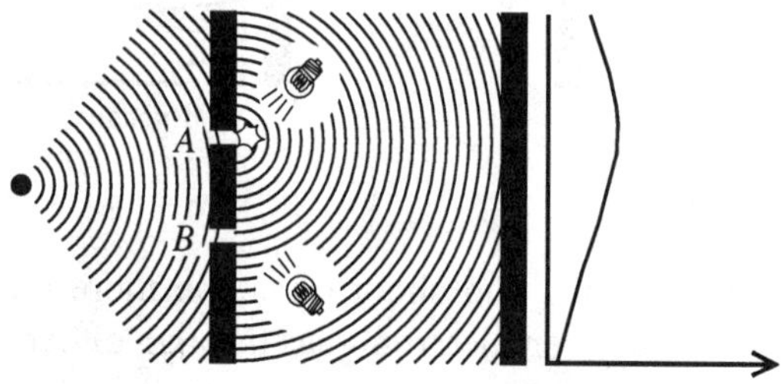

When this happens, the electron wave will pass only through slit *A* and interference will not occur.

If it is not observed which slit the electron went through, the electron wave will not shrink. The electron wave will go through both slits and interference will take place.

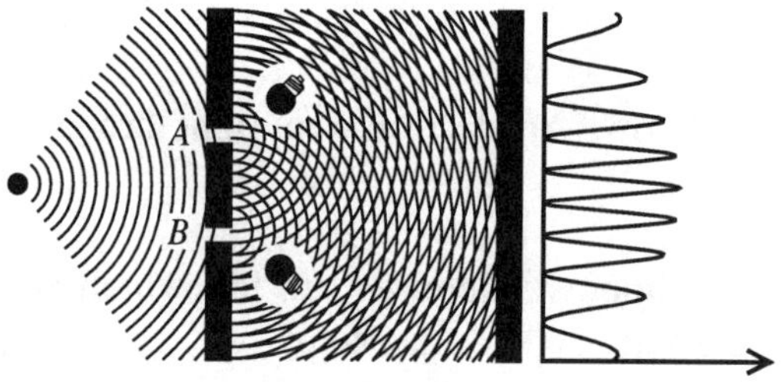

When an electron passes through only one of the slits and when it passes through both slits represent different sets of conditions. In the former case, the electron is observed; in the latter, it is not. It is impossible for both cases to occur at the same time. For that reason, these occurrences are not contradictory.

We've used the observation that an electron wave shrinks to explain a number of experiments. But what sort of mechanism do you suppose is at work when an electron wave shrinks? That mechanism has nothing to do with anything you can actually see happening. That goes without saying.

In the slit experiment, let's say that the lights were on, but you weren't looking at the passing electrons. Regardless of this, interference did not occur. Whether the electrons were observed or not observed, as long as the lights were turned on, conditions were satisfied and interference did not occur.

Next, let's consider that there is some kind of interaction involving the light from the bulbs that causes the electron wave to shrink. Since electrons are so minuscule, they may be disturbed when they are struck by light, and their movement is thrown into disorder.

But as the following experiment shows, this is not true.

We'll use the slit experiment setup, but this time we'll turn on just one light and point it toward slit *A*. That way, the electron will flicker only when it passes through slit *A* and at no other time.

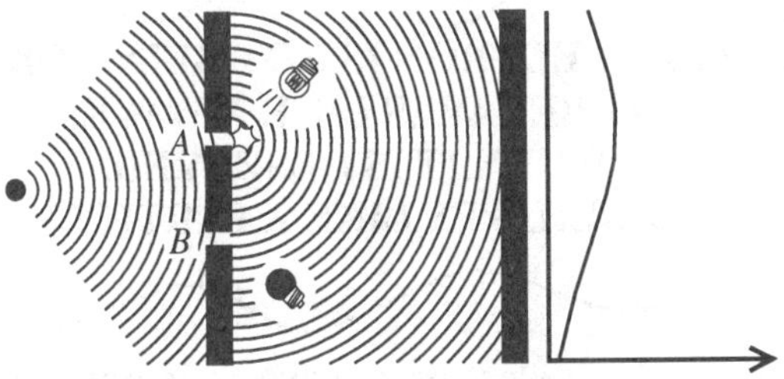

But the only other thing it can do is to pass through slit *B*. If the electron does not flash at slit *A*, you might think that it has passed through slit *B*. And lo and behold, the electron does not interfere in this experiment.

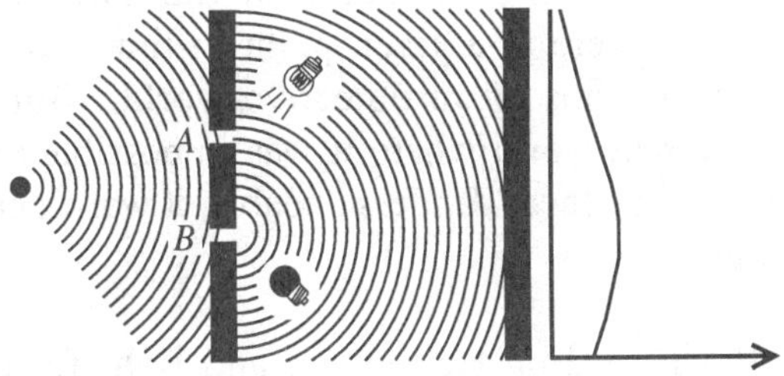

The electron did not flash at slit *A*, and therefore the electron wave shrank to slit *B*. Not only did the electron not flash at slit *A*, but there was no light bulb at slit *B* to begin with. Thus, in this case, it was not some interaction between electron and light that caused the electron wave to shrink. To put it another way, an electron wave shrinks when the observer, *in principal*, knows what slit the electron has passed through.

6. 4 WRAPPING UP QUANTUM MECHANICS

THE STRANGE RELATIONSHIP BETWEEN THE BEHAVIOR OF THE ELECTRON AND THE PEOPLE WHO OBSERVE IT

Throughout this adventure we have been trying to solve the mystery of the electron. Is it a particle or a wave? At last, we've found an answer!

**WHEN THE ELECTRON IS NOT BEING OBSERVED,
IT BEHAVES LIKE A WAVE;
WHEN IT IS OBSERVED,
IT BEHAVES LIKE A PARTICLE.**

Although we may call an electron a wave, it is not a wave with material properties. It is a "wave of possibility." And although we may call it a particle, its position and momentum cannot be known simultaneously according to the uncertainty principle. And finally, the very act of observing an electron affects the state it is in. The whole mystery of the electron may defy common sense, but unless we take a daring leap and go beyond the ideas of pre-quantum science, we aren't able to explain all the experimental facts staring at us.

For a long time the essential concern of the natural sciences was to determine where objects were at a given point in time. In this way, science described everything in terms of an objective world. But when it came to quanta, this was a different world where it was impossible to pinpoint exactly when and where things happened. Understandably, it wasn't easy to accept such a different world right off.

Einstein came down hard on Heisenberg and Bohr for their work on the uncertainty principle.

I CANNOT ACCEPT SUCH A THING!

Einstein did not object to the idea of describing things in terms of probability. That had been done before, especially when the number of particles was particularly large. In those cases, there were ways to determine the position and momentum of each and every particle if you were willing to go to all the trouble. But scientists weren't willing for it involved too much work.

But then Heisenberg announced that according to the uncertainty principle, there was absolutely no way to precisely determine both the position and momentum of quanta. Einstein could not accept this premise. "Fresh Fields," the sixth chapter of *Physics and Beyond*, describes the heated debate between Bohr and Einstein.

At the Solvay conference held in Brussels, Belgium, Einstein delivered a powerful refutation of Heisenberg and Bohr's hypotheses. Under no circumstances would he believe that electrons could only be described in terms of probability. Even worse, he balked at the suggestion that objective observation was not possible due to human observation influencing the behavior of electrons.

Each day during the Solvay conference, Einstein thought up a new hypothetical experiment in which the uncertainty principle would not hold up, and every time he challenged Heisenberg and Bohr to answer a very difficult question related to it. Heisenberg and Bohr would spend all day pondering the difficult questions posed by Einstein before presenting their solution to him in the evening. Then Einstein would come up with another hypothetical experiment, so complex that anyone would think, "Aha! He's got them for sure this time!" But the uncertainty principle did not fall apart. It held up and let Bohr and Heisenberg counter every challenge by Einstein.

"Watching from the sidelines, a friend of Einstein is said to have admonished him: 'Einstein, I am ashamed of you; you are arguing against the new quantum theory just as your opponents argue about relativity theory.' But Einstein wasn't really listening."

Physics and Beyond

"A number of years later, Einstein died. To the very end he was unable to accept quantum theory as valid science, saying over and over again, 'God does not throw dice.'

Schrödinger too, regretting having ever set foot in the world of quantum physics, ended up switching to molecular biology."

Physics and Beyond

More than sixty years after the uncertainty principle was discovered in 1927, an empirical proof or theory that might overthrow the uncertainty principle has yet to be discovered, despite the attempts of many physicists. Even today, quantum mechanics as Heisenberg and the rest developed it is held to be valid. In fact, we can no longer do without quantum mechanics, for it has become part of the scientific fabric of civilized society today.

NATURAL SCIENCE IN THE 21ST CENTURY

Thinking about electrons as quantum mechanics sees them, they seem to resemble people in various ways. And people, too, sometimes behave in ways that could be explained by quantum mechanics.

When a person is born, he or she has the potential of becoming or doing anything in life. But through their individual experiences in the cloud chamber known as society, they are observed through the eyes of other people. Individuals are assigned a value by others, and from that point on find it difficult to think beyond the value they have been assigned or their confirmed status within society. However, there are endless possibilities in life, and a person's potential to grow is always present.

At Hippo, too, every time we sing the words of a language and are praised by our friends for our accomplishments, we feel very good about ourselves. Bolstered by our sense of accomplishment, we go on to put even more effort into learning. This is but one example to illustrate that is not possible to go through life without being influenced by other people's observations.

Moreover, some aspects of the uncertainty principle remind us of the process by which a toddler acquires language.

When you observe a toddler, his manner changes. You have an effect on him. It is impossible to observe the way a toddler's language ability forms in a situation where there is no human influence, for if he is kept alone in a room, he will not learn to speak. We are unable to observe behavior that is completely uninfluenced by others.

When we see something, we see it in a shower of light. When a young child learns to speak, he hears a shower of words that we send forth. These showers, of light and of words, have an influence on the electron and the baby, respectively. There are similar aspects between the behavior of an electron and that of a baby. There are also similarities between light and language. Perhaps the relationship between light and the behavior of electrons will offer a clue to the relationship between toddlers and language, which may be explained scientifically. In any case, the world of light and electrons has produced a startling conclusion that common sense alone could never have conceived.

Recently, a physicist named Stephen Hawking has been saying some interesting things about the macro world, about space and the universe.

A black hole is commonly thought of as a place from which nothing emerges. It swallows up all matter, even light. Because it appears black, this phenomenon is called a black hole.

It so happens that the uncertainty principle is involved here. In theory, in a black hole, matter and light keep getting packed more and more tightly into a small space. When that happens, Δx in the black hole becomes smaller and smaller and dispersion of momentum Δp_x becomes proportionately larger. Hawking suggests that one result is the formation of something even faster than the speed of light. Somehow overcoming the force sucking it into the black hole, it springs forth and produces light or matter. If it is matter, it is of course impossible that it can exceed the speed of light, but if we are speaking of "waves of possibility," then it is conceivable. This theory, based on actual observation, proposes that the uncertainty principle is at work in the macro world called the universe.

Our day-to-day world is a macro world made up of light and electrons. Viewing it from space, it is a very tiny part of the universe. We believe that human beings, existing between the micro world of electrons and the macro world of the universe, cannot be fully explained without using the terms and concepts of quantum mechanics.

With regard to language, in particular, there is much that a quantum-type analysis might reveal. Using language, we are able to create images that express our future and our past, the micro world as well as the universe. How can we describe so strange and wonderful a thing as language that can leap across time and space?

For those of us who are treating language as a natural science, Heisenberg's *Physics and Beyond* inspires courage and the spirit of adventure. When we err, when we think and even when we lose hope, we always return to these pages for inspiration. There are still many, many worlds that remain unknown, some right at our doorstep. As we go forth to turn those worlds into language, we must always remember the wisdom and the courage of those who have preceded us.

For those of us now who have experienced the adventure of quantum mechanics and witnessed this grand drama, taking the stage in the world of natural science in the 21st Century may not be so far away.

Recently, a physicist named Stephen Hawking has been saying some interesting things about the macro world, about space and the universe.

[illegible] everything, and [illegible] cannot [illegible] up all matter, even light. [illegible] appears [illegible] this phenomenon [illegible] called a black hole.

It so happens [illegible] uncertainty principle [illegible] theory in a black hole [illegible] is the [illegible] tightly into a [illegible] space [illegible] what happens [illegible] becomes [illegible] and [illegible] and uncertainty of momentum [illegible] becomes disproportionately larger. Hawking suggested that one result [illegible] the possibility of something every faster than the speed of light. Since [illegible] force sucking it into the black hole, it springs forth and [illegible] It is of course impossible that [illegible] can exceed [illegible] light [illegible] we are speaking of "waves of probability" [illegible] able. This theory, based on actual observation, proposes that [illegible] principle [illegible] in the macro world called the universe.

[illegible] world [illegible] made [illegible] of light and electrons, [illegible] from space [illegible] tiny part of the universe. We believe that [illegible] beings [illegible] the micro world of atoms, and the macro world of the universe, cannot be fully explained without using the terms and concepts of [illegible].

[illegible] quantum-type analysis [illegible] are able to create images [illegible] and [illegible] world [illegible] universe [illegible] can [illegible] that can help [illegible].

[illegible] are the [illegible] a [illegible] physics and [illegible] inspires [illegible] the spirit of [illegible]. When we [illegible] when we think, and even when we lose hope, we always return to these pages for inspiration. There are still many, many worlds that remain unknown, some right at our doorstep. As we go forth to turn those worlds into language, we must always remember the [illegible] and the courage of those who have preceded us.

For those of us now who have experienced the adventure of quantum mechanics and witnessed this grand drama taking the stage in the world of natural science in the 21st Century may not be so far away.

AFTERWORD

It feels like we've been romping around in a delightful park where the words of quantum mechanics fly about us. The language of quantum mechanics was probably familiar to those who participated in the seminars over the past year, but it may have seemed like incomprehensible gibberish to all the new students.

Five-year-old Taro came from Japan to America when his father's job took the family there. The first time he went to the neighborhood park, the English language he heard all around him was completely new to him. For a month or two he played along by watching and imitating the other children, and he gradually began to understand the words they said. After another month or two, he could understand more clearly, and at some point he began to say a few things in English himself. His American friends would come over and listen intently, trying to pick up what he was saying. Something was being communicated. Their eyes shone as more words flew back and forth. The immense pleasure and satisfaction in understanding each other's words were apparent when watching Taro play with his new American friends. As more of Taro's words were understood, he had more fun playing. After about a year, he could speak English with no trouble. There are many similarities between that sort of good, natural setting that Taro found himself in and the warm, fun-filled atmosphere of our quantum mechanics seminars.

"Nature works and behaves like this."

Natural science is finding a language to describe how nature works and behaves. Since the ancient past, generations of people have culled out and examined the most reliable knowledge about how the nature around them was formed, and what human beings existing as part of nature really were. They sought a language to explain these things.

What was observed were repeated occurrences in nature, such as the movements of stars and seasonal changes in weather. That was because a phenomenon that occurred only once could not be confirmed a second time. Starting at the beginning with broad, general descriptions, words to depict ever greater detail were gradually found.

Newton is said to have opened the door to modern natural science. In order to describe the behavior of nature, he appropriated the abstract and rigid language of mathematics and used it with stunning success. But as people turned increasingly from explaining the macro world to the micro world, they found themselves at a loss to explain the world of atoms, those tiny things that make up the existence of all matter. It was found that these atoms could not be explained using Newtonian language.

What were the parts of the atom called the nucleus (protons) and electrons? What was the light emitted by an electron when it moved? Electrons and photons were too small to see. How did they behave? Because they were not directly visible, people could only theorize that they must be moving in such and such a way. In contrast to the world of Newtonian mechanics, people in recent times have been able to do no more than discuss possibilities.

Nevertheless, as long as we allow ourselves to suppose from evidence that things behave in a certain manner (theories), a way to determine whether our assumptions are correct can be devised (experiments). When an experiment proceeds according to the predictions of theory (language), it is considered a success, thereby confirming the theory. At that point the theory has been proven correct, and we can then say that nature behaves according to the predictions of language. Here, rather than saying that theory (language) describes natural phenomena, it is more suitable to say that nature demonstrates whether a theory (language) is correct (reality). The new theory (language) that Heisenberg and his colleagues formulated, quantum mechanics, was very successful in explaining the behavior of light and electrons. It was new and expansive, pushing out beyond the framework of Newtonian mechanics.

During these six months, as we played in a "park" with the language of quantum mechanics flying around us, we grew closer and closer to Heisenberg and the rest of his colleagues. Even so, we don't quite dare to dream that we understand the greater part of quantum mechanics. We are still just looking into the garden beyond the wall. Yet for all that, we have experienced the satisfaction of having glimpsed the beautiful and delicate tensions of nature and coming to know firsthand the language that describes it.

Anyone would agree that nature can be described through language, but we must not forget that language itself is a part of nature. We have the feeling that we are at last on solid ground, supported by the goal of describing language itself as a natural phenomenon. As the Dean of TCL always says, "Nature as humans know it does not exist beyond what can be described through words."

Students at the Transnational College of Lex

INDEX of Point

INDEX

Q

R

S

T

U

V

W

Y

Bibliography

Bohr, N. 井上健 訳 原子理論と自然記述 (**Atomic Theory and the Description of Nature, Atomic Physics and Human Knowledge, Essays 1958-1962 on Atomic Physics and Human Knowledge**), Misuzu Book Co., 1990

Born, M. and Einstein, A. ボルン・アインシュタイン往復書簡集 (**Nymphenburger Verlagshandlung, Albert Einstein, Hedwig und Max Born : Briefwechsel 1916-1955, Kommentiert von Max Born**), Sanshu-Sha Co., 1976

Dirac, P. A. M. 量子力学 (**The Principle of Quantum Mechanics**), Misuzu Book Co., 1963

Feynman, R. **The Feynman Lectures on Physics vol. I, II, III**, Addison-Wesley, 1965

Feynman, R. ファインマン物理学(全５巻) (**The Feynman Lectures on Physics**), Iwanami Book Co, 1967

Feynman, R. 光と物質の不思議な理論 (**QED : The Strange Theory of Light and Matter**), Iwanami Book Co., 1987

Gribbin J. 山崎和夫 訳 シュレディンガーの猫 上下巻 (**In Search of Schrödinger's Cat**), Chijin Shokan Co., 1989

Heisenberg, W. **Physics and Beyond**, Harper & Row, 1972

Heisenberg, W. 山崎和夫 訳 部分と全体 (**Physics and Beyond**), Misuzu Book Co., 1974

Heisenberg, W. 現代物理学の思想 (**Physics and Philosophy - The Revolution in Modern Science**), Misuzu Book Co., 1989

Kelman, P. and Stone, A. H. **Ernest Rutherford, Architect of the Atom**, Englewood Cliffs, 1969

The Nobel Foundation ノーベル賞講演 物理学 ３，４，５，７ 巻 (**Nobel Lectures — Physics**), Kodan-Sha Co., 1980

Pargels, H. R. 量子の世界 (**The Cosmic Code : Quantum Physics as the Language of Nature**), Chijin Shokan Co., 1983

Przibram, K. 江沢洋 訳 波動力学形成史 (**Briefe zur Wellenmechanik**), Misuzu Book Co., 1982

Sakakibara, Y. 榊原 陽 ことばを歌え！こどもたち, Chikuma Book Co., 1985

Spiegel, M. R. 数学公式・数表ハンドブック (**Mathematical Handbook of Formulas and Tables**), McGraw-Hill Book, 1984

Toda, M. 戸田盛和 他 物理入門コース(全１０巻), Iwanami Book Co., 1983

Tomonaga, S. 朝永 振一郎 量子力学 I、量子力学 II, Misuzu Book Co., 1952, 1953

Tomonaga, S. 朝永 振一郎 量子力学的世界像, Misuzu Book Co., 1982

Transnational College of LEX **Who is Fourier? A Mathematical Adventure**, LRF, 1995

Transnational College of LEX フーリエの冒険 (**Who is Fourier? A Mathematical Adventure**), Hippo Family Club, 1988

Transnational College of LEX 量子力学の冒険 (**What is Quantum Mechanics? A Physics Adventure**), Hippo Family Club, 1991

Transnational College of LEX **ARTCL '84-'87** (**Annual Reports of TCL**), Hippo Family Club, 1985-1988

Weinberg, S. 電子と原子核の発見 (**The Discovery of Subatomic Particles**), Nikkei Science, Inc., 1986

物理学辞典編集委員会編 物理学辞典, Baifukan Co., 1984